BASIC CONCEPTS

OF CALCULUS

The Appleton-Century Mathematics Series

Raymond W. Brink and John M. H. Olmsted, *Editors*

A First Year of College Mathematics, 2nd ed., by Raymond W. Brink
Algebra—College Course, 2nd ed., by Raymond W. Brink
Analytic Geometry, rev. ed., by Raymond W. Brink
College Algebra, 2nd ed., by Raymond W. Brink
Plane Trigonometry, 3rd ed., by Raymond W. Brink
Spherical Trigonometry by Raymond W. Brink
An Introduction to Matrices, Vectors, and Linear Programming by Hugh G.
     Campbell
Modern Basic Mathematics by Hobart C. Carter
Elementary Concepts of Modern Mathematics by Flora Dinkines
    Parts also available individually under the following titles:
        Part I, *Elementary Theory of Sets*
        Part II, *Introduction to Mathematical Logic*
        Part III, *Abstract Mathematical Systems*
Introduction to the Laplace Transform by Dio L. Holl, Clair G. Maple, and Bernard
     Vinograde
Introductory Analysis by V. O. McBrien
College Geometry by Leslie H. Miller
Advanced Calculus by John M. H. Olmsted
Calculus with Analytic Geometry (2 volumes) by John M. H. Olmsted
Intermediate Analysis by John M. H. Olmsted
Real Variables by John M. H. Olmsted
Solid Analytic Geometry by John M. H. Olmsted
The Real Number System by John M. H. Olmsted
Analytic Geometry by Edwin J. Purcell
Calculus with Analytic Geometry by Edwin J. Purcell
Analytic Geometry and Calculus by Lloyd L. Smail
Calculus by Lloyd L. Smail
The Mathematics of Finance by Franklin C. Smith

BASIC CONCEPTS

OF **CALCULUS**

John M. H. Olmsted

Southern Illinois University

 **New York**
APPLETON-CENTURY-CROFTS
DIVISION OF MEREDITH CORPORATION

TO CYNTHIA

PREFACE

This volume is the second of a set of three containing the material of a first course in calculus, and the subject matter immediately prerequisite thereto. The first volume is entitled *Prelude to Calculus and Linear Algebra,* and the third volume is entitled *A Second Course in Calculus.* As stated in the Preface to the preceding volume, the three-volume set is a condensation of the author's two-volume *Calculus with Analytic Geometry,* in this same Appleton-Century Mathematics Series, obtained by deleting from the earlier book all honors sections, most of the especially difficult and sophisticated proofs, and many of the more advanced exercises.

For statements of purpose and objectives, as well as suggestions for course outlines, the reader is referred to the preface of the preceding volume, *Prelude to Calculus and Linear Algebra,* which also contains a copy of the preface of *Calculus with Analytic Geometry.* As explained in the earlier preface, frequent cross references among the different volumes just named call for abbreviations. The following are used:

CWAG: *Calculus with Analytic Geometry,*
PCLA: *Prelude to Calculus and Linear Algebra,*
BCC: *Basic Concepts of Calculus,*
SCC: *A Second Course in Calculus.*

Prerequisite for work in the present volume are the first five chapters of *PCLA,* although some portions of Chapter 6, *PCLA,* would be needed for problems on the reflecting properties of the conics (Exs. 34-36, §709).

This volume, *BCC,* is designed for a 5-hour, 1-semester course of approximately 60 class meetings (aside from tests and reviews), although other possibilities are indicated in the preface of *PCLA.* A further possibility is for two 3-hour, 1-semester courses, such as those labeled Math 1 and 2 by the Committee on the Undergraduate Program in Mathematics, of the Mathematical Association of America, in their booklet entitled *A General Curriculum in Mathematics for Colleges,* published in 1965.

J.M.H.O.

Carbondale, Illinois

CONTENTS

Preface vii

1   THE DEFINITE INTEGRAL

101   The idea of area; ordinate sets 1
102   The integral of a step-function 4
103   The integral as a positive linear functional on S 7
104   Exercises 8
105   Riemann-integrability; vector space structure 9
106   Integrability of monotonic functions 13
107   Products and absolute values of integrable functions 15
108   Exercises 16
109   The Riemann integral 16
110   The integral as a linear functional 18
111   The integral as a positive linear functional 19
112   Integrability on subintervals 20
113   Additivity on adjacent intervals 21
114   Other theorems 23
115   Exercises 28

2   APPLICATIONS OF THE DEFINITE INTEGRAL

201   Area as a positive additive function 30
202   Areas of ordinate sets 33
203   Sets between two graphs 37
204   Exercises 39
205   Volume as a positive additive function 42
206   Volumes of revolution by cylinders and washers 43
207   Exercises 48
208   Volumes of revolution by cylindrical shells 49
209   Volumes of known cross section area 54

210   Exercises 58
211   Force and work 60
212   Distance and velocity 62
213   Exercises 63

3   UNIFORM CONTINUITY

301   Uniform continuity 65
302   Negation of uniform continuity 70
303   Vector space structure 75
304   Algebra structure 76
305   Exercises 78
306   Composite functions 79
307   Integrability of uniformly continuous functions 80
308   Exercises 83

4   CONTINUITY

401   Continuity at a point 84
402   Exercises 90
403   Negation of continuity at a point 90
404   Vector space and algebra 92
405   Exercises 93
406   Composite functions; quotients 94
407   One-sided continuity; types of discontinuity 97
408   Exercises 101
409   Intermediate-value property 103
410   Inverses of monotonic functions 104
411   Roots and rational powers 106
412   Exercises 109
413   Continuity and uniform continuity 110
414   Boundedness and extrema 111
415   Exercises 113

5   LIMITS

501   Deleted neighborhoods and the limit concept 114
502   Limit at a point 115
503   One-sided limits 117
504   Continuity and limits 119
505   Exercises 121

506 Limit of a composite function 122
507 Limit theorems 123
508 Exercises 129
509 Limits at infinity 129
510 Infinite limits 135
511 Exercises 139
512 Curve sketching 140
513 Exercises 141
514 The integral as the limit of a sum 142
515 Bliss's theorem 144
516 Exercises 145

6   THE DERIVATIVE

601 The idea of a tangent line 146
602 Average and instantaneous velocity 149
603 The derivative 153
604 Exercises 157
605 Laws of derivatives; polynomials; higher orders 157
606 Exercises 161
607 Differentiability and continuity; products and quotients 161
608 Exercises 164
609 Differentiation of powers 164
610 Composite functions and the chain rule 166
611 Exercises 169
612 One-sided derivatives 170
613 The law of the mean 171
614 Monotonic differentiable functions 175
615 Vertical tangents 177
616 Exercises 180
617 The intermediate-value property for derivatives 180
618 Differentiability of inverse functions 182
619 Differentiation of rational powers 185
620 Exercises 186
621 The formula for differentiating the sine function 188
622 The derivatives of the other trigonometric functions 189
623 Exercises 190
624 Counterexamples 191

7   DIFFERENTIALS AND IMPLICIT FUNCTIONS

701 Differentials 194
702 Identity, inverse, and composite functions 198

703 Exercises 201
704 Approximations by differentials 202
705 Exercises 204
706 Functions defined implicitly 205
707 The use of differentials 208
708 Second-order derivatives 208
709 Exercises 209
710 Curves defined parametrically 211
711 Second-order derivatives 215
712 The generalized law of the mean 216
713 Exercises 218

8 EXTREMA AND RELATED RATES

801 Global extrema 220
802 Exercises 223
803 Local extrema 224
804 The first derivative test; points of inflection .227
805 Exercises 232
806 Concavity and the second derivative test 233
807 Open-ended intervals; substitution techniques 239
808 Exercises 242
809 The extended law of the mean 244
810 Exercises 247
811 Applied problems 247
812 Exercises 254
813 Implicit functions and extrema 256
814 Exercises 258
815 Related rates 260
816 Exercises 262

9 CURVE SKETCHING

901 Points of inflection 265
902 Exercises 268
903 Polynomials in factored form 269
904 Graphical solutions of inequalities 271
905 Local behavior and dominant terms 272
906 Exercises 273

10 THE FUNDAMENTAL THEOREM OF CALCULUS

1001 Strict positivity of the integral for continuous functions 274
1002 The mean value theorem for integrals 275

1003 Indefinite integrals and their continuity 277
1004 Exercises 280
1005 Differentiability; primitives and antiderivatives 281
1006 The symbol $\int$ 284
1007 The fundamental theorem of calculus 286
1008 Exercises 289
1009 Some integration formulas 290
1010 Exercises 292
1011 Integration by substitution 293
1012 Definite integrals by substitution 297
1013 Exercises 299
1014 Work 301
1015 Hydrostatic force 305
1016 Exercises 308

11   LOGARITHMIC AND EXPONENTIAL FUNCTIONS

1101 Introduction; algebraic and transcendental functions 310
1102 The function ln 312
1103 Laws of ln 315
1104 The function exp 316
1105 General characteristics 317
1106 Laws of exp 319
1107 The number e 319
1108 Exercises 320
1109 The general exponential function a^x 321
1110 Laws of exponents 323
1111 The general power function x^b 324
1112 Logarithmic differentiation 325
1113 The general logarithmic function 327
1114 Exercises 329
1115 Integration formulas 331
1116 Exercises 333
1117 Functional definitions of sine and cosine 334

12   ELEMENTARY DIFFERENTIAL EQUATIONS

1201 The differential equation $dy/dx = f(x)$ 336
1202 The differential equation $d^2y/dx^2 = f(x)$ 339
1203 Rectilinear motion; the falling body 340
1204 Separable equations; orthogonal trajectories 342
1205 Exercises 345
1206 The differential equation $dy/dt = ky$ 347
1207 Applications to radioactive decay and bacterial growth 348
1208 Exercises 351

13   INDETERMINATE FORMS

1301   The indeterminate form 0/0 353
1302   Proof of l'Hospital's rule 355
1303   The indeterminate form ∞ / ∞ 356
1304   Exercises 358
1305   Other indeterminate forms 359
1306   Exercises 361
1307   Determinate expressions; curve sketching 361
1308   Exercises 363

APPENDIX

Table I   Squares, cubes, roots, reciprocals 366
Table II   Four-place common logarithms 368
Table III   Natural logarithms 370
Table IV   Numerical constants 372
Table V   Exponential function 373
Table VI   Natural trigonometric functions, degree measure 377
Table VII   Natural trigonometric functions, radian measure 378
Table VIII   Degrees, minutes, and seconds to radians 379
Table IX   Radians to degrees, minutes, and seconds 379
Table X   Formulas from geometry 380
Table XI   Greek alphabet 380

ANSWERS AND HINTS........................381

SPECIAL SYMBOLS 399

INDEX 401

1

The Definite Integral

101 THE IDEA OF AREA; ORDINATE SETS

The geometric concept that underlies the analytic ideas of this chapter is that of *area*, whereby to certain subsets of the Euclidean plane E_2 are assigned nonnegative numbers called their *areas*. It is too much to expect *every* set in E_2 to possess an area, even when the set is bounded (a set in E_2 is **bounded** if and only if it is contained in some circular disk). However, there are a few properties that a "satisfactory" *area function* should have when it is applied to those sets for which area *is* defined. ("Satisfactory" in the present instance means "intuitively appealing to most rational beings.") Aside from what has already been said, there are four of these "intuitively appealing" properties, which we shall discuss only informally in this chapter. In the next chapter (§§201, 202) these properties will be stated more formally, and several consequences will be established. We shall denote by A the area function under discussion, and by $A(S)$ the area of a set S that has area.

The first of these properties (perhaps the most "natural" of all) is that whenever two sets S_1 and S_2 in the plane are congruent* and either one possesses area, then the other must also, and the areas of these two sets must be equal; in brief:

$$(1) \qquad\qquad S_1 \cong S_2 \;\Rightarrow\; A(S_1) = A(S_2).$$

This property will be referred to as **congruence-invariance**.

The second property is that whenever a set S in E_2 is made up of two disjoint parts

---

*Two sets A and B in the Euclidean plane are said to be **congruent** if and only if there exists a one-to-one correspondence between their members that is *distance-preserving;* that is, if a_1 and a_2 are any two points of A and if b_1 and b_2 are the two corresponding points of B, then the distance between a_1 and a_2 must be equal to the distance between b_1 and b_2. Congruence of A and B is denoted $A \cong B$.

S_1 and S_2 — that is, $S = S_1 \cup S_2$ and $S_1 \cap S_2 = \emptyset$ — such that each set S_1 and S_2 has area, then so does S, and the area of the total set S is the sum of the areas of the two parts S_1 and S_2:

(2) $$A(S_1 \cup S_2) = A(S_1) + A(S_2).$$

This property is called **additivity.**

The third property is the most complicated of all, although it dates back to the ancient Greeks under the title of the method of *exhaustion.* For example, Archimedes (287–212 B.C.) used this technique for determining areas of certain special figures such as circular disks and parabolic segments. By this method the given figure S (a circular disk, for instance, as shown in Figure 101-1) is caused to lie *between* two simpler sets S_1 and S_2 (regular polygons in Figure 101-1):

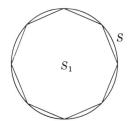

Figure 101-1

(3) $$S_1 \subset S \subset S_2,$$

where the areas of S_1 and S_2 are either known or can be computed, and such that the areas of S_1 and S_2 can be made arbitrarily close to each other. The third property — known as **completeness** or **continuity** — asserts that from the existence of the sets S_1 S_2 we can infer that the set S must be one for which the area function is defined. It can then be *proved* that the area $A(S)$ is simultaneously the least upper bound of the set $\{A(S_1)\}$ and the greatest lower bound of the set $\{A(S_2)\}$, where S_1 and S_2 are arbitrary sets of the types specified in connection with (3).

The fourth (and final) property to be assumed for an area function is that its values for certain particularly simple plane sets shall be in conformity with our intuitive convictions. The "particularly simple" sets whose areas are to be postulated will be open rectangles, where an **open rectangle** is defined to be any set R in E_2 that is congruent to a set of the form

(4) $$(a, b) \times (c, d) = \{(x, y) \mid a < x < b, c < y < d\},$$

where $a < b$ and $c < d$. The area of such a rectangle R is then required to be the product of its length and width:

(5) $$A(R) = (b - a)(d - c).$$

If a **closed rectangle** is defined to be any set R in E_2 that is congruent to a set of the form

(6) $$[a, b] \times [c, d] = \{(x, y) \mid a \leq x \leq b, c \leq y \leq d\},$$

where $a < b$ and $c < d$, then it can be *proved* that the area of any such closed rectangle is equal to that of the corresponding open rectangle:

(7) $$A(R) = (b - a)(d - c).$$

It can also be proved that any subset of any bounded closed line segment is a set with area equal to zero.

We summarize the preceding collection of assumed properties by stating that *area is a complete congruence-invariant positive additive function defined on certain sets in the Euclidean plane such that every open rectangle has area equal to the product of the lengths of two adjacent edges.* Proofs alluded to above are provided in connection with a discussion of area functions given in Chapter 2 (particularly in §§201 and 202). Finally, in Chapter 9, *SCC**, a definition is given for an area function that satisfies all requirements postulated.

In the present chapter we shall view an area function primarily as a useful geometric concept to accompany the analytic study of the integral. It should be appreciated that the development of properties of the integral does not depend in any way on those of an area function. Rather, area will be viewed in the next chapter as an *application* of the integral, and will be used in this chapter only informally as a pictorial or suggestive device.

The first general class of sets for which we shall attempt to attack the problem of assigning area is the class of *ordinate sets of nonnegative functions on compact intervals*, according to the definition:

Definition. *Let f be a nonnegative real-valued function defined on a compact interval* [a, b]:

(8) $$a \leq x \leq b \Rightarrow f(x) \geq 0.$$

*The **ordinate set** of f is the set (cf. Fig. 101-2):*

(9) $$\{(x, y) \mid a \leq x \leq b, \; 0 \leq y \leq f(x)\}.$$

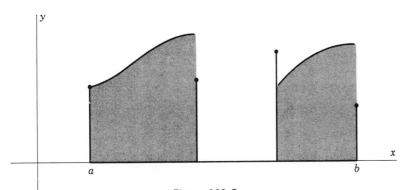

Figure 101-2

The type of *simpler set* (playing the role of S_1 and S_2 in Figure 101-1, and (3)) that will be used to "approximate" a given *ordinate set S* is one made up of open rectangles with sides parallel to the coordinate axes, together possibly with portions of horizontal or vertical line segments, as indicated in Figure 101-3.

*As stated in the Preface, the following abbreviations are used for closely related volumes by the author: *CWAG* for *Calculus with Analytic Geometry*, *PCLA* for *Prelude to Calculus and Linear Algebra*, and *SCC* for *A Second Course in Calculus*.

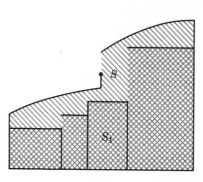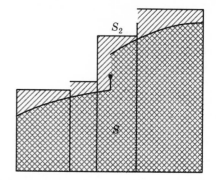

Figure 101-3

These considerations lead in a natural way to a closer look at the vector space of step-functions on an interval $[a, b]$, with particular attention to the ordinate sets of those step-functions that are nonnegative. However, in order to carry through an effective study of the linear functional known as the *integral*, we shall find it desirable to include in our considerations step-functions that have at least some negative values rather than restricting ourselves exclusively to those that are nonnegative.

102   THE INTEGRAL OF A STEP-FUNCTION

Definition.   *Let $s : x \to s(x)$ be a step-function on the compact interval $[a, b]$, and assume that s is constant in each of the open intervals of the net $\mathfrak{N} : \{a_0, a_1, \cdots, a_n\}$. Then the **Riemann integral*** or **definite integral** or **integral of s on $[a, b]$** or **from a to b** is denoted and defined:*

$$(1) \quad \int_a^b s = \int_a^b s(x)dx \equiv \sum_{i=1}^n s_i(a_i - a_{i-1})$$
$$= s_1(a_1 - a_0) + s_2(a_2 - a_1) + \cdots + s_n(a_n - a_{n-1}),$$

*where s_i is the constant value of s in the ith open interval (a_{i-1}, a_i) of $\mathfrak{N}$, $i = 1, 2, \cdots, n$. (Cf. Fig. 102-1.) The function s is called the **integrand** of the integral $\int_a^b s$.*

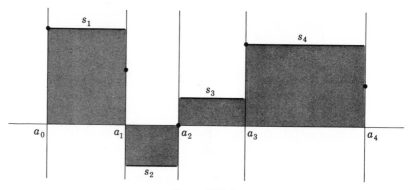

Figure 102-1

*After the German mathematician G.F.B. Riemann (1826–1866).

Example. If s is the step-function defined on the interval [2, 11] by the table:

x	2	(2, 4)	4	(4, 8)	8	(8, 11)	11
$s(x)$	1	5	8	-3	-1	7	4

then the integral of s from 2 to 11 is

$$\int_2^{11} s = 5(4-2) - 3(8-4) + 7(11-8) = 10 - 12 + 21 = 19.$$

NOTE 1. The symbol $\int$ for integration, the so-called **integral sign** was introduced by G. W. Leibniz (German, 1646–1716) and may be thought of as an elongated letter S which is the initial letter of the Latin word *summa* (and the English words *sum* and *summation*). In the first part of this book the notation $\int_a^b s$ of (1) will be used predominantly. The second form for writing the integral in (1), $\int_a^b s(x)dx$, contains what appears to be a variable x, together with a combination dx of two letters that seem to be extraneous to the situation. In subsequent chapters, starting with Chapter 10, this second notation (also due to Leibniz) will be used extensively, and an effort will be made to explain and exploit its many merits. For the present let it suffice to mention that the letter x that appears in (1) is a *dummy variable*, much as the k is that appears in the last part of (3), §510, *PCLA*, for the sigma summation notation. That is, the *value* of (1) is independent of the letter that is used in place of x:

$$(2) \qquad \int_a^b s(x)dx = \int_a^b s(t)dt = \int_a^b s(u)du = \cdots.$$

The variable x in (1) is called the **variable of integration.**

NOTE 2. Since the values of the step-function s at the points of the net $\mathfrak{N}$ do not appear on the right of (1), *the integral of a step-function for a net $\mathfrak{N}$ is independent of its values at the points of the net.*

NOTE 3. If a step-function s is nonnegative, then its integral is equal to the sum of the areas of a set of open rectangles whose union, supplemented by portions of horizontal and vertical line segments, constitutes the ordinate set of s, as shown in Figure 102-2. The integral of a nonnegative step-function assigns to its ordinate set precisely that number that our intuition tells us *should* be assigned as the area of its ordinate set.

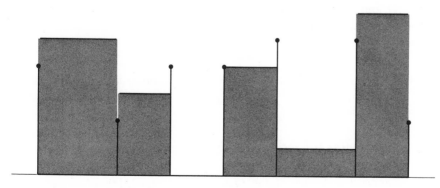

Figure 102-2

An essential theoretical consideration related to the preceding Definition has not yet been mentioned, and that is the question of whether or not the definition is *meaningful*. It was pointed out in §512, *PCLA*, that any step-function is a step-function for many distinct nets, and that whenever a function is a step-function for a net $\mathfrak{N}$, it is also a step-function for any supernet of $\mathfrak{N}$. Since formula (1), above, is expressed in terms of a *particular* net $\mathfrak{N}$, it is at least *conceivable* that when the value of (1) is determined by some *other* net for which s is a step-function the resulting number *might* be different from the number $\int_a^b s$ originally defined by (1). The fact that this cannot occur is guaranteed by the following theorem:

Theorem I. *The value (1) of the integral of any step-function s is independent of the net $\mathfrak{N}$ for which s is a step-function.*

Proof. Since any two nets $\mathfrak{M}$ and $\mathfrak{N}$ possess a common supernet $\mathfrak{P}$, it will be sufficient to prove that the values of (1) determined by two nets $\mathfrak{M}$ and $\mathfrak{N}$ for which s is a step-function are both equal to the value of (1) determined by any common supernet $\mathfrak{P}$. In other words, it will be sufficient to prove that the value of (1) for any supernet $\mathfrak{P}$ is the same as that of (1) for the given net $\mathfrak{N}$. Since $\mathfrak{P}$ is determined by adjoining to $\mathfrak{N}$ a finite set of points, it will be enough to show that as these points are added one at a time, no change in the value of (1) results. Suppose just one point c is added to $\mathfrak{N}$, then, and let it be added between a_{i-1} and a_i: $a_{i-1} < c < a_i$. Then the terms in (1) for the net $\mathfrak{P}$ are identical with those for $\mathfrak{N}$, except that $s_i(a_i - a_{i-1})$ is replaced by two terms with sum

$$(3) \qquad s_i(c - a_{i-1}) + s_i(a_i - c) = s_i[(c - a_{i-1}) + (a_i - c)] = s_i(a_i - a_{i-1}).$$

Therefore the new sum is identical with the original. Since the sum is unchanged with the addition of each new point, the sum for $\mathfrak{P}$ is equal to that for $\mathfrak{N}$, and the proof is complete.

Corollary. *If s and t are two step-functions on the interval [a, b] that are equal for all but a finite number of points of [a, b], then $\int_a^b s = \int_a^b t$.*

Proof. Let $\mathfrak{N}$ be a net for which both s and t are step-functions (Theorem I, §512, *PCLA*), and let $\mathfrak{P}$ be a supernet of $\mathfrak{N}$ that includes all points x at which $s(x) \neq t(x)$. Then by Note 2, above, $\int_a^b s = \int_a^b t$.

Another corollary gives an evaluation for the simplest kind of step-function:

Theorem II. *If f is a function defined on the closed interval [a, b] and constant on the open interval (a, b), then the integral of f on [a, b] is the product of that constant and the length of the interval:*

$$(4) \qquad\qquad f(x) = k \text{ for } a < x < b \Rightarrow \int_a^b f = k(b - a).$$

Proof. Choose for the net $\mathfrak{N}$ the two-point set consisting of a and b only: $\mathfrak{N} : \{a, b\}$. Then the sum (1) consists of one term only, $k(b - a)$.

NOTE 4. In the sequel it will sometimes be notationally convenient to suppress the letters a and b in the symbol $\int_a^b$, when there is no likelihood of confusion, and to write simply:

$$(5) \qquad \int \equiv \int_a^b, \qquad \int f \equiv \int_a^b f.$$

103 THE INTEGRAL AS A POSITIVE LINEAR FUNCTIONAL ON $\mathcal{S}$

Let us recall from §509, *PCLA*, that a real-valued function ϕ on a vector space $\mathcal{V}$ over $\mathcal{R}$ is a *linear functional* on $\mathcal{V}$ if and only if it is *additive* (f and $g \in \mathcal{V} \Rightarrow \phi(f + g) = \phi(f) + \phi(g)$) and *homogeneous* ($\lambda \in \mathcal{R}$ and $f \in \mathcal{V} \Rightarrow \phi(\lambda f) = \lambda \phi(f)$). We shall see that many of the important properties of the Riemann integral are contained in the simple statement: "The integral $\int_a^b$ is a linear functional." More precisely:

Theorem. *If $\mathcal{S}$ is the vector space of all step-functions on a fixed compact interval $[a, b]$, then $\int_a^b$ is a linear functional on $\mathcal{S}$.*

Proof. That $\int_a^b$ is real-valued and well-defined has already been established in §102. To prove additivity, let s and t be any two step-functions on $[a, b]$, let $\mathfrak{N}$: $\{a_0, a_1, \cdots, a_n\}$ be a net for which *both* s and t are step-functions, and let the values of s and t on the ith open interval of $\mathfrak{N}$ be s_i and t_i, respectively, $i = 1, 2, \cdots, n$. Then

$$(1) \qquad \int_a^b (s + t) = \sum_{i=1}^n (s_i + t_i)(a_i - a_{i-1})$$

$$= \sum_{i=1}^n s_i(a_i - a_{i-1}) + \sum_{i=1}^n t_i(a_i - a_{i-1}) = \int_a^b s + \int_a^b t.$$

That $\int_a^b$ is homogeneous is easier to prove:

$$(2) \qquad \int_a^b \lambda s = \sum_{i=1}^n \lambda s_i(a_i - a_{i-1}) = \lambda \sum_{i=1}^n s_i(a_i - a_{i-1}) = \lambda \int_a^b s.$$

Example. If f and g are the functions defined in Example 2, §512, *PCLA*

x	2	(2, 3)	3	(3, 4)	4	(4, 5)	5
$f(x)$	3	1	1	1	5	2	4
$g(x)$	5	3	1	4	4	4	3

then

$$\int_2^5 f = 1(4 - 2) + 2(5 - 4) = 4, \quad \int_2^5 g = 3(3 - 2) + 4(5 - 3) = 11,$$

and

$$\int_2^5 (f + g) = 4(3 - 2) + 5(4 - 3) + 6(5 - 4) = 15 = \int_2^5 f + \int_2^5 g.$$

Furthermore,

$$\int_2^5 7f = 7(4 - 2) + 14(5 - 4) = 28 = 7 \int_2^5 f.$$

In Definition III, §509, *PCLA*, a functional ϕ on a vector space $\mathcal{U}$ of functions was defined to be *positive* if and only if for every f of $\mathcal{U}$ such that $f \geq 0$, $\phi(f) \geq 0$, and there exists an $f \in \mathcal{U}$ such that $\phi(f) \neq 0$. The *integral* defined in §102 is a positive functional on the space $\mathcal{S}$ of step-functions on a compact interval $[a, b]$. This follows in part from the fact that the inequalities

$$(3) \qquad\qquad s_1 \geq 0, \qquad s_2 \geq 0, \qquad \cdots, \qquad s_n \geq 0$$

imply $s_1(a_1 - a_0) \geq 0$, $s_2(a_2 - a_1) \geq 0, \cdots$, $s_n(a_n - a_{n-1}) \geq 0$, and therefore

$$(4) \qquad\qquad \sum_{i=1}^{n} s_i(a_i - a_{i-1}) \geq 0.$$

This fact can be written, for a step-function s on $[a, b]$:

$$(5) \qquad\qquad s \geq 0 \Rightarrow \int_a^b s \geq 0.$$

Finally, the function identically equal to 1 on $[a, b]$ has a positive integral: $\int_a^b 1 = b - a > 0$.

As shown in Note 2, §514, *PCLA*, since $\int_a^b$ is a *linear* functional, (5) has as a consequence:

$$(6) \qquad\qquad s \leq t \Rightarrow \int_a^b s \leq \int_a^b t.$$

In other words, $\int_a^b$ is an *increasing* linear functional on $\mathcal{S}$.

104   EXERCISES

In Exercises 1–4, sketch the ordinate set of the given nonnegative function on the indicated interval. The functions sgn x and $[x]$ are defined in Examples 2 and 3, §115, *PCLA*.

1. $|x|$, $[-2, 3]$.   **2.** $2 + \text{sgn } x$, $[-3, 5]$.

3. $[x]$, $[0, 4]$.   **4.** $x - [x]$, $[-3, 3]$.

In Exercises 5 and 6, evaluate $\int f$, $\int g$, and $\int (f + g)$ and show that $\int (f + g) = \int f + \int g$. Draw graphs.

5.

x	$[1, 3]$	$(3, 4]$
$f(x)$	1	3

x	$[1, 2)$	$[2, 4]$
$g(x)$	4	2

6.

x	$[0, 4)$	$[4, 7]$
$f(x)$	-1	2

x	$[0, 2]$	$(2, 7]$
$g(x)$	2	-4

In Exercises 7 and 8, evaluate $\int (3f - 2g)$ and show that $\int (3f - 2g) = 3 \int f - 2 \int g$, for the functions of the indicated exercise above. Draw graphs.

7. Exercise 5.   **8.** Exercise 6.

9. Construct an example to illustrate Theorem I, §102.

105   RIEMANN-INTEGRABILITY; VECTOR SPACE STRUCTURE

Rectangles can be thought of as the building blocks for a theory of area. By extending our considerations to step-functions that are not restricted to nonnegative values we have been able to use techniques of vector spaces of functions, and linear functionals on them, to introduce the concept of the particular linear functional known as the *integral*, on the space S of step-functions on a fixed bounded closed interval I. We wish now to extend the space S to a much larger space of real-valued functions defined on I, and ultimately to extend the linear functional $\int_a^b$ to this larger space as well. The underlying idea is that of *exhaustion* mentioned in §101, whereby a plane figure is thought of as being "approximated" both from within and from without by simpler figures whose areas can be determined. For more efficacious study of integration, the idea of approximating an *area* from *within* and *without* by *simpler figures* will be replaced by a slightly different approach, that of approximating a *function* from *below* and *above* (in the sense of inequalities relating the functional values) by *simpler functions*, the simpler functions being step-functions. We make this precise in the Definition given below. First, however, it will be convenient to introduce some notation.

Notation. Let f be a real-valued function on a compact interval I. Any step-function s on I satisfying the inequality $s \leq f$ on I is called a **lower step-function for** f (or **of** f), and the class of *all* lower step-functions for f is called the **lower class for** f (or **of** f), and denoted $\mathcal{L}_f$:

$$(1) \qquad \mathcal{L}_f \equiv \{s \mid s \in S, \, s \leq f\}.$$

Any step-function t on I satisfying the inequality $t \geq f$ on I is called an **upper step-function for** f (or **of** f), and the class of *all* upper step-functions for f is called the **upper class for** f (or **of** f), and denoted $\mathcal{U}_f$:

$$(2) \qquad \mathcal{U}_f \equiv \{t \mid t \in S, \, t \geq f\}.$$

The lower class for f is nonempty if and only if f is bounded below (if f is bounded below then there exists a *constant* function belonging to the lower class, and if there exists a member s of the lower class, then since s is bounded below so is f).

Similarly, the upper class for f is nonempty if and only if f is bounded above.

Definition. *Let f be a real-valued function defined on a compact interval $[a, b]$. Then f is **Riemann-integrable** or **integrable on** $[a, b]$ if and only if corresponding to an arbitrary positive number ϵ there exist step-functions s and t belonging to the lower class for f and the upper class for f, respectively, such that $\int_a^b (t - s) < \epsilon$, or in terms of quantifiers:*

$$(3) \qquad \forall \, \epsilon > 0, \, \exists \, (s, t) \in \mathcal{L}_f \times \mathcal{U}_f \ni \int_a^b (t - s) < \epsilon.$$

The class of integrable functions will be denoted $\mathfrak{D}$.* *(Cf. Fig. 105-1.)*

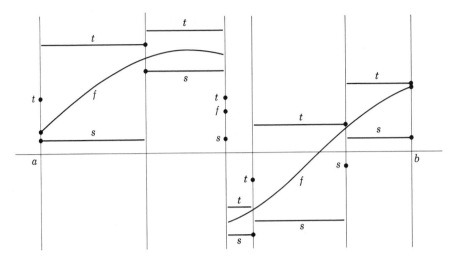

Figure 105-1

We shall defer until §109 any attempt to assign a numerical value to what will be known as the *integral* of f, and content ourselves for the present with a brief study of the behavior of the class $\mathfrak{D}$. We can think of the members of $\mathfrak{D}$ as being those functions that are sufficiently well-behaved to permit themselves to be arbitrarily closely "squeezed" or "pinched" by step-functions, in the sense of (3). As we shall see, this class of functions is a very extensive one.

Our first comment is that the class $\mathfrak{D}$ is not empty:

Theorem I. *Every step-function is integrable.*

Proof. If f is a step-function, then for every $\epsilon > 0$ there exist the step-functions s and t: $s = t = f$ satisfying (trivially) the inequalities $s \leqq f \leqq t$ and $\int_a^b (t - s) = 0 < \epsilon$.

On the other hand, *not every* function defined on $[a, b]$ belongs to $\mathfrak{D}$. In particular, no unbounded function can be a member of $\mathfrak{D}$ by virtue of the theorem:

Theorem II. *Every function integrable on $[a, b]$ is bounded there.*

Proof. If f is integrable on $[a, b]$ its lower class and upper class are both nonempty, and therefore f is bounded both below and above.

It is not too simple a matter to find a *bounded* function that fails to be integrable, but we shall exhibit one in the Example below. For this purpose, as well as for future use, it will be helpful to formulate the negation of (3) in positive terms:

*The letter $\mathfrak{D}$ can be thought of as standing for the word *definite*, since the class $\mathfrak{D}$ consists of all functions that possess a *definite* integral on $[a, b]$. The letters $\mathfrak{R}$ (for *Riemann*) and $\mathfrak{s}$ (for *integrable*) are already otherwise appropriated.

Theorem III. Negation of integrability. *A real-valued function f defined on* [a, b] **fails** *to be integrable there if and only if*

(4) $$\exists \, \epsilon > 0 \ni \forall \, (s, t) \in \mathcal{L}_f \times \mathcal{U}_f, \, \int_a^b (t - s) \geq \epsilon.$$

Proof. We should first recall the general form for the negations of statements expressed in terms of a single quantifier (§206, *PCLA*):

(5) $$\sim (\forall \, x \in A, \, p(x) \text{ is true}) \Leftrightarrow \exists \, x \in A \ni p(x) \text{ is false},$$

(6) $$\sim (\exists \, x \in A \ni p(x) \text{ is true}) \Leftrightarrow \forall \, x \in A, \, p(x) \text{ is false}.$$

We start by using (5) and writing the negation of (3):

(7) $$\sim (\forall \, \epsilon > 0, \, \exists \cdots) \Leftrightarrow \exists \, \epsilon > 0 \ni \sim (\exists \cdots).$$

The next step is to reformulate $\sim (\exists \cdots)$, by use of (6):

(8) $$\sim (\exists \, (s, t) \in \mathcal{L}_f \times \mathcal{U}_f \ni \int_a^b (t - s) < \epsilon)$$
$$\Leftrightarrow \forall \, (s, t) \in \mathcal{L}_f \times \mathcal{U}_f, \, \sim (\int_a^b (t - s) < \epsilon).$$

Since the negation of the inequality $\int_a^b (t - s) < \epsilon$ is the inequality $\int_a^b (t - s) \geq \epsilon$, we have only to fit together the pieces on the right of the equivalences (7) and (8) to obtain (4).

Example. Show that the function f defined on the interval $[0, 1]$ and equal to 1 if x is rational and $0 \leq x \leq 1$, and equal to 0 if x is irrational and $0 < x < 1$ (cf. the Example, §316, *PCLA*), is not integrable on $[0, 1]$.

Solution. We start by examining the nature of step-functions s and t satisfying the in-equalities $s \leq f \leq t$ on $[0, 1]$. Consider an arbitrary open interval (a_{i-1}, a_i) of a net $\mathfrak{N}$ on $[0, 1]$ for which s and t are lower and upper step-functions, respectively, for f. Since the set of rational numbers is dense in $[0, 1]$ (cf. §315, *PCLA*), there must exist a rational number r_i between a_{i-1} and a_i, and therefore belonging to the open interval (a_{i-1}, a_i). By definition, $f(r_i) = 1$, and therefore $t(r_i) \geq f(r_i) = 1$. If the constant value of t on the open interval (a_{i-1}, a_i) is t_i, $i = 1, 2, \cdots, n$, then $\int_a^b t$ satisfies the inequality:

(9) $$\int_a^b t = \sum_{i=1}^n t_i(a_i - a_{i-1}) \geq \sum_{i=1}^n 1 \cdot (a_i - a_{i-1}) = a_n - a_0 = 1.$$

By a similar argument, using the fact that the set of irrational numbers is dense in $[0, 1]$ (cf. §316, *PCLA*), and inequalities of the form $s_i = s(x_i) \leq f(x_i) = 0$, we have

(10) $$\int_a^b s = \sum_{i=1}^n s_i(a_i - a_{i-1}) \leq \sum_{i=1}^n 0 \cdot (a_i - a_{i-1}) = 0.$$

Therefore, since $\int_a^b t \geq 1$ and $-\int_a^b s \geq 0$, addition gives the inequality: $\int_a^b (t - s) = \int_a^b t - \int_a^b s \geq 1$, and we have only to choose ϵ equal to 1 in order to establish (4) for the given function f.

One of the more useful facts regarding integrable functions is that as a class they form a space having a structure with which we are becoming familiar:

Theorem IV. *The function space $\mathfrak{D}$ of all real-valued functions integrable on a fixed compact interval I is a vector space.*

Proof. The first part is to prove:

$$(f, g) \in \mathfrak{D} \times \mathfrak{D} \Rightarrow f + g \in \mathfrak{D}. \tag{11}$$

Accordingly, for a given positive number ϵ, we are to construct step-functions flanking $f + g$ (one belonging to the lower class of $f + g$ and one belonging to the upper class of $f + g$) such that the integral of the larger minus the smaller is less than ϵ. It is clear that this "pinch" on $f + g$ must be achieved as the result of separate "pinches" on f and g. It is also not unreasonable to expect that if we are to combine two "squeezes" into a resultant "squeeze" involving a measure of accuracy equal to ϵ, then each constituent "squeeze" should be regulated by at most *half* of ϵ. This is the way we start, therefore, for f and g separately. Let s and t be two step-functions on I such that $s \leq f \leq t$ and $\int_a^b (t - s) < \frac{1}{2}\epsilon$, and let σ and τ be two step-functions on I such that $\sigma \leq g \leq \tau$ and $\int_a^b (\tau - \sigma) < \frac{1}{2}\epsilon$. Then, combining the preceding inequalities, we have:

$$s + \sigma \leq f + g \leq t + \tau, \tag{12}$$

and since the space $\mathcal{S}$ of all step-functions on I is a vector space, $s + \sigma$ and $t + \tau$ are two step-functions of the desired nature, provided the integral of the larger minus the smaller is less than ϵ. That this is true follows from the fact that $\int_a^b$ is a linear functional on $\mathcal{S}$:

$$(13) \quad \int_a^b [(t + \tau) - (s + \sigma)] = \int_a^b [(t - s) + (\tau - \sigma)]$$
$$= \int_a^b (t - s) + \int_a^b (\tau - \sigma) < \frac{1}{2}\epsilon + \frac{1}{2}\epsilon = \epsilon.$$

In the second part of the proof we wish to show:

$$(\lambda, f) \in \mathfrak{R} \times \mathfrak{D} \Rightarrow \lambda f \in \mathfrak{D}. \tag{14}$$

The details depend on the nature of λ. Assume first that $\lambda > 0$. If s and t are step-functions such that $s \leq f \leq t$ then λs and λt are step-functions such that $\lambda s \leq \lambda f \leq \lambda t$, and

$$\int_a^b (\lambda t - \lambda s) = \int_a^b \lambda(t - s) = \lambda \int_a^b (t - s),$$

by the linearity of $\int_a^b$ on $\mathcal{S}$. We wish to find s and t such that

$$\int_a^b (\lambda t - \lambda s) = \lambda \int_a^b (t - s) < \epsilon. \tag{15}$$

The inequality in (15) tells us how to obtain s and t in terms of f: we require that $s \leq f \leq t$, and furthermore, in terms of the positive number ϵ/λ, that:

$$\int_a^b (t - s) < \frac{\epsilon}{\lambda}. \tag{16}$$

As a consequence of the requirement (16), the inequality of (15) is true, and the second part of the proof is complete if $\lambda > 0$. Assume next that $\lambda = 0$. Then $\lambda f = 0$, and the zero function is integrable. In the third place, assume that $\lambda = -1$, and let ϵ be an arbitrary positive number. From the fact that there exist step-functions s and t such that

$$s \leq f \leq t \quad \text{and} \quad \int_a^b (t - s) < \epsilon \tag{17}$$

we can infer immediately that there exist step-functions $-t$ and $-s$ such that

(18) $-t \leq -f \leq -s$ and $\int_a^b [(-s) - (-t)] < \epsilon,$

since (17) and (18) are equivalent. Therefore $\lambda f = -f$ is integrable. Finally, if $\lambda < 0$ and $f \in \mathfrak{D}$, since $-f \in \mathfrak{D}$ and $\lambda f = (-\lambda)(-f)$, λf has the form of a positive constant $(-\lambda)$ times a member $(-f)$ of $\mathfrak{D}$, and is therefore a member of $\mathfrak{D}$. This completes the proof.

NOTE. In terms of the notation $\mathfrak{S}$ for the vector space of step-functions on $[a, b]$, $\mathfrak{D}$ for the vector space of functions integrable on $[a, b]$, and $\mathfrak{B}$ for the vector space of functions bounded on $[a, b]$ (§507, *PCLA*), the statement of Theorems I and II can be expressed by the double inclusion:

(19) $\mathfrak{S} \subset \mathfrak{D} \subset \mathfrak{B}.$

106   INTEGRABILITY OF MONOTONIC FUNCTIONS

We already know (Theorem I, §105) that every step-function is integrable. With the aid of the next theorem we shall be able to extend the class of functions known to be integrable to the class of all functions monotonic on a compact interval.

Theorem I.   *Every real-valued function defined and increasing on a compact interval is integrable there.*

Proof.   Assume that f is defined and increasing on $[a, b]$. If f is constant then f is integrable. Assume now that f is *not* constant, so that $f(a) < f(b)$, and let ϵ be a given positive number. We propose now to construct step-functions s and t such that $s \leq f \leq t$ and $\int_a^b (t - s) < \epsilon$. For simplicity, and ease in evaluating the integral of $t - s$, we divide the interval $[a, b]$ into n subintervals of *equal length*, where n is a positive integer, by letting $\mathfrak{N}$ be a net of the form:

$$\mathfrak{N} = \{a_0, a_1, a_2, \cdots, a_n\} = \left\{a, a + \frac{1}{n}(b - a), a + \frac{2}{n}(b - a), \cdots, b\right\},$$

where $a_i = a + \dfrac{i}{n}(b - a)$, $i = 0, 1, 2, \cdots, n$. We next define the step-functions s and t, as indicated in Figure 106-1:

(1) $s(x) \equiv \begin{cases} f(a_{i-1}) & \text{if } a_{i-1} < x < a_i, \ i = 1, 2, \cdots, n, \\ f(a_i) & \text{if } x = a_i, \qquad\quad i = 0, 1, 2, \cdots, n, \end{cases}$

(2) $t(x) \equiv \begin{cases} f(a_i) & \text{if } a_{i-1} < x < a_i, \ i = 1, 2, \cdots, n, \\ f(a_i) & \text{if } x = a_i, \qquad\quad i = 0, 1, 2, \cdots, n. \end{cases}$

Then the inequalities

(3) $s(x) \leq f(x) \leq t(x)$

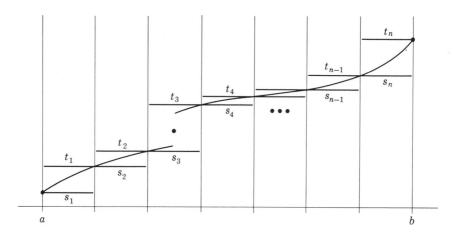

Figure 106-1

hold for every x: if $a_{i-1} < x < a_i$, then $s(x) = f(a_{i-1}) \leq f(x) \leq f(a_i) = t(x)$; if $x = a_i$, then $s(x) = f(a_i) = t(x)$. The integral of $t - s$ is equal to

$$(4) \quad \int_a^b (t - s) = \sum_{i=1}^n (f(a_i) - f(a_{i-1}))(a_i - a_{i-1})$$

$$= \sum_{i=1}^n (f(a_i) - f(a_{i-1}))\left(\frac{b - a}{n}\right) = \frac{b - a}{n} \sum_{i=1}^n (f(a_i) - f(a_{i-1}))$$

$$= \frac{b - a}{n} [-f(a_0) + f(a_1) - f(a_1) + f(a_2) - \cdots - f(a_{n-1}) + f(a_n)]$$

$$= \frac{b - a}{n} [-f(a_0) + f(a_n)].$$

With $a_0 = a$ and $a_n = b$, this takes the form

$$(5) \qquad\qquad\qquad \int_a^b (t - s) = \frac{b - a}{n}(f(b) - f(a)).$$

In order to make this less than ϵ, we have only to choose n sufficiently large. To be specific we solve the inequality $(b - a)(f(b) - f(a))/n < \epsilon$ to obtain:

$$(6) \qquad\qquad\qquad n > \frac{(b - a)(f(b) - f(a))}{\epsilon}.$$

By the Archimedean property for real numbers (§315, *PCLA*), there exists a positive integer n satisfying (6), and therefore step-functions s and t such that $s \leq f \leq t$ and $\int_a^b (t - s) < \epsilon$. With this, the proof of the integrability of f is complete.

Theorem I can be extended immediately:

Theorem II.   *Every real-valued function defined and monotonic on a compact interval is integrable there.*

Proof.   If f is monotonic on $[a, b]$, then either f is increasing or f is decreasing there. If f is increasing it is integrable by Theorem I. If f is decreasing, then $-f$ is increasing and hence integrable on $[a, b]$. By Theorem IV, §105, $f = -(-f)$ is integrable on $[a, b]$.

107 PRODUCTS AND ABSOLUTE VALUES OF INTEGRABLE FUNCTIONS

It is proved in H§609, *CWAG*, that the vector space $\mathfrak{D}$ of functions integrable on a compact interval has structure properties going well beyond those of a vector space. In particular, it is shown that $\mathfrak{D}$ is an algebra of functions. We record this fact in the following form:

Theorem I.   *The product of two functions each of which is integrable on a compact interval I is integrable on I.*

We also record one further fact that is established in H§609, *CWAG:*

Theorem II.   *If the function f is integrable on a compact interval I, then its absolute value $|f|$ is also integrable there.*

Let $I = [a, b]$ be an arbitrary compact interval and let $\mathfrak{D}$ be the vector space of functions integrable on I. Since the constant function 1 and the identity function $x \to x$ are both monotonic on I, they both belong to $\mathfrak{D}$. By Theorem I, above, the product of the identity function and itself, $x \to x^2$, also belongs to $\mathfrak{D}$. Similarly, the product of the two functions $x \to x$ and $x \to x^2$, or $x \to x^3$, also is a member of $\mathfrak{D}$. By induction, the following functions are all members of $\mathfrak{D}$, where elliptic notation is used:

(1) $1, x, x^2, \cdots, x^n,$

for any positive integer n. Since any polynomial

(2) $a_n + a_{n-1}x + a_{n-2}x^2 + \cdots + a_1 x^{n-1} + a_0 x^n$

is a linear combination of the members (1) of the vector space $\mathfrak{D}$, and since $\mathfrak{D}$ is closed under all linear combinations, we have the additional result:

Theorem III.   *Every polynomial is integrable on every compact interval.*

NOTE 1.   The actual *evaluation* of definite integrals of polynomials will be presented in §114, and for certain other functions in Chapter 10.

NOTE 2.   Theorem III can be expressed as follows in terms of the vector space Π of polynomials on $[a, b]$ and the vector space $\mathfrak{D}$ of functions integrable on $[a, b]$:

(3) $\Pi \subset \mathfrak{D}.$

108 EXERCISES

In Exercises 1–14, give an adequate set of reasons why the given function is integrable on the specified interval. The functions sgn x and $[x]$ are defined in Examples 2 and 3, §115, *PCLA*.

1. $3x^2 + 5x - 8$, $[-2, 10]$.

2. $x^2 - 8x - 11$, $[-5, 2]$.

3. sgn x, $[-6, 8]$.

4. $[x]$, $[-2, 9]$.

5. $|x|$, $[-4, 4]$.

6. $|5x - 3|$, $[-1, 8]$.

7. $|5x^2 - 7x - 3|$, $[-1, 7]$.

8. $|16 - 8x^2 + 5x^4|$, $[-6, 9]$.

9. $8 \operatorname{sgn} x - 5[x]$, $[-6, 2]$.

10. $4[x + 1] - |6x^2 - 8|$, $[-6, 7]$.

11. $f(x) \equiv \begin{cases} 5 - 2x, & -2 \leq x < 1, \\ 4 - 3x, & 1 \leq x \leq 3, \end{cases}$ $[-2, 3]$.

12. $f(x) \equiv \begin{cases} x^2, & 0 \leq x \leq 2, \\ x^3, & 2 < x \leq 4, \end{cases}$ $[0, 4]$.

13. $[x] \cdot (x^2 - 5)$, $[-4, 6]$.

14. $(x - [x])^2$, $[-2, 5]$.

109 THE RIEMANN INTEGRAL

In §105 we defined *integrability* of a function in terms of upper and lower step-functions that closely flank the given function. We are ready now to proceed to the next major step by assigning to each integrable function a numerical value called its **integral**. This process of obtaining integrals of integrable functions is called **integration**, and depends on the completeness axiom of the real number system.

Definition. *Let f be a real-valued function defined and integrable on a compact interval* $I = [a, b]$, *and let* $\mathcal{L}_f$ *and* $\mathcal{U}_f$, *respectively, denote the lower and upper classes (of step-functions) for f on the interval I. The* **Riemann integral** *or* **definite integral** *or* **integral of f on** $[a, b]$ *or* **from a to b** *is denoted and defined:*

(1)
$$\int_a^b f = \int_a^b f(x)dx \equiv \sup \left\{ \int_a^b s \, \middle| \, s \in \mathcal{L}_f \right\}$$
$$\equiv \inf \left\{ \int_a^b t \, \middle| \, t \in \mathcal{U}_f \right\}.$$

That is, the integral of f is the least upper bound of the set of integrals of all lower step-functions for f, and also the greatest lower bound of the set of integrals of all upper step-functions for f, where the integral of a step-function is the integral defined in §102. The function f is called the **integrand** *of the integral* $\int_a^b f$. *The variable x appearing in (1) is called the* **variable of integration**. *The numbers a and b are called the* **limits of integration**, *a being the* **lower limit** *and b being the* **upper limit**. *To integrate f from a to b means to determine the value of (1).*

The first essential is to prove that the two formulas of (1) — one for the lower step-functions of f and one for the upper step-functions of f — give the same result.

Define the two sets:

(2) $$L \equiv \{\int_a^b s \mid s \in \mathcal{L}_f\},$$

(3) $$U \equiv \{\int_a^b t \mid t \in \mathcal{U}_f\}.$$

Then every member of L is less than or equal to every member of U:

(4) $$(l, u) \in L \times U \Rightarrow l \leq u.$$

This follows from the fact that $s \leq f \leq t \Rightarrow s \leq t \Rightarrow \int_a^b s \leq \int_a^b t$ (cf. (6), §103).

Since every u in U is an upper bound of L, we have sup $L \leq u$. But this means than sup L is a lower bound for U and hence less than or equal to inf U, or:

(5) $$\text{sup } L \leq \text{inf } U.$$

We wish to prove that equality must hold in (5). To do this we assume that sup $L < $ inf U, and let $\epsilon \equiv$ inf $U -$ sup L. Then for *every* pair of step-functions s and t such that $s \in \mathcal{L}_f$ and $t \in \mathcal{U}_f$, since $\int_a^b s \leq$ sup L and $\int_a^b t \geq$ inf U, it must follow that $\int_a^b t \geq$ inf U and $- \int_a^b s \geq -$ sup L and therefore, by addition,

(6) $$\int_a^b (t - s) \geq \text{inf } U - \text{sup } L = \epsilon.$$

By Theorem III, §105, the function f is shown to be *not* integrable on $[a, b]$ and a contradiction is obtained on the basis of the assumption sup $L <$ inf U. By (5), therefore, it is established that sup $L =$ inf U, and the preceding Definition is proved to be consistent in the two evaluations for the integral $\int_a^b f$.

Since by definition, from (1), for any function f integrable on $[a, b]$, $\int_a^b f$ is an upper bound of the set L, we have the inequality $\int_a^b f \geq \int_a^b s$ for every lower step-function s of f. Similarly, $\int_a^b f \leq \int_a^b t$ for every upper step-function t of f. Combining these, we have:

(7) $$(s, t) \in \mathcal{L}_f \times \mathcal{U}_f \Rightarrow \int_a^b s \leq \int_a^b f \leq \int_a^b t.$$

An easy consequence of (7) is the fact that the integral as defined in this section is consistent with that given in §102 in the particular case that the function is a step-function. In other words, if f is a step-function on $[a, b]$, then $\int_a^b f$, as given by (1) above, is equal to the value given in §102, in the definition of the integral of a step-function. It is therefore of no serious moment that we have used the same notation $\int_a^b$ for two different integrals; on the space $\mathcal{S}$ of step-functions they are identical. In the language of §111, *PCLA*, the integral $\int_a^b$ of this section is an **extension** of that of §102.

A useful criterion for the value of the integral of an integrable function is given in the theorem:

Theorem .   *If f is integrable on the compact interval $[a, b]$, and if γ is a number, then γ is the value of the integral of f on $[a, b]$:*

(8) $$\gamma = \int_a^b f$$

if and only if, for an arbitrary positive number ϵ, *there exist step-functions s such that* $s \leqq f$ *and* $\int_a^b s > \gamma - \epsilon$, *and* t *such that* $t \geqq f$ *and* $\int_a^b t < \gamma + \epsilon$:

(9) $$\forall \epsilon > 0, \exists (s, t) \in \mathcal{L}_f \times \mathcal{U}_f \ni \int_a^b t - \epsilon < \gamma < \int_a^b s + \epsilon.$$

Proof. First assume (8), and let $\epsilon > 0$ be given. Since $\gamma - \epsilon$ is less than γ and since γ is the *least* upper bound of the set L defined in (2), than $\gamma - \epsilon$ is *not* an upper bound for L and there must exist a lower step-function s, for f, such that $\int_a^b s > \gamma - \epsilon$. This gives the right-hand inequality of (9). Similarly, since $\gamma + \epsilon$ is not a lower bound for the set U defined in (3), there must exist an upper step-function t, for f, such that $\int_a^b t < \gamma + \epsilon$, and the left-hand inequality of (9) must hold.

Now assume that (9) is true, let ϵ be an arbitrary positive number, and let s and t be step-functions satisfying (9). Then from (7) and (9) together, we have

(10) $$\int_a^b f - \epsilon < \gamma < \int_a^b f + \epsilon.$$

The inequalities (10) can be written in the form

(11) $$-\epsilon < \gamma - \int_a^b f < \epsilon,$$

or by Theorem I(*iv*), §311, *PCLA*:

(12) $$|\gamma - \int_a^b f| < \epsilon.$$

Since ϵ is an *arbitrary* positive number and the left-hand member of (12) is a non-negative *constant*, this constant must be equal to zero (cf. Exercise 15, §305, *PCLA*), and the equality (8) is established.

110   THE INTEGRAL AS A LINEAR FUNCTIONAL

Many of the basic properties of the Riemann integral follow from the fact that it is a linear functional on the space $\mathfrak{D}$:

Theorem. *Let* $\mathfrak{D}$ *be the vector space of integrable functions on the compact interval* [*a, b*], *and for each* $f \in \mathfrak{D}$ *let the integral* $\int_a^b$ *be defined as prescribed in §109. Then* $\int_a^b$ *is a linear functional on* $\mathfrak{D}$.

Proof. For the first part of the proof we assume that f and g belong to $\mathfrak{D}$, and we wish to prove that

(1) $$\int_a^b (f + g) = \int_a^b f + \int_a^b g.$$

The technique for establishing (1) is to use the Theorem, §109, and show that the number $\gamma \equiv \int_a^b f + \int_a^b g$ on the right-hand side of (1) is such that for every positive number ϵ there exist step-functions S and T belonging respectively to the lower class and the upper class of $f + g$ and such that

(2) $$\int_a^b T - \epsilon < \gamma < \int_a^b S + \epsilon.$$

In order to find the step-functions S and T we combine step-functions associated separately with f and g, and as in the proof of Theorem IV, §105, we shall use a

"$\frac{1}{2}\epsilon$" type of argument. Accordingly, by (8) and (9) of §109, with $\frac{1}{2}\epsilon$ playing the role of ϵ, we let s, t, σ, and τ be step-functions such that $s \leqq f \leqq t$, $\sigma \leqq g \leqq \tau$, and:

(3) $$\int_a^b t - \tfrac{1}{2}\epsilon < \int_a^b f < \int_a^b s + \tfrac{1}{2}\epsilon,$$

(4) $$\int_a^b \tau - \tfrac{1}{2}\epsilon < \int_a^b g < \int_a^b \sigma + \tfrac{1}{2}\epsilon,$$

and therefore, by addition and the linearity of $\int_a^b$ on the space $\mathcal{S}$:

(5) $$\int_a^b (t + \tau) - \epsilon < \int_a^b f + \int_a^b g < \int_a^b (s + \sigma) + \epsilon.$$

This is precisely of the form (2), with $S \equiv s + \sigma$ and $T \equiv t + \tau$, since $s + \sigma \leqq f + g \leqq t + \tau$. By the Theorem, §109, with $\gamma \equiv \int_a^b f + \int_a^b g$, the equality (1) is established.

For the second part of the proof, we assume that $f \in \mathcal{D}$ and that $\lambda \in \mathcal{R}$, and we wish to prove that

(6) $$\int_a^b \lambda f = \lambda \int_a^b f.$$

As in the proof of Theorem IV, §105, the details depend on the nature of λ. Assume first that $\lambda > 0$, and in terms of an arbitrary positive number ϵ let s and t be step-functions on $[a, b]$ such that $s \leqq f \leqq t$ and, by the Theorem, §109:

(7) $$\int_a^b t - \frac{\epsilon}{\lambda} < \int_a^b f < \int_a^b s + \frac{\epsilon}{\lambda},$$

whence (by the linearity of $\int_a^b$ for step-functions):

(8) $$\int_a^b \lambda t - \epsilon < \lambda \int_a^b f < \int_a^b \lambda s + \epsilon.$$

But since λs and λt are lower and upper step-functions, respectively, of λf, the inequalities (8) provide an implication of the type of (9), §109, where $\gamma \equiv \lambda \int_a^b f$, and where the function λf is the function under consideration. By the Theorem, §109, the constant $\lambda \int_a^b f$ must be equal to the integral $\int_a^b \lambda f$, and (6) is established for the case $\lambda > 0$. For the case $\lambda = 0$, (6) is trivially true. Now assume $\lambda = -1$. Then since additivity is already proved for $\int_a^b$, we know that

(9) $$\int_a^b f + \int_a^b (-f) = \int_a^b (f + (-f)) = \int_a^b 0 = 0,$$

and therefore

(10) $$\int_a^b (-f) = - \int_a^b f,$$

which is (6) for $\lambda = -1$. Finally, if $\lambda < 0$, from cases already proved:

(11) $$\int_a^b \lambda f = \int_a^b (-\lambda)(-f) = (-\lambda) \int_a^b (-f) = (-\lambda)(-\int_a^b f) = \lambda \int_a^b f,$$

and the proof is complete.

111   THE INTEGRAL AS A POSITIVE LINEAR FUNCTIONAL

The inequalities (5) and (6), §103, established for the linear functional $\int_a^b$ on the space $\mathcal{S}$ of step-functions, apply as well on the space $\mathcal{D}$ of integrable functions:

Theorem I. *If f and g are real-valued functions integrable on a compact interval* [a, b], *then*

(1)
$$f \geqq 0 \Rightarrow \int_a^b f \geqq 0,$$

(2)
$$f \leqq g \Rightarrow \int_a^b f \leqq \int_a^b g.$$

Therefore, since there exist functions with positive integrals, the linear functional $\int_a^b$ *is positive (and increasing) on the vector space* $\mathfrak{D}$ *of functions integrable on* [a, b].

Proof. By (7), §109, since the zero function is a lower step-function for any non-negative integrable function f, $\int_a^b f \geqq \int_a^b 0 = 0$, and (1) is proved. The implication (2) follows from (1) as in §103, by the linearity of $\int_a^b : f \leqq g \Rightarrow \int_a^b g - \int_a^b f = \int_a^b (g - f) \geqq 0$.

To help in establishing the fact that the ordinate set of any nonnegative integrable function has area equal to the integral of that function (cf. §201), we state the following theorem, which says in brief that for purposes of approximating the integral of a nonnegative integrable function by means of integrals of lower step-functions, we may assume that *only nonnegative lower step-functions are being considered.* Because of its intuitively simple nature the proof is omitted. Details are given in §613, *CWAG*.

Theorem II. *If f is nonnegative and integrable on* [a, b], *then*

(3)
$$\int_a^b f = \sup \left\{ \int_a^b s \,\middle|\, s \in \mathfrak{L}_f, s \geqq 0 \right\}.$$

112 INTEGRABILITY ON SUBINTERVALS

Many important properties pertaining to functions defined on a compact interval I are inherited by the restrictions of these functions to an arbitrary closed subinterval of I. Since one of these properties is integrability, we shall find it convenient to have the following simplifying definition:

Definition. *If $a \leqq b < c \leqq d$ and if a function f is defined on the interval* [a, d], *then f is said to be* **integrable** *on the subinterval* [b, c] *if and only if the restriction g of f to* [b, c] *is integrable on* [b, c]. *If f is integrable on* [b, c], *its* **integral** *there is defined to be that of its restriction g on that interval, with the notation:*

(1)
$$\int_b^c f \equiv \int_b^c g, \quad or \quad \int_b^c f(x)\,dx \equiv \int_b^c g(x)\,dx.$$

Theorem I. *If $a \leqq b < c \leqq d$, and if s is a step-function on* [a, d], *then the restriction of s to* [b, c] *is a step-function on* [b, c].

Proof. This is easy and is left to the reader.

Theorem II.   *If $a \leqq b < c \leqq d$ and if s is a nonnegative step-function on $[a, d]$, then*

$$(2) \qquad \int_b^c s \leqq \int_a^d s.$$

Proof.   Let $\mathfrak{N} : \{a_0, a_1, a_2, \cdots, a_n\}$ be a net on $[a, d]$ that includes the points b and c and for which s is a step-function, and assume that $b = a_i$ and $c = a_j$, where $0 \leqq i < j \leqq n$. If $s_k \equiv s(x)$ for $a_{k-1} < x < a_k$, $k = 1, 2, \cdots, n$, then every s_k is nonnegative, for $k = 1, 2, \cdots, n$, and therefore

$$(3) \qquad \int_a^d s = \sum_{k=1}^n s_k(a_k - a_{k-1})$$

$$= \sum_{k=1}^i s_k(a_k - a_{k-1}) + \sum_{l=i+1}^j s_l(a_l - a_{l-1}) + \sum_{m=j+1}^n s_m(a_m - a_{m-1})$$

$$\geqq \sum_{l=i+1}^j s_l(a_l - a_{l-1}) = \int_b^c s.$$

(It should be understood that if $i = 0$ then the first sum on the second line of (3) is absent and that if $j = n$ then the third sum on the second line of (3) is absent.)

We now turn our attention to more general functions than step-functions:

Theorem III.   *If $a \leqq b < c \leqq d$ and if f is integrable on $[a, d]$, then f is integrable on $[b, c]$. That is, every function integrable on a bounded closed interval is integrable on every closed subinterval.*

Proof.   If ϵ is an arbitrary positive number, let s and t be lower and upper step-functions, respectively, for f on the interval $[a, d]$ such that

$$(4) \qquad \int_a^d (t - s) < \epsilon.$$

Then the restrictions σ and τ of s and t, respectively, to the interval $[b, c]$ are lower and upper step-functions, respectively, for the restriction g of f to the interval $[b, c]$, and by Theorem II, since $t - s$ is a nonnegative step-function on $[a, d]$

$$(5) \qquad \int_b^c (\tau - \sigma) = \int_b^c (t - s) \leqq \int_a^d (t - s) < \epsilon.$$

113   ADDITIVITY ON ADJACENT INTERVALS

The two theorems of this section describe a kind of additivity of the integral operator $\int$ that is distinct from that of (1), §110.

Theorem I.   *If $a < b < c$ and if s is any step-function on $[a, c]$, then*

$$(1) \qquad \int_a^c s = \int_a^b s + \int_b^c s.$$

Proof.   Let $\mathfrak{N} = \{a_0, a_1, \cdots, a_n\}$ be a net on $[a, c]$ with $b = a_k$, and let $s(x) = s_i$ for $a_{i-1} < x < a_i$, $i = 1, 2, \cdots, n$. Then

$$(2) \qquad \int_a^c s = \sum_{i=1}^k s_i(a_i - a_{i-1}) + \sum_{i=k+1}^n s_i(a_i - a_{i-1}) = \int_a^b s + \int_b^c s.$$

The following theorem differs from Theorem III, §112, in that assumptions for subintervals are now transmitted into a conclusion valid for a superinterval (cf. Fig. 113-1):

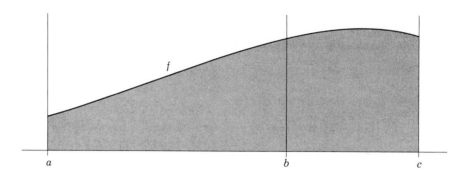

Figure 113-1

Theorem II.   *If $a < b < c$, if f is defined on $[a, c]$, and if f is integrable on both $[a, b]$ and $[b, c]$, then f is integrable on $[a, c]$ and*

$$(3) \qquad \int_a^c f = \int_a^b f + \int_b^c f.$$

Proof.   Let ϵ be an arbitrary positive number, let s and t be lower and upper step-functions, respectively, for the restriction of f to $[a, b]$ and let σ and τ be lower and upper step-functions, respectively, for the restriction of f to $[b, c]$, such that

$$(4) \qquad \int_a^b (t - s) < \tfrac{1}{2}\epsilon \quad \text{and} \quad \int_b^c (\tau - \sigma) < \tfrac{1}{2}\epsilon.$$

Let the step-functions S and T be defined (cf. Fig. 113-2):

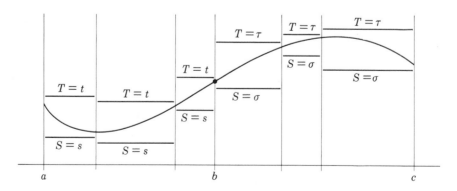

Figure 113-2

(5)
$$S(x) \equiv \begin{cases} s(x) & \text{if } a \leqq x < b, \\ f(b) & \text{if } x = b, \\ \sigma(x) & \text{if } b < x \leqq c, \end{cases}$$

(6)
$$T(x) \equiv \begin{cases} t(x) & \text{if } a \leqq x < b, \\ f(b) & \text{if } x = b, \\ \tau(x) & \text{if } b < x \leqq c. \end{cases}$$

Then S and T are lower and upper step-functions, respectively, for f on the interval $[a, c]$. Furthermore, S is identical to s on $[a, b]$ except possibly at the point b and is identical to σ on $[b, c]$ except possibly at the point b, and T is identical to t on $[a, b]$ except possibly at the point b and is identical to τ on $[b, c]$ except possibly at the point b. Therefore, by Note 2, §102, and Theorem I, above,

(7)
$$\int_a^c S = \int_a^b s + \int_b^c \sigma, \quad \int_a^c T = \int_a^b t + \int_b^c \tau.$$

Therefore, by subtraction and use of (4):

(8)
$$\int_a^c (T - S) = \int_a^b (t - s) + \int_b^c (\tau - \sigma) < \tfrac{1}{2}\epsilon + \tfrac{1}{2}\epsilon = \epsilon.$$

This proves that f is integrable on $[a, c]$.

To prove the equality (3) we use the Theorem, §109, with $\gamma \equiv \int_a^b f + \int_b^c f$. That is, we shall show that this number γ is such that for every positive number ϵ there exist step-functions S and T belonging respectively to the lower class and the upper class of f on $[a, c]$ and such that

(9)
$$\int_a^c T - \epsilon < \gamma < \int_a^c S + \epsilon.$$

The step-functions S and T are defined in the manner of (5) and (6) in terms of step-functions s and t on $[a, b]$ and σ and τ on $[b, c]$ which, in turn, are subject (by the Theorem, §109) to the inequalities:

(10)
$$\int_a^b t - \tfrac{1}{2}\epsilon < \int_a^b f < \int_a^b s + \tfrac{1}{2}\epsilon.$$

(11)
$$\int_b^c \tau - \tfrac{1}{2}\epsilon < \int_b^c f < \int_b^c \sigma + \tfrac{1}{2}\epsilon.$$

By addition of these inequalities and use of (7), we have (9), as desired. This completes the proof.

NOTE. If follows from Theorem II by mathematical induction that if f is defined on $[a_0, a_n]$ and integrable on each interval $[a_0, a_1], [a_1, a_2], \cdots, [a_{n-1}, a_n]$, then f is integrable on $[a_0, a_n]$ and

(12)
$$\int_{a_0}^{a_n} f = \int_{a_0}^{a_1} f + \int_{a_1}^{a_2} f + \cdots + \int_{a_{n-1}}^{a_n} f.$$

(Give the induction proof in Ex. 17, §115.)

114 OTHER THEOREMS

In this section we present five additional theorems concerning the Riemann integral.

Theorem I. *If f is integrable on a compact interval [a, b], and if g is defined on [a, b] and equal to f at all but a finite number of points of [a, b], then g is integrable on [a, b] and*

$$(1) \qquad \int_a^b g = \int_a^b f.$$

In other words, changing the values of a function, defined and integrable on a compact interval, at a finite number of points affects neither its integrability nor the value of its integral.

Proof. Since $g - f$ is equal to 0 at all but a finite number of points it is a step-function with integral equal to 0:

$$(2) \qquad \text{if } s \equiv g - f, \text{ then } \int_a^b s = 0.$$

Since $g = f + s$, g is the sum of two integrable functions and is therefore integrable. Furthermore

$$(3) \qquad \int_a^b g = \int_a^b f + \int_a^b s = \int_a^b f.$$

Some useful corollaries of Theorem I, in combination with results of earlier sections, are now possible, in terms of properties of *sectional behavior*, exemplified in the definition:

Definition. *A real-valued function f defined on a compact interval [a, b] is **sectionally monotonic** there if and only if f is bounded there and there exists a net $\mathfrak{N}$ on [a, b] such that on every open interval of $\mathfrak{N}$, f is monotonic. A real-valued function f defined on [a, b] is **sectionally linear** there if and only if there exists a net $\mathfrak{N}$ on [a, b] such that on every open interval of $\mathfrak{N}$, f is linear. (Cf. Fig. 114-1.)*

Before stating the next theorem, let us observe that every function that is sectionally linear on a compact interval is also sectionally monotonic there, since boundedness

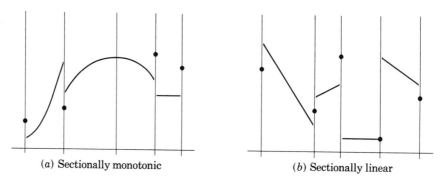

(a) Sectionally monotonic   (b) Sectionally linear

Figure 114-1

for any sectionally linear function is a consequence of its being bounded on each closed interval of any net for which it is sectionally linear. It should also be noted that sectionally linear functions are generalizations of step-functions; that is, every step-function is sectionally linear (it could be called *sectionally constant*).

Theorem II. *Any function that is sectionally monotonic on a compact interval is integrable there. In particular, any function that is sectionally linear on a compact interval is integrable there.*

Proof. We first show that if f is defined and bounded on a compact interval $[c, d]$ and monotonic on (c, d), then f is integrable on $[c, d]$. We do this by defining a new function g on $[c, d]$ identically equal to f on (c, d) and having values at c and d such that g is monotonic on $[c, d]$. Then, by §106, g is integrable on $[c, d]$, and by Theorem I, above, f is also integrable on $[c, d]$. As a consequence of this special case, under the assumptions of this theorem f is integrable on every closed interval of some net on $[a, b]$. By the Note, §113, f is integrable on $[a, b]$.

Theorem III. *If f is an even function on the interval $[-a, a]$ and integrable there, then (cf. Fig. 114-2):*

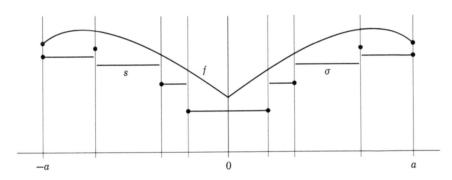

Figure 114-2

$$(4) \qquad \int_{-a}^{0} f = \int_{0}^{a} f \quad and \quad \int_{-a}^{a} f = 2 \int_{0}^{a} f.$$

Proof. By §112, all integrals in (4) exist, and by the additivity of the integral the second equality of (4) is a consequence of the first, which we shall now proceed to prove. If s is an arbitrary lower step-function for f on $[-a, 0]$ and if $\sigma(x) \equiv s(-x)$ for $0 \leq x \leq a$, then σ is a lower step-function for f on $[0, a]$ (cf. Fig. 114-2). Similarly, if σ is an arbitrary lower step-function for f on $[0, a]$, and if $s(x) \equiv \sigma(-x)$ for $-a \leq x \leq 0$, then s is a lower step-function for f on $[-a, 0]$. In each case $\int_{-a}^{0} s = \int_{0}^{a} \sigma$. Therefore the set $\{\int_{-a}^{0} s\}$ of integrals for all lower step-functions s for the interval $[-a, 0]$ is the same as the set $\{\int_{0}^{a} \sigma\}$ of integrals for all lower step-functions σ for the interval $[0, a]$. Since the least upper bound for this set is the same whether it is regarded as $\{\int_{-a}^{0} s\}$ or as $\{\int_{0}^{a} \sigma\}$, the desired first equality of (4) is established.

Theorem IV. *If f is an odd function on the interval $[-a, a]$ and integrable there, then (cf. Fig. 114-3):*

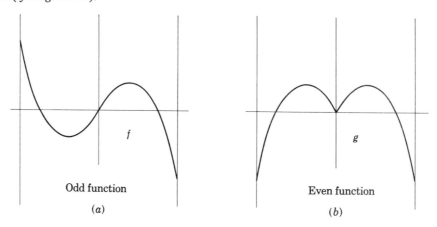

Odd function

(a)

Even function

(b)

Figure 114–3

(5)
$$\int_{-a}^{0} f = -\int_{0}^{a} f \text{ and } \int_{-a}^{a} f = 0.$$

Proof. As with Theorem III, all integrals in (5) exist, and it is necessary only to prove the first equality. Let the function g be defined on $[-a, a]$:

(6)
$$g(x) \equiv \begin{cases} -f(x) \text{ if } -a \leq x \leq 0, \\ f(x) \text{ if } 0 \leq x \leq a. \end{cases}$$

(Since f is odd, $-f(0) = f(0)$ and $f(0) = 0$.) Then g is an even function, integrable on both $[-a, 0]$ and $[0, a]$, and by Theorem III,

(7)
$$\int_{-a}^{0} g = \int_{0}^{a} g.$$

But since $\int_{-a}^{0} g = \int_{-a}^{0} (-f) = -\int_{-a}^{0} f$, and $\int_{0}^{a} g = \int_{0}^{a} f$, the first equality of (5) is established as desired.

Theorem V. *If f is integrable on the interval $[a, b]$ and if $|f|$ is the absolute value of f ($|f|(x) \equiv |f(x)|$) then $|f|$ is integrable on $[a, b]$ and*

(8)
$$\left| \int_{a}^{b} f \right| \leq \int_{a}^{b} |f|.$$

Proof. The integrability of $|f|$ is guaranteed by Theorem II, §107. To prove (8) we write, for each $x \in [a, b]$:

(9)
$$-|f(x)| \leq f(x) \leq |f(x)|,$$

and infer from (2), §111:

(10)
$$-\int_{a}^{b} |f| \leq \int_{a}^{b} f \leq \int_{a}^{b} |f|,$$

from which (8) follows (cf. Theorem I(v), §311, *PCLA*).

A proof of the following theorem is given in H§619, *CWAG*, by means of inequalities established by mathematical induction and suitably related to upper and lower step-functions. An independent proof is given in Example 1, §1007, of the present volume, using techniques that will be introduced and developed in the intervening chapters.

Theorem VI. *If n is a nonnegative integer* and if a < b, then*

(11)
$$\int_a^b x^n \, dx = \frac{b^{n+1} - a^{n+1}}{n + 1}.$$

Example 1. $\displaystyle\int_2^5 x^2 \, dx = \frac{5^3 - 2^3}{3} = \frac{117}{3} = 39,$

$$\int_{-1}^6 dx = \int_{-1}^6 1 \, dx = \int_{-1}^6 x^0 \, dx = \frac{6^1 - (-1)^1}{1} = 7,$$

$$\int_3^9 x \, dx = \frac{9^2 - 3^2}{2} = \frac{72}{2} = 36,$$

$$\int_0^1 x^{10} \, dx = \frac{1^{11} - 0^{11}}{11} = \frac{1}{11}.$$

Since any polynomial is a linear combination of nonnegative integral powers of the independent variable, and since $\int_a^b$ is a linear functional, Theorem VI provides a formula for integrating any polynomial on any compact interval.

Example 2. $\displaystyle\int_4^5 6x^2 \, dx = 6 \int_4^5 x^2 \, dx = 6\,\frac{125 - 64}{3} = 122,$

$$\int_4^5 (7 - 8x)dx = \int_4^5 7dx - 8 \int_4^5 x \, dx = 7 + 8 \cdot \frac{9}{2} = -29,$$

$$\int_4^5 (13 - 3x + 2x^3)dx = 13 - 3 \cdot \frac{9}{2} + 2 \cdot \frac{369}{4} = 184.$$

Example 3. Evaluate $I \equiv \displaystyle\int_{-2}^2 (5 - 7x + 3x^2 + 11x^3 - 2x^4)dx.$

Solution. We start (using elliptic notation) by writing the integrand of *I* as the sum of the odd function $-7x + 11x^3$ and the even function $(5 + 3x^2 - 2x^4)$, and use Theorems III and IV to write

$$I = \int_{-2}^2 (-7x + 11x^3)dx + \int_{-2}^2 (5 + 3x^2 - 2x^4)dx = 0 + 2\int_0^2 (5 + 3x^2 - 2x^4)dx.$$

*By Definition II, §309, *PCLA*) the function x^0 is identically equal to 1 for all x, including $x = 0$. For the case $n = 0$, formula (11) can be written in the following form:

$$\int_a^b 1 = \int_a^b 1 \, dx = \int_a^b dx = b - a.$$

We proceed with the evaluation:

$$I = 2\left[5 \cdot 2 + 3\frac{8-0}{3} - 2\frac{32-0}{5}\right] = 2 \cdot \frac{26}{5} = \frac{52}{5} = 10\frac{2}{5}.$$

Example 4.   Evaluate $I = \int_1^6 f(x)dx$, where

$$f(x) \equiv \begin{cases} 7, & x = 1, \\ 2x^3, & 1 < x \leq 3, \\ 4x^2, & 3 < x \leq 6. \end{cases}$$

Solution.   Since f is sectionally monotonic on $[1, 6]$, the integral exists, and by Theorem II, §113,

(12) $$I = \int_1^3 f(x)\, dx + \int_3^6 f(x)\, dx.$$

Since an integral is unaffected by changes in the values of the integrand at any finite number of points, the first integral on the right of (12) is the same as that of the function $2x^3$ on the interval $[1, 3]$, and the second integral is the same as that of $4x^2$ on $[3, 6]$.   Therefore

$$I = \int_1^3 2x^3\, dx + \int_3^6 4x^2\, dx = 2\frac{81-1}{4} + 4\frac{216-27}{3} = 40 + 252 = 292.$$

115   EXERCISES

In Exercises 1–16, evaluate the integral.   The functions sgn x and $[x]$ are defined in Examples 2 and 3, §115, *PCLA*.

1. $\int_1^4 x^2\, dx.$ 2. $\int_0^2 t^7\, dt.$

3. $\int_{-2}^3 2u^4\, du.$ 4. $\int_{-1}^5 4v^3\, dv.$

5. $\int_{-2}^2 (5x^3 - 6x^2 - 7x)dx.$ 6. $\int_3^4 (4x^2 + 5)dx.$

7. $\int_{-1}^2 (s^3 - 10s + 7)ds.$ 8. $\int_2^4 (6u^2 + 12u - 5)du.$

9. $\int_{-3}^4 \operatorname{sgn} x\, dx.$ 10. $\int_{-3}^4 [x]dx.$

11. $\int_0^3 (x - [x])dx.$ 12. $\int_0^3 (x - [x])^2 dx.$

13. $\int_0^5 f(x)dx, f(x) \equiv \begin{cases} 4x - 1, & 0 \leq x < 2, \\ 2x + 1, & 2 \leq x \leq 5. \end{cases}$

14. $\int_{-3}^3 f(x)dx, f(x) \equiv \begin{cases} 3x - 1, & -3 \leq x < -1, \\ 2x, & -1 \leq x \leq 1, \\ 3x + 1, & 1 < x \leq 3. \end{cases}$

15. $\displaystyle\int_{-2}^{3} f(x)dx, f(x) \equiv \begin{cases} 6x^2, -2 \leqq x \leqq 1, \\ 6x^3, 1 < x \leqq 3. \end{cases}$

16. $\displaystyle\int_{-3}^{3} f(x)dx, f(x) \equiv \begin{cases} -3x + 1, -3 \leqq x < -1, \\ |x|, -1 \leqq x \leqq 1, \\ 3x + 1, 1 < x \leqq 3. \end{cases}$

17. Prove the Note, §113.

18. Assume a function f is integrable on the interval $[1, 4]$ and on the interval $[2, 7]$. Prove that f is integrable on $[1, 7]$.

2

Applications of the Definite Integral

201 AREA AS A POSITIVE ADDITIVE FUNCTION

In §101 area was discussed informally as a complete congruence-invariant positive additive function defined on certain sets in the Euclidean plane such that every open rectangle has area equal to the product of the lengths of two adjacent edges. In the present section we shall state with greater precision just what this statement about area really means in terms of a set of axioms.

The axioms for area will be divided into three groupings. The first grouping concerns only the class of sets for which area is defined, and says nothing about the area function itself. The second grouping gives properties of the area function without specifying anything regarding the class of sets having area. The third grouping consists only of the single axiom of completeness, which states that whenever a set can be suitably "squeezed" between two sets that possess area, then this set must also possess area.

We start with a definition:

Definition. *A ring of sets is a nonempty class $\mathcal{E}$ of sets that is closed with respect to unions and set differences:*

(i) S_1 *and* $S_2 \in \mathcal{E} \Rightarrow S_1 \cup S_2 \in \mathcal{E}$,

(ii) S_1 *and* $S_2 \in \mathcal{E} \Rightarrow S_1 \setminus S_2 \in \mathcal{E}$.

Example 1. An example of a ring of sets in the Euclidean plane E_2 is the class of all finite subsets of E_2. Another example is the class of all bounded subsets of E_2. (Recall that a set is

30

bounded if and only if it is contained in some disk.) A third example is the class of *all* subsets of E_2. An example of a class of sets that is *not* a ring of sets is the class of all open rectangles of E_2. (This class is closed with respect to *neither* unions *nor* set differences.)

One immediate consequence of the preceding definition is that *every ring $\mathcal{E}$ of sets contains the empty set $\emptyset$.* This is true since, if S is an arbitrary member of $\mathcal{E}$, then by *(ii)*, $S \setminus S = \emptyset \in \mathcal{E}$. Another consequence is that *every ring of sets is closed with respect to intersections:*

(1) $$S_1 \text{ and } S_2 \in \mathcal{E} \Rightarrow S_1 \cap S_2 \in \mathcal{E}.$$

(This follows from the identity $S_1 \cap S_2 = S_1 \setminus (S_1 \setminus S_2)$.) The implications *(i)* of the preceding Definition, and (1), can be extended by mathematical induction to the statement that *every ring $\mathcal{E}$ of sets is closed with respect to arbitrary finite unions and intersections:*

(2) $$S_1, S_2, \cdots, S_n \in \mathcal{E} \Rightarrow S_1 \cup S_2 \cup \cdots \cup S_n \in \mathcal{E},$$

(3) $$S_1, S_2, \cdots, S_n \in \mathcal{E} \Rightarrow S_1 \cap S_2 \cap \cdots \cap S_n \in \mathcal{E}.$$

The class of sets that will be assumed to have area will be denoted $\mathcal{J}$, after the French mathematician C. Jordan (1838–1922), who studied the properties of area, its counterpart in three dimensions known as *volume*, and its extensions to higher dimensional spaces known as *Jordan content*. We are ready for our first set of axioms:

I. Axioms for $\mathcal{J}$. *The class $\mathcal{J}$ of subsets of E_2 that have area is a ring of sets that (i) is closed with respect to congruence and (ii) contains all open rectangles:*

(i) $(S_1 \cong S_2 \text{ and } S_1 \in \mathcal{J}) \Rightarrow S_2 \in \mathcal{J},$
(ii) S *is an open rectangle* $\Rightarrow S \in \mathcal{J}.$

The area function will be denoted A and assumed to possess the following properties:

II. Axioms for A. *The area function A is a nonnegative-valued function with domain $\mathcal{J}$ such that*

(i) *A is **additive**:* $(S_1 \text{ and } S_2 \in \mathcal{J} \text{ and } S_1 \cap S_2 = \emptyset) \Rightarrow$
$$A(S_1 \cup S_2) = A(S_1) + A(S_2).$$
(ii) *A is **congruence-invariant**:* $(S_1 \text{ and } S_2 \in \mathcal{J} \text{ and } S_1 \cong S_2) \Rightarrow$
$$A(S_1) = A(S_2).$$
(iii) *If S is an open rectangle and if a and b are lengths of two adjacent edges of S, then*
$$A(S) = ab.$$

From II(*i*) and the fact that $\emptyset \in \mathcal{J}$ it follows that *the area of the empty set is zero:*

(4) $$A(\emptyset) = 0.$$

(Since $\emptyset \cap \emptyset = \emptyset$, the equation for II($i$) gives $A(\emptyset) = A(\emptyset) + A(\emptyset)$.) If S_1 and $S_2 \in \mathcal{g}$ and if $S_1 \subset S_2$, then since $S_1 \cap (S_2 \setminus S_1) = \emptyset$ and $S_2 = S_1 \cup (S_2 \setminus S_1)$, we have $A(S_2) = A(S_1) + A(S_2 \setminus S_1)$, or

(5) $((S_1, S_2) \in \mathcal{g} \times \mathcal{g}$ and $S_1 \subset S_2) \Rightarrow A(S_2 \setminus S_1) = A(S_2) - A(S_1)$.

From (5), since $A(S_2 \setminus S_1) \geq 0$ it follows that *the area function A is increasing:*

(6) $((S_1, S_2) \in \mathcal{g} \times \mathcal{g}$ and $S_1 \subset S_2) \Rightarrow A(S_1) \leq A(S_2)$.

Mathematical induction extends II(i) to general **finite additivity**:

(7) $(S_1, S_2, \cdots, S_n \in \mathcal{g}$ and $S_i \cap S_j = \emptyset$ for $i \neq j$, i and $j = 1, 2, \cdots, n) \Rightarrow$
        $A(S_1 \cup S_2 \cup \cdots \cup S_n) = A(S_1) + A(S_2) + \cdots + A(S_n)$.

The axiom of completeness has the following formulation:

III. Axiom of Completeness.   *If S is any subset of E_2 and if*

(8) $\forall \epsilon > 0, \exists (S_1, S_2) \in \mathcal{g} \times \mathcal{g} \ni S_1 \subset S \subset S_2$ *and* $A(S_2) - A(S_1) < \epsilon$,

then $S \in \mathcal{g}$.

If, in Axiom III, we take S_1 to be the empty set, we have the theorem:

Theorem I.   *If S is any subset of E_2 and if*

(9) $\forall \epsilon > 0, \exists S_2 \in \mathcal{g} \ni S \subset S_2$ *and* $A(S_2) < \epsilon$,

then $S \in \mathcal{g}$. *Furthermore,* $A(S) = 0$.

Proof.   That $S \in \mathcal{g}$ follows immediately. To prove $A(S) = 0$, assume $A(S) > 0$ and let $\epsilon \equiv A(S)$. Since (9) is assumed to be true there exists a set $S_2 \in \mathcal{g}$ such that $S \subset S_2$ and $A(S_2) < \epsilon$. By (6), $A(S) \leq A(S_2) < \epsilon = A(S)$. (Contradiction.)
Another consequence, even more immediate, is:

Theorem II.   *If S is any subset of E_2 and if there exist sets S_1 and S_2 of $\mathcal{g}$ such that*

(10) $S_1 \subset S \subset S_2$ *and* $A(S_1) = A(S_2)$,

then $S \in \mathcal{g}$ and $A(S) = A(S_1) = A(S_2)$. Any subset of a set of zero area is a set of zero area.

Proof.   The fact that $S \in \mathcal{g}$, in the first part of Theorem II, follows directly from Axiom III, since (8) holds for every $\epsilon > 0$. The equality $A(S) = A(S_1) = A(S_2)$ follows from the chain of inequalities:

(11) $A(S_1) \leq A(S) \leq A(S_2) = A(S_1)$.

Finally, the last statement of Theorem II is proved from the first part by letting S_1 be the empty set.
Since any closed line segment in E_2 is contained in an open rectangle of arbitrarily small positive area, we have as a corollary to Theorems I and II:

Theorem III. *Any subset of any closed line segment in E_2 is a set of zero area.*

An immediate consequence of Theorem III and the additivity of A given in Axiom II(i) is that *any closed rectangle has area equal to the product of the lengths of two adjacent edges.*

As was mentioned in §101, there is discussed in Chapter 9, *SCC*, a class $\mathscr{g}$ and an area function A that satisfy all of Axioms I, II, and III of this section. It should be emphasized, however, that such classes $\mathscr{g}$ and functions A are by no means unique. The function defined in Chapter 9, *SCC*, is *Jordan content*. Another function which, together with its domain of sets, satisfies the axioms given above is known as *Lebesgue measure*, after the French mathematician H. Lebesgue (1875–1941). Lebesgue measure, which extends the finite additivity of (7) to *infinite additivity*, has become one of the most important parts of the graduate (and to an increasing extent the undergraduate) mathematical curriculum. Most of the important generalizations of Jordan content and Lebesgue measure apply to Euclidean spaces of any number of dimensions. The general subject of measure and integration is one of continuing research activity and creative productivity today.

202 AREAS OF ORDINATE SETS

Our main goal in this section will be to establish and illustrate the following theorem regarding the ordinate set S of a nonnegative function f on an interval $[a, b]$,

$$S = \{(x, y) \mid a \leqq x \leqq b, 0 \leqq y \leqq f(x)\}:$$

Theorem. *If f is a nonnegative function defined and integrable on a compact interval $[a, b]$, then the ordinate set S of f has area equal to*

$$(1) \qquad\qquad A(S) = \int_a^b f.$$

Proof. We first prove the theorem for the special case where f is a step-function, $f = s$, with nonnegative values $s_1, s_2, \cdots, s_n$ on the n open intervals of a net $\mathfrak{N} = \{a_0, a_1, \cdots, a_n\}$. Whenever $s_i > 0$, $i = 1, 2, \cdots, n$, the open rectangle $(a_{i-1}, a_i) \times (0, s_i)$, with area $s_i(a_i - a_{i-1})$, is a portion of the ordinate set S of s corresponding to the term $s_i(a_i - a_{i-1})$ of the sum that defines the integral $\int_a^b s$. (Cf. Fig. 202-1.)

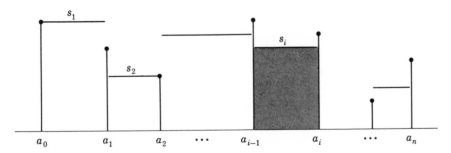

Figure 202-1

Whenever $s_i = 0$, $i = 1, 2, \cdots, n$, the term $s_i(a_i - a_{i-1})$ is equal to zero, corresponding to the area of the empty set $\varnothing$. Since the ordinate set of s consists of the open rectangles of the form $(a_{i-1}, a_i) \times (0, s_i)$, together with portions of horizontal or vertical line segments all of which have zero area, the area of the ordinate set is equal to the sum

$$(2) \qquad\qquad \sum_{i=1}^{n} s_i(a_i - a_{i-1}) = \int_a^b s,$$

and the theorem is proved for the case when f is a step-function.

Now let f be an arbitrary nonnegative function integrable on $[a, b]$ and let S be the ordinate set of f. We shall prove first that $S \in \mathcal{G}$. If ϵ is an arbitrary positive number, then by Theorem II, §111, and the definition of the Riemann integral, §109, there exist step-functions s and t on $[a, b]$ such that

$$(3) \qquad 0 \leqq s \leqq f \leqq t, \qquad \int_a^b s > \int_a^b f - \tfrac{1}{2}\epsilon, \qquad \int_a^b t < \int_a^b f + \tfrac{1}{2}\epsilon,$$

and consequently such that

$$(4) \qquad\qquad \int_a^b t - \int_a^b s < \epsilon.$$

If S_1 and S_2 are the ordinate sets of s and t, respectively, then by the first part of the proof already completed, $A(S_1) = \int_a^b s$ and $A(S_2) = \int_a^b t$, so that

$$(5) \qquad\qquad S_1 \subset S \subset S_2 \quad \text{and} \quad A(S_2) - A(S_1) < \epsilon.$$

Therefore, by the axiom of completeness (III, §201), $S \in \mathcal{G}$.

Finally, in order to prove that $A(S) = \int_a^b f$, we use the inequalities $A(S_1) \leqq A(S) \leqq A(S_2)$ and (4) to infer

$$(6) \qquad\qquad \int_a^b t - \epsilon < \int_a^b s \leqq A(S) \leqq \int_a^b t < \int_a^b s + \epsilon$$

and consequently, from the Theorem, §109, with $\gamma \equiv A(S)$, the desired equality $A(S) = \int_a^b f$, and the proof is complete.

Example 1.   Find the area of the ordinate set of the function $x^2 + 4$, $0 \leqq x \leqq 3$.

Solution.   The area desired is (cf. Theorem VI, §114):

$$\int_0^3 (x^2 + 4)\, dx = \int_0^3 x^2\, dx + \int_0^3 4\, dx = \frac{3^3 - 0^3}{3} + 4\frac{3 - 0}{1} = 21.$$

(Cf. Fig. 202-2a.)

Example 2.   Find the area of the set S bounded above by the curve $y = 2 + x - x^2$ and below by the x-axis: $S = \{(x, y) \mid 0 \leqq y \leqq 2 + x - x^2\}$.

Solution.   Since the solution set for the inequality $2 + x - x^2 \geqq 0$ is $[-1, 2]$, the area desired is

$$\int_{-1}^2 (2 + x - x^2)dx = 2 \cdot \frac{2 - (-1)}{1} + \frac{2^2 - (-1)^2}{2} - \frac{2^3 - (-1)^3}{3} = 6 + \frac{3}{2} - 3 = \frac{9}{2} = 4\tfrac{1}{2}.$$

(Cf. Fig. 202-2b.)

Symmetry can often be used to simplify calculation.

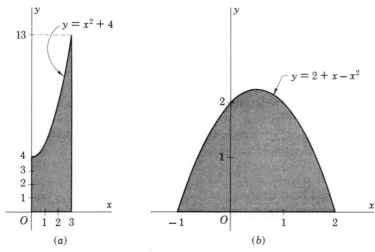

Figure 202-2   (a)   (b)

Example 3.   Find the area of the set S bounded by the curve $y = 9 - x^2$ and the x-axis.

Solution.   The set S is the union of two parts, S_1 in the first quadrant and S_2 in the second quadrant, where S_1 and S_2 are congruent (by reflection across the y-axis) and have a set of zero area in common. (Cf. Fig. 202-3a.) Equivalently, the function $9 - x^2$ is even. The area of S is therefore twice the area of S_1, or

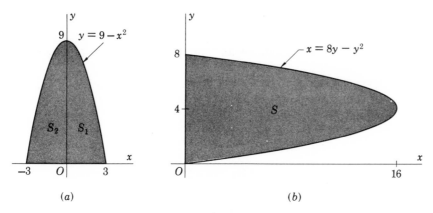

(a)   (b)

Figure 202-3

$$A(S) = \int_{-3}^{3} (9 - x^2)dx = 2\int_{0}^{3} (9 - x^2)dx = 2 \cdot 9(3 - 0) - 2 \cdot \frac{27 - 0}{3} = 54 - 18 = 36.$$

The roles of the variables x and y can often be interchanged to advantage.

Example 4.   Find the area of the set S bounded by the curve $x = 8y - y^2$ and the y-axis.

Solution.   Considering S as an "abscissa set" instead of an "ordinate set" (cf. Fig. 202-3b), we have

$$A(S) = \int_{0}^{8} (8y - y^2)dy = 8 \cdot \frac{64 - 0}{2} - \frac{512 - 0}{3} = \frac{256}{3} = 85\tfrac{1}{3}.$$

We close this section with a few facts concerning some familiar plane sets of a particularly simple character. Proofs are requested in Exercises 33–38, §204, where suggestions are provided.

If p, q, and r are three noncollinear points, let pq denote the line segment joining p and q, and similarly for pr and qr, and let Π_p be the open half-plane containing p and determined by the line through q and r, and similarly for Π_q and Π_r. Then the **triangle** pqr is the union $pq \cup pr \cup qr$. The intersection $\Pi_p \cap \Pi_q \cap \Pi_r$ is called the **open triangular region** or, for simplicity, the **open triangle**, determined by p, q, and r. It is also called the **inside** of the triangle pqr. A **closed triangular set** or, for simplicity, a **closed triangle**, is the union of a triangle and its inside. A **triangular set** is the union of the inside of a triangle and any subset of the triangle. When the meaning is clear from context the single word *triangle* is sometimes used to mean a triangular set. In any case, p, q, and r are the **vertices** and the segments pq, pr, and qr are the **edges** or **sides** of a triangular set determined by p, q, and r.

Any triangular set has area (cf. Ex. 33, §204), and its area is equal to half the product of the length of any side and the length of the altitude perpendicular to that side (cf. Ex. 36, §204).

Any set that is the union of a finite number of triangular sets has area (cf. Ex. 34, §204). In particular, any parallelogram or trapezoid has area, whether the figure is *open* (being the intersection of four open half-planes) or *closed* (being the intersection of four closed half-planes) or neither (being the union of an open figure and subsets of line segments). The area of any parallelogram is the product of the length of any side and the length of an altitude perpendicular to that side (cf. Ex. 35 §204). The area of any trapezoid is the product of the average of the lengths of the parallel sides and the length of an altitude perpendicular to those two sides (cf. Ex. 37, §204).

If (x_1, y_1), (x_2, y_2), and (x_3, y_3) are any three noncollinear points, the area of any triangular set with these points as vertices is half the absolute value of the third-order determinant

$$(7) \qquad \begin{vmatrix} x_1 & y_1 & 1 \\ x_2 & y_2 & 1 \\ x_3 & y_3 & 1 \end{vmatrix}.$$

(Cf. Ex. 38, §204.) If (x_1, y_1), (x_2, y_2), and (x_3, y_3) are three vertices of a parallelogram the area of this parallelogram is the absolute value of (7) (cf. Ex. 38, §204). The vanishing of the determinant (7) is a necessary and sufficient condition for the three points (x_1, y_1), (x_2, y_2), and (x_3, y_3) to be collinear.

If the point (x_3, y_3) is the origin $(0, 0)$, then the statements of the preceding paragraph reduce to corresponding statements concerning the second-order determinant

$$(8) \qquad \begin{vmatrix} x_1 & y_1 \\ x_2 & y_2 \end{vmatrix}.$$

If (x_1, y_1) and (x_2, y_2) are any two distinct points, the equation of the line through these two points can be written

(9)
$$\begin{vmatrix} x & y & 1 \\ x_1 & y_1 & 1 \\ x_2 & y_2 & 1 \end{vmatrix} = 0.$$

If (x_1, y_1) is any point distinct from the origin, the equation of the line through this point and the origin can be written

(10)
$$\begin{vmatrix} x & y \\ x_1 & y_1 \end{vmatrix} = 0.$$

(Cf. Ex. 39, §204.)

203 SETS BETWEEN TWO GRAPHS

Definition. *Let f and g be any two real-valued functions integrable on a compact interval [a, b], and such that f ≤ g there. Then the **set between their graphs** is*

(1) $S = \{(x, y) \mid a \leq x \leq b,\ f(x) \leq y \leq g(x)\}.$

(*Cf. Fig. 203-1.*)

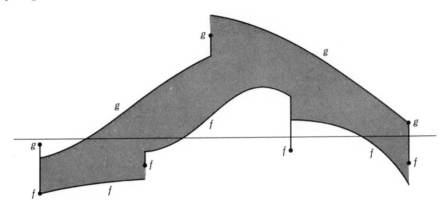

Figure 203-1

Considerations similar to those used in this section lead to the following theorem (cf. H§709, *CWAG*):

Theorem. *Under the assumptions of the preceding definition, the set S between the graphs of f and g has area equal to*

(2) $$A(S) = \int_a^b (g - f) = \int_a^b (g(x) - f(x))dx.$$

Example 1. Find the area of the set between the graphs of $y = x + 1$ and $y = x^2 - x$, for $0 \leq x \leq 2$.

Solution. Since, for $0 \leq x \leq 2$, $x + 1 \geq x^2 - x$, the area sought is

$$\int_0^2 [(x + 1) - (x^2 - x)]dx = \int_0^2 (-x^2 + 2x + 1)dx = -\frac{8}{3} + 4 + 2 = \frac{10}{3} = 3\frac{1}{3}.$$

(Cf. Fig. 203-2*a*.)

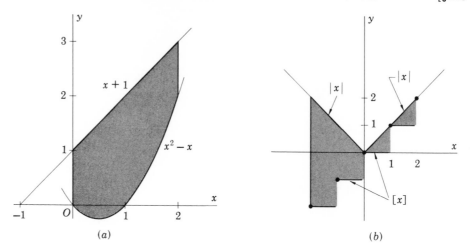

Figure 203-2

Example 2. Find the area of the set between the graphs of $|x|$ and $[x]$, for $-2 \leqq x \leqq 2$, where $[x]$ is the greatest integer function of Example 3, §115, *PCLA*.

Solution. As shown in Figure 203-2*b*, the area is

$$\int_{-2}^{2} (|x| - [x])dx = \int_{-2}^{-1} (-x + 2)dx + \int_{-1}^{0} (-x + 1)dx + \int_{0}^{1} xdx + \int_{1}^{2} (x - 1)dx$$

$$= -\frac{1 - 4}{2} + 2 - \frac{0 - 1}{2} + 1 + \frac{1}{2} + \frac{4 - 1}{2} - 1 = 6.$$

Example 3. Find the area of the bounded set S between the curves $y = x^3 - 2x^2 + 2$ and $y = x$.

Solution. Solving simultaneously the two equations $y = x^3 - 2x^2 + 2$ and $y = x$ gives $x^3 - 2x^2 - x + 2 = 0$, or $x = -1, 1$, and 2. Therefore, as shown in Figure 203-3*a*, the set S consists of two parts, one for $-1 \leqq x \leqq 1$ and one for $1 \leqq x \leqq 2$. The total area, with proper consideration given to the order relation between $x^3 - 2x^2 + 2$ and x, is therefore (cf. Theorems III and IV, §114)

$$\int_{-1}^{1} (x^3 - 2x^2 - x + 2)dx + \int_{1}^{2} (-x^3 + 2x^2 + x - 2)dx$$

$$= 2\int_{0}^{1} (-2x^2 + 2)dx + \frac{1 - 16}{4} + \frac{2(8 - 1)}{3} + \frac{4 - 1}{2} - 2 = \frac{8}{3} + \frac{5}{12} = \frac{37}{12} = 3\tfrac{1}{12}.$$

Example 4. Find the area of the bounded set S between the curves $x + y + 1 = 0$ and $x = 2 + y - y^2$.

Solution. The graphs (cf. Fig. 203-3*b*) show that the problem is best solved by interchanging the usual roles of x and y. Solving $x = -y - 1$ and $x = 2 + y - y^2$ simultaneously gives $y^2 - 2y - 3 = 0$, or $y = -1$ and 3. Since, for $-1 \leqq y \leqq 3$, $-y - 1 \leqq 2 + y - y^2$, or $3 + 2y - y^2 \geqq 0$, the desired area is

$$\int_{-1}^{3} (3 + 2y - y^2)dy = 3 \cdot 4 + (9 - 1) - \frac{27 + 1}{3} = \frac{32}{3} = 10\tfrac{2}{3}.$$

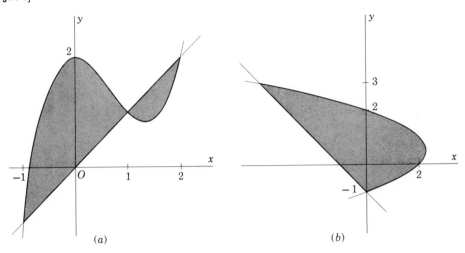

Figure 203-3

We shall find occasion to use the following corollary to the preceding theorem:

Corollary. *If f is integrable on the interval* [a, b], *then the graph of* $y = f(x)$, *for* $a \leqq x \leqq b$, *has zero area.*

Proof. In the Theorem let $g \equiv f$.

Example 5. Show that the circle $x^2 + y^2 = r^2$, where $r > 0$, has zero area.
Solution. The given circle is the union of the graphs of the two functions

$$x \to \sqrt{r^2 - x^2}, x \in [-a, a], x \to -\sqrt{r^2 - x^2}, x \in [-a, a].$$

204 EXERCISES

The functions sgn x and $[x]$ occurring in some of the following exercises are defined in Examples 2 and 3, §115, *PCLA*. A graph should accompany each of Exercises 1–30.

In Exercises 1–7, find the area of the ordinate set of the given function.

1. $4x - 3, 1 \leqq x \leqq 5$.

2. $7 - 2x, 0 \leqq x \leqq 3$.

3. $x^2 + 6, -2 \leqq x \leqq 2$.

4. $3x^2 - 2x + 4, -3 \leqq x \leqq 3$.

5. $|[x]|, -3 \leqq x \leqq 4$.

6. $f(x) \equiv \begin{cases} 2x, 0 \leqq x < 2, \\ 8 - 2x, 2 \leqq x \leqq 4. \end{cases}$

7. $f(x) \equiv \begin{cases} x^2, \quad 0 \leqq x \leqq 1, \\ 4 - 2x, 1 < x \leqq 2. \end{cases}$

In Exercises 8–10, find the area of the set bounded by the given curve and the x-axis.

8. $y = 4 - x^2$.

9. $y = 6x - x^2$.

10. $y = -2 + 3x - x^2$.

In Exercises 11–13, find the area of the set bounded by the given curve and the y-axis.

11. $x = 1 - y^2$.   **12.** $x = 10y - y^2$.

13. $x = -4y - y^2$.

In Exercises 14–23, find the area of the bounded set lying between the two indicated graphs.

14. $y = x^2 + 4$, $y = 4 - x$, $1 \leq x \leq 4$.   **15.** $y = 2x + 6$, $y = -x^2$, $-3 \leq x \leq 3$.

16. $y = x^2 - x$, $y = 2x$.   **17.** $y = x - x^2$, $x + y + 8 = 0$.

18. $x = 3y - y^2$, $x + 3y = 0$.   **19.** $x = y^2 - 4y$, $x - y + 4 = 0$.

20. $y = x^3 - 4x^2$, $3x + y = 0$.   **21.** $y = 2x^2 - x^3$, $3x + y = 0$.

22. $y = \operatorname{sgn} x$, $y = -x - 3$, $-1 \leq x \leq 2$.   **23.** $y = x^2$, $y = [x]$, $-2 \leq x \leq 3$.

In Exercises 24–26, use (7) or (8), §202, to find the area of the closed triangle having the three points as vertices.

24. $(0, 0)$, $(2, 5)$, $(-4, 3)$.   **25.** $(-1, 3)$, $(1, -4)$, $(6, 5)$.

26. $(-3, 2)$, $(4, 1)$, $(8, -1)$.

In Exercises 27–30, use (7) or (8), §202, to find the area of the open parallelogram having the four points as vertices.

27. $(0, 0)$, $(-3, 1)$, $(5, 2)$, $(2, 3)$.   **28.** $(0, 0)$, $(1, 4)$, $(7, 1)$, $(8, 5)$.

29. $(3, 5)$, $(4, 2)$, $(5, 12)$, $(6, 9)$.   **30.** $(1, 1)$, $(5, -6)$, $(-3, 0)$, $(9, -5)$.

31. Prove that if S is a set with area and Z is a set of zero area, then the sets $S \cup Z$ and $S \backslash Z$ have area and

$$A(S \cup Z) = A(S \backslash Z) = A(S).$$

32. Prove that if S_1 and S_2 are sets with area whose intersections $S_1 \cap S_2$ has zero area, then

$$A(S_1 \cup S_2) = A(S_1) + A(S_2).$$

33. Prove that any triangular set has area. *Suggestion:* Show first that any closed triangular set is congruent to the ordinate set of a sectionally linear nonnegative function as shown in Figure 204-1.

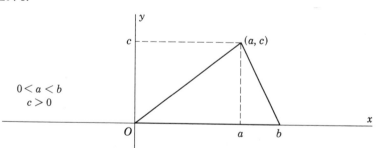

Figure 204-1

34. Prove that any finite union of triangular sets has area. In particular, show that any parallelogram or trapezoid has area.

35. Prove that any parallelogram has area equal to the product of the length of any side and the length of an altitude perpendicular to that side. *Suggestion:* Start by establishing this for a closed parallelogram with a horizontal base as shown in Figure 204-2, and with the steps suggested below:

$$\text{Area} = \text{Area}(PQRU, \text{closed}) - \text{Area}(SRU, \text{open on } SR)$$
$$= \text{Area}(PQRU, \text{closed}) - \text{Area}(PQT, \text{open on } QT)$$
$$= \text{Area}(TQRU, \text{closed}) = bh.$$

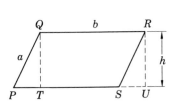 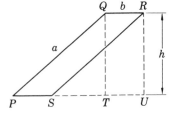

Figure 204-2

36. Prove that any triangular set has area equal to half the product of the length of any side and the length of the altitude perpendicular to that side. *Suggestion:* Start by establishing this for a closed triangular set as indicated in Figure 204-3, and with the steps suggested below:

$$\text{Area}(PQRS, \text{closed}) = \text{Area}(PQS, \text{closed}) + \text{Area}(SQR, \text{open on } QS)$$
$$= \text{Area}(PQS, \text{closed}) + \text{Area}(PQS, \text{open on } QS)$$
$$= 2 \,\text{Area } (PQS, \text{closed}).$$

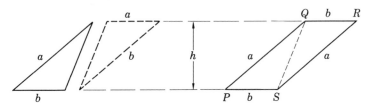

Figure 204-3

37. Prove that any trapezoid has area equal to the product of the average of the lengths of the parallel sides and the length of an altitude perpendicular to these two sides. (Cf. Fig. 204-4.)

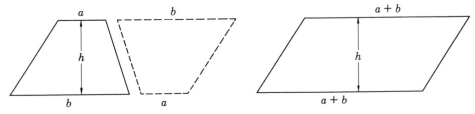

Figure 204-4

38. Prove the statements regarding areas of parallelograms and triangular sets made in §202 in connection with (7), §202. *Suggestions:* (*i*) An equation of the line through (x_1, y_1) and (x_2, y_2) is $(y_2 - y_1)(x - x_1) - (x_2 - x_1)(y - y_1) = 0$. (*ii*) The distance between this line and (x_3, y_3) is $|(y_2 - y_1)(x_3 - x_1) - (x_2 - x_1)(y_3 - y_1)|/d$, where d is the distance between (x_1, y_1) and (x_2, y_2).

39. Prove the statements of the paragraph containing (9) and (10), §202.

205   VOLUME AS A POSITIVE ADDITIVE FUNCTION*

Properties that will be assumed for a volume function V for certain subsets of three-dimensional Euclidean space E_3 are very similar to those given in §201 for the postulated area function.   Before stating these we give a definition:

Definition.   *A **cylindrical set** in E_3 is any set congruent to a Cartesian product of the form*

$$(1) \qquad\qquad S \times I = \{(p, z) \mid p \in S, z \in I\},$$

where S is a subset of E_2 and I is an interval.   For convenience of notation, the set $S \times I$ will also be denoted

$$(2) \qquad\qquad S \times I = \{(x, y, z) \mid (x, y) \in S, z \in I\}.$$

(*Cf. Fig. 205-1.*)

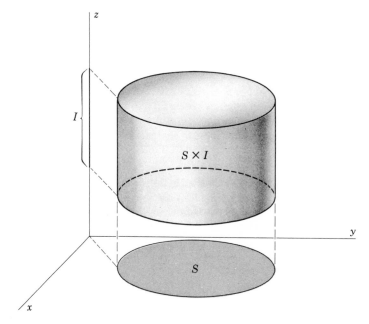

Figure 205-1

The same letter $\mathcal{J}$ will be used to designate the class of sets in E_3 that possess volume as was used in §201 for sets possessing area.   When there is a possibility of confusion we shall use subscripts 2 and 3, $\mathcal{J}_2$ being the class $\mathcal{J}$ of §201 and $\mathcal{J}_3$ being the new class of subsets of E_3 that have volume.

The axioms prescribing the properties of the class $\mathcal{J}_3$ and the volume function V state that volume is a complete congruence-invariant positive additive function defined on the sets of $\mathcal{J}_3$ such that every suitably restricted cylindrical set is a member of $\mathcal{J}_3$ with an appropriate volume, thus:

*Before proceeding to a study of volume, the student should first review the basic definitions and facts concerning rectangular coordinates in three-dimensional space, as given in §1001, *PCLA*.

I.   Axioms for $\mathfrak{J}_3$.   *The class $\mathfrak{J}_3$ of subsets of E_3 that have volume is a ring of sets such that*

(*i*) $W_1 \cong W_2$ *and* $W_1 \in \mathfrak{J}_3 \Rightarrow W_2 \in \mathfrak{J}_3$,

(*ii*) $S \in \mathfrak{J}_2$ *and* I *is an interval* $\Rightarrow S \times I \in \mathfrak{J}_3$.

II.   Axioms for V.   *The volume function V is a nonnegative-valued function with domain $\mathfrak{J}_3$ such that*

(*i*)   *V is **additive**:* $(W_1$ *and* $W_2 \in \mathfrak{J}_3$ *and* $W_1 \cap W_2 = \emptyset) \Rightarrow$
$$V(W_1 \cup W_2) = V(W_1) + V(W_2).$$

(*ii*)   *V is **congruence-invariant**:* $(W_1$ *and* $W_2 \in \mathfrak{J}_3$ *and* $W_1 \cong W_2) \Rightarrow$
$$V(W_1) = V(W_2).$$

(*iii*) $S \in \mathfrak{J}_2$ *and* I *is an interval of length* $l(I) \Rightarrow V(S \times I) = A(S) \cdot l(I)$.

III.   Axiom of Completeness.   *If W is any subset of E_3 and if*

(3) $\forall \epsilon > 0, \exists (W_1, W_2) \in \mathfrak{J}_3 \times \mathfrak{J}_3 \ni W_1 \subset W \subset W_2$ *and* $V(W_2) - V(W_1) < \epsilon$,

then $W \in \mathfrak{J}_3$.

The consequences of the axioms for area, as presented in §201, have almost exact analogues for volume, which will be assumed without separate recapitulation here.

A particular case of II(*iii*) should be noted: If an open rectangular parallelepiped is defined to be the Cartesian product of an open rectangle and a bounded open interval, then the volume of such a parallelepiped is the product of the lengths of three adjacent edges.

206   VOLUMES OF REVOLUTION BY CYLINDERS AND WASHERS

For purposes of application we shall now assume a formula to be established later (§512, *SCC*), namely, the formula for the area of an open or closed circular disk of radius r:

(1) $A(\{(x, y) \mid x^2 + y^2 < r^2\}) = A(\{(x, y) \mid x^2 + y^2 \leq r^2\}) = \pi r^2$.

By II(*iii*), §205, a solid right circular cylinder of base radius r and altitude h, open or closed, has volume $\pi r^2 h$, thus:

(2) $\begin{cases} \textbf{Open cylinder:} & V(\{(x, y, z) \mid x^2 + y^2 < r^2, 0 < z < h\}) = \pi r^2 h, \\ \textbf{Closed cylinder:} & V(\{(x, y, z) \mid x^2 + y^2 \leq r^2, 0 \leq z \leq h\}) = \pi r^2 h. \end{cases}$

The following theorem specifies two types of sets of zero volume that will appear in our work on volumes:

Theorem I.   *Any bounded plane set has zero volume. Any subset of the surface of a right circular cylinder has zero volume.*

Proof.   Any bounded plane set S is contained in a circular disk, and therefore, by formula (2), in a right circular cylinder of arbitrarily small volume. By the analogue of Theorem I, §201, S has zero volume. By Example 5, §203, and the formula of II(*iii*), §205, the lateral surface of any right circular cylinder has zero volume. Since the total surface of a right circular cylinder is the union of its lateral surface and two plane disks, the total surface has zero volume by the additivity of the volume function. Consequently (cf. Theorem II, §201) any subset of the surface of a right circular cylinder has zero volume.

We now turn our attention to the determination of certain volumes of revolution. Let f be a nonnegative function integrable on a compact interval $[a, b]$, and let W be the set obtained by revolving the ordinate set S of f about the x-axis, as shown in Figure 206-1.

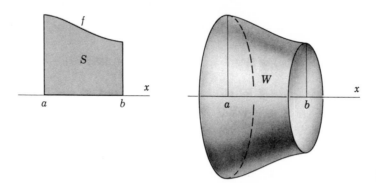

Figure 206-1

For an arbitrary net $\mathfrak{N} : \{a_0, a_1, \cdots, a_n\}$ on $[a, b]$, let s be a nonnegative lower step-function for f and let t be an upper step-function for f, and consider the sets W_1 and W_2 obtained by revolving about the x-axis the ordinate sets of s and t, respectively (cf. Fig. 206-2). Since $0 \leqq s \leqq f \leqq t$, the following inclusions hold:

$$(3) \qquad\qquad W_1 \subset W \subset W_2.$$

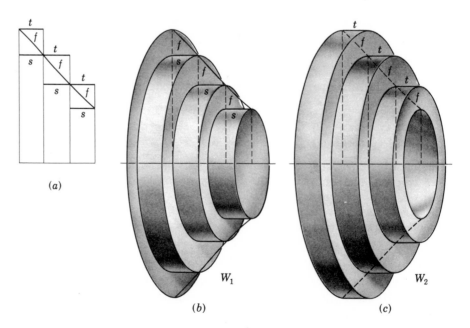

Figure 206-2

If the values of s and t on the ith open subinterval (a_{i-1}, a_i) of $\mathfrak{N}$ are s_i and t_i, respectively, then since each of W_1 and W_2 is the union of open cylinders and portions of their surfaces, we have from formula (2) and Theorem I:

$$\text{(4)} \qquad V(W_1) = \sum_{i=1}^{n} \pi s_i^2(a_i - a_{i-1}),$$

$$\text{(5)} \qquad V(W_2) = \sum_{i=1}^{n} \pi t_i^2(a_i - a_{i-1}).$$

In order to show that W has a volume, and to find a formula for it, we wish to show that the values of $V(W_1)$ and $V(W_2)$ can be made arbitrarily close to each other and that these values approximate a certain definite integral. To this end we let ϵ denote an arbitrary positive number and define the function

$$\text{(6)} \qquad g \equiv \pi f^2.$$

Since g is a nonnegative integrable function (cf. Theorem I, §107) there exist nonnegative step-functions σ and τ such that $\sigma \leq g \leq \tau$ and $\int_a^b (\tau - \sigma) < \epsilon$. In terms of σ and τ we define nonnegative step-functions s and t:

$$\text{(7)} \qquad s \equiv \sqrt{\sigma/\pi}, \qquad t \equiv \sqrt{\tau/\pi},$$

with W_1 and W_2 defined as before, and with $s \leq f \leq t$ and (3)–(5) holding. Since $V(W_2) - V(W_1) = \pi \int_a^b t^2 - \pi \int_a^b s^2 = \int_a^b (\tau - \sigma) < \epsilon$, we infer from the Axiom III of completeness, §205, that the set W has volume. Furthermore, the following inequalities hold:

$$\int_a^b \tau - \epsilon < \int_a^b \sigma = V(W_1) \leq V(W) \leq V(W_2) = \int_a^b \tau < \int_a^b \sigma + \epsilon.$$

Therefore, by the Theorem, §109, with $\gamma \equiv V(W)$ and g in the role of f of that theorem:

$$\text{(8)} \qquad V(W) = \int_a^b g = \int_a^b \pi f^2$$

and we have established the theorem:

Theorem II. *If f is a nonnegative function integrable on the compact interval $[a, b]$, and if W is the set obtained by revolving the ordinate set S of f, for $a \leq x \leq b$, about the x-axis, then W has volume given by*

$$\text{(9)} \qquad V(W) = \pi \int_a^b f^2 = \pi \int_a^b f^2(x)\, dx.$$

One way to remember formula (9) is by the corollary:

Corollary. *Under the assumptions of Theorem II, the volume of revolution may be computed by evaluating an integral, where the integrand is the area of the cross section perpendicular to the axis of revolution, expressed in terms of the variable of that axis as the variable of integration.*

Example 1. Find the volume of a solid sphere (also called a **spherical ball**) of radius $a > 0$.

Solution. By symmetry, we double the volume of the set W obtained by revolving about the x-axis the first-quadrant quarter-disk that is the ordinate set of the function $f(x) = \sqrt{a^2 - x^2}$, got by solving $x^2 + y^2 = a^2$ for y, for $0 \leq x \leq a$ (cf. Fig. 206-3a):

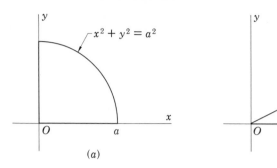

Figure 206-3

$$2V(W) = 2\pi \int_0^a [\sqrt{a^2 - x^2}]^2 dx = 2\pi \int_0^a (a^2 - x^2) dx = 2\pi \left[a^2(a - 0) - \frac{a^3 - 0^3}{3} \right] = \frac{4}{3}\pi a^3.$$

Example 2. Find the volume of a solid right circular cone of base radius r and altitude h.

Solution. The volume V desired can be obtained by revolving about the x-axis the right triangle shown in Figure 206-3b, with vertices $(0, 0)$, $(h, 0)$, and (h, r). Since the slope of the hypotenuse is r/h its equation is $y = (r/h)x$, and

$$V = \pi \int_0^h \left(\frac{rx}{h}\right)^2 dx = \frac{\pi r^2}{h^2} \frac{h^3 - 0^3}{3} = \frac{1}{3}\pi r^2 h.$$

Volumes of revolution can sometimes be found by interchanging the roles of the variables x and y.

Example 3. Find the volume of the set W obtained by revolving about the y-axis the set S bounded in the first quadrant by the curve $x + 4y^2 = 4$ and the two coordinate axes.

Solution. The set S can be described:

$$S = \{(x, y) \mid 0 \leq y \leq 1, 0 \leq x \leq 4 - 4y^2\}$$

(cf. Fig. 206-4). Using the Corollary to Theorem II, we cut W by a plane perpendicular to the y-axis corresponding to the point y on the y-axis, the resulting section of W being a disk of radius $x = 4 - 4y^2$ and area $\pi(4 - 4y^2)^2$. We therefore have for the volume of W:

$$V(W) = \pi \int_0^1 (4 - 4y^2)^2 dy = 16\pi \int_0^1 (1 - 2y^2 + y^4) dy = 16\pi(1 - \tfrac{2}{3} + \tfrac{1}{5}) = \frac{128\pi}{15}.$$

Consider now the case of revolving about a coordinate axis the set between two graphs. Specifically, let f and g be two nonnegative integrable functions on a compact interval $[a, b]$, assume $f \leq g$ there, and let S be the set between their graphs:

$$S \equiv \{(x, y) \mid a \leq x \leq b, f(x) \leq y \leq g(x)\}.$$

If W is the set obtained by revolving S about the x-axis (cf. **Fig.** 206-5), then it can be shown (cf. H§709, *CWAG*) that W has volume equal to the volume of revolution of the ordinate set of g minus the volume of revolution of the ordinate set of f:

$$(10) \qquad V(W) = \pi \int_a^b g^2 - \pi \int_a^b f^2 = \pi \int_a^b (g^2 - f^2) = \pi \int_a^b [g^2(x) - f^2(x)] dx.$$

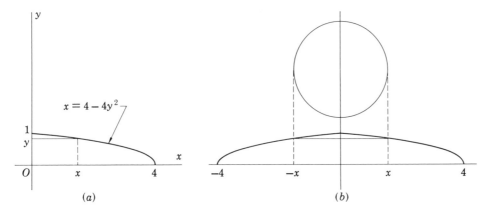

Figure 206-4

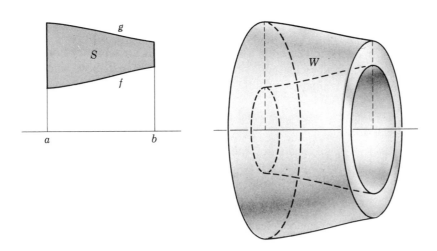

Figure 206-5

Notice that (10) reduces to (9) when $f = 0$. The Corollary to Theorem II applies also to the present case.

The determination of volumes by formula (10) is sometimes called the **method of washers** since the approximating cylinders of Figure 206-2 are replaced by approximating "reamed-out cylinders" or "washers."

Example 4. A set S is bounded in the first quadrant by the line $x = 2y$ and the curve $x = y^2$. Find the volume of the set W obtained by revolving S about the x-axis.

Solution. A figure (cf. Fig. 206-6) shows that the curve $x = y^2$ lies above the line $x = 2y$. For the formula (10) we can therefore take $g(x) \equiv \sqrt{x}$ and $f(x) \equiv \frac{1}{2}x$, and since the two graphs meet at $(0, 0)$ and $(4, 2)$, we have

$$V(W) = \pi \int_0^4 \left(x - \frac{x^2}{4}\right)dx = \pi\left(\frac{16}{2} - \frac{64}{12}\right) = \frac{8\pi}{3}.$$

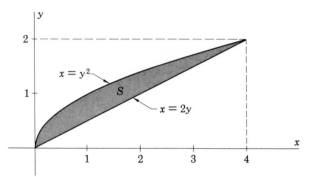

Figure 206-6

Example 5. Find the volume of the set obtained by revolving about the y-axis the set S of Example 4.

Solution. With an interchange of the roles of x and y, we have for the desired volume

$$\pi \int_0^2 [(2y)^2 - (y^2)^2]dy = \pi \int_0^2 (4y^2 - y^4)dy = \pi\left(\frac{4\cdot 8}{3} - \frac{32}{5}\right) = \frac{64\pi}{15}.$$

Volumes of revolution where the axis of revolution is an arbitrary horizontal or vertical line are obtained by methods similar to those discussed above where the axis of revolution is a coordinate axis.

Example 6. Find the volume obtained by revolving about the line $x = 4$ the set S of Examples 4 and 5.

Solution. The area of the section of the set of revolution corresponding to the ordinate y, where $0 \leq y \leq 2$, is the difference between the areas of two circular disks, of radius $4 - x = 4 - y^2$, and $4 - x = 4 - 2y$:

$$\text{Area} = \pi(4 - y^2)^2 - \pi (4 - 2y)^2 = \pi(y^4 - 12y^2 + 16y),$$

and the volume sought is therefore obtained by integration, according to the principle stated in the Corollary to Theorem II:

$$\text{Volume} = \pi \int_0^2 (y^4 - 12y^2 + 16y)dy = \pi\left(\frac{32}{5} - 32 + 32\right) = \frac{32\pi}{5}.$$

207 EXERCISES

In Exercises 1–4, find the volume obtained by revolving about the x-axis the ordinate set of the given function. (Cf. Example 3, §115, *PCLA*, for Exs. 3 and 4.)

1. $y = x^2, 0 \leq x \leq 3$.   **2.** $y = |x - 2|, 1 \leq x \leq 4$.

3. $y = [x], 0 \leq x \leq 6$.   **4.** $y = x - [x], 0 \leq x \leq 6$.

In Exercises 5–8, find by integration the volume obtained by revolving the given set about the y-axis.

5. $\{(x, y) \,|\, 0 \leq x \leq 2, 0 \leq y \leq 4 - 2x\}$.   **6.** $\{(x, y) \,|\, 0 \leq x \leq 4, 3x \leq y \leq 12\}$.

7. $\{(x, y) \,|\, 0 \leq x \leq 1, \sqrt{x} \leq y \leq 1\}$.   **8.** $\{(x, y) \,|\, 0 \leq x \leq 1, 0 \leq y \leq 1 - x^2\}$.

In Exercises 9–12, find the volume obtained by revolving about the x-axis the set bounded by the given curves.

9. $y = x^2, y = x^3$.

10. $y = x, y = \sqrt{x}$.

11. $y = x^2 + x, y = 4x$.

12. $y = 9 - x^2, y = 9 - 3x$.

In Exercises 13–16, find the volume obtained by revolving about the y-axis the set bounded by the given curves.

13. $x = y^2, x = y^4, y \geq 0$.

14. $y = x, y = \sqrt{x}$.

15. $y = x^2, y = 4x$.

16. $y = 9 - x^2, y = 9 - 3x$.

In Exercises 17–20, find the volume obtained by revolving about the given line L the set bounded by the given curves C_1 and C_2.

17. $L: y = 1, C_1: y = x^2, C_2: y = x^3$.
18. $L: y = 16, C_1: y = x^2, C_2: y = 4x$.

19. $L: x = 1, C_1: x = y^2, C_2: x = y^4, y \geq 0$.

20. $L: x = 2, C_1: x + 2y^2 = 2, C_2: x + 2y = 2$.

208 VOLUMES OF REVOLUTION BY CYLINDRICAL SHELLS

It may happen that a volume of revolution cannot be determined (at least readily) by the method of cylinders and washers discussed in §206. In some cases such a volume can be calculated by another method, called the method of **cylindrical shells,** which we shall now discuss.

Let f be a nonnegative function integrable on the compact interval $[a, b]$, where $0 \leq a < b$, and let W be the set obtained by revolving the ordinate set S of f about the y-axis (cf. Fig. 208-1).

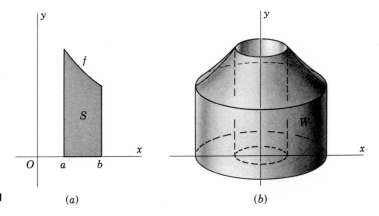

Figure 208-1   (a)   (b)

For an arbitrary net $\mathfrak{N} : \{a_0, a_1, \cdots, a_n\}$ on $[a, b]$, let s be a nonnegative lower step-function for f and let t be an upper step-function for f, and consider the sets W_1 and W_2 obtained by revolving about the y-axis the ordinate sets of s and t, respectively (cf. Fig. 208-2). Since $0 \leq s \leq f \leq t$ the following inclusions hold:

(1) $$W_1 \subset W \subset W_2.$$

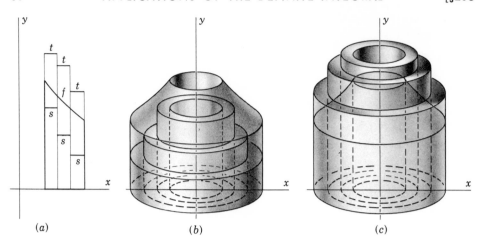

Figure 208-2

An **open circular annulus** of radii r_1 and r_2, where $r_1 < r_2$, is defined to be the set between two concentric circles of radii r_1 and r_2, congruent to a plane set of the form $\{(x, y) \mid r_1{}^2 < x^2 + y^2 < r_2{}^2\}$, as shown in Figure 208-3a. By formula (1), §206, the area of such a circular annulus is equal to $\pi r_2{}^2 - \pi r_1{}^2 = \pi(r_2{}^2 - r_1{}^2) = \pi(r_2 - r_1)(r_2 + r_1) = 2\pi \dfrac{r_1 + r_2}{2}(r_2 - r_1)$. The volume of a cylindrical set of altitude h whose base is an open circular annulus of radii r_1 and r_2 (Fig. 208-3b), congruent to a set of the form $\{(x, y, z) \mid r_1{}^2 < x^2 + y^2 < r_2{}^2, 0 < z < h\}$ is therefore equal to

$$(2) \qquad \text{Volume} = 2\pi \frac{r_1 + r_2}{2}(r_2 - r_1)h.$$

Such a cylindrical set will be called an **open cylindrical shell.**

If the values of s and t in the ith open interval (a_{i-1}, a_i) of $\mathfrak{N}$ are s_i and t_i, respectively, then since each of W_1 and W_2 is the union of open cylindrical shells, together with sets of zero volume, we have from formula (2):

$$(3) \qquad V(W_1) = \sum_{i=1}^{n} 2\pi s_i \frac{a_{i-1} + a_i}{2}(a_i - a_{i-1}),$$

$$(4) \qquad V(W_2) = \sum_{i=1}^{n} 2\pi t_i \frac{a_{i-1} + a_i}{2}(a_i - a_{i-1}).$$

In order to show that W has a volume, and to find a formula for it, we wish to show that the values of $V(W_1)$ and $V(W_2)$ can be made arbitrarily close to each other and that these values approximate a certain definite integral. To facilitate this objective, if ϵ denotes an arbitrary positive number, we let s and t be nonnegative step-functions such that $s \leqq f \leqq t$ and $\int_a^b (t - s) < \epsilon/2\pi b$ (we shall soon see the reason for the constant $\epsilon/2\pi b$), and define the three functions u, g, and v:

$$(5) \qquad u(x) \equiv 2\pi x\, s(x), \quad g(x) \equiv 2\pi x\, f(x), \quad v(x) \equiv 2\pi x\, t(x).$$

Then u, g, and v are integrable on $[a, b]$ since each is the product of two integrable

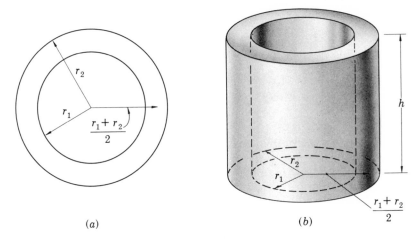

(a)   (b)

Figure 208-3

functions (cf. §107), and since all functions involved have nonnegative values, the following inequalities hold for $a \leq x \leq b$:

(6) $$u(x) \leq g(x) \leq v(x),$$

and therefore

(7) $$\int_a^b u \leq \int_a^b g \leq \int_a^b v.$$

The integrals $\int_a^b u$ and $\int_a^b v$ can be explicitly evaluated. For example,

$$\int_a^b u = \sum_{i=1}^n 2\pi \int_{a_{i-1}}^{a_i} s_i\, x\, dx = \sum_{i=1}^n 2\pi s_i \frac{a_i^2 - a_{i-1}^2}{2}$$

$$= \sum_{i=1}^n 2\pi s_i \frac{a_{i-1} + a_i}{2} (a_i - a_{i-1}) = V(W_1).$$

Similarly, $\int_a^b v = V(W_2)$, and we have from (7),

(8) $$V(W_1) \leq \int_a^b g \leq V(W_2).$$

We now compare the volumes of W_1 and W_2:

(9) $$V(W_2) - V(W_1) = \int_a^b v - \int_a^b u = \int_a^b (v - u) = 2\pi \int_a^b x(t(x) - s(x))dx$$

$$\leq 2\pi \int_a^b b(t(x) - s(x))dx = 2\pi b \int_a^b (t - s) < (2\pi b) \frac{\epsilon}{2\pi b} = \epsilon.$$

We now see the reason for the earlier choice of the constant $\epsilon/2\pi b$, since by the axiom of completeness for volume (Axiom III, §205), we can infer that the set W has volume.

Finally, from the inequalities (8) and $V(W_1) \leq V(W) \leq V(W_2)$, in the form

(10) $$-V(W_2) \leq -V(W) \leq -V(W_1),$$

we have by addition

(11) $-(V(W_2) - V(W_1)) \leqq \int_a^b g - V(W) = V(W_2) - V(W_1),$

and hence, by Theorem I(v), §311, *PCLA*, and (9),

(12) $\left| \int_a^b g - V(W) \right| \leqq V(W_2) - V(W_1) < \epsilon.$

Since ϵ is an *arbitrary* positive number, the nonnegative constant on the left of (12) must be equal to zero (cf. Ex. 15, §305, *PCLA*), and we have proved the theorem:

Theorem I.   *If f is a nonnegative function defined and integrable on the compact interval [a, b], where $0 \leqq a < b$, the set W obtained by revolving about the y-axis the ordinate set of f has volume equal to*

(13) $$V(W) = 2\pi \int_a^b x \, f(x) \, dx.$$

By subtraction of volumes, much as was done in §206 for volumes of revolution about the x-axis (cf. Ex. 21, H§720, *CWAG*), we have the theorem:

Theorem II.   *If f and g are functions defined and integrable on the compact interval [a, b], where $0 \leqq a < b$, if $f \leqq g$ there, and if W is the set obtained by revolving about the y-axis the set between the graphs of f and g (cf. Fig. 208-4), then W has volume equal to*

(14) $$V(W) = 2\pi \int_a^b x(g(x) - f(x))dx.$$

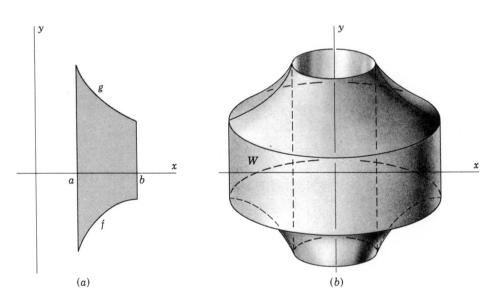

Figure 208-4

Intuitive discussion.   In the Corollary to Theorem II, §206, it was mentioned that each volume of revolution considered in §206 can be obtained by evaluating an integral where the integrand is the area of the cross section perpendicular to the axis of the variable of integration. This is not possible in the present instance, but something not entirely dissimilar *is* possible. The value of the function

$$(15) \qquad\qquad 2\pi x(g(x) - f(x))$$

integrated in (14) is an area (cf. §112, *SCC*), but the surface of which (15) is the area is not a plane surface. However, this surface *is*, in a sense, perpendicular to the x-axis (the axis of the variable of integration). The area in question is that of the lateral surface of a right circular cylinder, with base radius x and altitude $g(x) - f(x)$ (cf. Fig. 208-5). The circumference of the base circle is $2\pi x$ (cf. §107, *SCC*) and therefore the area is the product (15). One of the main purposes of such intuitive ideas as the preceding is the quick reconstruction of formulas like (14), and hence the elimination of a certain amount of memorization of formulas.

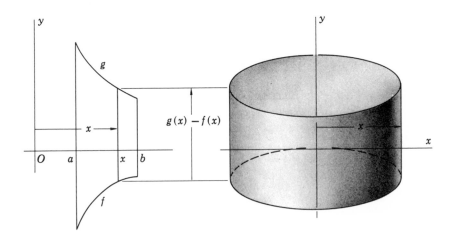

Figure 208-5

Example 1. Find the volume of the set obtained by revolving about the y-axis the ordinate set of the function $4x - x^2, 0 \leqq x \leqq 4$.

Solution. By Theorem I, the desired volume is

$$2\pi \int_0^4 x(4x - x^2)dx = 2\pi \int_0^4 (4x^2 - x^3)dx = 2\pi\left[4 \cdot \frac{64}{3} - \frac{256}{4}\right] = \frac{128\pi}{3}.$$

(Cf. Fig. 208-6*a*.)

Example 2. Find the volume of the set obtained by revolving about the x-axis the set bounded by the curve $x = -y^2 + 6y - 8$ and the line $x = y - 4$ (cf. Fig. 208-6*b*).

Solution. The method of cylinders and washers (§206) does not lend itself easily to this problem. We use the method of cylindrical shells (Theorem II) with the roles of x and y reversed:

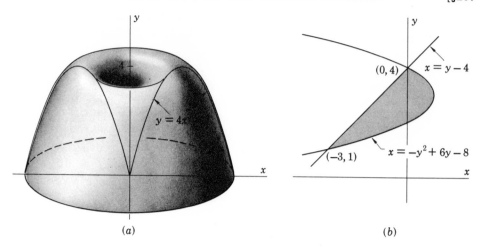

Figure 208-6

$$2\pi \int_1^4 y[(-y^2 + 6y - 8) - (y - 4)]dy = \pi \int_1^4 (-2y^3 + 10y^2 - 8y)dy$$

$$= \pi \left[-\frac{256 - 1}{2} + 10 \cdot \frac{64 - 1}{3} - 4(16 - 1) \right] = \pi \left(-128 + \frac{1}{2} + 210 - 60 \right) = \frac{45\pi}{2}.$$

As in §206, volumes of revolution where the axis of revolution is an arbitrary horizontal or vertical line are obtained by methods similar to those discussed above where the axis of revolution is a coordinate axis.

Example 3. Find the volume of the set obtained by revolving about the line $x = 7$ the ordinate set of the function $4x - x^2$, $0 \leq x \leq 4$.

Solution. The procedure is the same as with Example 1, except that the right circular cylinder of the preceding *intuitive discussion* has radius $7 - x$ instead x. The volume is thus

$$2\pi \int_0^4 (7 - x)(4x - x^2)dx = 2\pi \int_0^4 (28x - 11x^2 + x^3)dx = \frac{320\pi}{3}.$$

209 VOLUMES OF KNOWN CROSS SECTION AREA

Let W be a solid figure such that every section $S(x)$ of W by a plane perpendicular to the x-axis for $a \leq x \leq b$ has an area $\alpha(x) \equiv A(S(x))$, and assume furthermore that S is a *decreasing* set function* of x in the sense that orthogonal projections onto the yz-plane of sections perpendicular to the x-axis are related by inclusion as follows (cf. Fig. 209-1):

(1) $a \leq x_1 < x_2 \leq b \Rightarrow \{(y, z) \mid (x_2, y, z) \in S(x_2)\} \subset \{(y, z) \mid (x_1, y, z) \in S(x_1)\}$, or equivalently,

$$\{(y, z) \mid (x_2, y, z) \in W\} \subset \{(y, z) \mid (x_1, y, z) \in W\}.$$

*The case of an *increasing* set function is defined and treated similarly, with an identical resulting formula.

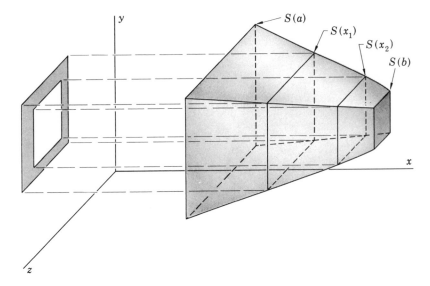

Figure 209-1

The principal theorem regarding volumes of sets of the type described above is:

Theorem. *If W is a solid figure having the properties enumerated above, then W has a volume $V(W)$, the function $\alpha : x \rightarrow \alpha(x) = A(S(x))$ is integrable on $[a, b]$, and*

$$(2) \qquad\qquad V(W) = \int_a^b \alpha(x)dx.$$

Proof. Let $\mathfrak{N} : \{a_0, a_1, \cdots, a_n\}$ be a net on $[a, b]$ of equally spaced points, with $a_i - a_{i-1} = (b - a)/n$, for $i = 1, 2, \cdots, n$ (cf. the proof of Theorem I, §106); for each x between a_{i-1} and a_i, for $i = 1, 2, \cdots, n$, let the sets W_1 and W_2 be defined to have the sections:

$$(3) \qquad\qquad W_1 : S(a_i); \qquad W_2 : S(a_{i-1});$$

and for each point of the net $\mathfrak{N}$, let both W_1 and W_2 have the same section as W (cf. Fig. 209-2). If the step-functions s and t are defined:

$$(4) \qquad\qquad s(x) \equiv A\{(y, z) \mid (x, y, z) \in W_1\},$$

$$(5) \qquad\qquad t(x) \equiv A\{(y, z) \mid (x, y, z) \in W_2\},$$

then we have the following inclusions and inequalities:

$$(6) \qquad\qquad W_1 \subset W \subset W_2,$$

$$(7) \qquad\qquad s(x) \leqq \alpha(x) \leqq t(x), \quad \text{for} \quad a \leqq x \leqq b.$$

Furthermore, since W_1 and W_2 are unions of cylindrical sets, together with sets of zero volume, their volumes can be specifically evaluated in terms of the integrals of s and t:

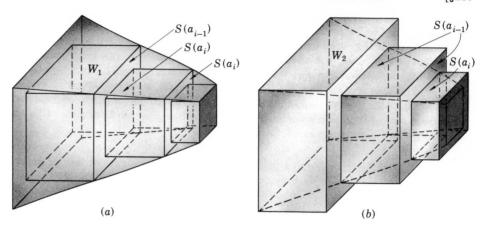

Figure 209-2

(8)
$$V(W_1) = \int_a^b s, \qquad V(W_2) = \int_a^b t,$$

and the integrals of s and t are related:

(9)
$$\int_a^b t - \int_a^b s = \int_a^b (t - s) = \sum_{i=1}^n [\alpha(a_{i-1}) - \alpha(a_i)](a_i - a_{i-1})$$

$$= \frac{b-a}{n} \sum_{i=1}^n [\alpha(a_{i-1}) - \alpha(a_i)] = \frac{b-a}{n}[\alpha(a) - \alpha(b)].$$

If ϵ is an arbitrary positive number, there exists a positive integer n so large that the final quantity of (9) is less than ϵ, and

(10)
$$V(W_2) - V(W_1) = \int_a^b (t - s) < \epsilon.$$

Therefore, by the axiom of completeness for volume (III, §205), W has a volume $V(W)$, and by (6) and (8),

(11)
$$\int_a^b t - \epsilon < \int_a^b s = V(W_1) \leqq V(W) \leqq V(W_2) = \int_a^b t < \int_a^b s + \epsilon.$$

Since the function $\alpha(x)$, as a function of x, is decreasing on $[a, b]$ it is integrable there. Therefore, by (7) and the Theorem, §109, with $\gamma \equiv V(W)$ and $\alpha(x)$ in the role of $f(x)$, $V(W)$ must be equal to $\int_a^b \alpha(x)dx$, and the proof is complete.

It should be noted that the formula for the volume of revolution by the method of cylinders and washers (§206) is a special case of (2) when the function involved is increasing (or decreasing). Finally, volumes of sets that are composites of portions for each of which the sections are either increasing or decreasing can be obtained by adding the volumes of the constituent parts.

NOTE. The condition that $S : x \to S(x)$ be increasing or decreasing can be omitted completely in case W is assumed to have volume, but the proof then becomes very much more difficult. The volume of a parallelepiped can be obtained as a special case of this more general result. If a parallelepiped Π is placed in a rectangular coordinate system so that its base lies in the yz-plane, then all sections perpendicular to the x-axis are congruent parallelograms and the function $x \to \alpha(x)$ of the preceding theorem is *constant* on the interval $[a, b]$ and equal to the area A of the base of Π. Therefore formula (2) becomes $V(W) = \int_a^b A\,dx = A \cdot (b - a)$. Since the length $b - a$ of the interval $[a, b]$ is the altitude of Π, we conclude that *the volume of a parallelepiped is equal to the product of its base area and its altitude.*

Example 1. A solid figure W has a base in the xy-plane that is a circular disk of radius $a > 0$, and every section of W by a plane perpendicular to the x-axis is a square. Find the volume of W.

Solution. For convenience we choose a coordinate system having its origin at the center of the base of W and with W situated so that the z-coordinates of points of W are nonnegative (cf. Fig. 209-3). Since the edge of the square $S(x)$ is of length $2\sqrt{a^2 - x^2}$ for each $x \in [-a, a]$, the area $\alpha(x)$ of the section $S(x)$ is $4(a^2 - x^2)$, and by symmetry the volume of W is

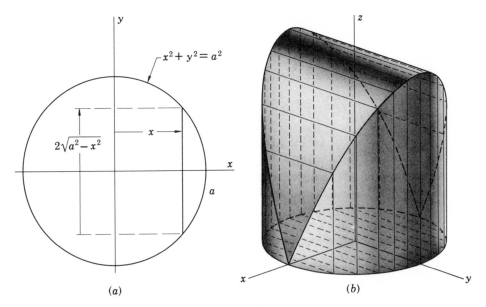

Figure 209-3

$$V(W) = \int_{-a}^{a} 4(a^2 - x^2)dx = 8 \int_0^a (a^2 - x^2)dx = 8\left[a^2 \cdot a - \frac{a^3}{3}\right] = \frac{16a^3}{3}.$$

Example 2. Let W be a pyramid with base area B and altitude h, and such that a line through the vertex of W perpendicular to the base passes through a point of the base. Assuming that areas of similar plane sets are proportional to the squares of corresponding dimensions of these plane sets, derive the formula for the volume of W:

(12) $V(W) = \frac{1}{3} Bh.$

Solution. Choose a coordinate system with the vertex of W at the origin and the base of W in the plane perpendicular to the x-axis at $x = h$ (cf. Fig. 209-4a). Because of linearity and the fashion in which lines of the figure issue from the origin, the dimensions of the section

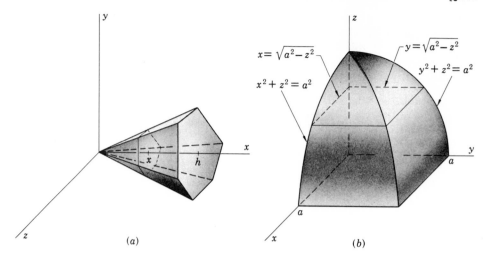

Figure 209-4

of W at the abscissa x vary directly with x itself. Therefore the assumption concerning similar plane sets can be formulated:

$$(13) \qquad \frac{\alpha(x_1)}{\alpha(x_2)} = \frac{x_1^2}{x_2^2},$$

so that with $x = x_1$ and $h = x_2$, we have for the cross-section area at $x \in [0, h]$:

$$(14) \qquad \alpha(x) = \frac{B}{h^2} x^2.$$

By (2), the volume of the pyramid is

$$(15) \qquad V(W) = \int_0^h \alpha(x)dx = \frac{B}{h^2} \int_0^h x^2 \, dx = \frac{1}{3} Bh.$$

Example 3. Two right circular solid cylinders of equal radius have axes that intersect at right angles. Find the volume of their common set W of intersection.

Solution. Choose a coordinate system with the x-axis and y-axis the axes of the two cylinders, and let $a > 0$ be their common radius. Then (cf. Fig. 209-4b) the section of one cylinder by the xz-plane is the disk given by $x^2 + z^2 \leqq a^2$ and the section of the other cylinder by the yz-plane is the disk given by $y^2 + z^2 \leqq a^2$. The simplest sections of W are those parallel to the xy-plane. Such a section corresponding to a point z on the z-axis is a square of area

$$(16) \qquad \alpha(z) = (2\sqrt{a^2 - z^2})(2\sqrt{a^2 - z^2}) = 4(a^2 - z^2).$$

Therefore the volume $V(W)$ is

$$(17) \qquad V(W) = \int_{-a}^a 4(a^2 - z^2)dz = 8 \int_0^a (a^2 - z^2)dz = \frac{16}{3} a^3.$$

210   EXERCISES

A figure should accompany each of the following exercises.

In Exercises 1–4, use the method of cylindrical shells to find the volume obtained by revolving about the y-axis the ordinate set of the given function. (Cf. Example 3, §115, *PCLA*, for Exs. 3 and 4.)

1. $y = x^2, 0 \leq x \leq 3$.

2. $y = |x - 2|, 1 \leq x \leq 4$.

3. $y = [x], 0 \leq x \leq 4$.

4. $y = x - [x], 0 \leq x \leq 4$.

In Exercises 5–8, use the method of cylindrical shells to find the volume obtained by revolving the given set about the x-axis.

5. $\{(x, y) \mid 0 \leq x \leq 2, 0 \leq y \leq 4 - 2x\}$.

6. $\{(x, y) \mid 0 \leq x \leq 4, 3x \leq y \leq 12\}$.

7. $\{(x, y) \mid 0 \leq x \leq 1, \sqrt{x} \leq y \leq 1\}$.

8. $\{(x, y) \mid 0 \leq x \leq 1, 0 \leq y \leq 1 - \sqrt{x}\}$.

In Exercises 9–12, use the method of cylindrical shells to find the volume obtained by revolving about the y-axis the set bounded by the given curves.

9. $y = x^2, y = x^3$.

10. $y = x^2 + x, y = 4x$.

11. $y = 1/x, y = -\frac{1}{2}x + \frac{3}{2}$.

12. $y = 9 - x^2, y = 9 - 3x$.

In Exercises 13–16, use the method of cylindrical shells to find the volume obtained by revolving about the x-axis the set bounded by the given curves.

13. $x = y^2, x = y^4, y \geq 0$.

14. $y = x, y = \sqrt{x}$.

15. $y = 1/x, y = -\frac{1}{2}x + \frac{3}{2}$.

16. $x = 3y - y^2, x = -2y$.

In Exercises 17–20, use the method of cylindrical shells to find the volume obtained by revolving about the given line L the set bounded by the curves C_1 and C_2.

17. $L: x = 1, C_1: y = x^2, C_2: y = x^3$.

18. $L: x = 4, C_1: y = x^2, C_2: y = 4x$.

19. $L: y = 1, C_1: x = y^2, C_2: x = y^4, y \geq 0$.

20. $L: y = 2, C_1: x + 2y^2 = 2, C_2: x + 2y = 2$.

In Exercises 21 and 22, a solid figure W has a base in the xy-plane that is a circular disk of radius $a > 0$, and every section of W by a plane perpendicular to the x-axis is a closed triangle as described. Find the volume of W.

21. Isosceles, altitude twice the base.

22. Equilateral.

In Exercises 23–26, a solid figure W has a base in the xy-plane, and every section of W by the plane parallel to the xy-plane that corresponds to the z-coordinate z is a square with vertices $(f(z), f(z), z)$, $(f(z), -f(z), z)$, $(-f(z), f(z), z)$, and $(-f(z), -f(z), z)$, for the specified function $f(z)$ and range of the variable z. Find the volume of W.

23. $f(z) = 2z + 1, 0 \leq z \leq 3$.

24. $f(z) = 2 - \frac{1}{2}z, 0 \leq z \leq 2$.

25 $f(z) = \frac{1}{2}\sqrt{4 - z}, 0 \leq z \leq 4$.

26. $f(z) = 2 - \frac{1}{2}z^2, 0 \leq z \leq 1$.

27. A log has the form of a right circular cylinder of radius 2 feet. A wedge is removed from the log by means of two cuts, one of which is perpendicular to the axis of the log. If the two cuts form an angle of $\frac{1}{4}\pi$ radians and meet in a line that passes through the axis of the log, find the volume of the wedge.

211   FORCE AND WORK

The physical concept of **work** done by a force is defined, in case a constant force is applied in the direction of motion over a certain distance, as the product of the force and the distance. The units of work incorporate those used for force and distance.

Example 1.   The work done by a force of 3 pounds acting over a distance of 5 feet is 15 foot-pounds.

Example 2.   An object weighing 8 ounces is raised a distance of 90 inches. The work done in raising this object is 720 inch-ounces, or $\frac{8}{16} \cdot 90 = 45$ inch-pounds $= 8 \cdot \frac{90}{12} = 60$ foot-ounces $= \frac{8}{16} \cdot \frac{90}{12} = \frac{15}{4} = 3\frac{3}{4}$ foot-pounds.

In case a *variable force* is in operation, work is defined in such a way as to be consistent with the special case of a constant force, just discussed, and the two principles of additivity and positivity, in the form:

(*i*)   **Additivity:** *The work for the distance interval* [a, b] *plus the work for the distance interval* [b, c] *is equal to the total work for the distance interval* [a, c], *where* a < b < c.

(*ii*)   **Positivity:** *If* F_1 *and* F_2 *are two force functions for the interval* [a, b], *and if* $F_1 \leq F_2$ *there, then the work* W_1 *done by* F_1 *is less than or equal to the work* W_2 *done by* $F_2 : F_1 \leq F_2 \Rightarrow W_1 \leq W_2$.

As a consequence of these two principles, we have the theorem:

Theorem.   *Let* [a, b] *be a compact interval, as the range of a distance variable x, and let F be a nonnegative function integrable on* [a, b] *whose values represent force applied in the direction of the positive x-axis. Then the work W done by the force F over the interval* [a, b] *is:*

(1)
$$W = \int_a^b F(x)\,dx.$$

(Cf. Fig. 211-1.)

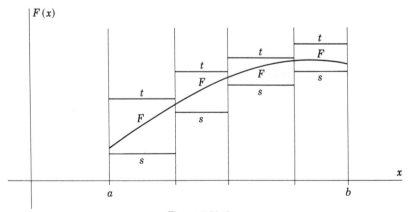

Figure 211-1

Proof. If ϵ is an arbitrary positive number, let s and t be nonnegative lower and upper step functions for F, for some common net $\mathfrak{N} : \{a_0, a_1, \cdots, a_n\}$ on $[a, b]$ such that $\int_a^b (t - s) < \epsilon$. Then interpreting s as a force function constant on subintervals we have the corresponding work achieved by s as the sum of the individual items of work done by s over these subintervals (by the additivity (*i*) extended to n terms), and if the value of s on the *i*th interval of $\mathfrak{N}$ is s_i, since the work done by s over this interval is by definition the product $s_i(a_i - a_{i-1})$, we have for the work done by s:

$$(2) \qquad\qquad W_s = \int_a^b s = \sum_{i=1}^n s_i(a_i - a_{i-1}).$$

In a similar way, and for similar reasons, the work done by t is

$$(3) \qquad\qquad W_t = \int_a^b t = \sum_{i=1}^n t_i(a_i - a_{i-1}).$$

By the positivity assumption (*ii*), and by the positivity of the integral functional $\int_a^b$, we have the two sets of inequalities:

$$(4) \qquad\qquad \int_a^b s = W_s \leq W \leq W_t = \int_a^b t,$$
$$(5) \qquad\qquad W_s = \int_a^b s \leq \int_a^b F \leq \int_a^b t = W_t.$$

If the central inequalities of (5) are written $-\int_a^b t \leq -\int_a^b F \leq -\int_a^b s$, then addition with (4) gives $-\int_a^b (t - s) \leq W - \int_a^b F \leq \int_a^b (t - s)$, or

$$(6) \qquad\qquad |W - \int_a^b F| \leq \int_a^b (t - s) < \epsilon.$$

Since ϵ is an arbitrary positive number, the constant on the left of (6) must be zero, and (1) follows.

Example 3. **Hooke's law** in physics states that if a spring (or similar elastic object) is stretched or compressed within the "elastic limit" of the material, then the force used is proportional to the amount of extension or compression from the equilibrium position. A force of 12 pounds stretches a certain spring whose natural length is 5 inches to an extended length of 7 inches. Find the work done in stretching the spring one more inch, to a total length of 8 inches.

Solution. Letting x denote the amount of extension of the spring from equilibrium position, in inches, we can represent the force function F by means of a straight line through the origin, and since F is equal to 12 when $x = 2$, we have $F(x) = 6x$. The work done for $2 \leq x \leq 3$ is therefore

$$W = \int_2^3 6x \, dx = 6 \cdot \frac{9 - 4}{2} = 15 \text{ inch-pounds.}$$

This work is shown in Figure 211–2*a* by the shaded area.

Example 4. A cable hanging vertically from a scaffold is 50 feet long and weighs 3 pounds per foot. How much work is done in winding up the cable by means of a winch on the scaffold?

Solution. If x is the number of feet of cable wound onto the winch, the force of the remaining $50 - x$ feet is $3(50 - x)$. Therefore the work done is

$$\int_0^{50} 3(50 - x)dx = 3\left[50\frac{50}{1} - \frac{50^2}{2}\right] = 3750 \text{ foot-pounds.}$$

(Cf. Fig. 211-2*b*.)

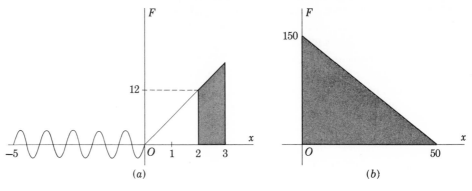

Figure 211-2

Other types of work problems are treated in §1014.

212   DISTANCE AND VELOCITY

The concept of *instantaneous velocity* will be defined and given considerable attention in later sections of this book. However, it is possible at present to treat a simple
relationship between distance and velocity in a manner quite similar to that between
work and force, given in §211. The principal difference is that in the present instance the independent variable is *time*, denoted by the letter *t*. Corresponding to the
fundamental definition of work as force times distance, when *force* is constant, is the
relationship of distance as the product of velocity times time, when *velocity* is constant. For present purposes let it suffice to consider velocity, as a function of time,
in a purely intuitive manner. Motion will be restricted to *rectilinear* motion (motion
of a particle on the real axis), the *sense* of the motion being to the *right;* that is,
distance *x* as a function of *t*: $t \to x(t)$, is an increasing function. Another way of
expressing the idea of *forward* motion is to say that velocity *v* as a function of *t*:
$t \to v(t)$, is nonnegative.

With distance properties of *additivity* and *positivity* expressed as under (*i*) and (*ii*),
§211, we have a similar result (cf. Fig. 212-1*a*).

Theorem.   *Let* [*a, b*] *be a compact interval, as the range of a time variable t, and let
v be a nonnegative function integrable on* [*a, b*] *whose values represent velocity. Then
the distance d traveled by the point having velocity v over the interval* [*a, b*] *is*

(1) $$d = \int_a^b v(t)dt.$$

If velocity is measured in feet per second and time in seconds, then the distance *d*
in (1) is measured in feet. If velocity is in miles per hour and time in hours, then
distance is in miles.

Example.   A car is speeding up in such a way that its velocity increases linearly from 30
feet per second to 50 feet per second over a 10-second time-interval. How far does it go
during these 10 seconds?

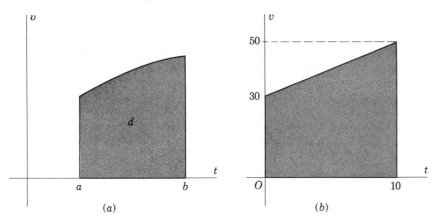

Figure 212-1

Solution. For convenience we choose the time units so that the beginning of the time interval corresponds to $t = 0$. Then, since $v(0) = 30$ and $v(10) = 50$ and the function $v(t)$ is linear, $v(t) = 2t + 30$ (cf. Fig. 212-1b). Therefore

$$d = \int_0^{10} (2t + 30)dt = 2 \cdot \frac{10^2}{2} + 30 \cdot \frac{10}{1} = 400 \text{ feet.}$$

213   EXERCISES

In Exercises 1 and 2, force in pounds as a function of distance x in feet is applied to a sled according to the given formula for $F(x)$. Find the total work done over the prescribed distance interval.

1. $F(x) \equiv \begin{cases} 100 - 4x, 0 \leq x \leq 10, \\ \qquad 60, 10 < x \leq 25, \end{cases} \quad 0 \leq x \leq 25.$

2. $F(x) \equiv \begin{cases} 50 - 3x, 0 \leq x \leq 2, \\ \qquad 44, \ \ 2 < x \leq 10, \end{cases} \quad 2 \leq x \leq 10.$

3. A leaky bucket containing sand is being raised at such a rate that at a height of x feet from its initial position it weighs $100 - 3x$ pounds. Find the work done in raising it 30 feet.

4. A water tank containing 200 cubic feet of water is being raised, but as it is being raised, water spills out at such a rate that when the tank has been raised x feet, $2x$ cubic feet of water have been lost. Find the total work done in raising the tank 10 feet. Assume the weight of water to be 62.4 pounds per cubic foot.

5. A force of 5 pounds extends a spring whose natural length is 7 inches to a new length of 10 inches. Find the work done in stretching the spring from its original position to an extended length of 15 inches.

6. How far will 60 inch-pounds stretch the spring of Exercise 5?

7. A force of 8 pounds extends a spring whose natural length is 6 inches to a new length of 10 inches. Find the work done in stretching the spring from a length of 11 inches to a length of 13 inches.

8. The spring of Exercise 7 is stretched by 2 inches from one position to another with an expenditure of 30 inch-pounds of work. What is the beginning total length?

9. How much work is done in winding up the cable of Example 4, §211, halfway?

10. How far is the cable of Example 4, §211, raised by half the total amount of work of that example, or 1875 foot-pounds?

11. A cable hanging vertically down a well is 100 feet long, weighs 5 pounds per foot, and has suspended from the lower end an additional weight of 200 pounds. Find the total work done in hoisting the cable and weight to the top of the well.

12. A cable suspended from the top of a building is 100 feet long and consists of two 50-foot pieces. The upper 50-foot portion weighs 2 pounds per foot and the lower 50-foot portion weighs 1 pound per foot. Find the total work performed in raising the 100-foot cable to the top of the building.

13. A car is slowing down in such a way that its velocity decreases linearly from 20 feet per second to 15 feet per second over a 20-second time-interval. How far does it go in these 20 seconds?

14. A car is speeding up in such a way that its velocity increases linearly from 5 feet per second to 25 feet per second over a 12-second time-interval. How far does it go during these 12 seconds?

15. A particle is moving along a straight line with velocity given by the formula $v = 80 - 32t$ feet per second where t represents time in seconds. How far does the particle go in the 2-second interval $[0, 2]$?

16. A toy cart is rolling down an inclined plane with velocity given by the formula $v = 8 + 4t$ inches per second, where t represents time in seconds. How far does the cart go from time $t = 3$ to time $t = 10$?

3

Uniform Continuity

301 UNIFORM CONTINUITY

Certain functions defined on an interval* I have a property known as *uniform continuity*, which is of great importance in the theory of integration, and in mathematical analysis in general. (The property of *continuity*, unmodified by the adjective *uniform* will be considered in the next chapter.) In this chapter *all functions considered will be assumed to be real-valued.*

The general *idea* of uniform continuity is best appreciated when the function f under consideration is looked at as a *mapping*. Crudely expressed, the property of uniform continuity for f means that *points that are close together are mapped by f onto points that are close together.* A little more precisely, this means that if we are told in advance how close the images $f(x_1)$ and $f(x_2)$ must be, then we can determine a measure of closeness for x_1 and x_2 that will guarantee the required measure of closeness of $f(x_1)$ and $f(x_2)$. Again in still different wording: the distance between $f(x_1)$ and $f(x_2)$ will be less than any preassigned positive number provided the distance between x_1 and x_2 is sufficiently small.

The definition in precise terms, with the aid of quantifiers is as follows:

Definition. *A function whose domain contains an interval I is **uniformly continuous on I** if and only if*

(1) $\quad \forall \epsilon > 0, \exists \delta > 0 \ni$
$$\left. \begin{array}{l} (x_1, x_2) \in I \times I \\ |x_1 - x_2| < \delta \end{array} \right\} \Rightarrow |f(x_1) - f(x_2)| < \epsilon.$$

*The interval I can be replaced, in nearly all the definitions and theorems that follow, by any nonempty set.

If the domain of a function f is an interval on which f is uniformly continuous, then f is simply called **uniformly continuous.**

The following theorem follows immediately from the preceding Definition:

Theorem I. *A function uniformly continuous on an interval I is uniformly continuous on any subinterval J of I.*

Proof. Assume that the function f is uniformly continuous on I and let J be any subinterval of I. If ϵ is an arbitrary positive number, let $\delta > 0$ be such that whenever x_1 and $x_2 \in I$ and $|x_1 - x_2| < \delta$, then $|f(x_1) - f(x_2)| < \epsilon$. It follows, then, that if x_1 and $x_2 \in J$ and $|x_1 - x_2| < \delta$, since x_1 and x_2 must belong to I, the quantity $|f(x_1) - f(x_2)|$ must be less than ϵ.

It will be shown in §304 that *every polynomial is uniformly continuous on every bounded interval*. In the first two examples that follow we shall verify this general theorem for linear functions, and shall illustrate the general principle by finding a positive number δ in terms of a given positive number ϵ, for a certain specific polynomial. We shall continue to use the single word *polynomial* to mean *polynomial function*, and the elliptic notation $P(x)$ for the polynomial that maps x onto $P(x)$.

Example 1. Prove that every linear function $ax + b$ is uniformly continuous on $\mathfrak{R}$.

Solution. The special case of a constant function given by $a = 0$ is considered in Example 4, below. We shall now assume that $a \neq 0$. If ϵ is an arbitrary positive number and if $f(x) \equiv ax + b$, we wish to find a positive number δ such that for any real numbers x_1 and x_2, $|x_1 - x_2| < \delta$ implies $|f(x_1) - f(x_2)| < \epsilon$ or, since $f(x_1) - f(x_2) = (ax_1 + b) - (ax_2 + b) = ax_1 - ax_2$,

$$|x_1 - x_2| < \delta \Rightarrow |a| \cdot |x_1 - x_2| < \epsilon.$$

Since $|a| > 0$, the implication that we are seeking to prove is equivalent to

$$|x_1 - x_2| < \delta \Rightarrow |x_1 - x_2| < \frac{\epsilon}{|a|}.$$

If the basic question that we have been asking ourselves is now rephrased, "How small must δ be in order that $|x_1 - x_2|$ is less than $\epsilon/|a|$ whenever $|x_1 - x_2|$ is less than δ?" the answer is immediate: The number δ can be any number between 0 and $\epsilon/|a|$, including $\epsilon/|a|$. We can choose δ to be $\epsilon/|a|$, or $\epsilon/2|a|$, or $\epsilon/3|a|$, or any other positive number less than or equal to $\epsilon/|a|$. The simplest and most natural choice is probably $\epsilon/|a|$, and so we define $\delta \equiv \epsilon/|a|$. With this value of δ the desired implication $|x_1 - x_2| < \delta \Rightarrow |f(x_1) - f(x_2)| < \epsilon$ reduces to

$$|x_1 - x_2| < \frac{\epsilon}{|a|} \Rightarrow |a| \cdot |x_1 - x_2| < \epsilon$$

and the solution is complete.

Example 2. Use the preceding Definition to prove that the polynomial $2x^2 - 3x + 5$ is uniformly continuous on the closed interval $[-3, 6]$.

Solution. With the notation $f(x) \equiv 2x^2 - 3x + 5$ we wish to obtain an inequality of the form $|f(x_1) - f(x_2)| < \epsilon$, or

(2) $|(2x_1{}^2 - 3x_1 + 5) - (2x_2{}^2 - 3x_2 + 5)| < \epsilon,$

if x_1 and x_2 are points of $[-3, 6]$ that are sufficiently near each other. If we simplify the left-hand member of (2) to

(3) $$|2x_1{}^2 - 2x_2{}^2 - 3x_1 + 3x_2| = |2(x_1{}^2 - x_2{}^2) - 3(x_1 - x_2)|,$$

we can factor the quantity within the absolute values signs and hence rewrite (3):

(4) $$|2(x_1 - x_2)(x_1 + x_2) - 3(x_1 - x_2)| = |(x_1 - x_2)(2x_1 + 2x_2 - 3)|,$$

and therefore obtain the following inequality that is equivalent to (2):

(5) $$|x_1 - x_2| \cdot |2x_1 + 2x_2 - 3| < \epsilon.$$

The question now takes the form: "How small must the first factor of (5) be in order that the product on the left side be less than the given positive number ϵ?" The answer depends on how large the second factor $|2x_1 + 2x_2 - 3|$ is. We now obtain an upper bound for this second factor, using two methods.

The first method for estimating the magnitude of $|2x_1 + 2x_2 - 3|$ makes use of inequalities derived from $-3 \leqq x_1 \leqq 6$ and $-3 \leqq x_2 \leqq 6$, and a simple equality:

$$-6 \leqq 2x_1 \leqq 12,$$
$$-6 \leqq 2x_2 \leqq 12,$$
$$-3 = -3 = -3.$$

By addition, we have

$$-15 \leqq (2x_1 + 2x_2 - 3) \leqq 21$$

and therefore, since $-21 < -15$,

(6) $$|2x_1 + 2x_2 - 3| \leqq 21.$$

The second method for estimating the magnitude of $|2x_1 + 2x_2 - 3|$ is simpler but cruder, making use of the triangle inequality:

(7) $$|2x_1 + 2x_2 - 3| \leqq 2|x_1| + 2|x_2| + 3 \leqq 2 \cdot 6 + 2 \cdot 6 + 3 = 27.$$

For the rest of the work on Example 2 we shall use the cruder result (7), rather than (6), since it will be sufficient for our purposes. (The number 27 could be replaced by 21, but the details would not otherwise be essentially changed.) Accordingly, since

(8) $$|x_1 - x_2| \cdot |2x_1 + 2x_2 - 3| \leqq 27|x_1 - x_2|,$$

we can now formulate a *new* question: "How small must $|x_1 - x_2|$ be in order that $27|x_1 - x_2|$ be less than ϵ?" It should be clear that if $|x_1 - x_2| < \epsilon/27$, then $27|x_1 - x_2| < \epsilon$, and hence, from (8) and the earlier equalities (3) and (4), it follows that $|f(x_1) - f(x_2)| < \epsilon$. We therefore can always choose

(9) $$\delta \equiv \frac{\epsilon}{27},$$

for (1) to hold for this example.

From the first method of estimating the magnitude of $|2x_1 - 2x_2 - 3|$ we know that δ could be chosen equal to $\epsilon/21$, with the same resulting implication. Actually, δ could be chosen to be *any* constant multiple of ϵ, $k\epsilon$, where k is a positive constant less than or equal to $1/21$.

The preceding two examples illustrate the following theorem, which is often used for establishing uniform continuity (the proof follows immediately from the preceding Definition):

Theorem II. *If f is defined on an interval I and if there exists a positive-valued function $\delta(\epsilon)$ with domain equal to the set $\mathcal{P}$ of all positive numbers such that*

(10) $\forall\, \epsilon > 0,$

$$\left.\begin{array}{c}(x_1, x_2) \in I \times I \\ |x_1 - x_2| < \delta(\epsilon)\end{array}\right\} \Rightarrow |f(x_1) - f(x_2)| < \epsilon,$$

then f is uniformly continuous on I.

NOTE. The elliptic notation $\delta(\epsilon)$ for "a function δ whose value for ϵ is $\delta(\epsilon)$" is a particularly convenient one to use, since the single letter δ has already been used to represent a *number* rather than a *function*. We shall continue to use the letter δ for a number, but think of "δ as a function of ϵ" when it is used in the context of the preceding theorem. The preceding Example 2 could have been phrased "Find δ as a function of ϵ in order to prove that $\cdots$."

We give four more illustrative examples:

Example 3. Prove that the absolute value function $|x|$ is uniformly continuous on every interval I by finding δ as a function of ϵ, according to the preceding Theorem II.

Solution. The problem is to find a function $\delta(\epsilon)$ such that for every positive number ϵ and for every x_1 and x_2 in I,

(11) $|x_1 - x_2| < \delta(\epsilon) \Rightarrow \big||x_1| - |x_2|\big| < \epsilon.$

By Theorem I(*xi*), §311, *PCLA*, $\big||x_1| - |x_2|\big| \leq |x_1 - x_2|$, and therefore $\delta(\epsilon)$ can be taken as the identity function: $\delta(\epsilon) = \epsilon$, since $|x_1 - x_2| < \epsilon \Rightarrow \big||x_1| - |x_2|\big| \leq |x_1 - x_2| < \epsilon.$

Example 4. Prove that any constant function K is uniformly continuous on every interval I by finding δ as a function of ϵ, according to the preceding Theorem II.

Solution. The problem is to find a positive-valued function $\delta(\epsilon)$ such that for every positive number ϵ and for every x_1 and x_2 in I,

(12) $|x_1 - x_2| < \delta(\epsilon) \Rightarrow |K - K| < \epsilon.$

Since the right-hand side of (12) is the inequality $0 < \epsilon$ which is *always* true for every positive number ϵ, the implication (12) is *always true* for *every* positive-valued function $\delta(\epsilon)$. (Cf. (17), §204, *PCLA*.) Therefore we can choose *any* positive-valued function $\delta(\epsilon)$ we wish. One choice is $\delta(\epsilon) \equiv 1$; another is $\delta(\epsilon) \equiv \epsilon$; another is $\delta(\epsilon) \equiv \epsilon^2$; another is $\delta(\epsilon) \equiv 1/\epsilon$. Probably the simplest is $\delta(\epsilon) \equiv 1$.

Example 5. Prove that the function $f(x) = 1/x$ is uniformly continuous on every interval of the form $[\eta, +\infty)$, and also on every interval of the form $(-\infty, -\eta]$, where η is a positive number.

Solution. We shall give the details only for the interval $[\eta, +\infty)$ since those for the interval $(-\infty, -\eta]$ are essentially identical. For a given positive number ϵ, then, the problem is to find a positive number δ such that

(13) $\left.\begin{array}{c}x_1 \geq \eta \\ x_2 \geq \eta \\ |x_1 - x_2| < \delta\end{array}\right\} \Rightarrow |f(x_1) - f(x_2)| = \left|\dfrac{1}{x_1} - \dfrac{1}{x_2}\right| < \epsilon.$

Since the right-hand inequality in (13) can be written

(14)
$$\frac{|x_1 - x_2|}{x_1 x_2} < \epsilon,$$

and since for $x_1 \geqq \eta$ and $x_2 \geqq \eta$,

(15)
$$\frac{|x_1 - x_2|}{x_1 x_2} \leqq \frac{|x_1 - x_2|}{\eta^2},$$

we see that (14) is guaranteed by $|x_1 - x_2|/\eta^2 < \epsilon$, or equivalently, $|x_1 - x_2| < \eta^2 \epsilon$. Therefore, if we choose $\delta \equiv \eta^2 \epsilon$, the implication (13) is guaranteed. (Cf. Fig. 301-1a.)

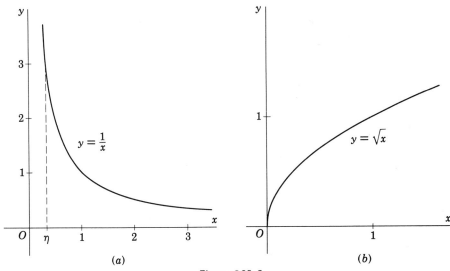

(a) (b)

Figure 301-1

Example 6. Prove that the function $\sqrt{x}$ is uniformly continuous on the interval $[0, +\infty)$. (Cf. Fig. 301-b.)

Solution. If ϵ is an arbitrary positive number, we wish to find a positive number δ such that for nonnegative numbers x_1 and x_2,

(16)
$$|x_1 - x_2| < \delta \Rightarrow |\sqrt{x_1} - \sqrt{x_2}| < \epsilon.$$

A little experimentation leads to the *guess* that δ can be chosen to be equal to ϵ^2. We shall now show that this is the case. To be specific, we shall show that

(17)
$$|x_1 - x_2| < \epsilon^2 \Rightarrow |\sqrt{x_1} - \sqrt{x_2}| < \epsilon,$$

and we shall do this by establishing the inequality

(18)
$$|\sqrt{x_1} - \sqrt{x_2}| \leqq \sqrt{|x_1 - x_2|}.$$

To prove (18) we define

(19)
$$a \equiv \min (\sqrt{x_1}, \sqrt{x_2}), \quad b \equiv \max (\sqrt{x_1}, \sqrt{x_2}),$$

so that, since $\sqrt{x}$ is a strictly increasing function on $[0, +\infty)$ (cf. (2), §316, *PCLA*),

(20)
$$a^2 = \min (x_1, x_2), \quad b^2 = \max (x_1, x_2).$$

Inequality (18), to be established, can be written $b - a \leqq \sqrt{b^2 - a^2}$, or, since $\sqrt{x}$ is a strictly increasing function,

(21)
$$(b - a)^2 \leqq b^2 - a^2.$$

Inequality (21) is true since it is equivalent to $2a^2 \leq 2ab$, which follows by multiplication of both members of the inequality $a \leq b$ by the nonnegative quantity $2a$. With (18) now proved, we have the chain of implications:

(22) $$|x_1 - x_2| < \epsilon^2 \Rightarrow \sqrt{|x_1 - x_2|} < \epsilon \Rightarrow |\sqrt{x_1} - \sqrt{x_2}| < \epsilon,$$

and (17) follows as desired.

We conclude this section by stating without proof a fact that we shall wish to use in subsequent illustrative examples (for a proof, see §622):

Theorem III. *For any real number k, the functions*

(23) $$\sin kx \quad and \quad \cos kx$$

are uniformly continuous on $(-\infty, +\infty) = \Re$.

302 NEGATION OF UNIFORM CONTINUITY

In the preceding section we saw a few examples of uniformly continuous functions. In this section we shall look at four specific examples of functions that are *not* uniformly continuous. In the remainder of this chapter we shall concentrate again almost exclusively on functions that *are* uniformly continuous, and study the structures of certain *systems* of uniformly continuous functions.

If a function fails to be uniformly continuous, then in a sense that will be made precise soon, points that are near each other are mapped onto points that are *not* near each other. This does not mean that *all* points close together are thus "pulled apart," but rather that *some* points close together are separated by the mapping. The idea is that there must be a portion of the domain of the function where points *arbitrarily* close to each other are mapped onto points separated by at least a certain amount. In order to put this rather vague idea into exact terms we appeal to the language and notation of quantifiers:

Theorem. Negation of Uniform Continuity. *A function f whose domain contains an interval I fails to be uniformly continuous on I if and only if*

(1) $\exists \epsilon > 0 \ni \forall \delta > 0, \exists (x_1, x_2) \in I \times I \ni |x_1 - x_2| < \delta$ and $|f(x_1) - f(x_2)| \geq \epsilon$.

Proof. As in the proof of Theorem III, §105, we recall the general form for the negations of statements expressed in terms of a single quantifier:

(2) $$\sim (\forall x \in A, p(x) \text{ is true}) \Leftrightarrow \exists x \in A \ni p(x) \text{ is false},$$

(3) $$\sim (\exists x \in A \ni p(x) \text{ is true}) \Leftrightarrow \forall x \in A, p(x) \text{ is false}.$$

We start by using (2) and writing the negation of (1), §301:

(4) $$\sim (\forall \epsilon > 0, \exists \cdots) \Leftrightarrow \exists \epsilon > 0 \ni \sim (\exists \cdots).$$

The next step is to reformulate $\sim (\exists \cdots)$, by use of (3):

(5) $$\sim (\exists \delta > 0 \ni \cdots) \Leftrightarrow \forall \delta > 0, \sim (\cdots),$$

where the statement $(\cdots)$ being negated is the implication on the second line of (1), §301. Finally, from §204, *PCLA*, we use the fact that the negation of the implication $p \Rightarrow q$ is the statement that there exists a member x of the domain of p and q such that $p(x)$ is true and $q(x)$ is false, to express $\sim (\cdots)$ as follows:

$$(6) \qquad \exists\, (x_1, x_2) \in I \times I \ni |x_1 - x_2| < \delta \text{ and } |f(x_1) - f(x_2)| \geqq \epsilon.$$

When the component parts of the compound statement negating (1), §301, are assembled, (1), above, is the result.

We now turn our attention to some examples of functions that are not uniformly continuous. These examples illustrate the four principal ways in which a function may fail to be uniformly continuous.

The first example illustrates a "jump."

Example 1. Prove that any step-function that is not constant cannot be uniformly continuous; in other words, *the only uniformly continuous step-functions are constants.*

Solution. If s is a nonconstant step-function for a net $\mathfrak{N} : \{a_0, a_1, \cdots, a_n\}$ on $I = [a, b]$, and if the value of s on (a_{i-1}, a_i) is s_i, $i = 1, 2, \cdots, n$, then there must be a point $a_k \in \mathfrak{N}$ such that *either* $s(a_k) \neq s_k$ *or* $s(a_k) \neq s_{k+1}$ (or both). Assume for definiteness that

$$(7) \qquad\qquad\qquad s(a_k) \neq s_k,$$

the argument for the case $s(a_k) \neq s_{k+1}$ being entirely similar (cf. Fig. 302-1).

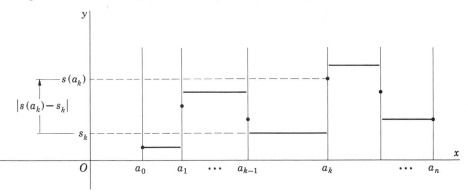

Figure 302-1

It is evident from Figure 302-1 that points near a_k can be found that are arbitrarily near each other and at which the values of s are separated by a fixed positive amount. To be more specific, we can choose one point to be a_k itself and the other point to be arbitrarily near a_k and to the left of a_k, the values of their images, then, being $s(a_k)$ and s_k, which are separated by the distance $|s(a_k) - s_k|$. In the notation of the preceding Theorem, we let ϵ be the positive number $|s(a_k) - s_k|$, and for an arbitrary given positive number δ, we define x_1 to be a_k and x_2 to be a point of the open interval (a_{k-1}, a_k) whose distance from a_k is less than δ. A specific point x_2 having these properties is given by subtracting from a_k a positive quantity that is simultaneously less than δ and less than the length $a_k - a_{k-1}$ of the interval (a_{k-1}, a_k):

$$(8) \qquad\qquad\qquad x_2 \equiv a_k - \min\!\left(\frac{\delta}{2}, \frac{a_k - a_{k-1}}{2}\right).$$

Then both x_1 and x_2 belong to I,

(9) $$|x_1 - x_2| = \min\left(\frac{\delta}{2}, \frac{a_k - a_{k-1}}{2}\right) \leqq \frac{\delta}{2} < \delta,$$

and since $x_2 \in (a_{k-1}, a_k)$ (this is true since $x_2 < a_k$, and $a_k - x_2 = \min\left(\frac{\delta}{2}, \frac{a_k - a_{k-1}}{2}\right) \leqq$

$\frac{a_k - a_{k-1}}{2} < a_k - a_{k-1}$ so that $x_2 > a_{k-1}$),

(10) $$|s(x_1) - s(x_2)| = |s(a_k) - s_k| = \epsilon \geqq \epsilon.$$

The next example illustrates the case of an unbounded function on a bounded interval.

Example 2.   Prove that the function $f(x) \equiv 1/x$ is not uniformly continuous on the half-open interval $(0, 1]$.

Solution.   The graph (Fig. 302-2) shows that points are increasingly "pulled apart" to the extent that they are chosen near the origin. It should seem plausible that no matter what

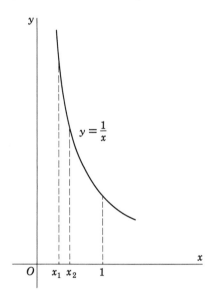

Figure 302-2

positive number we may choose for ϵ, positive numbers x_1 and x_2 can be found arbitrarily near each other such that their images $1/x_1$ and $1/x_2$ are separated by a distance at least equal to that ϵ. To be quite specific, let us choose ϵ to be 1, and let δ be an arbitrary positive number. In our search for the two numbers x_1 and x_2, which are to "crowd in" toward the origin, it will be helpful to let one number be half the other, and then seek a suitable value for the larger. Accordingly, if $x_1 \equiv \frac{1}{2}x_2$, the requirement $|f(x_1) - f(x_2)| \geqq \epsilon$ takes the form

(11) $$\left|\frac{1}{x_1} - \frac{1}{x_2}\right| = \left|\frac{2}{x_2} - \frac{1}{x_2}\right| = \frac{1}{x_2} \geqq 1,$$

which is automatically satisfied for all $x_2 \leqq 1$. The requirement $|x_1 - x_2| < \delta$ becomes

(12) $$|x_1 - x_2| = |\tfrac{1}{2}x_2 - x_2| = \tfrac{1}{2}x_2 < \delta,$$

or:

(13) $$x_2 < 2\,\delta.$$

To find a *specific* positive number x_2 satisfying *both* (13) *and* the inequality $x_2 \leqq 1$, we may define x_2 as follows:

(14) $$x_2 \equiv \min(\delta, 1).$$

Finally, with

(15) $$x_1 \equiv \tfrac{1}{2}x_2 = \tfrac{1}{2}\min(\delta, 1),$$

we have the required pair of points.

The third example illustrates the case of an unbounded function on an unbounded interval whose graph has chords of arbitrarily large slope.

Example 3. Prove that the function $f(x) = x^2$ is not uniformly continuous on the open interval $(0, +\infty)$.

Solution. In this case (cf. Fig. 302-3) we must move far to the right to find points close together whose images are far apart. As in Example 2, we choose $\epsilon \equiv 1$, and let $\delta > 0$ be

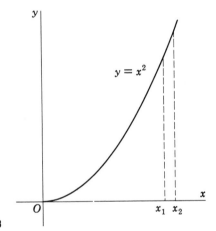

Figure 302-3

given. The search for x_1 and x_2 can be simplified in this case by letting $x_2 \equiv x_1 + \tfrac{1}{2}\delta$, and focusing on finding x_1. Since the inequality $|x_1 - x_2| < \delta$ is now guaranteed, we look at the inequality $|f(x_1) - f(x_2)| \geqq \epsilon$, which takes the form

(16) $$|x_1^2 - (x_1 + \tfrac{1}{2}\delta)^2| = |x_1 \delta + \tfrac{1}{4}\delta^2| \geqq 1.$$

The problem of finding a positive number x_1 so large that (16) is true can be replaced by the simpler problem of finding x_1 so that

(17) $$x_1 \delta \geqq 1,$$

since whenever (17) is true, (16) must be also. We therefore define our two numbers x_1 and x_2:

(18) $$x_1 \equiv \frac{1}{\delta}, \quad x_2 \equiv \frac{1}{\delta} + \frac{\delta}{2},$$

and have as a consequence that both x_1 and x_2 belong to $(0, +\infty)$, $|x_1 - x_2| < \delta$, and $|f(x_1) - f(x_2)| \geqq 1$.

Our final example illustrates an extreme oscillatory misbehavior.

Example 4. Prove that the function

(19) $$f(x) \equiv \sin \frac{1}{x}, \text{ if } x \neq 0,$$

is not uniformly continuous on the half-open interval $(0, 1]$.

Solution. The graph (Fig. 302-4) reveals that, as in the function of Example 2, the trouble lies near the origin. It appears that since the values of the function oscillate infinitely many

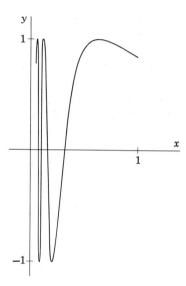

Figure 302-4

times between 1 and -1, points arbitrarily close to each other can be found such that the corresponding values of the function are separated by a distance equal to 2. Let us choose ϵ this time to be equal to 2. If n is a large positive integer, and if

(20) $$x_1 \equiv \frac{1}{(2n + \frac{1}{2})\pi}, \quad x_2 \equiv \frac{1}{(2n - \frac{1}{2})\pi},$$

then the inequality $|f(x_1) - f(x_2)| \geq \epsilon$ becomes

(21) $$\left| \sin (2n + \tfrac{1}{2})\pi - \sin (2n - \tfrac{1}{2})\pi \right| = \sin \frac{\pi}{2} - \sin \left(-\frac{\pi}{2} \right) = 2 \geq 2,$$

true for all positive integers n. If δ is a given positive number, the inequality $|x_1 - x_2| < \delta$ is guaranteed by a sufficiently large value of n. This is "intuitively obvious," but the details are less than obvious. Perhaps the simplest way to see this is the somewhat brutal method of using the triangle inequality to reduce the problem thus:

(22) $$|x_1 - x_2| \leq x_1 + x_2 < 2x_2 < \frac{2}{(2n - 2)\pi} = \frac{1}{(n - 1)\pi}.$$

We can now ensure that $|x_1 - x_2| < \delta$ by requiring:

(23) $$\frac{1}{(n - 1)\pi} \leq \delta,$$

or finally, as a result of solving (23):

(24) $$n \geq 1 + \frac{1}{\pi\delta}.$$

Since there exist positive integers greater than or equal to $1 + (1/\pi\delta)$, we can obtain a specific n as the least positive integer greater than or equal to $1 + (1/\pi\delta)$.

NOTE. The curve $y = \sqrt{x}$ of Example 6, §301, shows that a function may be uniformly continuous on an interval even though its graph has chords of arbitrarily large slope (the slope of the chord that joins the points $(0, 0)$ and $(h, \sqrt{h})$ is $1/\sqrt{h}$, which is arbitrarily large for small positive h). This is of interest in connection with Examples 2, 3, and 4, above, where the idea was to find "steep" chords in order to demonstrate *failure* of uniform continuity.

303 VECTOR SPACE STRUCTURE

Some of the most useful properties of uniformly continuous functions are contained in the theorem:

Theorem I. *The set $\mathfrak{U}$ of all functions uniformly continuous on an interval I is a vector space.*

Proof. Assume that $f \in \mathfrak{U}$ and $g \in \mathfrak{U}$. In order to show that $f + g \in \mathfrak{U}$ we use an "$\epsilon/2$" argument similar to that employed before in §§105, 110, and 113. The idea is that by restricting the spread for *each* of f and g to something less than $\frac{1}{2}\epsilon$, we can guarantee that the (combined) spread of $f + g$ is less than $\frac{1}{2}\epsilon + \frac{1}{2}\epsilon = \epsilon$. We now give the details by starting with an arbitrary given positive number ϵ. Since f is uniformly continuous on I there exists a positive number δ_1 such that

$$(1) \qquad \left.\begin{array}{r} (x_1, x_2) \in I \times I \\ |x_1 - x_2| < \delta_1 \end{array}\right\} \Rightarrow |f(x_1) - f(x_2)| < \frac{\epsilon}{2}.$$

Similarly, for g, there exists a positive number δ_2 such that

$$(2) \qquad \left.\begin{array}{r} (x_1, x_2) \in I \times I \\ |x_1 - x_2| < \delta_2 \end{array}\right\} \Rightarrow |g(x_1) - g(x_2)| < \frac{\epsilon}{2}.$$

We now wish to use the two implications (1) and (2) *simultaneously*, and for this reason we must arrange to have the *two* inequalities $|x_1 - x_2| < \delta_1$ and $|x_1 - x_2| < \delta_2$ holding. The simplest way to do this is to define the positive number δ to be the minimum of δ_1 and δ_2:

$$(3) \qquad\qquad\qquad \delta \equiv \min (\delta_1, \delta_2).$$

Then if x_1 and x_2 are points of I such that $|x_1 - x_2| < \delta$ we must have the two inequalities on the right of (1) and (2) both holding so that, by the triangle inequality, if $h \equiv f + g$:

$$|h(x_1) - h(x_2)| = |(f(x_1) - f(x_2)) + (g(x_1) - g(x_2))|$$
$$\leq |f(x_1) - f(x_2)| + |g(x_1) - g(x_2)| < \tfrac{1}{2}\epsilon + \tfrac{1}{2}\epsilon = \epsilon.$$

In other words,

$$(4) \qquad \left.\begin{array}{r} (x_1, x_2) \in I \times I \\ |x_1 - x_2| < \delta \end{array}\right\} \Rightarrow |h(x_1) - h(x_2)| < \epsilon,$$

and $h = f + g \in \mathfrak{U}$.

We now show that if $f \in \mathfrak{u}$ and if λ is any real number, then $F \equiv \lambda f \in \mathfrak{u}$. There are two cases. The first case, $\lambda = 0$, is trivial since $0 \cdot f$ is a constant function and every constant function is uniformly continuous (Example 4, §301). We now assume $\lambda \neq 0$, and seek to show that, if ϵ is a given positive number, there must exist a positive number δ such that

$$(5) \qquad \left.\begin{array}{r}(x_1, x_2) \in I \times I \\ |x_1 - x_2| < \delta\end{array}\right\} \Rightarrow |\lambda f(x_1) - \lambda f(x_2)| < \epsilon.$$

Since the inequality on the right of (5) is equivalent to $|f(x_1) - f(x_2)| < \epsilon/|\lambda|$, we have only to use the assumed uniform continuity of f, with the positive number $\epsilon/|\lambda|$ playing the role of the given positive number ϵ in the Definition, §301. That is, from (1), §301, we know that there must be a positive number δ having the property that

$$(6) \qquad \left.\begin{array}{r}(x_1, x_2) \in I \times I \\ |x_1 - x_2| < \delta\end{array}\right\} \Rightarrow |f(x_1) - f(x_2)| < \frac{\epsilon}{|\lambda|}.$$

Since (6) is equivalent to (5) the proof is complete.

Example. Since the functions x and $|x|$ are separately uniformly continuous on $\mathfrak{R}$, so is their linear combination $3x - 4|x|$.

304 ALGEBRA STRUCTURE

In case the interval I is unbounded, the vector space $\mathfrak{u}$ of functions that are uniformly continuous on I is *not* an algebra (§515, *PCLA*). The reason for this is indicated by Example 3, §302, with the aid of Example 1, §301: The identity polynomial x is a member of the vector space of functions uniformly continuous on $(0, +\infty)$, but its square, x^2, is not. We shall show in this section (Theorem II) that if the interval is *bounded*, then the vector space $\mathfrak{u}$ *is* an algebra.

We start by establishing the *boundedness* of any function uniformly continuous on a bounded interval I:

Theorem I. *If f is uniformly continuous on a bounded interval I, then f is bounded there.*

Proof. To establish the boundedness of f on I we need to find specific numbers to serve as upper and lower bounds. To do this we begin with a specific positive number to serve as ϵ, namely 1. That is, we use the fact that there must exist a positive number δ such that

$$(1) \qquad \left.\begin{array}{r}(x_1, x_2) \in I \times I \\ |x_1 - x_2| < \delta\end{array}\right\} \Rightarrow |f(x_1) - f(x_2)| < 1.$$

If the interval I has endpoints a and b, with $a < b$, let $\mathfrak{N}$ be a net on the *closed* interval $[a, b]$ with every interval of $\mathfrak{N}$ having length less than 2δ. (This can be done, for instance, by dividing $[a, b]$ into n equal parts, with $n > (b - a)/2\delta$.) If the *midpoints* of the intervals of $\mathfrak{N}$ are denoted $b_1, b_2, \cdots, b_n$, then these midpoints all belong to I, and *every* point x of I is within a distance less than δ from at least *one* of these midpoints. As a consequence of (1), therefore, for *every* $x \in I$ an inequality of the form $|f(x) - f(b_i)| < 1$, or

$$(2) \qquad\qquad\qquad f(b_i) - 1 < f(x) < f(b_i) + 1,$$

must hold for some $i = 1, 2, \cdots, n$. Consequently, if we define

$$(3) \qquad\qquad\qquad M \equiv \max\,(f(b_1), f(b_2), \cdots, f(b_n)),$$

$$(4) \qquad\qquad\qquad m \equiv \min\,(f(b_1), f(b_2), \cdots, f(b_n)),$$

we must have for every $x \in I$:

$$(5) \qquad\qquad\qquad m - 1 < f(x) < M + 1.$$

In other words, the values of $f(x)$ are bounded above by $M + 1$ and below by $m - 1$.

Theorem II. *The vector space $\mathfrak{U}$ of functions uniformly continuous on a bounded interval I is an algebra.*

Proof. By Theorem III, §515, *PCLA*, we have only to show that $\mathfrak{U}$ is closed under squaring; that is, that $f \in \mathfrak{U} \Rightarrow f^2 \in \mathfrak{U}$. Let f be an arbitrary member of $\mathfrak{U}$. Then by Theorem I, above (and Theorem I, §507, *PCLA*), there exists a positive number K such that

$$(6) \qquad\qquad\qquad x \in I \Rightarrow |f(x)| < K.$$

If $h \equiv f^2$, we shall wish to examine an inequality of the form

$$(7) \qquad\qquad |h(x_1) - h(x_2)| = |f^2(x_1) - f^2(x_2)| < \epsilon,$$

where ϵ is an arbitrary positive number and x_1 and $x_2 \in I$. In order to ensure the inequality $|f^2(x_1) - f^2(x_2)| < \epsilon$ as a consequence of the uniform continuity of f, we rewrite its left-hand member, and make use of (6):

$$(8) \quad \begin{aligned} |f^2(x_1) - f^2(x_2)| &= |f(x_1) - f(x_2)| \cdot |f(x_1) + f(x_2)| \\ &\leq |f(x_1) - f(x_2)| \cdot (|f(x_1)| + |f(x_2)|) \leq 2K\,|f(x_1) - f(x_2)|. \end{aligned}$$

To obtain (7) we see now that we must make $|f(x_1) - f(x_2)|$ less than $\epsilon/2K$. Therefore, we let δ be a positive number such that

$$(9) \qquad \left. \begin{aligned} (x_1, x_2) &\in I \times I \\ |x_1 - x_2| &< \delta \end{aligned} \right\} \Rightarrow |f(x_1) - f(x_2)| < \frac{\epsilon}{2K}.$$

With this δ, then, by (8) and the definition of $h \equiv f^2$,

$$(10) \qquad \left. \begin{aligned} (x_1, x_2) &\in I \times I \\ |x_1 - x_2| &< \delta \end{aligned} \right\} \Rightarrow |h(x_1) - h(x_2)| < \epsilon,$$

and the proof is complete. (For an alternative proof, cf. Ex. 13, §308.)

A useful corollary to Theorem II is the following:

Theorem III. *Every polynomial is uniformly continuous on every bounded interval.*

Proof. Denote by $\mathfrak{U}$ the algebra of all functions uniformly continuous on a given bounded interval I. Since the identity function x is a member of $\mathfrak{U}$, every positive integral power x^n is also a member of $\mathfrak{U}$, by Theorem II. If n is any positive integer, then the $n + 1$ functions $1, x, \cdots, x^n$ all belong to $\mathfrak{U}$, and therefore so does any linear combination $a_n + a_{n-1}x + a_{n-2}x^2 + \cdots + a_0x^n$.

Example. Show that the function $3x^2 - 5x\sqrt{x}$ is uniformly continuous on the interval $[0, a]$, where $a > 0$.

Solution. If $\mathfrak{U}$ is the algebra of functions uniformly continuous on $[0, a]$, then the polynomials $3x^2$ and x are members of $\mathfrak{U}$, by Theorem III, and the function $\sqrt{x}$ is a member of $\mathfrak{U}$ by Example 6, §301, and Theorem I, §301. Since $\mathfrak{U}$ is an algebra, the product $x\sqrt{x}$ belongs to $\mathfrak{U}$, and since $\mathfrak{U}$ is a vector space, the linear combination $3x^2 - 5x\sqrt{x}$ belongs to $\mathfrak{U}$.

305 EXERCISES

In Exercises 1–6, show that the given function is uniformly continuous on the specified interval by finding δ as a function of ϵ, according to Theorem II, §301.

1. $5x - 7$, $\mathfrak{R}$.   **2.** $7x + 4$, $\mathfrak{R}$.   **3.** $x^2 + 2x - 4$, $[2, 5]$.

4. $\dfrac{1}{x}$, $(3, +\infty)$.   **5.** $\dfrac{1}{x + 3}$, $[2, +\infty)$.   **6.** $\dfrac{x + 1}{x + 4}$, $\mathfrak{P}$.

In Exercises 7 and 8, use an equation of the form $\sqrt{u} - \sqrt{v} = (u - v)/(\sqrt{u} + \sqrt{v})$ to find δ as a linear function of ϵ, according to Theorem II, §301, for the given function on the specified interval.

7. $\sqrt{2x + 3}$, $[0, +\infty)$.   **8.** $\sqrt{3x - 1}$, $(2, +\infty)$.

In Exercises 9–11, use the Theorem, §302, to show that the given function is not uniformly continuous on the specified interval. Actually find explicit values of x_1 and x_2 for an arbitrary $\delta > 0$ and $\epsilon \equiv 1$.

9. $\dfrac{1}{x^2}$, $(0, 2]$.   **10.** $\dfrac{1}{\sqrt{x}}$, $(0, 4]$.   **11.** x^3, $\mathfrak{P}$.

12. Assume that f is a function that is defined on an interval $[a, b]$ but not uniformly continuous there, that g is uniformly continuous on $[a, b]$, and that λ is a nonzero real number. Prove that the functions $f + g, f - g, g - f$, and λf all fail to be uniformly continuous on $[a, b]$.

In Exercises 13 and 14, show that the function is not uniformly continuous on the interval $[-2, 3]$. The functions sgn x and $[x]$ are defined in Examples 2 and 3, §115, *PCLA*.

13. sgn x.   **14.** $[x]$.

In Examples 15–18, use theorems from §§301–304 to show that the given function is uniformly continuous on the specified interval.

15. $2x^3 + 4x + 7 + (3x - 5)\sqrt{x}$, $[0, 10]$. **16.** $x^2 + (5x^3 - 8x - 11)|x|$, $[-2, 3]$.

17. $(x^2 + 4) + \dfrac{x - 5}{x}$, $[1, 8)$.   **18.** $(x + \sqrt{x})^3 - 7(x^2 - |x|) + \dfrac{1}{x}$, $[2, 5]$.

306 COMPOSITE FUNCTIONS

A significant property of uniform continuity is that *it is preserved by composition.* Expressed in simplified terms this means that *a uniformly continuous function of a uniformly continuous function is uniformly continuous.* The exact statement follows:

Theorem I. *If f is uniformly continuous on an interval I, if g is uniformly continuous on an interval J, and if the range of f (for the interval I) is a subset of J, then the composite function g ∘ f, whose values are given by g(f(x)), is uniformly continuous on I.*

Before attempting a proof, let us spend a little time in a very informal way seeing what this theorem says, and why our intuition should say that it must be true. Let us look at the composite mapping $g \circ f$ in terms of input-output machines (cf. Fig. 306-1), and think of different values of x being fed in. The object is to prove that if these values are sufficiently close together, then the resulting values produced by the composite machine $g \circ f$ are not spread apart too much. A little more to the point: if the outgoing values of $g(f(x))$, for various values of x, are to be held within a certain control size, the question is whether the x's can be properly controlled to achieve this limitation. From the first part of Figure 306-1, it appears that we must first control the spread of the points $f(x)$ (for various values of x) that are going into the "g machine," and then determine the type of "squeeze" to apply to the x's going into the "f machine." All this discussion is imprecise, to be sure, but its intent is "heuristic," or designed to point the way toward a true proof. We should now be ready.

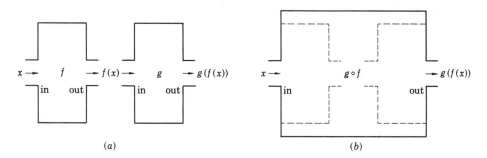

(a)   (b)

Figure 306-1

Proof. Let $\epsilon > 0$ be given. Then, since g is uniformly continuous on J there exists a positive number η such that

(1)
$$\left.\begin{array}{l}(y_1, y_2) \in J \times J \\ |y_1 - y_2| < \eta\end{array}\right\} \Rightarrow |g(y_1) - g(y_2)| < \epsilon.$$

In terms of the positive number η, since f is uniformly continuous on I, there exists a positive number δ such that

(2)
$$\left.\begin{array}{l}(x_1, x_2) \in I \times I \\ |x_1 - x_2| < \delta\end{array}\right\} \Rightarrow |f(x_1) - f(x_2)| < \eta.$$

For any x_1 and x_2 of I, let $y_1 \equiv f(x_1)$ and $y_2 \equiv f(x_2)$. Then y_1 and y_2 belong to J, and if $|x_1 - x_2| < \delta$, $|y_1 - y_2| < \eta$. If $h \equiv g \circ f$, we therefore have $h(x_1) - h(x_2) = g(y_1) - g(y_2)$, and hence the implication:

$$(3) \qquad \left. \begin{array}{l} (x_1, x_2) \in I \times I \\ |x_1 - x_2| < \delta \end{array} \right\} \Rightarrow |h(x_1) - h(x_2)| < \epsilon.$$

This completes the proof.

A number of applications of the preceding theorem are now possible. A few of these are illustrated in the following theorem and examples:

Theorem II. *The function $|f|$ is uniformly continuous on any interval I on which f is uniformly continuous.*

Proof. The function $h : x \to h(x) \equiv |f(x)|$ is the composite of the function $x \to f(x)$ by the function $x \to |x|$. Since the absolute value function $|x|$ is uniformly continuous on the interval $(-\infty, +\infty) = \Re$, which automatically contains the range of f, the composite function $|f|$ is uniformly continuous on I if f is.

Example. Prove that the function $\sqrt{a^2 - x^2}$ is uniformly continuous on the interval $[-a, a]$, where a is a positive number (cf. Fig. 306-2).

Solution. The function $H(x) \equiv \sqrt{a^2 - x^2}$ is the composite function of $f(x) \equiv a^2 - x^2$ by $g(x) \equiv \sqrt{x}$, which are uniformly continuous on the intervals $[-a, a]$ and $[0, +\infty)$, respectively (cf. Example 6, §301, and Theorem III, §304), and the range of the function $a^2 - x^2$, for $-a \leqq x \leqq a$, is a subset of $[0, +\infty)$.

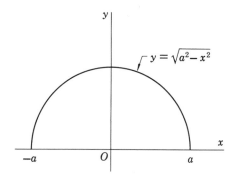

Figure 306-2

307 INTEGRABILITY OF UNIFORMLY CONTINUOUS FUNCTIONS

One of the most important facts concerning uniformly continuous functions relates to their integrability.

Theorem. *Every function uniformly continuous on a compact interval is Riemann-integrable there.*

Proof. Assume that f is uniformly continuous on the interval $I = [a, b]$, and let $\epsilon > 0$. We now choose δ to be a positive number such that

(1)
$$\left.\begin{array}{l}(x_1, x_2) \in I \times I \\ |x_1 - x_2| < \delta\end{array}\right\} \Rightarrow |f(x_1) - f(x_2)| < \frac{\epsilon}{4(b-a)}.$$

(The reason for the particular positive number $\epsilon/4(b-a)$ on the right of (1) will become apparent presently; this is a multiple of ϵ that "makes things come out right." In practice, any multiple, such as $\eta\epsilon$, can be used, with η to be determined at a later stage.) As in the proof of Theorem I, §304, we let $\mathfrak{N} : \{a_0, a_1, \cdots, a_n\}$ be a net on $[a, b]$ with every interval of length $< 2\delta$. If the *midpoints* of the intervals of $\mathfrak{N}$ are denoted $b_1, b_2, \cdots, b_n$, then *every* point x of I is within a distance less than δ from at least *one* of these midpoints. As a consequence of (1), therefore, for every $x \in (a_{i-1}, a_i)$, $i = 1, 2, \cdots, n$, the following inequalities hold: $|f(x) - f(b_i)| < \frac{\epsilon}{4(b-a)}$,

or

(2)
$$f(b_i) - \frac{\epsilon}{4(b-a)} < f(x) < f(b_i) + \frac{\epsilon}{4(b-a)}.$$

Now define two step-functions (cf. Fig. 307-1):

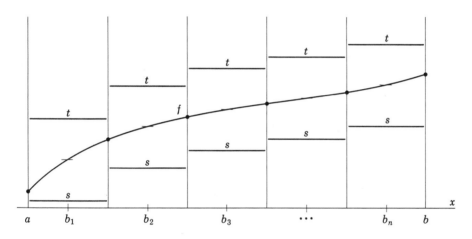

Figure 307-1

(3)
$$s(x) \equiv \begin{cases} f(b_i) - \dfrac{\epsilon}{4(b-a)} & \text{if } a_{i-1} < x < a_i, \, i = 1, 2, \cdots, n, \\ f(a_i) & \text{if } x = a_i, \, i = 0, 1, \cdots, n, \end{cases}$$

(4)
$$t(x) \equiv \begin{cases} f(b_i) + \dfrac{\epsilon}{4(b-a)} & \text{if } a_{i-1} < x < a_i, \, i = 1, 2, \cdots, n, \\ f(a_i) & \text{if } x = a_i, \, i = 0, 1, \cdots, n. \end{cases}$$

Then $s(x) \leqq f(x) \leqq t(x)$ for $a \leqq x \leqq b$, and

(5)
$$\int_a^b (t - s) = \sum_{i=1}^n \frac{\epsilon}{2(b-a)} (a_i - a_{i-1})$$

$$= \frac{\epsilon}{2(b-a)} \sum_{i=1}^n (a_i - a_{i-1}) = \frac{\epsilon}{2(b-a)} (b-a) = \frac{\epsilon}{2} < \epsilon.$$

This completes the proof.

The catalog of the seven principal vector spaces of functions that have been presented up to this point — all of which are algebras as well — can be represented schematically by a Venn diagram, as in Figure 307-2. Every function space is assumed to be for functions having a compact interval as common domain. Places in the book(or in *PCLA*)where these function spaces are shown to be vector spaces and algebras are indicated.

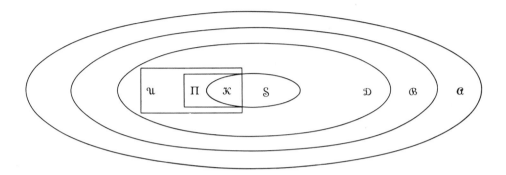

$\mathcal{K}$: Constant functions (Example 3, §506, and §515, *PCLA*),
Π : Polynomials (Example 4, §506, and §515, *PCLA*),
$\mathcal{S}$: Step-functions (Theorem II, §512, and Theorem II, §515, *PCLA*),
$\mathcal{U}$: Uniformly continuous functions (Theorem I, §303; Theorem II, §304),
$\mathcal{D}$: Integrable functions (Theorem IV, §105; Theorem I, §107),
$\mathcal{B}$: Bounded functions (Theorem II, §507, and Theorem I, §515, *PCLA*),
$\mathcal{A}$: All functions (Example 5, §506, and §515, *PCLA*).

Figure 307-2

The inclusions indicated in Figure 807-2 are established in the following places:

$\mathcal{K} \subset \mathcal{S}$: Definition II, §512, *PCLA*,
$\mathcal{K} \subset \Pi$: Example 16, §111, *PCLA*,
$\mathcal{S} \subset \mathcal{D}$: Theorem I, §105,
$\Pi \subset \mathcal{U}$: Theorem III, §304,
$\mathcal{U} \subset \mathcal{D}$: Theorem, §307,
$\mathcal{D} \subset \mathcal{B}$: Theorem II, §105,
$\mathcal{B} \subset \mathcal{A}$: Definition, §507, *PCLA*.

The fact, indicated in Figure 307-2, that

(6) $\mathcal{U} \cap \mathcal{S} = \mathcal{K}$

is proved in Example 1, §302. It follows from this (give a proof in Ex. 14, §308) that

(7) $\Pi \cap \mathcal{S} = \mathcal{K}.$

308 EXERCISES

In Exercises 1–12, use Theorem I, §306, together with theorems from §§301-304, to show that the given function is uniformly continuous on the specified interval.

1. $\dfrac{1}{2x+3}$, $[0,+\infty)$.

2. $\sqrt{2x+3}$, $[0,+\infty)$.

3. $|5x+1|$, $(-\infty,+\infty)$.

4. $|\sqrt{x}-4|$, $[0,+\infty)$.

5. $\dfrac{1}{x^2+2}$, $[-10, 20]$.

6. $\sqrt{x^4+9}$, $(-30, 15)$.

7. $\left|\dfrac{2}{x}-\sqrt{x}\right|$, $[1,+\infty)$.

8. $|x^2-4x-17|$, $(-10, 10]$.

9. $\sqrt{|x|+1}$, $(-\infty,+\infty)$.

10. $\sqrt{|3x-5|}$, $(-\infty,+\infty)$.

11. $\dfrac{1}{\sqrt{x^4+x^2+1}}$, $[-6, 6)$.

12. $\dfrac{x^7-11x^4+8}{x^4+x^2+1}$, $[-9, 9]$.

13. Use Theorem I, §306, to prove that whenever a function f is uniformly continuous on a bounded interval I, then so is its square f^2. Thus give a second proof for Theorem II, §304.

14. Prove (7), §307.

4

Continuity

401 CONTINUITY AT A POINT

At this point in our development of the subject of calculus we introduce a change in focus or point of view. In the first three chapters of this volume (and in Chapter 5, *PCLA*, as well) we have studied collections of functions and looked at them in terms of their properties on intervals. To express it differently, we have been studying properties that are defined and conceived of *on sets*. Such properties are called **global properties**, or **properties in the large.** In contrast to this, we shall introduce in this and the following two chapters concepts that are defined and conceived of *at individual points*, or in *arbitrarily small neighborhoods* of individual points. Such properties are called **local properties**, or **point properties**, or **properties in the small.** Local properties will receive our main attention for the next few chapters. In Chapter 10 a basic global concept — the Riemann integral — and a basic local concept — the derivative — will be brought together in one of the great intellectual achievements of mankind, known as *the fundamental theorem of calculus.*

Our presentation of calculus follows in spirit its historical development. The ancient Greeks, for instance, studied such global concepts as area, volume, and centroids, which are basic to the part of calculus known as *integral calculus*. Centuries later, Sir Isaac Newton (English, 1642–1727) and Gottfried Wilhelm Leibniz (German, 1646–1716) attacked the problem of instantaneous rates of change, and were led independently to the invention of *differential calculus*. It was only with this latter development that the fundamental theorem became possible.

If we take the general ideas discussed in the preceding chapter, but concentrate on the points in the domain of the function under consideration that are near a particular fixed point of the domain of that function, we have the concept of *con-

tinuity at a point, in distinction to *uniform continuity on an interval.* Continuity at a point c of the domain D of a function f means, crudely, that points near c are mapped by f onto points near $f(c)$, the image of c. More precisely, this means that no matter how small a neighborhood may be taken around the point $f(c)$, a sufficiently small neighborhood may be found around the point c to ensure that all points within this neighborhood of c are carried by f onto points within the given neighborhood of $f(c)$. (All of this applies only to points of the domain and range of f.)

The definition in precise terms, with quantifiers, follows closely the form of the definition of uniform continuity, §301. In nearly all specific applications the domain of the function considered will be an interval, or a union of intervals, but the following definition is framed in terms of a general nonempty domain D.

All functions in this chapter will be assumed to be real-valued functions of a real variable.

Definition. *A function f with domain D is* **continuous at a point** *c if and only if $c \in D$ and*

(1) $\forall \epsilon > 0, \exists \delta > 0 \ni$

$$\left. \begin{array}{l} x \in D \\ |x - c| < \delta \end{array} \right\} \Rightarrow |f(x) - f(c)| < \epsilon.$$

A function f is said to be **continuous on a set** *A if and only if A is a subset of the domain of f and f is continuous at every point of A.*

This definition can be rephrased in a number of equivalent ways, in terms of neighborhoods, sets, and mappings. Let us recall the definition and notation for a **neighborhood** of a point c of radius δ (§311, *PCLA*):

(2) $N_c = N_c(\delta) \equiv (c - \delta, c + \delta) = \{x \mid |x - c| < \delta\},$

and the **image** of a subset A of the domain of f ((8), §111, *PCLA*):

(3) $f(A) \equiv \{f(x) \mid x \in A\}.$

The following theorem presents a reformulation of the preceding Definition couched in the language of neighborhoods and mappings. The proof is left as an exercise (Ex. 13, §402).

Theorem I. *A function f is continuous at a point c of its domain D if and only if*

(4) $\forall$ *neighborhood $N_{f(c)}$ of $f(c)$, $\exists$ a neighborhood N_c of c $\ni$*

$$f(D \cap N_c) \subset N_{f(c)},$$

that is, if and only if for every neighborhood $N_{f(c)}$ of $f(c)$, there exists a neighborhood N_c of c such that every point of $D \cap N_c$ is mapped by f into $N_{f(c)}$.

The preceding Definition and Theorem I are illustrated in Figure 401-1.

NOTE 1. From Theorem I it follows that if f is continuous at c and if its domain D is restricted to any smaller domain E containing c ($c \in E \subset D$), then the restriction of f to E is also continuous at c. (Cf. the Note, §403.) Also, if f is continuous on B and if $A \subset B$, then f is continuous on A.

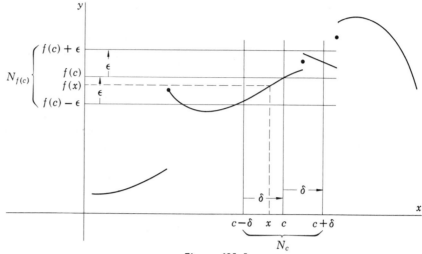

Figure 401-1

Corresponding to Theorem II, §301, is the following, whose proof is immediate, and which will be illustrated in the Examples below.

Theorem II. *Let c be a point of the domain D of a function f. If there exists a positive-valued function $\delta(\epsilon)$ with domain equal to the set $\wp$ of all positive numbers such that*

(5)　$\forall \epsilon > 0,$

$$\left.\begin{array}{l} x \in D \\ |x - c| < \delta(\epsilon) \end{array}\right\} \Rightarrow |f(x) - f(c)| < \epsilon,$$

then f is continuous at c.

Example 1. Show that the function $3x + 5$ is continuous at the point $x = 4$ by finding a function $\delta(\epsilon)$ as specified in Theorem II.

Solution. We start by examining the inequality on the right of (5), with $f(x) \equiv 3x + 5$ and $c = 4$:

$$|f(x) - f(c)| = |(3x + 5) - 17| = |3x - 12| = 3|x - 4| < \epsilon.$$

Since the inequality $3|x - 4| < \epsilon$ is equivalent to $|x - 4| < \epsilon/3$, we have only to define the function $\delta(\epsilon)$ to be $\epsilon/3 : |x - 4| < \epsilon/3 \Rightarrow 3|x - 4| < \epsilon$. (Cf. Fig. 401-2.)

Example 2. Show that the function $5x^2 - 8x - 17$ is continuous at the point $x = -3$ by finding a function $\delta(\epsilon)$ as specified in Theorem II.

Solution. With $f(x) \equiv 5x^2 - 8x - 17$ and $c \equiv -3$, the inequality on the right of (5) becomes

(6)　　　$|f(x) - f(c)| = |5x^2 - 8x - 69| = |x + 3| \cdot |5x - 23| < \epsilon.$

The problem of guaranteeing the inequality (6) by virtue of one of the form $|x - c| = |x + 3| < \delta$ is more difficult than the corresponding problem in Example 1, because of the presence of the *variable* factor $|5x - 23|$. It is essential to control this factor by keeping it bounded. We do this by ensuring that the variable x itself remains bounded. The simplest way to keep x

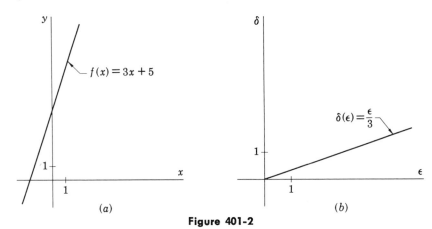

Figure 401-2

bounded is to require that the function $\delta(\epsilon)$ be bounded. In the present instance any positive upper bound will be satisfactory, and we choose 1 as the simplest positive number to use. We start, then, by defining $\delta_1 \equiv 1$, and requiring that $|x + 3| < \delta_1 = 1$, or $-1 < x + 3 < 1$. With $-4 < x < -2$, we have $|x| < 4$ and consequently

(7) $$|5x - 23| \leq 5|x| + 23 < 20 + 23 = 43.$$

Having guaranteed that the second factor of the product $|x + 3| \cdot |5x - 23|$ is less than 43 we can be assured that the product will be less than ϵ provided the first factor is less than $\epsilon/43$. We therefore let $\delta_2 \equiv \epsilon/43$, and define the function $\delta(\epsilon)$ in such a way that whenever $|x + 3| < \delta(\epsilon)$, then *both* inequalities $|x + 3| < \delta_1$ and $|x + 3| < \delta_2$ will be guaranteed. This is accomplished by means of the definition

(8) $$\delta(\epsilon) \equiv \min(\delta_1, \delta_2) = \min\left(1, \frac{\epsilon}{43}\right).$$

The inequality $|x + 3| < \delta(\epsilon)$ implies *both* $|x + 3| < 1$, and hence $|5x - 23| < 43$, *and* $|x + 3| < \epsilon/43$. Consequently, the inequality $|x + 3| < \delta(\epsilon)$ implies (6), and continuity at $x = -3$ is established. Figure 401-3 illustrates both functions $f(x)$ and $\delta(\epsilon)$ by means of coordinate systems with unequal units.

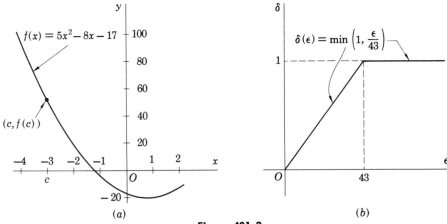

Figure 401-3

Example 3. Show that the function $\dfrac{1}{9x - 20}$, with domain $\mathcal{R} \setminus \left\{\dfrac{20}{9}\right\}$, is continuous at the point $x = 2$ by finding a function $\delta(\epsilon)$ as specified in Theorem II.

Solution. With $f(x) \equiv 1/(9x - 20)$ and $c \equiv 2$, the inequality on the right of (5) becomes

$$(9) \qquad |f(x) - f(c)| = \left|\frac{1}{9x - 20} - \frac{1}{-2}\right| = \left|\frac{9x - 18}{18x - 40}\right| = |x - 2| \cdot \frac{9}{|18x - 40|} < \epsilon.$$

This time we must control the denominator $|18x - 40|$ by keeping it from being too small, and this means keeping x away from $\frac{20}{9} = 2\frac{2}{9}$. This can be done by keeping x within a distance from 2 of less than $\frac{2}{9}$. A convenient positive number less than $\frac{2}{9}$ is $\frac{1}{9}$, and we therefore let $\delta_1 \equiv \frac{1}{9}$. The inequality $|x - 2| < \delta_1 = \frac{1}{9}$ is equivalent to $-\frac{1}{9} < x - 2 < \frac{1}{9}$, or $\frac{17}{9} < x < \frac{19}{9}$, and therefore to $34 < 18x < 38$ and $-6 < 18x - 40 < -2$. Since

$$|x - 2| < \delta_1 \Rightarrow |18x - 40| > 2 \Rightarrow \frac{9}{|18x - 40|} < \frac{9}{2} < 5,$$

we let $\delta_2 \equiv \epsilon/5$ and define

$$(10) \qquad\qquad \delta(\epsilon) \equiv \min(\delta_1, \delta_2) = \min\left(\frac{1}{9}, \frac{\epsilon}{5}\right).$$

The inequality $|x - 2| < \delta(\epsilon)$ therefore implies both $|x - 2| < 1/9$ and $|x - 2| < \epsilon/5$, and consequently (9), as desired. (Cf. Fig. 401-4.)

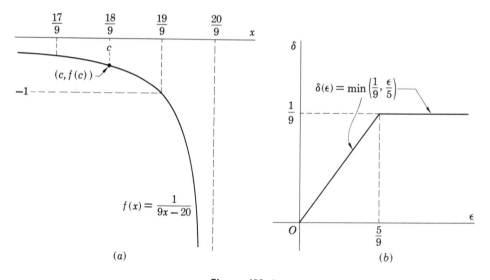

Figure 401-4

As might be expected, the two concepts of uniform continuity and continuity at a point are related. The simplest relationship is stated in the theorem:

Theorem III. *A function uniformly continuous on its domain is continuous at every point of its domain.*

Proof. If f is uniformly continuous on its domain D and if ϵ is an arbitrary positive number, then there exists a positive number δ such that for any points x_1 and x_2 of D,

$$(11) \qquad\qquad |x_1 - x_2| < \delta \Rightarrow |f(x_1) - f(x_2)| < \epsilon.$$

If c is any point of D, then f is continuous at c since for any point x of D such that $|x - c| < \delta$, then with $x_1 \equiv x$ and $x_2 \equiv c$, we conclude from (11) that $|f(x) - f(c)| < \epsilon$, as desired.

For *subsets* of the domain of a given function the situation is somewhat more complicated, as shown in the following Theorem IV. (The necessity of including the word *interior* is shown by Example 3, §403.) For statements concerning implications in the reverse direction see Note 2, below, and Theorem I, §413.

Theorem IV. *A function f uniformly continuous on an interval I, where I is a subset of the domain of f, is continuous at every, interior point of that interval.*

Proof. Assume that f is uniformly continuous on an interval I, and let c be any point interior to I. Then there exists a positive number η such that $(c - \eta, c + \eta) \subset I$. Since f is uniformly continuous on I, if ϵ is an arbitrary positive number there exists a positive number δ_1 such that whenever x_1 and x_2 are points of I such that $|x_1 - x_2| < \delta_1$ it follows that $|f(x_1) - f(x_2)| < \epsilon$. We now wish to find a positive number δ such that if x is any point of the domain of f and $|x - c| < \delta$, then $|f(x) - f(c)| < \epsilon$. Evidently we are to let one of the points, x_1 and x_2, be equal to c and the other equal to x, with δ small enough that the inequality $|x - c| < \delta$ will ensure that $x \in I$. To accomplish all this, we define δ to be the *smaller* of δ_1 and η: $\delta \equiv \min (\delta_1, \eta)$. Then the inequality $|x - c| < \delta$ implies that $|x - c| < \eta$ so that $x \in I$, and also that $|x - c| < \delta_1$, so that $|f(x) - f(c)| < \epsilon$. This completes the proof.

A corollary to Theorems III and IV and to facts regarding uniformly continuous functions given in Chapter 3 (the references to Chapter 3 are cited in the proof) is:

Theorem V. *Each of the following functions is continuous at every point of the specified set:*

    (i) $|x|;$ $(-\infty, +\infty) = \mathcal{R}.$
    (ii) *Any polynomial;* $(-\infty, +\infty) = \mathcal{R}.$
    (iii) $1/x;$ $\mathcal{R} \setminus \{0\} = (-\infty, 0) \cup (0, +\infty).$
    (iv) $\sqrt{x};$ $[0, +\infty).$
    (v) $\sin kx$ *and* $\cos kx;$ $(-\infty, +\infty) = \mathcal{R}.$

Proof. (i): The function $|x|$ is uniformly continuous on the interval $(-\infty, +\infty)$. (Example 3, §301.)

(ii): Let f be any polynomial and c any real number. Then c is an interior point of the bounded interval $(c - 1, c + 1)$, on which f is uniformly continuous. (Theorem III, §304.)

(iii): If c is any positive number, then c is an interior point of the interval $[\frac{1}{2}c, +\infty)$ on which $1/x$ is uniformly continuous, and if c is any negative number, then c is an interior point of the interval $(-\infty, \frac{1}{2}c]$, on which f is uniformly continuous. (Example 5, §301.)

(iv): $\sqrt{x}$ is uniformly continuous on $[0, +\infty)$. (Example 6, §301.)

(v): sin kx and cos kx are uniformly continuous on $(-\infty, +\infty)$. (Theorem III, §301.)

NOTE 2. The examples considered in parts (*ii*) and (*iii*) of Theorem V show that a function may be continuous at *every* point of an interval without being uniformly continuous there. The polynomial x^2 is continuous everywhere, and therefore on the interval $(0, +\infty)$, but it is not uniformly continuous there (Example 3, §302), and the function $1/x$ is continuous on the interval $(0, 1]$ without being uniformly continuous there (Example 2, §302).

Example 4. Prove that if s is a step-function for a net $\mathfrak{N} : \{a_0, a_1, \cdots, a_n\}$, then s is continuous at every point of every open interval of $\mathfrak{N}$.

Solution. If J is any open interval of $\mathfrak{N}$, then since s is constant on J, s is uniformly continuous on J (Example 4, §301). Since every point c of J is an interior point of J, s is continuous at c by Theorem IV.

402 EXERCISES

In Exercises 1–12, show that the given function is continuous at the specified point by finding a function $\delta(\epsilon)$ in accord with Theorem II, §401.

1. $3x - 2$, $x = 4$. **2.** $2x + 9$, $x = 3$. **3.** $x^2 + 7$, $x = 5$.

4. $2x^2$, $x = 3$. **5.** $x^2 + 3x - 1$, $x = 1$. **6.** $x^2 - 4x - 6$, $x = 1$.

7. $2x^2 - x - 7$, $x = 3$. **8.** $\dfrac{1}{2x}$, $x = 4$. **9.** $\dfrac{1}{x + 2}$, $x = 3$.

10. $\dfrac{1}{5x - 6}$, $x = 1$. **11.** $\dfrac{1}{6x - 5}$, $x = 1$. **12.** $\dfrac{x^2}{x + 3}$, $x = 2$.

13. Prove Theorem I, §401.

403 NEGATION OF CONTINUITY AT A POINT

Following the lines of the proof of the Theorem, §302, we have the corresponding statement concerning the *failure* of continuity at a point of the domain of a function:

Theorem I. Negation of Continuity at a Point. *If f is a function with domain D and if c is a point of D, then f fails to be continuous at c if and only if*

(1) $\quad \exists\, \epsilon > 0 \ni \forall\, \delta > 0, \exists\, x \in D \ni$
$$|x - c| < \delta \quad and \quad |f(x) - f(c)| \geq \epsilon.$$

In a similar fashion the formulation of Theorem I, §401, has the following negation:

Theorem II. *A function f fails to be continuous at a point c of its domain D if and only if*

(2) $\quad \exists\, a \ neighborhood\ N_{f(c)}\ of\ f(c) \ni \forall\ neighborhood\ N_c\ of\ c,$
$$f(D \cap N_c) \not\subset N_{f(c)},$$

that is, if and only if there exists a neighborhood $N_{f(c)}$ of $f(c)$ such that for every neighborhood N_c of c, at least one point of $D \cap N_c$ is mapped by f outside the neighborhood $N_{f(c)}$.

A function is said to be **discontinuous**, or to have a **discontinuity**, at a point c if and only if it fails to be continuous there. (A function is therefore discontinuous at every point not in its domain.) A point at which a function is discontinuous is a **point of discontinuity**.

Example 1. Prove that if s is a step-function for a net $\mathfrak{N} : \{a_0, a_1, \cdots, a_n\}$, if the value of s on the interval (a_{i-1}, a_i) is s_i, $i = 1, 2, \cdots, n$, and if either $s(a_k) \neq s_k$ or $s(a_k) \neq s_{k+1}$ for a particular $k = 0, 1, \cdots, n$, then s is discontinuous at a_k. Conclude that *the only continuous step-functions are constants.*

Solution. The proof is the same as that for Example 1, §302, except for the notation $c = a_k$ in place of $x_1 = a_k$, and x in place of x_2 for a point of the open interval (a_{k-1}, a_k) whose distance from a_k is less than δ.

Example 2. Prove that the function

$$f(x) \equiv \begin{cases} 1 \text{ if } x \text{ is rational,} \\ 0 \text{ if } x \text{ is irrational,} \end{cases}$$

(cf. the Example, §315, *PCLA*) is discontinuous at every $c \in \mathfrak{R}$.

Solution. If c is irrational, then by the density of the set $\mathfrak{Q}$ there are rational numbers x arbitrarily near c. Similarly, by the density of the set of irrational numbers, if c is rational there are irrational numbers x arbitrarily near c. Since the values of f on rational and irrational points differ by 1, we can take $\epsilon \equiv 1$ in Theorem I. Then for any $\delta > 0$, whether c is rational or irrational, there exists a point x such that $|x - c| < \delta$ and $|f(x) - f(c)| = |1 - 0| = 1 \geq \epsilon$.

Example 3. Show that the bracket (greatest integer) function (Example 3, §115, *PCLA*) is uniformly continuous on the half-open interval $[0, 1)$ although it is not continuous at 0, and therefore conclude that the word *interior* is essential in the statement of Theorem IV, §401.

Solution. With the elliptic notation $[x]$ for the bracket function, we can say that $[x]$ is constant on the interval $[0, 1)$, and therefore, by Example 4, §301, uniformly continuous there. However, by the same argument as that used in Example 2, $[x]$ is discontinuous at $x = 0$. Therefore, if the word *interior* were omitted from the statement of Theorem IV, §401, an endpoint such as 0 for the interval $[0, 1)$ would be admissible, and in such an example as the present one, lead to a false conclusion.

NOTE. While it is true that uniform continuity of a function on an interval ensures continuity on the interval provided that the interval is the entire domain of the function, Example 3 shows that in general *uniform continuity on an interval does not imply continuity on that interval*. It also illustrates the distinction between the two statements (*i*) *f is continuous on a set A* and (*ii*) *the restriction of f to A is continuous on A*. The first statement (*i*) *always* implies the second (*ii*) (cf. Note 1, §401), but Example 3 shows that (*ii*) does not imply (*i*). An argument similar to that given in the proof of Theorem IV, §401, can be used to prove that *if I is an open interval contained in the domain of a function f, then f is continuous on I if and only if the restriction of f to I is continuous on I.* In Example 3, for instance, since the restriction of $[x]$ to the *open* interval $(0, 1)$ is constant and therefore continuous there, the bracket function $[x]$ itself is continuous on $(0, 1)$.

404   VECTOR SPACE AND ALGEBRA

As might be expected from the similarity between the definitions of uniform continuity on an interval and continuity at a point, families of functions continuous at a given point c have a structure, as stated in Theorem II, below, that has now become familiar. Before we can prove that theorem, however, we must establish a fact regarding *local boundedness*, defined as follows:

Definition. *Let f be a function with domain D and let c be a point that is either a member of D or such that every neighborhood of c contains a point of D.* Then f is **locally bounded at** c if and only if there exists a neighborhood N_c of c such that f is bounded on $D \cap N_c$; that is, if and only if positive numbers δ and K exist such that $x \in D \cap (c - \delta, c + \delta) \Rightarrow |f(x)| < K$. The function f is **locally unbounded at** c if and only if it fails to be locally bounded there, that is, if and only if f is unbounded on $D \cap N_c$ for every neighborhood N_c of c.*

Theorem I. *A function is locally bounded at every point at which it is continuous.*

Proof. Assume that f is continuous at c. Then by Theorem I, §401, since the interval $(f(c) - 1, f(c) + 1)$ is a neighborhood of the point $f(c)$, there must exist a neighborhood N_c of c such that

$$(1) \qquad\qquad f(D \cap N_c) \subset (f(c) - 1, f(c) + 1).$$

Since the interval $(f(c) - 1, f(c) + 1)$ is bounded, f is bounded on $D \cap N_c$.

Theorem II. *Let c be a point of a set D. The family of all functions with domain D that are continuous at c is a vector space and an algebra. Consequently, the family of all functions with domain D that are continuous on D is a vector space and an algebra.*

Proof. The details are so similar to those of the proofs of Theorem I, §303, and Theorem II, §304, that most of these will be left as exercises. We shall prove only that the square of a function f that is continuous at c and has D as domain is continuous at c, following closely the pattern of the proof of Theorem II, §304. Since f is continuous at c, then by Theorem I there exist positive numbers δ_1 and K such that

$$(2) \qquad\qquad x \in D \cap (c - \delta_1, c + \delta_1) \Rightarrow |f(x)| < K.$$

If $h \equiv f^2$, we shall wish to examine an inequality of the form

$$(3) \qquad\qquad |h(x) - h(c)| = |f^2(x) - f^2(c)| < \epsilon,$$

where ϵ is an arbitrary positive number, and $x \in D$. In order to ensure the inequality $|f^2(x) - f^2(c)| < \epsilon$ as a consequence of the continuity of f at c, we rewrite its left-hand member, and make use of (2):

$$(4) \quad |f^2(x) - f^2(c)| = |f(x) - f(c)| \cdot |f(x) + f(c)|$$
$$\leq |f(x) - f(c)| \cdot (|f(x)| + |f(c)|) \leq 2K |f(x) - f(c)|.$$

---

*This latter case is closely related to the concept of *limit point*, or *cluster point*, treated in §501.

To obtain (3) we see that we must make $|f(x) - f(c)|$ less than $\epsilon/2K$. Therefore we let δ_2 be a positive number such that (by continuity of f at c):

(5)$$x \in D \cap (c - \delta_2, c + \delta_2) \Rightarrow |f(x) - f(c)| < \frac{\epsilon}{2K}.$$

Finally, with $\delta \equiv \min (\delta_1, \delta_2)$ and $N_c \equiv (c - \delta, c + \delta)$, we have, by virtue of (2), (4), and (5), and the definition of h:

(6)$$x \in D \cap N_c \Rightarrow |h(x) - h(c)| < \epsilon,$$

and the proof is complete. (For an alternative proof, cf. Ex. 28, §408.)

NOTE. The preceding theorem contains the precise formulations of the statements that *sums, differences, products,* and *constant multiples* of continuous functions are continuous. The case of *quotients* is treated in §406.

The following corollary to Theorem II is concerned with sums and differences and constant multiples. For products and quotients of two functions of which one is continuous and one is discontinuous, see §406.

Corollary.   *Let f and g be functions with domain D, let $c \in D$, and let λ be a nonzero constant. If f is discontinuous at c and g is continuous at c, then the functions*

(7)$$f + g, \ f - g, \ g - f, \ \lambda f$$

are all discontinuous at c.

Proof.   The proof is by the indirect method. Assume, for example, that $h \equiv f + g$ is continuous at c, and express f in terms of g and h: $f = h - g$. Then f, being a linear combination of two functions each of which is continuous at c, is continuous at c. (Contradiction.) The details for the remaining cases are left as an exercise.

Example.   Show that if two functions f and g continuous on an interval I are identical there except at a point c of I, then f and g must be identical at c as well : $f(c) = g(c)$.

Solution.   The function $h \equiv f - g$ is a continuous step-function, and therefore, by Example 1, §403, a constant. Since $h(x) = 0$ when $x \neq c$, $h(c) = 0$ and $f(c) = g(c)$.

405 EXERCISES

In Exercises 1–5, use Theorem I, §403, to show that the given function is not continuous at the specified point. Actually find an explicit value of x for an arbitrary $\delta > 0$ and $\epsilon = 1$. The functions sgn x and $[x]$ are defined in Examples 2 and 3, §115, *PCLA*.

1. sgn x, $x = 0$ **2.** $[x]$, $x = 2$.   **3.** $x + [x]$, $x = 1$.

4. $f(x) \equiv \begin{cases} \dfrac{1}{x}, \ x \neq 0, \\ 0, \ x = 0, \end{cases} x = 0.$ **5.** $f(x) \equiv \begin{cases} 3 - x, \ x < 2, \\ 2x, \ x \geq 2, \end{cases} x = 2.$

In Exercises 6–13, show that the given function is continuous at the specified point by making use of Theorem V, §401, and Theorem II, §404.

6. $x + \dfrac{1}{x}$, $x = 3$.

7. $x|x|$, $x = 2$.

8. $x^3 - 5x + 2$, $x = -3$.

9. $x^2 + 5\sqrt{x}$, $x = 1$.

10. $2\sqrt{x} - 3|x|$, $x = 10$.

11. $\dfrac{x^2 + 4\sqrt{x}}{x}$, $x = 4$.

12. $|x| \cdot (3x^5 - 8x + 2)$, $x = 0$.

13. $2x^2 + 7x - 18 + \dfrac{1}{x}$, $x = -5$.

406 COMPOSITE FUNCTIONS; QUOTIENTS

As with uniform continuity (cf. §306), *continuity at a point is preserved by composition*. In informal terms: *a continuous function of a continuous function is a continuous function*. The exact statement follows:

Theorem I. *If f is continuous at a point c, if g is continuous at a point d, if the range of f is a subset of the domain of g, and if $f(c) = d$, then the composite function $g \circ f$, whose values are given by $g(f(x))$, is continuous at c.*

Proof. Following the general outline of the proof of Theorem I, §306, we start with a positive number ϵ. Since g is continuous at the point d of its domain D, there exists a positive number η such that

(1) $$y \in D \cap (d - \eta, d + \eta) \implies |g(y) - g(d)| < \epsilon.$$

In terms of the positive number η, since f is continuous at the point c of its domain C, there exists a positive number δ such that

(2) $$x \in C \cap (c - \delta, c + \delta) \implies |f(x) - f(c)| < \eta.$$

For any x of C, let $y \equiv f(x)$. Then $y \in D$, and if $|x - c| < \delta$, $|y - d| < \eta$. If $h \equiv g \circ f$, we therefore have $h(x) - h(c) = g(y) - g(d)$, and hence the implication

(3) $$x \in C \cap (c - \delta, c + \delta) \implies |h(x) - h(c)| < \epsilon.$$

This completes the proof.

In order to visualize the ideas involved in the preceding theorem and its proof, it is helpful once more (as in §306) to think in terms of input-output machines (cf. Fig. 306-1 and Fig. 406-1). We start by feeding the number c to the "f machine," and passing along its output d to the "g machine." The idea now is to prove that the composite "machine" $h = g \circ f$ does not cause the two numbers x and c being fed into the machine to become too far separated, when they come out with the labels $h(x)$ and $h(c)$. A little more to the point: If the outgoing $h(x) = g(f(x))$ is to be within a certain "target range" of $h(c) = g(f(c)) = g(d)$, then the question is whether a control limitation about the point c can be determined so that every x within this limitation will "hit the target" when it comes out. The whole point of the η in the preceding proof is that we first determine a control limitation about the point d so that the "g machine" forces the point y, as limited, to "hit the target" about the point $g(d)$, and *then* regard this limitation around the point d as a target for the "f machine" to reckon with.

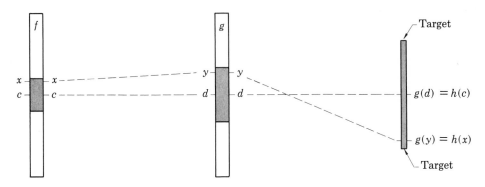

Figure 406-1

A simple application of the principle of the continuity of the composite of two continuous functions is a proof that *the reciprocal of a continuous function is continuous wherever it exists:*

Theorem II. *If f is continuous at a point c, if the domain of f is D, and if f(c) ≠ 0, then the reciprocal 1/f of f, with domain*

(4) $$E \equiv D \cap \{x \mid f(x) \neq 0\},$$

is continuous at c.

Proof. Define the functions g and h:

(5) $$g(x) \equiv \frac{1}{x}, \text{ domain } = (-\infty, 0) \cup (0, +\infty),$$

(6) $$h(x) \equiv g(f(x)) = 1/f(x), \text{ domain } = E.$$

By Note 1, §401, the restriction of the function f to the set E is continuous at the point c. Therefore, by Theorem V(*iii*), §401, and Theorem I above, h is continuous at c.

A generalization of Theorem II is that *the quotient of two continuous functions is continuous at any point where the denominator is not equal to zero:*

Theorem III. *If f and g are continuous at a point c, if the domains of f and g are both D, and if g(c) ≠ 0, then the quotient f/g, with domain*

(7) $$E \equiv D \cap \{x \mid g(x) \neq 0\},$$

is continuous at c.

Proof. By Theorem II, the function $1/g$ with domain E is continuous at c, and by Note 1, §401, f restricted to the domain E is continuous at c. Therefore, by Theorem II, §404, the product $f \cdot (1/g)$ is continuous at c.

Corresponding to the Corollary to Theorem II, §404, we have a further corollary to both that theorem and Theorem III, above (give a proof in Ex. 13, §408):

Corollary. *Let f and g be functions with domain D, let g be nonzero on D, and let c ∈ D. If f is discontinuous at c and g is continuous at c, then the functions*

(8) fg and f/g

are both discontinuous at c.

We can now extend slightly our collection of continuous functions (give proofs in Ex. 14, §408):

Theorem IV. *Each of the following is a continuous function on its domain:*

(i) *Any rational function (Example 17, §111, PCLA).*

(ii) *Any function of the form $\sqrt{f(x)}$, where $f(x)$ is continuous and nonnegative on its domain.*

(iii) *The trigonometric functions,* sin kx, cos kx, tan kx, cot kx, sec kx, csc kx.

Closely related to the subject of quotients of continuous functions is the concept of *boundedness from zero:*

Definition. *A function f is **bounded from zero** on a subset A of its domain if and only if there exists a positive number η such that*

(9) $x \in A \Rightarrow |f(x)| \geq \eta.$

NOTE.   Each of the following two statements is equivalent to (9):

(i) $x \in A \Rightarrow f(x) \in (-\infty, -\eta] \cup [\eta, +\infty),$

(ii) $f(A) \subset (-\infty, -\eta] \cup [\eta, +\infty).$

Furthermore, the following two statements follow directly from the preceding definition:

(iii) f is bounded from zero on A if and only if its absolute value $|f|$ is.

(iv) f is bounded from zero on A if and only if its reciprocal $1/f$ is defined and bounded there.

The simplest statement relating continuity and boundedness from zero is the following:

Theorem V. *If f is continuous at a point c, if the domain of f is D, and if $f(c) \neq 0$, then there exists a neighborhood N_c of c such that f is bounded from zero on $D \cap N_c$.*

We shall prove a stronger theorem from which Theorem V follows:

Theorem VI. *Under the assumptions of Theorem V and the additional assumption that $f(c) > 0$, there exist a positive number η and a neighborhood N_c of c such that*

(10) $x \in D \cap N_c \Rightarrow f(x) > \eta.$

Under the assumptions of Theorem V and the additional assumption that $f(c) < 0$, there exist a negative number $-\eta$ and a neighborhood N_c of c such that

(11) $x \in D \cap N_c \Rightarrow f(x) < -\eta$

Proof.   We shall give the details for the first part only, leaving those for the second part to the reader. The method of procedure is suggested by Figure 406-2. Since

$f(c)$ is positive, so is $\frac{1}{2}f(c)$. Also, any number closer to $f(c)$ than $\frac{1}{2}f(c)$ must be greater than $\frac{1}{2}f(c)$. It seems, therefore, that we should be able to use $\frac{1}{2}f(c)$ in the role of ϵ in the definition of continuity at c, and also to let η be defined to be $\frac{1}{2}f(c)$. The details to justify this conjecture follow.

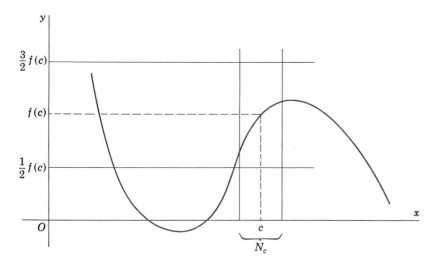

Figure 406-2

We start by letting ϵ be the positive number $\frac{1}{2}f(c)$ and use Theorem I, §401, to obtain a neighborhood N_c of c such that

(12) $f(D \cap N_c) \subset (f(c) - \frac{1}{2}f(c), f(c) + \frac{1}{2}f(c)),$

and therefore, with $\eta \equiv \frac{1}{2}f(c)$:

(13) $f(D \cap N_c) \subset (\frac{1}{2}f(c), \frac{3}{2}f(c)) \subset (\eta, +\infty).$

With this the proof is complete.

The following corollary to Theorem V is immediate:

Corollary. *Every function is nonzero in some neighborhood of every point at which it is both continuous and nonzero. That is, under the assumptions of Theorem V there exists a neighborhood N_c of c such that*

(14) $x \in D \cap N_c \Rightarrow f(x) \neq 0.$

We close this section with the following analogue of Theorem II, §306 (give a proof in Ex. 15, §408):

Theorem VII. *The function $|f|$ is continuous at any point at which f is continuous.*

407   ONE-SIDED CONTINUITY; TYPES OF DISCONTINUITY

The greatest integer function, as discussed in Example 3, §403, is discontinuous at the point 0, although its restriction to the closed interval $[0, \frac{1}{2}]$ is continuous at each point of that interval, and in particular at 0. This is an example, then, of a function that is discontinuous at a point c but whose restriction to an interval having c as endpoint is continuous there. The *one-sided continuity* thus illustrated has the following general definition:

Definition. *Let c be a point of the domain D of a function f. Then f is **continuous on the right**, or **right-continuous**, at c if and only if the restriction of f to $D \cap [c, +\infty]$ is continuous at c. The function f is **continuous on the left**, or **left-continuous**, at c if and only if the restriction of f to $D \cap (-\infty, c]$ is continuous at c.*

The two kinds of one-sided continuity specified in this definition are called **right-hand continuity** and **left-hand continuity**, respectively.

One-sided discontinuities are defined in terms of the absence of the corresponding type of one-sided continuity. For example, a function is **discontinuous on the right** or **right-discontinuous** if and only if it fails to be right-continuous there, and the function is said to have a **right-hand discontinuity** at the point. Similar definitions apply on the left. (Cf. Fig. 407-1.)

The relationship between continuity and one-sided continuity is easily stated:

Theorem. *Let c be a point of the domain D of a function f. Then f is continuous at c if and only if it is both right-continuous and left-continuous there.*

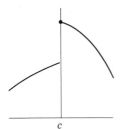

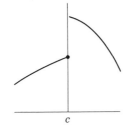

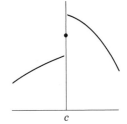

Right-hand continuity   Left-hand continuity   Two-sided discontinuity
Left-hand discontinuity   Right-hand discontinuity

Figure 407-1

Proof. Since $D \cap [c, +\infty) \subset D$, the restriction of f to $D \cap [c, +\infty)$ is continuous at c whenever f is, and similarly with $D \cap (-\infty, c]$ (cf. Note 1, §401). Therefore continuity at c implies both right-continuity and left-continuity there. Assume now that f is both right-continuous and left-continuous at c, and let $\epsilon > 0$. Then there exist positive numbers δ_1 and δ_2 such that (cf. Theorem I, §401):

(1) $f(D \cap [c, +\infty) \cap (c - \delta_1, c + \delta_1)) \subset (f(c) - \epsilon, f(c) + \epsilon)$,

(2) $f(D \cap (-\infty, c] \cap (c - \delta_2, c + \delta_2)) \subset (f(c) - \epsilon, f(c) + \epsilon)$,

and therefore, if $\delta \equiv \min(\delta_1, \delta_2)$,

(3) $f(D \cap [c, c + \delta)) \subset (f(c) - \epsilon, f(c) + \epsilon)$,

(4) $\qquad\qquad f(D \cap (c - \delta, c]) \subset (f(c) - \epsilon, f(c) + \epsilon)$,

and thus, finally,

(5) $f((D \cap [c, c + \delta)) \cup (D \cap (c - \delta, c]))$
$$= f(D \cap (c - \delta, c + \delta)) \subset (f(c) - \epsilon, f(c) + \epsilon).$$

Discontinuities of functions are of several types, the principal ones of which we can now enumerate.

I. Unbounded discontinuities. By Theorem I, §404, any function that is locally unbounded at the point c is discontinuous there, whether it is defined at that point or not. (Cf. Fig. 407-2.)

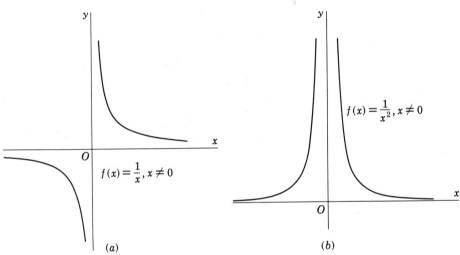

Unbounded discontinuities at $x = 0$

Figure 407-2

II. Removable discontinuities. If f is a function with domain D that is discontinuous at a point c, whether c is a member of D or not, and if g is a function with domain $D \cup \{c\}$ that is continuous at c and equal to f on $D \setminus \{c\}$:

(6) $\qquad\qquad \left.\begin{matrix} x \in D \\ x \neq c \end{matrix}\right\} \Rightarrow f(x) = g(x)$,

then f is said to have a **removable discontinuity** at c. The idea is that either $f(c)$ is not defined but may be assigned a value such that f "becomes continuous" on $D \cup \{c\}$, or $f(c)$ exists and is such that f is discontinuous with *this* value at c, but "becomes continuous" when it is appropriately *redefined* at c. (Cf. Fig. 407-3.)

III. Jump discontinuities. A function f with domain D has a **removable right-hand discontinuity** at a point c if and only if its restriction to $D \cap [c, +\infty)$ has a removable

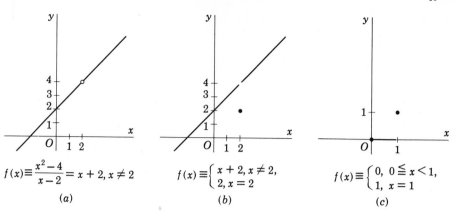

$$f(x) \equiv \frac{x^2 - 4}{x - 2} = x + 2, x \neq 2$$

(a)

$$f(x) \equiv \begin{cases} x + 2, x \neq 2, \\ 2, x = 2 \end{cases}$$

(b)

$$f(x) \equiv \begin{cases} 0, \ 0 \leq x < 1, \\ 1, \ x = 1 \end{cases}$$

(c)

Removable discontinuities

Figure 407-3

discontinuity there. A similar definition applies to a **removable left-hand discontinuity**. A function f that does *not* have a removable discontinuity at a point c has a **jump discontinuity** there if and only if: (*i*) f has both a removable right-hand discontinuity and a removable left-hand discontinuity at c (cf. Fig. 407-4*a*), or (*ii*) f is right-continuous and has a removable left-hand discontinuity at c (cf. Fig. 407-4*b*), or (*iii*) f is left-continuous and has a removable right-hand discontinuity at c (cf. Fig. 407-4*c*).

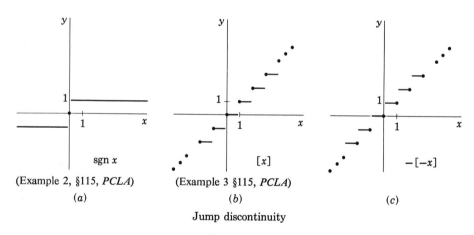

sgn x

(Example 2, §115, *PCLA*)

(a)

$[x]$

(Example 3 §115, *PCLA*)

(b)

$-[-x]$

(c)

Jump discontinuity

Figure 407-4

IV. Oscillatory discontinuities. The function $\sin (1/x)$, $x \neq 0$, provides an example of a discontinuity that does not fit either category II or III, above, regardless of the manner in which it may be defined at $x = 0$. The discontinuity is caused by the infinite number of oscillations occurring in every neighborhood of 0. (However, see I and II, §624, where an infinite number of oscillations occur near a point of continuity.) The functions

$$(7) \qquad g(x) \equiv \begin{cases} \sin \dfrac{1}{x} \text{ if } x > 0, \\[2mm] 0 \quad \text{if } x \leq 0, \end{cases} \qquad h(x) \equiv \begin{cases} 0 \quad \text{if } x \geq 0, \\[2mm] \sin \dfrac{1}{x} \text{ if } x < 0, \end{cases}$$

are modifications of the function f of Figure 407-5, where the oscillations give one-sided discontinuities only.

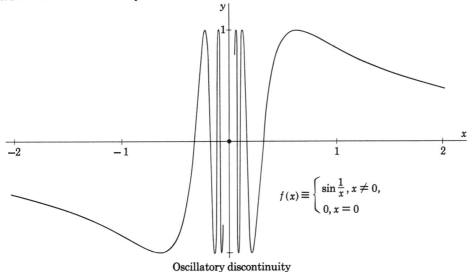

$$f(x) \equiv \begin{cases} \sin \dfrac{1}{x}, x \neq 0, \\[2mm] 0, x = 0, \end{cases}$$

Oscillatory discontinuity

Figure 407-5

V. Dense discontinuities. The function f defined so that $f(x) = 1$ if x is rational and $f(x) = 0$ if x is irrational is everywhere discontinuous (cf. Example 2, §403). In H§909, *CWAG*, is given an example of a function that is discontinuous at every rational number and continuous at every irrational number.

NOTE. One-sided continuity can be expressed in terms of *one-sided neighborhoods*, a **one-sided neighborhood** of a point c being defined as the intersection of a neighborhood N_c of c and one of the two unbounded closed intervals $[c, +\infty)$ or $(-\infty, c]$. One-sided neighborhoods of the point c are therefore either of the form

$$(8) \qquad N_{c+} \equiv N_c \cap [c, +\infty) = [c, c + \delta)$$

or of the form

$$(9) \qquad N_{c-} \equiv N_c \cap (-\infty, c] = (c - \delta, c]$$

where δ is a positive number. The neighborhoods N_{c+} and N_{c-} of (8) and (9) are called **right half-neighborhoods** and **left half-neighborhoods,** respectively, of the point c. Counterparts of Theorem I, §401, are available for one-sided continuity by simply replacing N_c by either N_{c+} or N_{c-}.

408   EXERCISES

The functions sgn x and $[x]$ occurring in some of the following exercises are defined in Examples 2 and 3, §115, *PCLA*.

In Exercises 1–8, show that the given function is continuous on the specified interval, with the aid of Theorem II, §404, and Theorems III and VII, §406.

1. $\dfrac{9 + x^2}{9 - x^2}$, $(-3, 3)$.   **2.** $\sqrt{x^2 - 16}$, $[4, +\infty)$.   **3.** $\left(\dfrac{|3x - 2| - 5}{|2x - 3| + 5}\right)^4$, $\mathfrak{R}$.

4. $\left|\sqrt{x - 2} - \dfrac{1}{2x - 3}\right|$, $[2, +\infty)$.   **5.** $(3x^4 + 7x - \sin x^2)^3$, $\mathfrak{R}$.

6. $\sin \sqrt{x} - \dfrac{1}{x^2}$, $(0, +\infty)$.   **7.** $x\sqrt{1 - \cos 3x}$, $\mathfrak{R}$.   **8.** $\dfrac{1 + \cos 2\pi x}{1 - \cos 2\pi x}$, $\mathfrak{R} \backslash \mathcal{I}$.

In Exercises 9–12, use the Corollaries to Theorem II, §404, and Theorem III, §406, to show that the given function is discontinuous at the specified point.

9. $\sin x^2 + 3 \operatorname{sgn} x$, $x = 0$.   **10.** $\sqrt{x^2 + 4} - 5 \operatorname{sgn} x$, $x = 0$.

11. $[x]\sqrt{x^4 - 20}$, $x = 3$.   **12.** $\dfrac{[x]}{1 + \tan (x - \frac{5}{4}\pi)}$, $x = 2$.

13. Prove the Corollary to Theorem III, §406.

14. Prove Theorem IV, §406.

15. Prove Theorem VII, §406.

In Exercises 16–19, show that the given function is continuous at the specified point. Draw a graph.

16. $f(x) \equiv \begin{cases} x - 2, x \leqq 5, \\ 8 - x, x > 5, \end{cases}$ $x = 5$.   **17.** $f(x) \equiv \begin{cases} 3x - 2, x < 3, \\ 2x + 1, x \geqq 3, \end{cases}$ $x = 3$.

18. $f(x) \equiv \begin{cases} x^2, x < 4, \\ 2x + 8, x \geqq 4, \end{cases}$ $x = 4$.   **19.** $f(x) \equiv \begin{cases} 3x - x^2, x \leqq 2, \\ x^2 - x, x > 2, \end{cases}$ $x = 2$.

In Exercises 20–27, discuss the location and nature of any discontinuity. Also discuss one-sided continuity where it exists at any point of discontinuity. Draw a graph.

20. $\dfrac{1}{(x - 2)^2}$.   **21.** $\dfrac{1}{x^2 - 4}$.

22. $f(x) \equiv \begin{cases} x + 3, x \leqq 1, \\ 6 - x, x > 1. \end{cases}$ **23.** $f(x) \equiv \begin{cases} \dfrac{x^2 + x - 2}{x - 1}, x \neq 1, \\ 5, \quad x = 1. \end{cases}$

24. $f(x) \equiv \begin{cases} \dfrac{x^2 - x - 6}{x - 3}, x \neq 3, \\ 5, \quad x = 3. \end{cases}$ **25.** $f(x) \equiv \begin{cases} x + 2, x < 1, \\ 4, \quad x = 1, \\ 5, \quad x > 1. \end{cases}$

26. $f(x) \equiv \begin{cases} 0, \quad x \leqq 0, \\ \cos \dfrac{1}{x}, x > 0. \end{cases}$ **27.** $f(x) \equiv \begin{cases} 2, x \text{ rational}, \\ 5, x \text{ irrational}. \end{cases}$

28. Use Theorem I, §406, to prove that whenever a function f is continuous at a point c, then so is its square f^2. Thus give a second proof of Theorem II, §404.

409   INTERMEDIATE-VALUE PROPERTY

Suppose f is a function continuous on the closed interval $[a, b]$, negative at a and positive at b (cf. Fig. 409-1). It "stands to reason" that the graph of f must "cross the x-axis" at some point c between a and b. In other words, there "should be" some number c between a and b such that $f(c) = 0$. This important fact is restated in the following theorem, and proved in §911, *CWAG*:

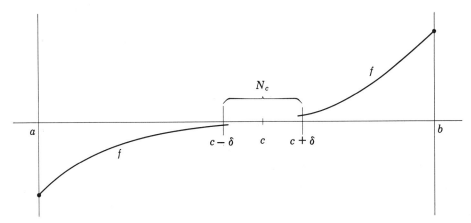

Figure 409-1

Theorem I.   *If f is continuous on $[a, b]$, if $f(a) < 0$, and if $f(b) > 0$, then there exists a number c such that $a < c < b$ and $f(c) = 0$.*

A consequence of Theorem I is the **intermediate-value property** of continuous functions:

Theorem II.   *If f is continuous on an interval I, if a and b are any two points of I such that $f(a) \neq f(b)$, and if d is any number between $f(a)$ and $f(b)$, then there exists a number c between a and b such that $f(c) = d$.*

Proof.   Let the notation be adjusted so that $a < b$, and assume first that $f(a) < d < f(b)$. Then the function

$$(5) \qquad\qquad\qquad g(x) \equiv f(x) - d$$

is continuous on the closed interval $[a, b]$, $g(a) < 0$, and $g(b) > 0$ (cf. Fig. 409-2). Therefore, by Theorem I, there exists a number c such that $a < c < b$ and $g(c) = 0$. But since $g(c) = f(c) - d$, this means that $f(c) = d$. The other case is handled similarly. If $f(a) > d > f(b)$, define

$$(6) \qquad\qquad\qquad h(x) \equiv -f(x) + d.$$

The remaining details are left for the student.

The intermediate-value property of continuous functions can be expressed as follows:

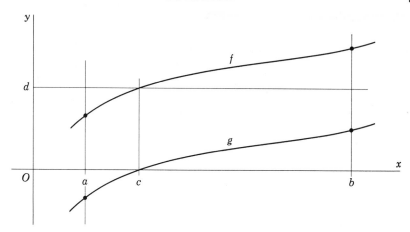

Figure 409-2

Theorem III. *If f is continuous on an interval I, then the image of every subinterval of I is either an interval or a degenerate interval consisting of one point.*

Proof. By Theorem II, if A is the image of an interval and if A consists of more than one point, then A has the intermediate-membership property of Note 4, §314, *PCLA*, and is therefore an interval.

410   INVERSES OF MONOTONIC FUNCTIONS

The intermediate-value property established in Theorem II, §409, provides a proof for the important fact that all strictly monotonic continuous functions on intervals have inverses. More precisely:

Theorem I. *If f is strictly monotonic and continuous on its domain and if its domain is an interval I, then its range is an interval J. The mapping of I onto J is one-to-one, so that the inverse function φ, defined*

(1) $$\phi(y) = x \iff f(x) = y, \text{ for } x \in I, \ y \in J,$$

exists.

Proof. By Theorem III, §409, if f is continuous on an interval I, then its range is either an interval or a degenerate interval consisting of one point. If f is in addition strictly monotonic on I, then its range consists of more than one point and hence must be an interval J. If f is strictly monotonic on I, two distinct points of I are mapped onto two distinct points of J, and the mapping is one-to-one. Therefore, for any $y \in J$ there is *exactly one* $x \in I$ such that $f(x) = y$, and therefore the inverse function ϕ exists, with domain J.

Proofs that *the inverse of a strictly increasing function is strictly increasing* and that *the inverse of a strictly decreasing function is strictly decreasing* are left as an exercise.

Under the conditions of Theorem I the inverse mapping not only exists but is *continuous:*

Theorem II.   *If f is a strictly monotonic and continuous mapping of an interval I onto an interval J, then the inverse function ϕ is a strictly monotonic and continuous mapping of the interval J onto the interval I.*

Proof.   We give the details for the case of a strictly increasing function f and for intervals I and J that are *open*. (The decreasing case differs in no essential manner and is left to the student. The case of continuity at an *endpoint* of an interval differs only to the extent that neighboring points on only *one* side of the endpoint in question are considered.)

Assume, then, that f is a strictly increasing function with domain and range open intervals I and J, respectively, and let v be an arbitrary point of J. In order to prove that ϕ is continuous at v, we wish to show (according to Theorem I, §401) that if $u = \phi(v)$, then

(2)   ∀ neighborhood N_u of u, ∃ a neighborhood N_v of v ∋ $\phi(J \cap N_v) \subset N_u$.

Since $u \in I$ and I is an open interval, u is an interior point of I and therefore there exists a neighborhood $U = (u - \epsilon, u + \epsilon)$ of u such that $U \subset N_u$ (cf. Fig. 410-1). We now define a neighborhood N_v of v by means of the positive number δ:

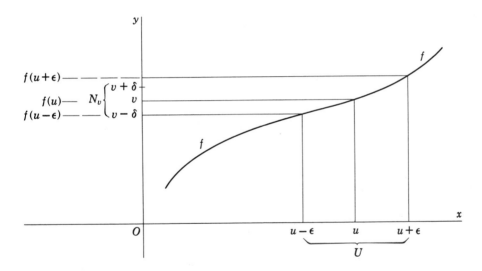

Figure 410-1

(3) $\delta \equiv \min (f(u) - f(u - \epsilon), f(u + \epsilon) - f(u))$,

with $N_v \equiv (v - \delta, v + \delta)$. Then (cf. Fig. 410-1)

(4) $N_v \subset (f(u - \epsilon), f(u + \epsilon)) \subset J$,

and therefore, since ϕ as well as f is strictly increasing,

(5) $\phi(J \cap N_v) = \phi(N_v) \subset \phi((f(u - \epsilon), f(u + \epsilon))) = (u - \epsilon, u + \epsilon) = U \subset N_u$,

and the proof is complete.

411   ROOTS AND RATIONAL POWERS

By Theorems I and II, §410, we can infer from the fact that the power function

(1) $$f(x) \equiv x^n,$$

where n is a positive integer, is continuous and strictly increasing on the interval $[0, +\infty)$ that the inverse function ϕ, denoted

(2) $$\phi(y) = \sqrt[n]{y},$$

is defined, continuous, and strictly increasing on the interval J that is the range of f. In order to establish the existence of nth roots of all positive numbers we have only to show, then, that the range of the function x^n is unbounded above:

Theorem I. *If n is a positive integer, the function x^n with domain $[0, +\infty)$ has a range that is unbounded above.*

Proof.   If b is an arbitrary positive number, we wish to find a positive number x such that $x^n > b$.   Such a number x is given by the formula $x \equiv b + 1$, since the inequality $b + 1 > 1$ implies

(3) $$(b + 1)^n \geqq b + 1 > b.$$

Three corollaries follow directly:

Corollary I. *If n is a positive integer, the range of the function x^n with domain $[0, +\infty)$ is $[0, +\infty)$.*

Proof.   The range R is an interval containing 0 that is an unbounded subset of $[0, +\infty)$. The only such interval is $[0, +\infty)$.

Corollary II. *If n is a positive integer and y is a nonnegative number, there exists a unique nonnegative number x such that $x^n = y$.*

Corollary III. *There exists a unique positive number whose square is equal to 2.*

We incorporate some of the preceding results into a theorem, with an extension based on symmetry (cf. Example 1, §514, *PCLA*):

Theorem II. *If n is a positive integer, the function*

(4) $$\sqrt[n]{x}, \ domain = [0, +\infty),$$

is a strictly increasing continuous function with range $[0, +\infty)$. The values of $\sqrt[n]{x}$ include $\sqrt[n]{0} = 0$ and $\sqrt[n]{1} = 1$. The function

(5) $$\sqrt[2n-1]{x}, \ domain = (-\infty, +\infty),$$

is a strictly increasing continuous function with range $(-\infty, +\infty)$. The values of $\sqrt[2n-1]{x}$ include $\sqrt[2n-1]{0} = 0$, $\sqrt[2n-1]{1} = 1$, and $\sqrt[2n-1]{-1} = -1$. (Cf. Fig. 411-1)

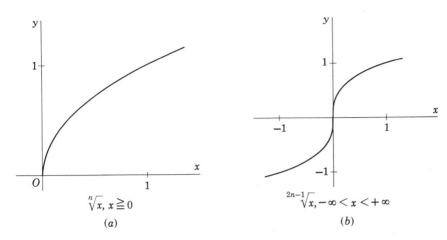

$\sqrt[n]{x},\, x \geqq 0$

(a)

$\sqrt[2n-1]{x},\, -\infty < x < +\infty$

(b)

Figure 411-1

With the existence of nth roots assured, it is now possible to extend the definition of powers to those with an arbitrary rational exponent and positive base:

Definition.   *Let x be a positive number, and let r be a rational number p/q, where p and q are integers and q is positive. Then x^r is defined:*

(6)
$$x^r = x^{\frac{p}{q}} \equiv \sqrt[q]{x^p}.$$

If in addition p is positive,

(7)
$$0^r = 0^{\frac{p}{q}} \equiv \sqrt[q]{0^p} = 0.$$

The following three theorems are proved in §§1005 and 1006 of the author's *The Real Number System:*

Theorem III.   *The value of x^r in the preceding Definition is independent of the form of r. That is, if $r = p/q = m/n$, where p, q, m, and n are integers and q and n are positive, then $\sqrt[q]{x^p} = \sqrt[n]{x^m}$.*

Theorem IV.   *Under the assumptions of the preceding Definition,*

(8)
$$(x^{\frac{p}{q}})^q = x^p,$$

(9)
$$x^{\frac{p}{q}} = \sqrt[q]{x^p} = (\sqrt[q]{x})^p.$$

Note 1.   The second equality of (9) has the following interpretation: *The functions x^p and $\sqrt[q]{x}$ commute with each other under composition.* More generally, by Theorem V(*iii*), below, if r and s are any rational numbers, the functions x^r and x^s, with domain $(0, +\infty)$, commute with each other under composition. (Cf. §501, *PCLA.*)

Theorem V. Laws of Exponents. *If x and y are any positive numbers and if r and s are any rational numbers, then*

(i) $x^r x^s = x^{r+s}$,

(ii) $\dfrac{x^r}{x^s} = x^{r-s}$,

(iii) $(x^r)^s = x^{rs}$,

(iv) $(xy)^r = x^r y^r$,

(v) $\left(\dfrac{x}{y}\right)^r = \dfrac{x^r}{y^r}$.

NOTE 2.   The preceding Definition and Theorems III–V can be extended to apply to *negative* x or y provided the exponents concerned are restricted to numbers of the form p/q, where p is an integer and q is a *positive odd* integer. In like fashion, if all exponents concerned are of the form p/q, where both p and q are positive integers and q is odd, then the preceding theorems apply to *all real numbers*, except for Theorem V(*ii*) and (*v*) when zero denominators occur.

Theorem VI. *If r is a positive rational number, then the function*

(10) x^r, *domain* $= [0, +\infty)$,

is a strictly increasing continuous function with range $[0, +\infty)$. *The values of* x^r *include* $0^r = 0$ *and* $1^r = 1$.

Proof. Let $r = p/q$, where p and q are positive integers. Then the function $h(x) = x^r$ is the composite of the two functions $f(x) = \sqrt[q]{x}$ and $g(x) = x^p$:

(11) $h = f \circ g, \quad h(x) = f(g(x)) = \sqrt[q]{x^p}$.

Each of the functions $\sqrt[q]{x}$ and x^p is strictly increasing and continuous on $[0, +\infty)$ with range $[0, +\infty)$. Since the composite of any two strictly increasing functions is strictly increasing, and since the composite of any two continuous functions is continuous (Theorem I, §406), the proof is complete.

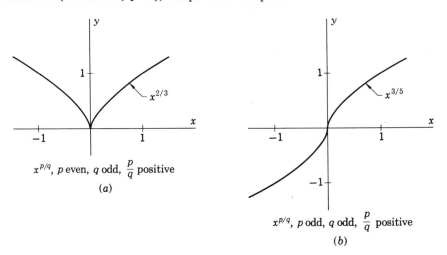

$x^{p/q}$, p even, q odd, $\dfrac{p}{q}$ positive

(a)

$x^{p/q}$, p odd, q odd, $\dfrac{p}{q}$ positive

(b)

Figure 411-2

NOTE 3.   If r is a positive rational number of the form p/q, where p and q are positive integers and q is *odd*, then the function x^r is continuous on $\Re = (-\infty, +\infty)$. It is even or odd according as p is even or odd. (Cf. Fig. 411-2.)

Theorem VII.   *If r is a negative rational number, then the function*

(12) x^r, *domain* $= (0, +\infty)$

is a strictly decreasing continuous function with range $(0, +\infty)$. *The values of x^r include* $1^r = 1$.

Proof.   The function x^r is the reciprocal of the function of Theorem VI:

(13) $$x^r = \frac{1}{x^{-r}}.$$

NOTE 4.   If r is a negative rational number of the form p/q, where p is a negative integer and q is a positive *odd* integer, then the function x^r is continuous on $\Re \setminus \{0\}$. It is even or odd according as p is even or odd. (Cf. Fig. 411–3.)

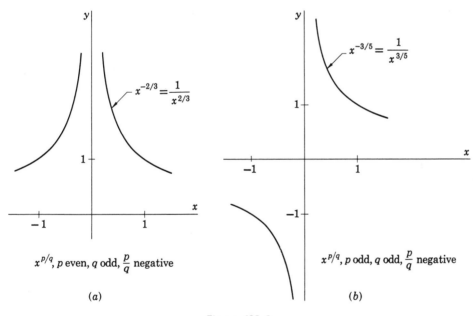

$x^{p/q}$, p even, q odd, $\dfrac{p}{q}$ negative

(a)

$x^{p/q}$, p odd, q odd, $\dfrac{p}{q}$ negative

(b)

Figure 411-3

NOTE 5.   In §1111 will be considered the *general power function* x^b with domain $(0, +\infty)$, where b is an arbitrary real number, rational or irrational.

412   EXERCISES

In Exercises 1–6, show that the given function is continuous on the prescribed interval.

1. $\sqrt[3]{x^2 - 8x - 1}$, $\Re$.   **2.** $\sqrt[4]{4 + 3x - x^2}$, $[-1, 4]$.

3. $(x^2 - 6x + 8)^{-\frac{3}{4}}$, $(4, +\infty)$.

4. $(x^2 - 4x + 3)^{-\frac{5}{3}}$, $(-\infty, 1)$.

5. $\cos^3(x^{\frac{3}{4}})$, $[0, +\infty)$.

6. $\sin^2(x^{\frac{2}{3}})$, $\mathfrak{R}$.

In Exercises 7–12, show that the given function is strictly monotonic on the given interval, and find the image of this interval under the prescribed mapping. Draw a graph.

7. $\sqrt[3]{x}$, $[-1, 8]$.

8. $\sqrt[3]{x^2}$, $(1, 8)$.

9. $x^3 + 4$, $(0, +\infty)$.

10. $x^4 - 3$, $[0, +\infty)$.

11. $x^2 - 8x$, $(4, 8]$.

12. $x^2 - 6x$, $[0, 3)$.

In Exercises 13–18, write out explicitly in the form $x = \phi(y)$ the inverse function of the function prescribed in the given exercise, and show that this inverse function is monotonic on its domain.

13. Exercise 7.   **14.** Exercise 8.   **15.** Exercise 9.   **16.** Exercise 10.

17. Exercise 11.   **18.** Exercise 12.

413 CONTINUITY AND UNIFORM CONTINUITY

One of the most important properties of continuous functions is stated in the following theorem, whose proof is given in §916 and H§919, *CWAG*:

Theorem I. *Every function continuous on a compact interval is uniformly continuous there.*

Since any function that is uniformly continuous on a compact interval is (Riemann-) integrable there, we have the immediate corollary:

Theorem II. *Every function that is continuous on a compact interval is integrable there.*

This result can be readily generalized:

Theorem III. *Every function that is defined on a compact interval, and continuous there except for a finite number of removable or jump discontinuities, is integrable there.*

Proof. Let f be defined on $[a, b]$ and continuous there except for the points of a net $\mathfrak{N} : \{a_0, a_1, \cdots, a_n\}$, at each point of which f has either a removable or a jump discontinuity. On each closed subinterval $[a_{i-1}, a_i]$, $i = 1, 2, \cdots, n$, f can be redefined at the endpoints a_{i-1} and a_i in such a way that it becomes continuous on $[a_{i-1}, a_i]$. Since the *redefined* function is integrable on $[a_{i-1}, a_i]$, so is the *original* function f by Theorem I, §114. Therefore, since f is integrable on every closed subinterval for the net $\mathfrak{N}$, f is integrable on the entire closed interval $[a, b]$ (cf. the Note, §113).

414 BOUNDEDNESS AND EXTREMA

Two fundamental properties of functions continuous on compact intervals — to be added to those of §§409 and 413 — follow quickly from §413:

Theorem I. *Every function that is continuous on a compact interval is bounded there.*

Proof. Every function continuous on a compact interval is uniformly continuous there and therefore bounded there, by Theorem I, §304.

Theorem II. *Every function that is continuous on a compact interval has both a maximum value and a minimum value there. That is, if f is continuous on [a, b], then there exist points c and d of [a, b] such that*

(1) $$x \in [a, b] \implies f(c) \leq f(x) \leq f(d).$$

Proof. We shall give the details for the existence of the point d such that $x \in [a, b] \implies f(x) \leq f(d)$. The case for c and the inequality $f(c) \leq f(x)$ is left as an exercise. By Theorem I, the function f is bounded on $[a, b]$. Define λ to be the least upper bound of its range:

(2) $$\lambda \equiv \sup \{f(x) \mid x \in [a, b]\},$$

and assume that there is *no point x* of $[a, b]$ such that $f(x) = \lambda$. Then the inequality $f(x) < \lambda$ must hold for every point x of $[a, b]$, and therefore the function g:

(3) $$g(x) \equiv \lambda - f(x),$$

is a continuous function with *positive* values on $[a, b]$. Consequently, $h \equiv 1/g$, the reciprocal of g:

(4) $$h(x) \equiv \frac{1}{g(x)} = \frac{1}{\lambda - f(x)},$$

is defined and continuous on $[a, b]$ (cf. Theorem II, §406). We can therefore conclude from Theorem I that h is bounded above by some positive number K:

(5) $$h(x) = \frac{1}{g(x)} = \frac{1}{\lambda - f(x)} < K.$$

Bearing in mind the positivity of the numerators and denominators appearing in (5) we can infer that $\lambda - f(x) > 1/K$, for all $x \in [a, b]$, and hence:

(6) $$x \in [a, b] \implies f(x) < \lambda - \frac{1}{K}.$$

But (6) means that the number $\lambda - (1/K)$ is an upper bound for the range of f on $[a, b]$, in contradiction to the assumption that λ is the *least* upper bound of that set.

We conclude that there must exist a point d of $[a, b]$ such that $f(d) = \lambda = \sup \{f(x) \mid x \in [a, b]\}$, and hence such that $x \in [a, b] \implies f(x) \leq f(d)$. This completes the proof.

Note. Theorem II of this section, in combination with Theorem III, §409, gives the following result concerning *continuous images of intervals:* If f is continuous on a compact interval I, then the image of I is either a compact interval or a degenerate interval consisting of one point.

Example 1. The following examples show that the conclusion to Theorem I is invalid if any one of the three assumptions of continuity of f, boundedness of the interval I, and closedness of I is absent (cf. Fig. 414-1):

    (i) $f(0) \equiv 0, f(x) \equiv 1/x$ for $0 < x \leqq 1$ on $[0, 1]$,
    (ii) x (the identity function) on $[0, +\infty)$,
    (iii) $1/x$ (the reciprocal function) on $(0, 1]$.

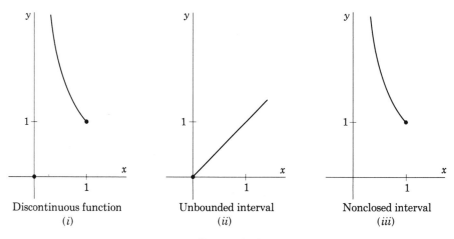

Discontinuous function   Unbounded interval   Nonclosed interval
      (i)   *(ii)*   *(iii)*

Figure 414-1

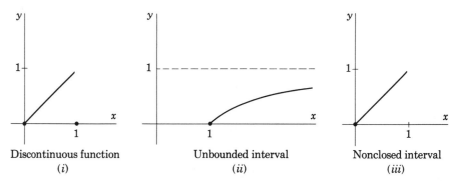

Discontinuous function   Unbounded interval   Nonclosed interval
      (i)   *(ii)*   *(iii)*

Figure 414-2

Example 2. The following examples show that the conclusion to Theorem II is invalid if any one of the three assumptions of continuity of f, boundedness of the interval I, and closedness of I is absent — even when the function under consideration is bounded (cf. Fig. 414-2).

    (i) $x - [x]$ on $[0, 1]$,
    (ii) $(x - 1)/x$ on $[1, +\infty)$,
    (iii) x on $[0, 1)$.

415 EXERCISES

In Exercises 1–8, show that the given function is integrable on the specified interval.

1. $\sqrt{x}$, $[0, 20]$.

2. $\sqrt[3]{x^2}$, $[0, 5]$.

3. $\dfrac{x^3 - 8x + 3}{x^2 + 4}$, $[-2, 3]$.

4. $\dfrac{x^2 + 4x + 1}{x^2 - 5x}$, $[6, 10]$.

5. $f(x) \equiv \begin{cases} \dfrac{x^2 + x - 20}{x - 4}, & x \neq 4, \\ 3, & x = 4, \end{cases}$ $[2, 5]$.

6. $f(x) \equiv \begin{cases} x^2, & x < 6, \\ 5x, & x \geq 6, \end{cases}$ $[4, 9]$.

7. $f(x) \equiv \begin{cases} \sqrt{x}, & 0 \leq x < 1, \\ 0, & x = 1, \\ \sqrt[3]{x}, & 1 < x \leq 3, \end{cases}$ $[0, 3]$.

8. $f(x) \equiv \begin{cases} x^{\frac{3}{5}}, & -1 \leq x < 1, \\ 2, & x = 1, \\ x^2 + 2, & 1 < x \leq 3, \end{cases}$ $[-1, 3]$.

In Exercises 9–14, construct a function defined at every point of the given interval and having the prescribed properties.

9. $[3, 5]$; unbounded.

10. $[3, 5)$; continuous and unbounded below.

11. $[3, +\infty)$; continuous and unbounded below.

12. $[3, 5]$; bounded and without a minimum value.

13. $[3, +\infty)$; continuous and bounded and without a minimum value.

14. $(3, 5]$; continuous and bounded and without a minimum value.

5

Limits

501   DELETED NEIGHBORHOODS AND THE LIMIT CONCEPT

The concept of *limit* of a function at a point c is similar in many ways to that of *continuity* of a function at a point c. The principal distinction is that with a limit at a point we are in no way concerned with the value of the function at that point, or whether, indeed, the function is defined there at all. When we say that a function f has a *finite limit* at c, we mean that there is a number d such that when a point x is near c but *not at c*, then $f(x)$ is near d (possibly at d). More precisely, this means that no matter how small a neighborhood may be taken around the point d, a sufficiently small neighborhood may be found around the point c to ensure that all points within this neighborhood of c — except perhaps for c itself — are carried by f onto points within the given neighborhood of d. (All of this applies only to points of the domain and range of f.)

Before we give precise formulations we need two definitions. First we define a *deleted neighborhood* of a point c, which means the same thing as a *neighborhood* of c except that the point c itself is removed or *deleted*.

Definition I.   *A **deleted neighborhood** D_c of a point c is any set having the form*

$$(1) \qquad\qquad D_c \equiv N_c \setminus \{c\},$$

where N_c is a neighborhood of c. In other words, if δ is any positive number, then

$$(2) \qquad\qquad D_c \equiv (c - \delta, c) \cup (c, c + \delta)$$

is a deleted neighborhood of c. The deleted neighborhood (2) can also be specified:

$$(3) \qquad\qquad D_c \equiv \{x \mid 0 < |x - c| < \delta\}.$$

114

Example 1.   Each of the following sets is a deleted neighborhood of the point 5:

(a) $(4, 6) \setminus \{5\}$,
(b) $(3, 5) \cup (5, 7)$,
(c) $\{x \mid 0 < |x - 5| < 3\}$.

Definition II.   *A point c is a **limit point** or **cluster point** of a set A if and only if every deleted neighborhood D_c of c has at least one point in common with A:*

(4) $$D_c \cap A \neq \emptyset.$$

This can be formulated equivalently:

   (i) $\forall$ *deleted neighborhood D_c of c, $\exists x \in D_c \cap A$,*
   (ii) $\forall \delta > 0, \exists x \in A \ni 0 < |x - c| < \delta$.*

Example 2.   The number 0 is a limit point of each of the following sets:

(a) the interval $(0, 1)$,
(b) the interval $(-\infty, 0]$,
(c) the set of rational numbers $\mathbb{Q}$,
(d) the set difference $(0, 1) \setminus \mathbb{Q}$.

By negation of Definition II we have:

Theorem.   *A point c fails to be a limit point of a set A if and only if there exists a deleted neighborhood D_c of c having no point in common with A:*

(5) $$D_c \cap A = \emptyset.$$

Example 3.   The number 0 fails to be a limit point of each of the following sets:

(a) the empty set $\emptyset$,
(b) the interval $[1, 5]$,
(c) the set of integers $\mathcal{I}$.

NOTE. A point c of a set A is called an **isolated point** of A if and only if it is not a limit point of A. If c is an isolated point of the domain D of a function f, then there exists a neighborhood N_c of c such that $D \cap N_c = \{c\}$. Since $f(c)$ belongs to every neighborhood $N_{f(c)}$ of $f(c)$, it follows from Theorem I, §401, that *every function is continuous at every isolated point of its domain*. The case of isolated points of the domain of a function will play no important role in this book.

502   LIMIT AT A POINT

We are now ready to define a finite limit of a function at a point c that is a limit point of the domain of the function.

Definition.   *Let c be a limit point of the domain D of a function f. Then f has a finite limit at c equal to a number d, written*

(1)
$$\lim_{x \to c} f(x) = d, \quad or \quad \lim_{x \to c} f(x) = d,$$

or

(2)
$$f(x) \to d \ as \ x \to c,$$

if and only if

(3) $\forall \, \epsilon > 0, \, \exists \, \delta > 0 \ni$

$$\left. \begin{array}{c} x \in D \\ 0 < |x - c| < \delta \end{array} \right\} \Rightarrow |f(x) - d| < \epsilon.$$

NOTE. The statement (1) is read "the limit of *f* at *c* is *d*," or "the limit of *f* of *x* as *x* approaches *c* is *d*," or "the limit of *f* of *x* as *x* tends toward *c* is *d*." In these latter cases it should be appreciated that the language of "*x* approaching *c*" or of "*x* tending toward *c*" is merely intended to be psychologically suggestive and should be viewed informally as a sort of "stage setting." Similarly, statement (2) is read "*f* of *x* approaches *d* as *x* approaches *c*," or "*f* of *x* tends toward *d* as *x* tends toward *c*," but in reality *f(x)* and *x* are numbers, and neither is endowed with attributes that permit it to "approach" or "tend toward" anything. In other words, any language of "approach" or "tending" should be interpreted only in the sense of a meaningful definition such as that embodied in the compound statement (3).

Corresponding to Theorem I, §401, we have for limits:

Theorem I.   *A function f has a limit d at a limit point c of its domain D if and only if*

(4) $\forall$ *neighborhood N_d of d, $\exists$ a deleted neighborhood D_c of c $\ni$ $f(D \cap D_c) \subset N_d$,*

that is, if and only if for every neighborhood N_d of d, there exists a deleted neighborhood D_c of c such that every point of $D \cap D_c$ is mapped by f into N_d.

Corresponding to Theorem II, §401, is:

Theorem II.   *Let c be a limit point of the domain D of a function f. If there exists a positive-valued function $\delta(\epsilon)$ with domain $\mathcal{P} = (0, +\infty)$ such that*

(5) $\forall \, \epsilon > 0, \qquad \left. \begin{array}{c} x \in D \\ 0 < |x - c| < \delta(\epsilon) \end{array} \right\} \Rightarrow |f(x) - d| < \epsilon,$

then $\lim_{x \to c} f(x) = d.$

Example.   Show that

$$\lim_{x \to 2} \sqrt{3x + 4} = \sqrt{10}$$

by finding a function $\delta(\epsilon)$ as specified in Theorem II.

Solution.   With $f(x) \equiv \sqrt{3x + 4}$ and $d \equiv \sqrt{10}$, the inequality on the right of (5) can be written

(6) $$\left|\frac{\sqrt{3x+4}-\sqrt{10}}{1}\cdot\frac{\sqrt{3x+4}+\sqrt{10}}{\sqrt{3x+4}+\sqrt{10}}\right| = \frac{3|x-2|}{\sqrt{3x+4}+\sqrt{10}} < \epsilon.$$

We first control the denominator $\sqrt{3x+4}+\sqrt{10}$ by letting $\delta_1 \equiv 2$ and requiring that $|x-2| < 2$, so that $x > 0$ and $\sqrt{3x+4}+\sqrt{10} > \sqrt{4}+\sqrt{10} > 2 + 3 = 5$. If $\delta_2 \equiv \frac{5}{3}\epsilon$ and $\delta(\epsilon) \equiv \min(\delta_1, \delta_2) = \min(2, \frac{5}{3}\epsilon)$,

(7) $$0 < |x-2| < \delta(\epsilon) \Rightarrow \frac{3|x-2|}{\sqrt{3x+4}+\sqrt{10}} < \frac{3}{5}|x-2| < \frac{3}{5}\cdot\frac{5}{3}\epsilon = \epsilon.$$

Since the existence and the value of a limit depend only on values of the function for values of the independent variable "near" but not at the point in question, any two functions that are equal for values of the independent variable near a point c must have equal limits at c, provided *one* of the functions has a limit at c:

Theorem III.   *Let c be a point that is a limit point both of the domain D of a function f and of the domain E of a function g, and assume that there exists a deleted neighborhood D_c of c such that $D \cap D_c = E \cap D_c$ and such that on the set $D \cap D_c = E \cap D_c$ the functions f and g are identical. If f has a finite limit at c, then g also has a finite limit at c and $\lim_{x\to c} g(x) = \lim_{x\to c} f(x)$.*

Proof.   Let $d \equiv \lim_{x\to c} f(x)$ and let $\epsilon > 0$. Then there exists a positive number δ_1 such that

(8) $$(x \in D \text{ and } 0 < |x-c| < \delta_1) \;\Rightarrow\; |f(x) - d| < \epsilon.$$

If $D_c = \{x \mid 0 < |x-c| < \delta_2\}$ and if $\delta \equiv \min(\delta_1, \delta_2)$, then

(9) $$(x \in E \text{ and } 0 < |x-c| < \delta) \;\Rightarrow\; x \in E \cap D_c = D \cap D_c,$$

and hence

(10) $$(x \in E \text{ and } 0 < |x-c| < \delta) \;\Rightarrow\; x \in D \text{ and } f(x) = g(x).$$

Finally, therefore,

(11) $$(x \in E \text{ and } 0 < |x-c| < \delta) \;\Rightarrow\; |g(x) - d| = |f(x) - d| < \epsilon,$$

and $\lim_{x\to c} g(x) = d$.

503   ONE-SIDED LIMITS

One-sided limits are defined in a manner similar to that used for one-sided continuity, and obtained by restricting a function f with domain D to a function with domain either $D \cap (c, +\infty)$ or $D \cap (-\infty, c)$:

Definition I.   *If c is a limit point of $D \cap (c, +\infty)$, where D is the domain of a function f, then f has a finite **limit from the right**, or **right-hand limit**, at c equal to a number d, written*

(1) $$\lim_{x\to c+} f(x) = d, \quad \text{or} \quad \lim_{x\to c+} f(x) = d,$$

or

(2) $$f(x) \rightarrow d \quad as \quad x \rightarrow c+,$$

if and only if the restriction of f to the domain $D \cap (c, +\infty)$ has a limit at c equal to d; that is, if and only if

(3) $\forall \epsilon > 0, \quad \exists \delta > 0 \ni$
$$\left. \begin{array}{c} x \in D \cap (c, +\infty) \\ 0 < |x - c| < \delta \end{array} \right\} \Rightarrow |f(x) - d| < \epsilon.$$

If c is a limit point of $D \cap (-\infty, c)$, where D is the domain of a function f, then f has a **finite limit from the left,** *or* **left-hand limit,** *at c equal to a number d, written*

(4) $$\lim_{x \rightarrow c-} f(x) = d, \quad or \quad \lim_{x \rightarrow c-} f(x) = d,$$

or

(5) $$f(x) \rightarrow d \quad as \quad x \rightarrow c-,$$

if and only if the restriction of f to the domain $D \cap (-\infty, c)$ has a limit at c equal to d; that is, if and only if

(6) $\forall \epsilon > 0, \exists \delta > 0 \ni$
$$\left. \begin{array}{c} x \in D \cap (-\infty, c) \\ 0 < |x - c| < \delta \end{array} \right\} \Rightarrow |f(x) - d| < \epsilon.$$

We state two alternative formulations for right-hand limits in the following theorem. (The corresponding formulations for left-hand limits are analogous.) For this purpose it will be convenient to speak of an open interval of the form $D_{c+} \equiv (c, c + \delta)$, where $\delta > 0$, as a **deleted right half-neighborhood** of the point c, and an open interval of the form $D_{c-} \equiv (c - \delta, c)$, where $d > 0$, as a **deleted left half-neighborhood** of c. In either case, a deleted right half-neighborhood or deleted left half-neighborhood is called a **deleted half-neighborhood,** or **deleted one-sided neighborhood,** of the point in question. (Cf. the Note, §407.)

Theorem I. *Let c be a limit point of $D \cap (c, +\infty)$, where D is the domain of a function f. Then each of the following two statements is a necessary and sufficient condition for f to have a right-hand limit d at c:*

(i) $\forall \epsilon > 0, \exists \delta > 0 \ni$
$$\left. \begin{array}{c} x \in D \\ c < x < c + \delta \end{array} \right\} \Rightarrow |f(x) - d| < \epsilon.$$
(ii) $\forall$ *neighborhood N_d of d, $\exists$ a deleted right half-neighborhood D_{c+} of c $\ni$*
$$f(D \cap D_{c+}) \subset N_d.$$

Monotonic bounded functions always have one-sided limits, as specified in the theorem:

Theorem II. *If f is monotonic and bounded on an interval having the point a as left-hand endpoint, then f has a finite right-hand limit at a. If f is monotonic and bounded on an interval having the point b as right-hand endpoint, then f has a finite left-hand limit at b.*

Proof. We give the details only for a left-hand endpoint a and a function f that is *increasing.* (Cf. Ex. 24, §505.) Accordingly, we assume that I is an interval having a as left-hand endpoint and on which f is increasing and bounded, and define

(7)
$$d \equiv \inf \{f(x) \mid x \in I \setminus \{a\}\}$$

(cf. Fig. 503-1). We wish to prove that

(8)
$$\lim_{x \to a+} f(x) = d.$$

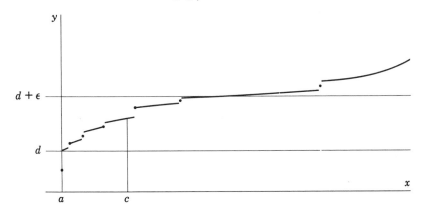

Figure 503-1

If ϵ is an arbitrary positive number, then since $d + \epsilon$ is a number greater than d, there must be a member of the set $\{f(x) \mid x \in I \setminus \{a\}\}$ less than $d + \epsilon$. In other words, there must be a point c of I that is greater than a and such that $f(c) < d + \epsilon$. Letting $\delta \equiv c - a$, we have $\delta > 0$ and $c = a + \delta$. Furthermore, since f is increasing on I,

(9)
$$a < x < a + \delta \implies d \leqq f(x) \leqq f(a + \delta) < d + \epsilon,$$

and therefore $d - \epsilon < f(x) < d + \epsilon$, or $|f(x) - d| < \epsilon$. By Theorem I(i), (8) is established.

One-sided limits are related to standard limits as follows (cf. the Theorem, §407):

Theorem III. *If f is a function with domain D, and if c is a limit point of both $D \cap (c, +\infty)$ and $D \cap (-\infty, c)$, then $\lim_{x \to c} f(x)$ exists if and only if both $\lim_{x \to c+} f(x)$ and $\lim_{x \to c-} f(x)$ exist and are equal. In case $\lim_{x \to c} f(x)$ exists,*

(10)
$$\lim_{x \to c} f(x) = \lim_{x \to c+} f(x) = \lim_{x \to c-} f(x).$$

504 CONTINUITY AND LIMITS

The relationship between continuity and limits is simple. We state it in two parts:

Theorem I. *Let f be a function with domain D and let c be a point of D that is also a limit point of D. Then f is continuous at c if and only if the limit of f at c exists and is equal to $f(c)$:*

(1) $$\lim_{x \to c} f(x) = f(c).$$

Proof. Assume first that f is continuous at c, and let $\epsilon > 0$. Then there exists $\delta > 0$ such that whenever $x \in D$ and $|x - c| < \delta$, the inequality $|f(x) - f(c)| < \epsilon$ must hold. Therefore, if $d \equiv f(c)$, whenever $x \in D$ and $0 < |x - c| < \delta$ the inequality $|f(x) - d| < \epsilon$ must hold, and hence $\lim_{x \to c} f(x) = d = f(c)$. Now assume that (1) holds, and let $\epsilon > 0$. Then there exists $\delta > 0$ such that

(2) $$\left. \begin{array}{r} x \in D \setminus \{c\} \\ |x - c| < \delta \end{array} \right\} \Rightarrow |f(x) - f(c)| < \epsilon,$$

and therefore, since for $x = c$, $|f(x) - f(c)| = 0 < \epsilon$,

(3) $$\left. \begin{array}{r} x \in D \\ |x - c| < \delta \end{array} \right\} \Rightarrow |f(x) - f(c)| < \epsilon,$$

and f is continuous at c.

Theorem I is most useful, probably, in permitting the evaluation of limits of continuous functions by means of simple substitution.

Example 1. Evaluate $\lim_{x \to 3} \sqrt{\dfrac{x^2 + 7}{5x - 2}}$.

Solution. The function $(x^2 + 7)/(5x - 2)$ with domain $(\frac{2}{5}, +\infty)$ is continuous (Theorem IV(*i*), §406) and has positive values, and therefore the function $\sqrt{(x^2 + 7)/(5x - 2)}$ is continuous on $(\frac{2}{5}, +\infty)$ (Theorem IV(*ii*), §406). Consequently the limit desired can be found by direct substitution, by Theorem I above:

$$\lim_{x \to 3} \sqrt{\frac{x^2 + 7}{5x - 2}} = \sqrt{\frac{3^2 + 7}{5 \cdot 3 - 2}} = \sqrt{\frac{16}{13}}.$$

Example 2. Evaluate the limit $\lim_{x \to 2} \dfrac{x^2 - x - 2}{x^2 - 4}$.

Solution. If $f(x) \equiv \dfrac{x^2 - x - 2}{x^2 - 4}$ with domain $\Re \setminus \{2, -2\}$, then $f(x) = \dfrac{(x - 2)(x + 1)}{(x - 2)(x + 2)} = \dfrac{x + 1}{x + 2}$ for every x of the domain of f. If the function g is defined by $g(x) = \dfrac{x + 1}{x + 2}$ with domain $\Re \setminus \{-2\}$, then f and g are identical on the domain of f. Since g is continuous at $x = 2$, the limit of g at 2 exists and is equal to its value there: $\lim_{x \to 2} g(x) = g(2) = \frac{3}{4}$. Since $f(x)$ and $g(x)$ are identical for x in a deleted neighborhood of the point 2, $\lim_{x \to 2} f(x) = \lim_{x \to 2} g(x) = \frac{3}{4}$, by Theorem III, §502.

Theorem II. *Let c be a limit point of the domain D of a function f. Then f has a finite limit at c if and only if f either is continuous at c or has a removable discontinuity at c.*

Proof. Assume first that f is continuous at c. Then, by the preceding theorem, the finite limit of f at c exists. Assume next that f has a removable discontinuity at c, and let g be a function with domain $D \cup \{c\}$ that is continuous at c and equal to f on $D \setminus \{c\}$. If $\epsilon > 0$ there exists $\delta > 0$ such that whenever $x \in D \cup \{c\}$ and $|x - c| < \delta$, the inequality $|g(x) - g(c)| < \epsilon$ must hold. Therefore, if $d \equiv g(c)$, whenever $x \in D$

and $0 < |x - c| < \delta$, the inequality $|g(x) - d| < \epsilon$ must hold, and since $f(x) = g(x)$ for $x \in D \setminus \{c\}$, the inequality $|f(x) - d| < \epsilon$ must also hold, and $\lim_{x \to c} f(x) = d$.

Now assume that the finite limit of f at c exists, and let d be this limit:

(4)
$$d \equiv \lim_{x \to c} f(x).$$

Define the function g:

(5)
$$g(x) \equiv \begin{cases} f(x) \text{ if } x \in D \setminus \{c\}, \\ d \quad \text{if } x = c. \end{cases}$$

If $\epsilon > 0$, there exists $\delta > 0$ such that

(6)
$$\left. \begin{array}{c} x \in D \setminus \{c\} \\ |x - c| < \delta \end{array} \right\} \Rightarrow |f(x) - d| = |g(x) - g(c)| < \epsilon,$$

and therefore, since for $x = c$, $|g(x) - g(c)| = 0 < \epsilon$,

(7)
$$\left. \begin{array}{c} x \in D \\ |x - c| < \delta \end{array} \right\} \Rightarrow |g(x) - g(c)| < \epsilon,$$

and g is continuous at c. If $f(c)$ exists and is equal to $g(c)$, then $f = g$ and f is continuous at c. Otherwise f has a removable discontinuity at c.

The situation with one-sided limits is similar. The following theorem is expressed in terms of a right-hand limit; the case of a left-hand limit is essentially identical.

Theorem III. *Let c be a limit point of $D \cap (c, +\infty)$, where D is the domain of a function f. Then f has a finite right-hand limit at c if and only if f either is right-continuous at c or has a removable right-hand discontinuity at c.*

Example 3. Evaluate $\lim_{x \to 3-} \sqrt{3 - x}$.

Solution. The function $3 - x$ with domain $(-\infty, 3]$ is continuous and has nonnegative values. Therefore the function $\sqrt{3 - x}$ with domain $(-\infty, 3]$ is continuous (Theorem IV(ii), §406). In particular, $\sqrt{3 - x}$ is left-continuous at 3 and therefore $\lim_{x \to 3-} \sqrt{3 - x} = \sqrt{3 - 3} = 0$.

505 EXERCISES

In Exercises 1–8, determine whether the given point is a limit point of the given set. Explain your conclusion.

1. 5, $\mathfrak{N}$. **2.** 2, $\mathcal{Q}$. **3.** 6, (3, 8). **4.** 4, [5, 10].

5. 7, (0, 7). **6.** -2, $\mathcal{J}$. **7.** $\sqrt{2}$, $\mathcal{Q}$. **8.** 3, $\mathcal{R} \setminus \mathcal{Q}$.

In Exercises 9–14, establish the given limit statement by finding δ as a function of ϵ, in accord with Theorem II, §502.

9. $\lim_{x \to 4} \sqrt{x} = 2$. **10.** $\lim_{x \to 2} \sqrt{x} = \sqrt{2}$. **11.** $\lim_{x \to 2} x^2 - 7x = -10$.

12. $\lim_{x\to 3} x^2 - 8x = -15.$ **13.** $\lim_{z\to -2} \dfrac{1}{3x+4} = -\dfrac{1}{2}.$ **14.** $\lim_{x\to -3} \dfrac{1}{4x+9} = -\dfrac{1}{3}.$

In Exercises 15–23, evaluate the given limit with the aid of theorems from §§ 503 and 504. Give reasons.

15. $\lim_{x\to a} (x^2 - ax).$ **16.** $\lim_{x\to b} (x^3 - 2bx^2 + 4b^3).$ **17.** $\lim_{y\to 3} \dfrac{y^2}{y^2+9}.$

18. $\lim_{z\to 2} \dfrac{z+3}{z^2+5z+1}.$ **19.** $\lim_{x\to 4+} \sqrt[3]{\dfrac{x^2+5x+9}{2x+7}}.$ **20.** $\lim_{x\to 1} \sqrt{\dfrac{x^2-4x+8}{3x+2}}.$

21. $\lim_{s\to -3} \dfrac{3s^2+5s-12}{s+3}.$ **22.** $\lim_{t\to 5-} \dfrac{4t^2-19t-5}{t-5}.$ **23.** $\lim_{u\to 2+} (\sqrt[4]{5u-10}+3)^4.$

24. Prove Theorem II, §503, for the case of the right-hand endpoint of an interval on which a function is increasing.

506   LIMIT OF A COMPOSITE FUNCTION

In §406 it was proved that a continuous function of a continuous function is a continuous function. For limits this theorem takes the following form:

Theorem. *If f has a finite limit d at a point c, where c is a limit point of the domain C of f, if g is continuous at d, and if the range of f is a subset of the domain D of g, then the composite function g ∘ f, whose values are given by g(f(x)), has the limit g(d) at c. In short, the limit of the function is the function of the limit:*

$$\lim_{x\to c} g(f(x)) = g(\lim_{x\to c} f(x)).$$

Proof. (Cf. Theorem I, §406.) If $\epsilon > 0$, since g is continuous at d there exists a neighborhood N_d of d such that

$$(1) \qquad\qquad g(D \cap N_d) \subset (g(d) - \epsilon, g(d) + \epsilon).$$

In terms of the neighborhood N_d of d, since $\lim_{x\to c} f(x) = d$, there exists a deleted neighborhood D_c of c such that

$$(2) \qquad\qquad f(C \cap D_c) \subset N_d.$$

Therefore, if $h \equiv g \circ f$,

$$(3) \qquad\qquad h(C \cap D_c) \subset (g(d) - \epsilon, g(d) + \epsilon),$$

since if $x \in C \cap D_c$, $f(x) \in N_d$, and hence $h(x) = g(f(x)) \in (g(d) - \epsilon, g(d) + \epsilon).$

Example 1. Since $g(x) = x^3$ is everywhere continuous,

$$\lim_{x\to c} f^3(x) = (\lim_{x\to c} f(x))^3$$

whenever $\lim_{x\to c} f(x)$ exists as a finite limit.

Example 2. Since $\sqrt{x}$ is a continuous function for nonnegative x,

$$\lim_{h\to 0} \sqrt{2+h} = \sqrt{\lim_{h\to 0}(2+h)} = \sqrt{\lim_{h\to 0} 2 + \lim_{h\to 0} h} = \sqrt{2+0} = \sqrt{2}.$$

507　LIMIT THEOREMS

Many of the continuity theorems of Chapter 4 have counterparts for limits, which are included among the *limit theorems* listed below. Indeed, some of these limit theorems can be proved by a simple appeal to results already established for functions continuous at a point. (Cf. Example 2, below.) However, since all the limit theorems of this section have duplicate reformulations in other contexts, it is desirable to give fresh proofs. The new proofs that are given below are formulated in terms of neighborhoods and deleted neighborhoods in order that these proofs may be available for the duplicate reformulations just alluded to. Some of the proofs will be left as exercises. The notation D_c for a deleted neighborhood of a point c will be extended to other letters, thus: $A_c, B_c, C_c, \cdots$, when more than one deleted neighborhood of c is under discussion.

Before attacking the limit theorems themselves let us observe that *the intersection of any two deleted neighborhoods of c is a deleted neighborhood of c:* If $A_c \equiv \{x \mid 0 < |x - c| < \delta_1\}$ and if $B_c \equiv \{x \mid 0 < |x - c| < \delta_2\}$, then

(1)　　　　　　$D_c \equiv A_c \cap B_c = \{x \mid 0 < |x - c| < \min(\delta_1, \delta_2)\}.$

A similar statement applies to the intersection of three or more deleted neighborhoods of the same point c.

We now state some of the principal limit theorems of analysis. After each statement we refer to any analogous proof already given for continuity, or uniform continuity, and either give the proof or refer to an exercise of §508. All of the following limit theorems have to do with limits of the form $\lim_{x\to c} f(x)$, and *it is assumed unless explicit exception is made that all functions concerned have a common domain D and that the point c is a limit point of D.* Each limit theorem can be restated (and proved) for one-sided limits by merely replacing $x \to c$ by $x \to c+$ throughout, or by replacing $x \to c$ by $x \to c-$ throughout, by rephrasing appropriately the assumption that the point c is a limit point of D, and by replacing deleted neighborhoods by deleted one-sided neighborhoods.

Theorem I. *If f has a finite limit at c, then this limit is unique.*

Proof. (Cf. the Example, §404.) Assume that $\lim_{x\to c} f(x) = d_1$ and $\lim_{x\to c} f(x) = d_2$, where $d_1 \neq d_2$, and let $\epsilon \equiv \frac{1}{2}|d_1 - d_2|$, so that the two neighborhoods of d_1 and d_2, respectively, of radius ϵ:

(2)　　　　　　$N_{d_1} \equiv (d_1 - \epsilon, d_1 + \epsilon), \quad N_{d_2} \equiv (d_2 - \epsilon, d_2 + \epsilon)$

have no points in common: $N_{d_1} \cap N_{d_2} = \varnothing$. Now let A_c and B_c be deleted neighborhoods of c such that (by Theorem I, §502):

(3)　　　　　　$f(D \cap A_c) \subset N_{d_1},$

(4) $$f(D \cap B_c) \subset N_{d_2}.$$

If $D_c \equiv A_c \cap B_c$, then $D \cap D_c$ is a nonempty set mapped by f into *both* N_{d_1} and N_{d_2}, and therefore into their intersection:

(5) $$f(D \cap D_c) \subset N_{d_1} \cap N_{d_2} = \emptyset.$$

With this contradiction (a nonempty set cannot be a subset of the empty set) the proof is complete.

Theorem II. *If f is a constant function on $D \setminus \{c\} : f(x) = k$, then the limit of f at c exists and is equal to k:*

(6) $$\lim_{x \to c} f(x) = k.$$

Proof. (Cf. Example 4, §301.) Give a proof in Exercise 9, §508.

Theorem III. *If $f \leqq g$ on $D \cap E_c$ for some deleted neighborhood E_c of c, and if f and g have finite limits at c, then*

(7) $$\lim_{x \to c} f(x) \leqq \lim_{x \to c} g(x).$$

Proof. Let $d_1 \equiv \lim_{x \to c} f(x)$ and $d_2 \equiv \lim_{x \to c} g(x)$, and assume $d_1 > d_2$. If $\epsilon \equiv \frac{1}{2}(d_1 - d_2)$, then the two neighborhoods of d_1 and d_2, respectively, with radius ϵ, defined

(8) $$N_{d_1} \equiv (d_1 - \epsilon, d_1 + \epsilon) \subset \left(\frac{d_1 + d_2}{2}, +\infty\right)$$

(9) $$N_{d_2} \equiv (d_2 - \epsilon, d_2 + \epsilon) \subset \left(-\infty, \frac{d_1 + d_2}{2}\right)$$

are disjoint and, in fact, such that every member of N_{d_2} is less than every member of N_{d_1} (Cf. Fig. 507-1). Now let A_c and B_c be deleted neighborhoods of c such that (Theorem I, §502):

(10) $$f(D \cap A_c) \subset N_{d_1}, \quad g(D \cap B_c) \subset N_{d_2},$$

and let $D_c \equiv A_c \cap B_c \cap E_c$. If x is an arbitrary point of $D \cap D_c$, then by (10):

(11) $$f(x) \in N_{d_1} \text{ and hence } f(x) > \frac{d_1 + d_2}{2},$$

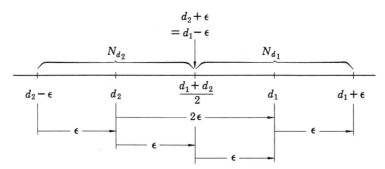

Figure 507-1

(12) $$g(x) \in N_{d_2} \text{ and hence } g(x) < \frac{d_1 + d_2}{2}.$$

But since $f(x) \leq g(x)$ for all $x \in E_c$, we have thus obtained a contradiction to the assumption that $d_1 > d_2$, and hence we have the conclusion (7) as desired.

Corollary. *Let f have a finite limit at c and let k be a constant. If $f \leq k$ on $D \cap E_c$ for some deleted neighborhood E_c of c, then*

(13) $$\lim_{x \to c} f(x) \leq k.$$

If $f \geq k$ on $D \cap E_c$ for some deleted neighborhood E_c of c, then

(14) $$\lim_{x \to c} f(x) \geq k.$$

Proof. Give a proof in Exercise 10, §508.

Theorem IV. *If $f \leq g \leq h$ on $D \cap E_c$ for some deleted neighborhood E_c of c, and if f and h have the same finite limit d at c, then g also has this same finite limit d at c.*

Proof. If ϵ is any positive number, let A_c and B_c be deleted neighborhoods of c such that (Theorem I, §502)·

(15) $$f(D \cap A_c) \subset (d - \epsilon, d + \epsilon),$$

(16) $$h(D \cap B_c) \subset (d - \epsilon, d + \epsilon).$$

If $D_c \equiv A_c \cap B_c \cap E_c$, then

(17) $$g(D \cap D_c) \subset (d - \epsilon, d + \epsilon),$$

since for all $x \in D \cap D_c$, by (15) and (16),

(18) $$d - \epsilon < f(x) \leq g(x) \leq h(x) < d + \epsilon.$$

Theorem V. *If f and g have finite limits at c, then $h \equiv f + g$ also has a finite limit, and*

(19) $$\lim_{x \to c} h(x) = \lim_{x \to c} [f(x) + g(x)] = \lim_{x \to c} f(x) + \lim_{x \to c} g(x).$$

In short, the limit of the sum is the sum of the limits. This rule extends to the sum of any finite number of functions.

Proof. (Cf. Theorem II, §404.) Let $d_1 \equiv \lim_{x \to c} f(x)$, $d_2 \equiv \lim_{x \to c} g(x)$, and $d \equiv d_1 + d_2$, and let $\epsilon > 0$. If N_{d_1} and N_{d_2} are neighborhoods of d_1 and d_2, respectively, of radius $\frac{1}{2}\epsilon$:

(20) $$N_{d_1} \equiv (d_1 - \tfrac{1}{2}\epsilon, d_1 + \tfrac{1}{2}\epsilon), \ N_{d_2} \equiv (d_2 - \tfrac{1}{2}\epsilon, d_2 + \tfrac{1}{2}\epsilon),$$

let A_c and B_c be deleted neighborhoods of c such that (by Theorem I, §502)

(21) $$f(D \cap A_c) \subset N_{d_1}, \ g(D \cap B_c) \subset N_{d_2}.$$

If $D_c \equiv A_c \cap B_c$, then

(22) $$f(D \cap D_c) \subset N_{d_1}, \quad g(D \cap D_c) \subset N_{d_2}.$$

We wish to prove that

(23) $$h(D \cap D_c) \subset N_d \equiv (d - \epsilon, d + \epsilon).$$

Accordingly, we let x be an arbitrary member of $D \cap D_c$, and use the triangle inequality:

(24) $$|h(x) - d| = |(f(x) - d_1) + (g(x) - d_2)|$$
$$\leqq |f(x) - d_1| + |g(x) - d_2| < \tfrac{1}{2}\epsilon + \tfrac{1}{2}\epsilon = \epsilon.$$

Therefore $h(x) \in N_d$, and (23) is proved. Proof of the extension to n functions is requested in Exercise 11, §508.

Theorem VI. *If f has a finite limit at c and if λ is any constant, then λf has a finite limit at c and*

(25) $$\lim_{x \to c} \lambda f(x) = \lambda \lim_{x \to c} f(x).$$

In short, the limit of a constant times a function is the constant times the limit of the function.

Proof. (Cf. Theorem II, §404.) Give a proof in Exercise 12, §508.

Theorem VII. *If f and g have finite limits at c, then so does $h \equiv f - g$, and*

(26) $$\lim_{x \to c} h(x) = \lim_{x \to c} [f(x) - g(x)] = \lim_{x \to c} f(x) - \lim_{x \to c} g(x).$$

In short, the limit of the difference is the difference of the limits.

Proof. (Cf. Theorem II, §404.) Give a proof in Exercise 13, §508.

Theorem VIII. *If f has a finite limit at c, then f is locally bounded at c.*

Proof. (Cf. Theorem I, §404.) Give a proof in Exercise 14, §508.

Theorem IX. *If f and g have finite limits at c, then $h \equiv fg$ also has a finite limit, and*

(27) $$\lim_{x \to c} h(x) = \lim_{x \to c} [f(x)g(x)] = \lim_{x \to c} f(x) \cdot \lim_{x \to c} g(x).$$

In short, the limit of the product is the product of the limits. This rule extends to the product of any finite number of functions.

Proof. (Cf. Theorem II, §404.) Because of the identity

(28) $$f(x)g(x) = \tfrac{1}{4}[f(x) + g(x)]^2 - \tfrac{1}{4}[f(x) - g(x)]^2,$$

and Theorems V, VI, and VII, we have only to prove the special case of Theorem IX where f and g are the *same function:*

(29) $$\lim_{x \to c} f^2(x) = [\lim_{x \to c} f(x)]^2,$$

since from (29) and Theorems V–VII we have

$$(30) \quad \lim_{x \to c} f(x)g(x) = \tfrac{1}{4} \lim_{x \to c} [f(x) + g(x)]^2 - \tfrac{1}{4} \lim_{x \to c} [f(x) - g(x)]^2$$

$$= \tfrac{1}{4}[\lim_{x \to c} f(x) + \lim_{x \to c} g(x)]^2 - \tfrac{1}{4}[\lim_{x \to c} f(x) - \lim_{x \to c} g(x)]^2 = \lim_{x \to c} f(x) \cdot \lim_{x \to c} g(x).$$

We proceed now to establish (29). This follows directly from the Theorem, §506, with $g(x) = x^2$, since g is everywhere continuous. Proof of the extension to n functions is requested in Exercise 11, §508.

Theorem X. *If* $\lim_{x \to c} f(x) = 0$, *if* g *is locally bounded at* c, *and if* $h \equiv fg$, *then*

$$(31) \qquad\qquad \lim_{x \to c} h(x) = \lim_{x \to c} f(x)g(x) = 0.$$

Proof. Let A_c be a deleted neighborhood of c such that g is bounded on $D \cap A_c$, and let K be a positive number such that $g(D \cap A_c) \subset (-K, K)$. If ϵ is any given positive number, let B_c be a deleted neighborhood of c such that $f(D \cap B_c) \subset (-\epsilon/K, \epsilon/K)$. If $D_c \equiv A_c \cap B_c$, and if $h \equiv fg$, then $h(D \cap D_c) \subset (-\epsilon, \epsilon)$, since for any $x \in D \cap D_c$

$$(32) \qquad |h(x)| = |f(x)g(x)| = |f(x)| \cdot |g(x)| < \frac{\epsilon}{K} \cdot K = \epsilon.$$

Theorem XI. *If* f *has a nonzero finite limit at* c, *then there exists a deleted neighborhood* D_c *of* c *such that* f *is bounded from zero on* $D \cap D_c$. *In fact, there also exists a positive number* η *such that if the limit of* f *at* c *is positive, then*

$$(33) \qquad\qquad f(D \cap D_c) \subset (\eta, +\infty),$$

and if the limit of f *at* c *is negative, then*

$$(34) \qquad\qquad f(D \cap D_c) \subset (-\infty, -\eta).$$

Proof. (Cf. Theorem VI, §406.) We shall prove the part concerning (33) and leave the part concerning (34) as an exercise. Assume, then, that

$$(35) \qquad\qquad \lim_{x \to c} f(x) = d > 0,$$

and let $\epsilon \equiv \tfrac{1}{2}d$. Then there exists a deleted neighborhood D_c of c such that

$$(36) \qquad f(D \cap D_c) \subset (d - \epsilon, d + \epsilon) = (\tfrac{1}{2}d, \tfrac{3}{2}d),$$

and therefore, if $\eta \equiv \tfrac{1}{2}d > 0$,

$$(37) \qquad\qquad f(D \cap D_c) \subset (\eta, +\infty).$$

Theorem XII. *If* f *has a nonzero limit* d *at* c, *and if* $g \equiv 1/f$, *with domain* $E \equiv D \cap \{x \mid f(x) \neq 0\}$, *then* g *has a finite limit at* c *equal to* $1/d$:

$$(38) \qquad \lim_{x \to c} g(x) = \lim_{x \to c} \frac{1}{f(x)} = \frac{1}{\lim\limits_{x \to c} f(x)} = \frac{1}{d}.$$

In short, the limit of the reciprocal is the reciprocal of the limit.

Proof. (Cf. Theorem II, §406.) Let A_c be a deleted neighborhood of c such that f is bounded from zero on $D \cap A_c$, and, in fact, as indicated in the proof of Theorem XI, such that

$$(39) \qquad f(D \cap A_c) \subset (-\infty, -\tfrac{1}{2}|d|] \cup [\tfrac{1}{2}|d|, +\infty).$$

If ϵ is an arbitrary positive number, let B_c be a deleted neighborhood of c such that

$$(40) \qquad f(D \cap B_c) \subset (d - \tfrac{1}{2}|d|^2\epsilon, d + \tfrac{1}{2}|d|^2\epsilon)$$

and let $D_c = A_c \cap B_c$. Then

$$(41) \qquad g(D \cap D_c) \subset \left(\frac{1}{d} - \epsilon, \frac{1}{d} + \epsilon\right)$$

since for any $x \in D \cap D_c$, $|f(x)| \geq \tfrac{1}{2}|d|$, and therefore

$$(42) \qquad \left|g(x) - \frac{1}{d}\right| = \left|\frac{1}{f(x)} - \frac{1}{d}\right| = \left|\frac{d - f(x)}{f(x) \cdot d}\right| = \frac{|f(x) - d|}{|f(x)| \cdot |d|} \leq \frac{|f(x) - d|}{\tfrac{1}{2}|d|^2} < \frac{\tfrac{1}{2}|d|^2\epsilon}{\tfrac{1}{2}|d|^2} = \epsilon.$$

Theorem XIII. *If f and g have finite limits at c, if the limit of g is nonzero, and if $h = f/g$ with domain $E \equiv \{x \mid g(x) \neq 0\}$, then h has a finite limit at c given by*

$$(43) \qquad \lim_{x \to c} h(x) = \lim_{x \to c} \frac{f(x)}{g(x)} = \frac{\lim\limits_{x \to c} f(x)}{\lim\limits_{x \to c} g(x)}.$$

In short, the limit of the quotient is the quotient of the limits, provided the limit in the denominator is nonzero.

Proof. (Cf. Theorem III, §406.) Give a proof in Exercise 15, §508.

Example 1. Use limit theorems of this section to evaluate $\lim\limits_{h \to 0} \dfrac{\sqrt{2+h} - \sqrt{2}}{h}$.

Solution. With $f(h) \equiv (\sqrt{2+h} - \sqrt{2})/h$, for $h \neq 0$, we can rewrite the expression for $f(h)$:

$$f(h) = \frac{\sqrt{2+h} - \sqrt{2}}{h} \cdot \frac{\sqrt{2+h} + \sqrt{2}}{\sqrt{2+h} + \sqrt{2}} = \frac{(2+h-2)}{h(\sqrt{2+h} + \sqrt{2})} = \frac{1}{\sqrt{2+h} + \sqrt{2}}.$$

By Theorem III, §502, we can evaluate $\lim\limits_{h \to 0} f(h)$ by evaluating $\lim\limits_{h \to 0} [1/(\sqrt{2+h} + \sqrt{2})]$, and since the limit of the reciprocal is the reciprocal of the limit (Theorem XII), the limit sought can be written $1/\lim\limits_{h \to 0} (\sqrt{2+h} + \sqrt{2})$, and since the limit of the sum is the sum of the limits (Theorem V) we have

$$\lim_{h \to 0} f(h) = \frac{1}{\lim\limits_{h \to 0} \sqrt{2+h} + \lim\limits_{h \to 0} \sqrt{2}}.$$

Finally, by Example 2, §506, $\lim_{h \to 0} \sqrt{2+h} = \sqrt{2}$, and since $\lim_{h \to 0} \sqrt{2} = \sqrt{2}$, we have the final result:

$$(44) \qquad \lim_{h \to 0} \frac{\sqrt{2+h} - \sqrt{2}}{h} = \lim_{h \to 0} \frac{1}{\sqrt{2+h} + \sqrt{2}} = \frac{1}{\sqrt{2} + \sqrt{2}} = \frac{1}{2\sqrt{2}} = \frac{\sqrt{2}}{4}.$$

Example 2. Use previously established results for continuous functions to prove Theorem V.

Solution. Let f and g be defined or redefined at the point c so that $f(c) \equiv \lim_{x \to c} f(x)$ and $g(c) \equiv \lim_{x \to c} g(x)$. Then by Theorem I, §504, f and g are continuous at c. By Theorem II, §404, the set of all functions defined on $D \cup \{c\}$ and continuous at c is a vector space, and consequently the function $h \equiv f + g$ on $D \cup \{c\}$ is continuous at c. Therefore, again by Theorem I, §504, $\lim_{x \to c} h(x) = h(c) = f(c) + g(c) = \lim_{x \to c} f(x) + \lim_{x \to c} g(x)$, and (19) is established.

508   EXERCISES

In Exercises 1–8, use limit theorems of §507 to evaluate the given limit. Explain your use of these limit theorems.

1. $\displaystyle \lim_{x \to 5} \frac{x^2 - 25}{x - 5}.$

2. $\displaystyle \lim_{h \to 0} \frac{(2 + h)^3 - 8}{h}.$

3. $\displaystyle \lim_{h \to 0} \frac{\sqrt{9 + h} - 3}{h}.$

4. $\displaystyle \lim_{x \to 5} \frac{\sqrt{x + 20} - 5}{x - 5}.$

5. $\displaystyle \lim_{x \to a} \frac{\dfrac{1}{x} - \dfrac{1}{a}}{x - a}.$

6. $\displaystyle \lim_{x \to 3} \frac{\dfrac{6}{x^2} + \dfrac{1}{x} - 1}{x - 3}.$

7. $\displaystyle \lim_{x \to 5} \frac{\sqrt{x^2 - 9} - 4}{x - 5}.$

8. $\displaystyle \lim_{h \to 0} \frac{\sqrt{16 - 6h - h^2} - 4}{h}.$

In Exercises 9–15, prove the indicated statement from §507.

9. Theorem II.
10. The Corollary to Theorem III.

11. The extensions to n functions of Theorems IV and IX.

12. Theorem VI.   **13.** Theorem VII.   **14.** Theorem VIII.   **15.** Theorem XIII.

In Exercises 16–18, assuming that $\lim_{x \to 3} f(x) = 2$, show that the given limit statement is true by virtue of certain continuity properties. Explain the role played by continuity.

16. $\displaystyle \lim_{x \to 3} f^2(x) = 4.$

17. $\displaystyle \lim_{x \to 3} \sqrt{f(x) + 2} = 2.$

18. $\displaystyle \lim_{x \to 3} \frac{1}{f(x)} = \frac{1}{2}.$

In Exercises 19–21, assuming that $\lim_{x \to 3} f(x) = 2$, establish the given limit statement. (*Warning:* This limit statement is not the result of any theorems of this chapter, but must be proved by direct application of the definition of a limit.)

19. $\displaystyle \lim_{x \to 4} f(2x - 5) = 2.$

20. $\displaystyle \lim_{z \to 2} f(z^2 - 1) = 2.$

21. $\displaystyle \lim_{t \to 0+} f(\sqrt{t} + 3) = 2.$

509   LIMITS AT INFINITY

A set that is unbounded above is said to have $+\infty$ as a *limit point*. This concept can be defined in a manner completely analogous to that used for finite limit points in §501, by means of *deleted neighborhoods of* $+\infty$:

Definition I. *A **deleted neighborhood** of $+\infty$ is any unbounded open interval of the form $(p, +\infty)$, where p is a positive number.* * A set A has $+\infty$ as a **limit point** or **cluster point** if and only if A is unbounded above, or equivalently:*

(i)   *$\forall$ deleted neighborhood $D_{+\infty}$ of $+\infty$, $D_{+\infty} \cap A \neq \varnothing$,*
(ii)   *$\forall p \in \mathcal{P}, \exists x \in A \ni x > p$.*

Limits at $+\infty$ are defined as are limits at points:

Definition II. *A function f whose domain is unbounded above has a **finite limit** at $+\infty$ equal to a number d, written*

(1) $$\lim_{x\to+\infty} f(x) = d, \quad or \quad \lim_{x\to+\infty} f(x) = d,$$

or

(2) $$f(x) \to d \quad as \quad x \to +\infty,$$

if and only if

(3) $\forall \epsilon > 0, \exists p \in \mathcal{P} \ni$

$$(x \in D \ and \ x > p) \Rightarrow |f(x) - d| < \epsilon.$$

The following two theorems are immediate consequences of the definitions.

Theorem I. *A function f whose domain D is unbounded above has a limit d at $+\infty$ if and only if*

(4)   *$\forall$ neighborhood N_d of d, $\exists$ a deleted neighborhood $D_{+\infty}$ of $+\infty$ $\ni$*
$$f(D \cap D_{+\infty}) \subset N_d,$$
that is, if and only if for every neighborhood N_d of d, there exists a deleted neighborhood $D_{+\infty}$ of $+\infty$ such that every point of $D \cap D_{+\infty}$ is mapped by f into N_d.

Theorem II. *Let f be a function whose domain is unbounded above. If there exists a positive-valued function $p(\epsilon)$ with domain $\mathcal{P} = (0, +\infty)$ such that*

(5) $$\forall \epsilon > 0, \begin{Bmatrix} x \in D \\ x > p(\epsilon) \end{Bmatrix} \Rightarrow |f(x) - d| < \epsilon,$$

then $\lim_{x\to+\infty} f(x) = d$.

Example 1. Show that $\lim_{x\to+\infty} \dfrac{1}{x} = 0$, by finding a function $p(\epsilon)$ as specified in Theorem II.

Solution.   With $f(x) \equiv 1/x$ and $d \equiv 0$, the inequality on the right of (5) is $|1/x| < \epsilon$. If we can guarantee that x is positive this inequality becomes $1/x < \epsilon$, which is equivalent to $x > 1/\epsilon$. If we take $p(\epsilon) \equiv 1/\epsilon$, then the inequality $x > p(\epsilon)$ implies that x is positive, and therefore that

$$|f(x) - d| = \left|\frac{1}{x}\right| = \frac{1}{x} < \frac{1}{1/\epsilon} = \epsilon.$$

*The requirement that p be *positive* is inessential. It is imposed only because of consequent simplifications.

Example 2. Show that $\lim\limits_{x \to +\infty} \dfrac{3x - 2}{4x + 5} = \dfrac{3}{4}$ by finding a function $p(\epsilon)$ as specified in Theorem II.

Solution. With $f(x) \equiv \dfrac{3x - 2}{4x + 5}$ and $d \equiv \dfrac{3}{4}$, the inequality on the right of (4) simplifies to

(6)
$$\left| \frac{3x - 2}{4x + 5} - \frac{3}{4} \right| = \left| \frac{12x - 8 - 12x - 15}{4(4x + 5)} \right| = \frac{23}{4|4x + 5|} < \epsilon.$$

If we can guarantee that x is positive, then $|4x + 5| = 4x + 5 > 4x$, and

(7)
$$\frac{23}{4|4x + 5|} < \frac{23}{4 \cdot 4x} < \frac{32}{16x} = \frac{2}{x}.$$

If we take $p(\epsilon) \equiv 2/\epsilon$, then the inequality $x > p(\epsilon)$ implies that x is positive, and therefore that

$$|f(x) - d| = \frac{23}{4|4x + 5|} < \frac{2}{x} < \frac{2}{2/\epsilon} = \epsilon.$$

All of the thirteen limit theorems of §507 hold for finite limits at $+\infty$. All that is necessary in the statements is to replace c by $+\infty$. All that is necessary in the proofs is to use the fact that the intersection of two deleted neighborhoods of $+\infty$ is a deleted neighborhood of $+\infty$:

(8)
$$(p, +\infty) \cap (q, +\infty) = (\max (p, q), +\infty),$$

and that this extends to the intersection of any finite number of deleted neighborhoods of $+\infty$.

Example 3. Prove that $\lim\limits_{x \to +\infty} \dfrac{\sin x}{x} = 0$.

Solution. By Theorem X, §507, adapted to limits at $+\infty$, $(\sin x)/x$ is the product of the function $1/x$ whose limit at $+\infty$ is 0 and the bounded function $\sin x$. Therefore $(\sin x)/x \to 0$ as $x \to +\infty$.

Example 4. Evaluate the limit in Example 2 by use of limit theorems.

Solution. We write the fraction $(3x - 2)/(4x + 5)$ for positive x by dividing every term in both numerator and denominator by x, and proceed thus:

$$\lim_{x \to +\infty} \frac{3x - 2}{4x + 5} = \lim_{x \to +\infty} \frac{3 - \dfrac{2}{x}}{4 + \dfrac{5}{x}} = \frac{\lim\limits_{x \to +\infty} \left(3 - \dfrac{2}{x} \right)}{\lim\limits_{x \to +\infty} \left(4 + \dfrac{5}{x} \right)} = \frac{\lim\limits_{x \to +\infty} 3 - 2 \lim\limits_{x \to +\infty} \left(\dfrac{1}{x} \right)}{\lim\limits_{x \to +\infty} 4 + 5 \lim\limits_{x \to +\infty} \left(\dfrac{1}{x} \right)},$$

where we have used successively Theorem XIII, §507 (the limit of a quotient is the quotient of the limits), Theorem V, §507 (the limit of a sum is the sum of the limits), and Theorem VI, §507 (the limit of a constant times a function is the constant times the limit of the function). Finally, by Theorem II, §507 (the limit of a constant function k is the constant k), and Example 1, above, we have the result $(3 - 2 \cdot 0)/(4 + 5 \cdot 0) = 3/4$.

The Theorem of §506 has a useful variant:

Theorem III. *If f has a domain that is unbounded above, if f has a finite limit equal to d at $+\infty$, if g is continuous at d and if the range of f is a subset of the domain of g, then the composite function $g \circ f$, whose values are given by the formula $g(f(x))$, has the limit $g(d)$ at $+\infty$. In short, the limit of the function is the function of the limit.*

Example 5. Evaluate $\lim\limits_{x \to +\infty} \dfrac{x}{x^2 - 5}$ by use of limit theorems.

Solution. We start, as in Example 4, by dividing every term of the numerator and denominator by x^2 (the highest power of x present):

$$(9) \qquad \lim_{x \to +\infty} \frac{x}{x^2 - 5} = \lim_{x \to +\infty} \frac{\dfrac{1}{x}}{1 - \dfrac{5}{x^2}}.$$

If we now write $f(x) = 1/x$ and $g(x) = x/(1 - 5x^2)$, then the given fraction, in the form given on the extreme right in (9), can be expressed by means of the composite function $g \circ f$:

$$g(f(x)) = \frac{\dfrac{1}{x}}{1 - 5\left(\dfrac{1}{x}\right)^2} = \frac{x}{x^2 - 5}.$$

Since $\lim_{x \to +\infty} f(x) = \lim_{x \to +\infty} (1/x) = 0$, and since g is continuous at 0, we can apply Theorem III to obtain

$$\lim_{x \to +\infty} \frac{x}{x^2 - 5} = \lim_{x \to +\infty} g(f(x)) = g(\lim_{x \to +\infty} f(x)) = g(0) = 0.$$

Definition III. *An infinite sequence is a function whose domain is the set $\mathfrak{N}$ of all natural numbers.*

Since $\mathfrak{N}$ is unbounded above, the preceding Definition and Theorems are immediately available for infinite sequences. If the letter n is used for a variable with range $\mathfrak{N}$, Examples 1, 2, and 5, above, give the following results:

$$\lim_{n \to +\infty} \frac{1}{n} = 0, \quad \lim_{n \to +\infty} \frac{3n - 2}{4n + 5} = \frac{3}{4}, \quad \lim_{n \to +\infty} \frac{n}{n^2 - 5} = 0.$$

The general topic of infinite sequences and their limits will be pursued more intensively in Chapter 10, *SCC*.

A set A that is unbounded below is said to have $-\infty$ as a limit point, or, in other terms:

Definition IV. *A deleted neighborhood of $-\infty$ is any unbounded open interval of the form $(-\infty, -p)$, where $p > 0$. A set A has $-\infty$ as a **limit point** or **cluster point** if and only if A is unbounded below, or equivalently:*

(i) *$\forall$ deleted neighborhood $D_{-\infty}$ of $-\infty$, $D_{-\infty} \cap A \neq \varnothing$,*

(ii) *$\forall p \in \mathcal{P}, \exists x \in A \ni x < -p$.*

Limits at $-\infty$ are defined almost exactly as are limits at $+\infty$. The analogues of Definition II and Theorems I, II, and III will be left to the reader to formulate.

A set A that is unbounded is said to have ∞ (unsigned infinity) as a limit point:

Definition V.   *A **deleted neighborhood** of ∞ is a set of the form*

$$(10) \qquad\qquad (-\infty,\ -p)\cup(p,\ +\infty) = \{x\mid |x| > p\},$$

*where p is a positive number. A set A has ∞ as a **limit point** or **cluster point** if and only if it is unbounded, or equivalently:*

(i) $\forall$ deleted neighborhood D_∞ of ∞, $D_\infty \cap A \neq \varnothing$,
(ii) $\forall p \in \mathscr{P}, \exists x \in A \ni |x| > p$.

Limits at ∞ are defined almost exactly as are limits at $+\infty$ or at $-\infty$. The analogues of Definition II and Theorems I, II, and III will be left to the reader to formulate.

NOTE.   The limits $\lim_{x\to+\infty} f(x)$, $\lim_{x\to-\infty} f(x)$, and $\lim_{x\to\infty} f(x)$ are all called "limits at infinity." The limit statement $\lim_{x\to+\infty} f(x) = d$ is read "the limit of f at $+\infty$ is d," or "the limit of f of x as x approaches (or tends toward) $+\infty$ is d," or "the limit of f of x as x becomes (positively) infinite is d." The limit statements $\lim_{x\to-\infty} f(x) = d$ and $\lim_{x\to\infty} f(x) = d$ have similar readings.

Definition VI.   *A horizontal line $y = d$ is an **asymptote** for the graph of the function f if and only if the domain of f is unbounded and at least one of the following two statements is true:*

$$(11) \qquad\qquad \lim_{x\to+\infty} f(x) = d, \quad \lim_{x\to-\infty} f(x) = d.$$

Example 6.   Prove that $\lim_{x\to\infty} (1/x) = 0$, and hence that the x-axis is a horizontal asymptote for the graph of $1/x$. (Cf. Fig. 407-2a.)

Solution.   By analogy with Example 1, the problem is to find a positive-valued function $p(\epsilon)$ with domain $\mathscr{P}$ such that

$$(12) \qquad\qquad |x| > p(\epsilon) \ \Rightarrow\ \left|\frac{1}{x}\right| < \epsilon.$$

Such a function is $p(\epsilon) \equiv 1/\epsilon$. The statement $\lim_{x\to\infty} (1/x) = 0$ implies both $\lim_{x\to+\infty} (1/x) = 0$ and $\lim_{x\to-\infty} (1/x) = 0$.

Example 7.   Show that $\lim_{x\to\infty} \dfrac{\sin x}{x} = 0$, $\lim_{x\to\infty} \dfrac{3x - 2}{4x + 5} = \dfrac{3}{4}$, and $\lim_{x\to\infty} \dfrac{x}{x^2 - 5} = 0$. Interpret these results in terms of horizontal asymptotes.

Solution.   With the aid of Example 6, the techniques of Examples 3, 4, and 5 give the desired results. The graphs of the functions $(\sin x)/x$, $(3x - 2)/(4x + 5)$, and $x/(x^2 - 5)$ have the horizontal asymptotes $y = 0$, $y = \frac{3}{4}$, and $y = 0$, respectively (cf. Fig. 509-1). (For the behavior of $(\sin x)/x$ near $x = 0$, cf. Example 4, §622, and Example 1, §1301.

We conclude this section with an analogue of Theorem II, §503. (A corresponding analogue for limits at $-\infty$ also holds).

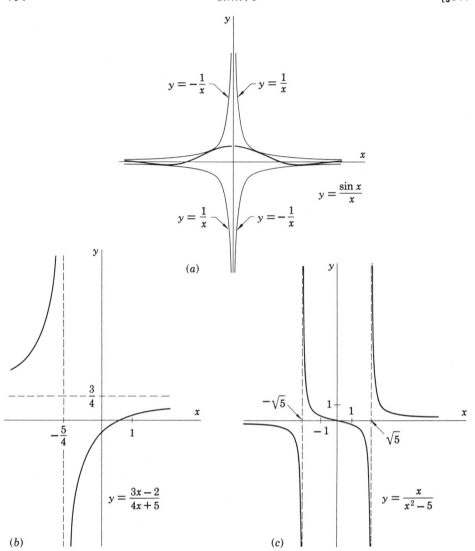

Figure 509-1

Theorem IV. *If f is monotonic and bounded on a domain D that is unbounded above, then f has a finite limit at* $+\infty$.

Proof. We give details for the case when f is *increasing.* (Proof for the decreasing case is entirely similar.) Accordingly, we define

$$(13) \qquad\qquad d \equiv \sup \{f(x) \mid x \in D\}$$

(cf. Fig. 509-2). We wish to prove that

$$(14) \qquad\qquad \lim_{x \to +\infty} f(x) = d.$$

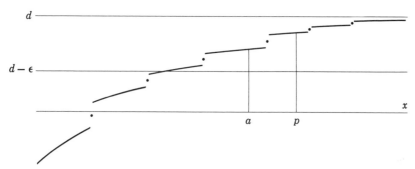

Figure 509-2

If ϵ is an arbitrary positive number, then since $d - \epsilon$ is a number less than d, there must be a member of the range of f greater than $d - \epsilon$. In other words, there must be a point a of D such that $f(a) > d - \epsilon$. Letting p be a positive number greater than a, and letting $D_{+\infty} \equiv (p, +\infty)$, we infer from the fact that f is increasing on $D \cap [a, +\infty)$:

$$(15) \qquad (x \in D \text{ and } x > p) \;\Rightarrow\; f(x) \geqq f(p) \geqq f(a) > d - \epsilon,$$

and therefore $d - \epsilon < f(x) \leqq d < d + \epsilon$, and $|f(x) - d| < \epsilon$. By Definition II, (14) is established.

510   INFINITE LIMITS

In order to introduce and study *infinite limits* (in distinction to *limits at infinity*) we shall find it convenient to have available the language of *neighborhoods* (as well as of *deleted neighborhoods*) of $+\infty$, $-\infty$, and ∞. In the case of a real number c, the only distinction between a neighborhood N_c of c and a deleted neighborhood D_c of c is that c is a member of N_c and not a member of D_c. For neighborhoods and deleted neighborhoods of $+\infty$, $-\infty$, and ∞ we shall make no such distinction since we shall be concerned only with sets of real numbers, and $+\infty$, $-\infty$, *and* ∞ *are not real numbers*. Accordingly, we define a **neighborhood** of $+\infty$, $-\infty$, or ∞ to be identical with a *deleted neighborhood* of $+\infty$, $-\infty$, or ∞, respectively. The reason for having distinct names for identical point sets is that these terms have distinct roles in limit statements. In formulations involving $+\infty$, $-\infty$, or ∞ that are closely analogous to finite counterparts we shall use the single word *neighborhood* in the context in which this single word was used before, and we shall incorporate the adjective *deleted* when the context is similar to that in which this adjective was previously employed.

Infinite limits of the following variety can be defined:

$$\lim_{x \to c} f(x) = +\infty, \quad \lim_{x \to c} f(x) = -\infty, \quad \lim_{x \to c} f(x) = \infty,$$

$$\lim_{x \to c+} f(x) = +\infty, \quad \lim_{x \to c+} f(x) = -\infty, \quad \lim_{x \to c+} f(x) = \infty,$$

with twelve more where $x \to c$ or $x \to c+$ is replaced by $x \to c-$, $x \to +\infty$, $x \to -\infty$, or $x \to \infty$. Since the idea is practically the same in every case, we shall content ourselves with two formulations.

Definition I. *Let f be a function with domain D and let c be a limit point of* $D \cap (c, +\infty)$. *Then*

(1) $$\lim_{x \to c+} f(x) = +\infty, \quad \text{or} \quad \lim_{x \to c+} f(x) = +\infty,$$

or

(2) $$f(x) \to +\infty \quad \text{as} \quad x \to c+,$$

if and only if

(3)   ∀ *neighborhood* $N_{+\infty}$ *of* $+\infty$, ∃ *a deleted right half-neighborhood* D_{c+} *of* c ∋

$$f(D \cap D_{c+}) \subset N_{+\infty}.$$

or, equivalently,

(4)   ∀ $p \in \mathcal{P}$, ∃ $\delta > 0$ ∋
$$x \in D \text{ and } c < x < c + \delta \implies f(x) > p.$$

Example 1. Show that $\lim_{x \to 0+} \dfrac{1}{x} = +\infty$. (Cf. Fig. 407-2*a*.)

Solution. If p is an arbitrary positive number, then the inequality $1/x > p$ is equivalent to $0 < x < 1/p$. In (4), then, δ can be defined: $\delta \equiv 1/p$.

Definition II. *If c is a limit point of the domain D of a function f, then*

(5) $$\lim_{x \to c} f(x) = \infty,$$

or

(6) $$f(x) \to \infty \quad \text{as} \quad x \to c,$$

if and only if

(7)   ∀ *neighborhood* N_∞ *of* ∞, ∃ *a deleted neighborhood* D_c *of* c ∋
$$f(D \cap D_c) \subset N_\infty,$$

or, equivalently,

(8)   ∀ $p > 0$, ∃ $\delta > 0$ ∋ $\left\{ \begin{matrix} x \in D \\ 0 < |x - c| < \delta \end{matrix} \right\} \implies |f(x)| > p.$

Example 2. Show that $\lim_{x \to 0} \dfrac{1}{x} = \infty$. Comment on the statement $\lim_{x \to 0} \dfrac{1}{x} = +\infty$. (Cf. Fig. 407-2*a*.)

Solution. If $p > 0$, the inequality $|1/x| > p$ is equivalent to $0 < |x| < 1/p$, and δ, in (8), can be taken to be $\delta \equiv 1/p$. The statement $\lim_{x \to 0} 1/x = +\infty$ is false since $1/x$ is negative for *some* values of x in *every* neighborhood of 0.

Example 3. Show that $\lim_{x \to 0} \dfrac{1}{x^2} = +\infty$. (Cf. Fig. 407-2*b*.)

Solution. If p is an arbitrary positive number, the inequality $1/x^2 > p$ is equivalent to

$1/|x| > \sqrt{p}$, and hence to $0 < |x| < 1/\sqrt{p}$. Therefore δ, in (8), can be taken to be $\delta \equiv 1/\sqrt{p}$.

A special relationship between infinite and finite limits is contained in the theorem:

Theorem I. *Let f be a function with domain D, and let c be a limit point of $D \cap (c, +\infty)$. If there exists a deleted right half-neighborhood A_{c+} of c such that f is nonzero on $D \cap A_{c+}$, then*

$$(9) \qquad \lim_{x \to c+} f(x) = \infty \text{ if and only if } \lim_{x \to c+} \frac{1}{f(x)} = 0;$$

or, equivalently,

$$(10) \qquad \lim_{x \to c+} f(x) = 0 \text{ if and only if } \lim_{x \to c+} \frac{1}{f(x)} = \infty.$$

If f is the quotient

$$(11) \qquad f = \frac{g}{h}$$

of two functions each of which is right-continuous at c, where $g(c) \neq 0$, $h(c) = 0$, and $h(x) \neq 0$ for x in some deleted right half-neighborhood of c, then

$$(12) \qquad \lim_{x \to c+} f(x) = \lim_{x \to c+} \frac{g(x)}{h(x)} = \infty.$$

Proof. The first part, involving (9) and (10), is established by standard techniques related to ϵ and its reciprocal, and the details will be omitted. Conclusion (12) follows from (9) since $h(x)/g(x) \to 0$ by Theorem XIII, §507.

Example 4. Since $g(x) \equiv x^2 + 4$ and $h(x) \equiv 3x^2 - 5x - 2$ are both continuous at $x = 2$, and since $g(2) = 8 \neq 0$, $h(2) = 0$, and $h(x) \neq 0$ for $0 < |x - 2| < 1$, $\lim\limits_{x \to 2} \dfrac{x^2 + 4}{3x^2 - 5x - 2} = \infty$.

Definition III. *A vertical line $x = c$ is an **asymptote** for the graph of the function f if and only if c is a limit point of the domain of f and at least one of the following four statements is true:*

$$(13) \quad \lim_{x \to c+} f(x) = +\infty, \quad \lim_{x \to c+} f(x) = -\infty, \quad \lim_{x \to c-} f(x) = +\infty, \quad \lim_{x \to c-} f(x) = -\infty.$$

From Theorem I, we know that whenever f has the form of a quotient g/h of (11), where g and h are continuous at c, with $g(c) \neq 0$, $h(c) = 0$, and $h(x)$ of one sign for x in a deleted one-sided neighborhood of c, then the line $x = c$ is a vertical asymptote for the graph of f.

Example 5. The graphs of $y = 1/x$ and $y = 1/x^2$ both have vertical asymptotes at $x = 0$ (the y-axis). (Cf. Fig. 407-2.)

Example 6. The graph of $(3x - 2)/(4x + 5)$ has the vertical asymptote $x = -\frac{5}{4}$ (cf. Fig. 509-1b), and the graph of $x/(x^2 - 5)$ has the two vertical asymptotes $x = \pm\sqrt{5}$ (cf. Fig. 509-1c).

For rational functions the following result is often useful:

Theorem II.   *Let f be a rational function:*

$$(14) \qquad f(x) \equiv \frac{g(x)}{h(x)} = \frac{a_0 x^m + a_1 x^{m-1} + \cdots + a_m}{b_0 x^n + b_1 x^{n-1} + \cdots + b_n},$$

where the leading coefficients a_0 and b_0 are nonzero, so that m and n are the degrees of g and h, respectively. Then:

(i)   *If $m < n$, $\lim\limits_{x \to +\infty} f(x) = 0$, and the x-axis is a horizontal asymptote for the graph of f.*

(ii)   *If $m = n > 0$, $\lim\limits_{x \to +\infty} f(x) = \dfrac{a_0}{b_0}$, and the line $y = \dfrac{a_0}{b_0}$ is a horizontal asymptote for the graph of f.*

(iii)   *If $m > n$, $\lim\limits_{x \to +\infty} f(x) = \infty$, and the graph of f has no horizontal asymptote.*

Proof.   (i): Write $f(x)$, for $x \neq 0$:

$$(15) \qquad f(x) = \frac{\dfrac{a_0}{x^{n-m}} + \dfrac{a_1}{x^{n-m+1}} + \cdots + \dfrac{a_m}{x^n}}{b_0 + \dfrac{b_1}{x} + \cdots + \dfrac{b_n}{x^n}}.$$

Define the function

$$(16) \qquad \phi(x) \equiv \frac{a_0 x^{n-m} + a_1 x^{n-m+1} + \cdots + a_m x^n}{b_0 + b_1 x + \cdots + b_n x^n}.$$

Then ϕ is the quotient of two polynomials each of which is continuous at 0, and the denominator of which is nonzero at 0. Therefore, by Theorem IV(i), §406, ϕ is continuous at 0. The function $f(x)$ is the composite of the functions $\phi(x)$ and $1/x$: $f(x) = \phi(1/x)$, and since $\lim_{x \to \infty} (1/x) = 0$, by the Theorem III, §509, with $x \to +\infty$ replaced by $x \to \infty$,

$$(17) \qquad \lim_{x \to \infty} f(x) = \lim_{x \to \infty} \phi(1/x) = \phi(0) = 0.$$

(ii): This is very similar to the case just proved, except that in this case

$$(18) \qquad \phi(x) = \frac{a_0 + a_1 x + \cdots + a_m x^n}{b_0 + b_1 x + \cdots + b_n x^n},$$

and $\phi(0) = a_0/b_0$.

(iii): This can be deduced from case (i) and Theorem I, above, by considering the reciprocal of f.

Example 7. $\lim\limits_{x \to \infty} \dfrac{5x^2 + 7x - 8}{16x^3 - 9x - 11} = 0,$

$$\lim_{x \to \infty} \frac{5x^2 + 7x - 8}{16x^2 - 9x - 11} = \frac{5}{16}, \quad \lim_{x \to \infty} \frac{5x^3 + 7x - 8}{16x^2 - 9x - 11} = \infty.$$

NOTE.   With both finite and infinite limits permitted, we can extend the statements of Theorem II, §503,   and Theorem V, §509,   to the very general statement that all *monotonic functions always have one-sided limits.* This statement should be interpreted as applying to both bounded and unbounded functions and to limits at $+\infty$ and limits at $-\infty$.

511 EXERCISES

In Exercises 1–3, prove the given limit statement by finding a function $p(\epsilon)$ as specified in Theorem II, §509.

1. $\lim\limits_{x\to+\infty} \dfrac{1}{\sqrt{x}} = 0.$

2. $\lim\limits_{x\to+\infty} \dfrac{1}{x^2} = 0.$

3. $\lim\limits_{x\to+\infty} \dfrac{2x-3}{4x+1} = \dfrac{1}{2},$

In Exercises 4–6, prove the given limit statement by use of an appropriate analogue of Theorem X, §507.

4. $\lim\limits_{x\to+\infty} \dfrac{1+\cos 2x}{x} = 0.$

5. $\lim\limits_{n\to+\infty} \dfrac{\sin^2 n}{n^2} = 0.$

6. $\lim\limits_{n\to+\infty} \dfrac{\cos(an+b)}{n+1} = 0.$

In Exercises 7–12, evaluate the limit by use of limit theorems.

7. $\lim\limits_{x\to\infty} \dfrac{5x+8}{7x-10}$

8. $\lim\limits_{x\to-\infty} \dfrac{11x+1}{5x-9},$

9. $\lim\limits_{s\to+\infty} \dfrac{3s^2+6s-4}{8s^2-2s+5},$

10. $\lim\limits_{t\to\infty} \dfrac{6t^2-7}{5t^2-2t},$

11. $\lim\limits_{n\to+\infty} \dfrac{3n}{6n^2-2},$

12. $\lim\limits_{y\to-\infty} \dfrac{y+3}{4y^2+25},$

In Exercises 13–18, evaluate the limit of the indicated exercise by use of Theorem III, §509, or an appropriate analogue.

13. Exercise 7.

14. Exercise 8.

15. Exercise 9.

16. Exercise 10.

17. Exercise 11.

18. Exercise 12.

In Exercises 19–21, establish the given limit statement by finding a suitable δ in terms of p, in accord with (4), §510.

19. $\lim\limits_{x\to0+} \dfrac{1}{x^2} = +\infty.$

20. $\lim\limits_{x\to0+} \dfrac{1}{\sqrt{x}} = +\infty.$

21. $\lim\limits_{x\to0+} \dfrac{1}{x-x^2} = +\infty.$

In Exercises 22–24, establish the given limit statement by finding a suitable δ in terms of p, in accord with (8) of Definition II, §510.

22. $\lim\limits_{x\to0} \dfrac{1}{x^3} = \infty.$

23. $\lim\limits_{x\to2} \dfrac{1}{x-2} = \infty.$

24. $\lim\limits_{x\to2} \dfrac{1}{x^2-4} = \infty.$

In Exercises 25–32, find all horizontal and vertical asymptotes of the graph of the given function. Justify your conclusions.

25. $\dfrac{3x-5}{4x+6},$

26. $\dfrac{5x+2}{3x-1},$

27. $\dfrac{x-3}{x^2-4},$

28. $\dfrac{x-4}{x^2+2x-3},$

29. $\dfrac{3x^2-1}{4x^2+5},$

30. $\dfrac{5x^2-4}{3x^2+2},$

31. $\dfrac{x^2-9}{x-2},$

32. $\dfrac{x^2+10}{x-1},$

In Exercises 33–38, find the indicated limit.

33. $\lim\limits_{y\to\infty} \dfrac{3y^5 - 5y^2 - 11}{y^2 + 2},$

34. $\lim\limits_{s\to-\infty} \dfrac{5s^3 - 2s}{10s^3 + s^2 - 7},$

35. $\lim\limits_{n\to+\infty} \dfrac{n + 8}{3n^4 - 7n^3},$

36. $\lim\limits_{z\to\infty} \dfrac{z^8 - 10z}{2z^3 + z^2 - 4},$

37. $\lim\limits_{t\to+\infty} \dfrac{8t^4 + 1}{2t^4 + 4t^2 + 1},$

38. $\lim\limits_{x\to-\infty} \dfrac{2x^2 + 3x + 1}{5x^3 + x^2 + 4},$

512   CURVE SKETCHING

In this section we shall consider certain aspects of the graphs of rational functions. The approximate shape of the graph can usually be inferred from the following information: (*i*) symmetry (cf. §115, *PCLA*), (*ii*) horizontal asymptotes, (*iii*) vertical asymptotes, and (*iv*) intercepts. The following examples illustrate these items. Later chapters (especially Chapter 9) will take up refinements in graphing.

Example 1.   Sketch the graph of $y = \dfrac{x^2 - 4}{x^2 - 9}.$

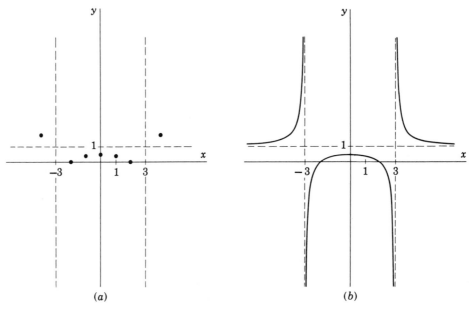

Figure 512-1

Solution. Since the function is even its graph is symmetric with respect to the y-axis; since $y = 0$ when $x = \pm 2$ the graph has the two x-intercepts $x = \pm 2$; since the denominator vanishes at $x = \pm 3$ and the numerator does not the graph has the two vertical asymptotes $x = \pm 3$; and since $\lim_{x\to\infty} (x^2 - 4)/(x^2 - 9) = 1$ the graph has the horizontal asymptote $y = 1$. Most of this information, together with the five points corresponding to $x = 0, \pm 1,$ and ± 4 is shown in Figure 512-1*a*. The total graph is indicated in Figure 512-1*b*.

Example 2.   Sketch the graph of $\dfrac{x^2 + 9}{x(x^2 - 4)}.$

Solution. Since the function is odd its graph is symmetric with respect to the origin; since the numerator never vanishes there are no x-intercepts; since the denominator vanishes at $x = 0$ and $x = \pm 2$ the graph has the three vertical asymptotes $x = 0, x = \pm 2$; and since $\lim_{x \to \infty} (x^2 + 9)/x(x^2 - 4) = 0$, the graph has the x-axis as horizontal asymptote. Most of this information, together with the four points corresponding to $x = \pm 1$ and ± 3, is shown in Figure 512-2a. The total graph is indicated in Figure 512-2b.

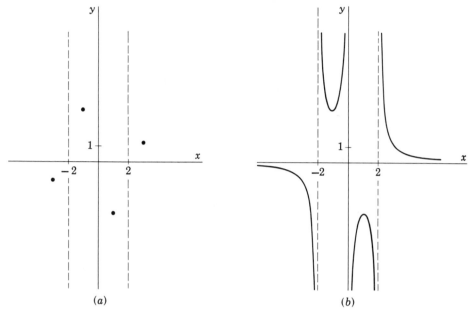

(a) $\qquad\qquad\qquad\qquad\qquad\qquad$ (b)

Figure 512-2

513 EXERCISES

In Exercises 1–34, sketch the graph of the given function, with special attention to symmetry, horizontal and vertical asymptotes, and intercepts. The general shape of the graph is more important than precision plotting of points.

1. $\dfrac{1}{x - 2}$. $\qquad$ **2.** $\dfrac{1}{1 - x}$. $\qquad$ **3.** $\dfrac{x - 1}{x - 2}$. $\qquad$ **4.** $\dfrac{x - 2}{x - 1}$.

5. $\dfrac{1}{x^2 + 1}$. $\qquad$ **6.** $\dfrac{1}{(x + 1)^2}$. $\qquad$ **7.** $\dfrac{1}{x^2 - 1}$. $\qquad$ **8.** $\dfrac{1}{4 - x^2}$.

9 $\dfrac{x}{x^2 + 1}$. $\qquad$ **10,** $\dfrac{x}{(x - 1)^2}$. $\qquad$ **11.** $\dfrac{x - 1}{x^2}$. $\qquad$ **12,** $\dfrac{x}{x^2 - 1}$.

13. $\dfrac{x + 1}{x(x - 1)}$. $\qquad$ **14.** $\dfrac{x - 1}{x(x + 1)}$. $\qquad$ **15.** $\dfrac{x^2 + 1}{x}$. $\qquad$ **16.** $\dfrac{(x - 1)^2}{x}$.

17. $\dfrac{x^2 - 1}{x}$. $\qquad$ **18.** $\dfrac{(x - 1)(x - 2)}{x}$. $\qquad$ **19.** $\dfrac{x^2 + 2}{x^2 + 1}$. $\qquad$ **20.** $\dfrac{x^2 + 1}{x^2 + 2}$.

21. $\dfrac{x^2}{x^2 + 1}$. $\qquad$ **22.** $\dfrac{x^2 - 1}{x^2 + 1}$. $\qquad$ **23.** $\dfrac{(x - 1)^2}{x^2}$. $\qquad$ **24.** $\dfrac{x^2 - 1}{x^2}$.

25. $\dfrac{(x-1)(x-2)}{x^2}$.   **26.** $\dfrac{x(x-1)}{(x-2)^2}$.   **27.** $\dfrac{x^2+1}{x^2-1}$.   **28.** $\dfrac{x^2}{x^2-1}$.

29. $\dfrac{(x-2)^2}{x^2-1}$.   **30.** $\dfrac{(2+x)^2}{1-x^2}$.   **31.** $\dfrac{x^2-1}{x^2-4}$.   **32.** $\dfrac{x^2-4}{x^2-1}$.

33. $\dfrac{x(x-2)}{(x-1)(x-3)}$.   **34.** $\dfrac{x(x-1)}{(x-2)(x-3)}$.

514   THE INTEGRAL AS THE LIMIT OF A SUM

Since Riemann integrability has been defined (Chapter 1) by means of approximations of a function by step-functions, and the integral of the function by integrals of step-functions, each of which is a finite sum, it might seem likely that the integral could be obtained as a specific *limit* of such sums, in a manner similar to the definitions of limits occurring earlier in this chapter. The fact that this is indeed possible is the main concern of the present section.

We start with a definition:

Definition I. *The norm* $|\mathfrak{N}|$ *of a net* $\mathfrak{N} : \{a_0, a_1, \cdots, a_n\}$ *on an interval* $[a, b]$ *is the maximum length of its subintervals:*

(1) $|\mathfrak{N}| \equiv \max\left((a_1 - a_0), (a_2 - a_1), \cdots, (a_n - a_{n-1})\right).$

Let f be defined on a compact interval $[a, b]$ on which the net $\mathfrak{N}$ is constructed. We wish to study approximating sums of the form

(2) $\displaystyle\sum_{i=1}^{n} f(x_i)(a_i - a_{i-1}) = f(x_1)(a_1 - a_0) + \cdots + f(x_n)(a_n - a_{n-1}),$

where for each $i = 1, 2, \cdots, n$, x_i is an arbitrary point of the *closed* ith subinterval: $a_{i-1} \leqq x_i \leqq a_i$. If the symbol Δx_i is defined to be the length of the ith subinterval, $\Delta x_i \equiv a_i - a_{i-1}$, $i = 1, 2, \cdots, n$, the sum (2) can be written

(3) $\displaystyle\sum_{i=1}^{n} f(x_i)\Delta x_i = f(x_1)\Delta x_1 + f(x_2)\Delta x_2 + \cdots + f(x_n)\Delta x_n.$

The limit that is now to be considered is defined as follows:

Definition II. *The sum* $\displaystyle\sum_{i=1}^{n} f(x_i)\,\Delta x_i$ *has a* **finite limit** L *as the norm of the net* $\mathfrak{N}$ *approaches zero, written*

(4) $\displaystyle\lim_{|\mathfrak{N}|\to 0} \sum_{i=1}^{n} f(x_i)\Delta x_i = L,$

if and only if

(5) $\forall\, \epsilon > 0, \exists\, \delta > 0 \ni$

$$\left.\begin{array}{l} |\mathfrak{N}| < \delta \\ x_i \in [a_{i-1}, a_i],\ i = 1, \cdots, n \end{array}\right\} \ \Rightarrow\ \left|\sum_{i=1}^{n} f(x_i)\Delta x_i - L\right| < \epsilon.$$

Our principal theorem can now be stated:

Theorem. *If f is Riemann-integrable on [a, b], then the limit* $\lim\limits_{|\mathfrak{N}|\to 0}\sum\limits_{i=1}^{n} f(x_i)\Delta x_i$ *exists and is equal to the integral* $\int_a^b f(x)dx$:

(6) $$\lim_{|\mathfrak{N}|\to 0}\sum_{i=1}^{n} f(x_i)\Delta x_i = \int_a^b f(x)dx.$$

(Cf. Fig. 513-1.)

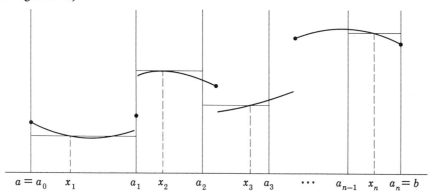

Figure 513-1

A proof of this theorem is given in §1016, *CWAG*. The general method is to make use of vector space concepts and techniques, with the aid of the following four lemmas:

Lemma 1. *The Theorem is true if f is the characteristic function of a one-point set. That is, if for some* $c \in [a, b]$,

$$f(x) = \begin{cases} 1 \ if \ x = c, \\ 0 \ if \ x \in [a, b] \setminus \{c\}, \end{cases}$$

then

$$\lim_{|\mathfrak{N}|\to 0}\sum_{i=1}^{n} f(x_i)\Delta x_i = 0.$$

Lemma 2. *The Theorem is true if f is the characteristic function of an open subinterval (c, d) of [a, b]. That is, if*

$$f(x) = \begin{cases} 1 \ if \ c < x < d, \\ 0 \ if \ x \in [a, b] \setminus (c, d), \end{cases}$$

where $a \leqq c < d \leqq b$, *then*

$$\lim_{|\mathfrak{N}|\to 0}\sum_{i=1}^{n} f(x_i)\Delta x_i = d - c.$$

Lemma 3. *The functions on [a, b] for which the Theorem is true form a vector space.*

Lemma 4. *The Theorem is true for every step-function.*

The final step in the proof combines Lemma 4 and a suitable "squeeze" on the given function by means of step-functions.

Example. Evaluate the limit

(7)
$$\lim_{n \to +\infty} \frac{1}{n^3} [1^2 + 2^2 + \cdots + n^2].$$

First solution. By formula (13) of Example 5, §510, *PCLA*,

$$\frac{1}{n^3} [1^2 + 2^2 + \cdots + n^2] = \frac{2n^2 + 3n + 1}{6n^2},$$

and therefore, by Theorem II, 510,

$$\lim_{n \to +\infty} \frac{1}{n^3} [1^2 + 2^2 + \cdots + n^2] = \lim_{n \to +\infty} \frac{2n^2 + 3n + 1}{6n^2} = \frac{2}{6} = \frac{1}{3}.$$

Second solution. The function x^2 is integrable on the interval $[0, 1]$ with integral

$$\int_0^1 x^2 dx = \frac{1^3 - 0^3}{3} = \frac{1}{3}.$$

Let $\mathfrak{N} = \left\{ 0, \frac{1}{n}, \frac{2}{n}, \cdots, \frac{n}{n} \right\}$ be the net on $[0, 1]$ with n subintervals of equal length $1/n$, so that $|\mathfrak{N}| = 1/n$. On the ith subinterval $[(i - 1)/n, i/n]$ let $x_i = i/n$, $i = 1, 2, \cdots, n$. Then the sum (3) becomes

(8)
$$\sum_{i=1}^n f(x_i)\Delta x_i = \sum_{i=1}^n \left(\frac{i}{n}\right)^2 \cdot \frac{1}{n} = \frac{1}{n^3} [1^2 + 2^2 + \cdots + n^2].$$

By the Theorem, above, the limit of (8) as $|\mathfrak{N}| \to 0$, or equivalently as $n \to +\infty$, is the value of the integral $\int_0^1 x^2 dx = \frac{1}{3}.$

515   BLISS'S THEOREM

If f and g are both integrable functions on the interval $[a, b]$, then their product is also (cf. §107), and therefore, for any $\epsilon > 0$ there exists a $\delta > 0$ such that

(1)
$$\left. \begin{array}{c} |\mathfrak{N}| < \delta \\ x_i \in [a_{i-1}, a_i], i = 1, \cdots, n \end{array} \right\} \Rightarrow \left| \sum_{i=1}^n f(x_i)g(x_i)\Delta x_i - \int_a^b fg \right| < \epsilon.$$

A fact of frequent practical application is that the two functions f and g can be evaluated at independent points x_i and x_i' of the ith interval, for each $i = 1, 2, \cdots, n$. This result is due to the American mathematician G. A. Bliss (1876–1951), and is known as *Bliss's Theorem*. A proof is given in H§1019, *CWAG*.

Theorem I.   Bliss's Theorem.   *Let f and g be integrable on $[a, b]$. Then*

(2) $\forall \epsilon > 0, \exists \delta > 0 \ni$

$$\left. \begin{array}{c} |\mathfrak{N}| < \delta \\ x_i \in [a_{i-1}, a_i], i = 1, \cdots, n \\ x_i' \in [a_{i-1}, a_i], i = 1, \cdots, n \end{array} \right\} \Rightarrow \left| \sum_{i=1}^n f(x_i)g(x_i')\Delta x_i - \int_a^b fg \right| < \epsilon,$$

or, in brief,

(3)
$$\lim_{|\mathfrak{N}| \to 0} \sum_{i=1}^n f(x_i)g(x_i')\Delta x_i = \int_a^b fg.$$

A companion theorem, whose proof is also to be found in H§1019, *CWAG*, is one that will be used later in connection with arc length (§105, *SCC*):

Theorem II. *Let f and g be integrable on [a, b]. Then the function $\sqrt{f^2 + g^2}$ is also integrable on [a, b] and*

(4) $\forall\, \epsilon > 0, \exists\, \delta > 0 \ni$

$$\left.\begin{array}{l} |\mathfrak{N}| < \delta \\ x_i \in [a_{i-1}, a_i], \ i = 1, \cdots, n \\ x_i' \in [a_{i-1}, a_i], \ i = 1, \cdots, n \end{array}\right\} \ \Rightarrow\ \left|\sum_{i=1}^{n}\sqrt{f^2(x_i) + g^2(x_i')}\,\Delta x_i - \int_a^b \sqrt{f^2 + g^2}\,\right| < \epsilon,$$

or, in brief,

(5) $$\lim_{|\mathfrak{N}|\to 0}\sum_{i=1}^{n}\sqrt{f^2(x_i) + g^2(x_i')}\Delta x_i = \int_a^b \sqrt{f^2 + g^2}.$$

516 EXERCISES

In Exercises 1–4, evaluate the given limit by the following two methods: (*i*) by using a formula from Example 4, §510, *PCLA*, or Exercises 10–12, §511, *PCLA*; (*ii*) by representing as the limit of a sum a certain integral on the interval [0, 1], with the integrand evaluated at the right-hand endpoint of every interval of some net on [0, 1].

1. $\lim\limits_{n\to+\infty} \dfrac{1}{n^2}(1 + 2 + 3 + \cdots + n).$

2. $\lim\limits_{n\to+\infty} \dfrac{1}{n^4}(1^3 + 2^3 + 3^3 + \cdots + n^3).$

3. $\lim\limits_{n\to+\infty} \dfrac{1}{n^5}(1^4 + 2^4 + 3^4 + \cdots + n^4).$

4. $\lim\limits_{n\to+\infty} \dfrac{1}{n^6}(1^5 + 2^5 + 3^5 + \cdots + n^5).$

In Exercises 5–7, evaluate the given limit by representing as the limit of a sum a certain integral on the interval [0, 1], with the integrand evaluated at the left-hand endpoint of every interval of some net on [0, 1].

5. $\lim\limits_{n\to+\infty} \dfrac{1}{n^3}(0^2 + 1^2 + 2^2 + \cdots + (n-1)^2).$

6. $\lim\limits_{n\to+\infty} \dfrac{1}{n^4}(0^3 + 1^3 + 2^3 + \cdots + (n-1)^3).$

7. $\lim\limits_{n\to+\infty} \dfrac{1}{n^5}(0^4 + 1^4 + 2^4 + \cdots + (n-1)^4).$

In Exercises 8–10, evaluate the given limit by representing as the limit of a sum a certain integral on the interval [0, 1], with the integrand evaluated at the midpoint of every interval of some net on [0, 1].

8. $\lim\limits_{n\to+\infty} \dfrac{1}{n^2}(1 + 3 + 5 + \cdots + (2n - 1)).$

9. $\lim\limits_{n\to+\infty} \dfrac{1}{n^3}(1^2 + 3^2 + 5^2 + \cdots + (2n - 1)^2).$

10. $\lim\limits_{n\to+\infty} \dfrac{1}{n^4}(1^3 + 3^3 + 5^3 + \cdots + (2n - 1)^3).$

6

The Derivative

601   THE IDEA OF A TANGENT LINE

Let $p : (a, b)$ be a fixed point on the graph C of a function whose domain includes a neighborhood of a, and let $q : (x, y)$ be a point on C that is "near" but not at p. It seems at least plausible that if q is very close to p, then the secant line pq through p and q should be very "near" the "tangent line" L to the curve C at p (cf. Fig. 601-1).

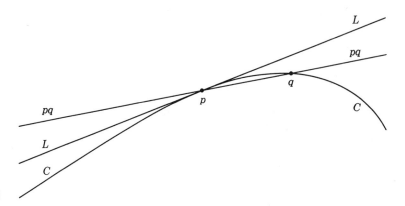

Figure 601-1

Let us try to give concrete meaning to these (admittedly rather vague) notions. There are different ways in which to define what is meant by the statement that a line is tangent to a curve at a certain point. One approach to this problem is to formulate definitions of "closeness" of lines passing through a point, and by means of "neighborhoods" construct appropriate related limit definitions. From *practical* considerations, however, it turns out to be much simpler to define the tangent line L in terms of the limit of the *slope* of a secant line pq, rather than in terms of the limit of pq itself. For present purposes we shall restrict ourselves to *finite* limits. (Infinite limits are treated in §615.)

Definition. *Let $p : (a, b)$ be a point on the graph C of a function f whose domain includes a neighborhood N_a of a, and let $q : (x, y)$ be a point of C such that $x \in N_a \setminus \{a\}$. Then C has a **nonvertical tangent**, or **tangent line**, at p if and only if the limit of the slope of the secant line pq exists as a finite quantity m, as $x \to a$:*

$$(1) \qquad \lim_{x \to a} (\text{slope of } pq) = \lim_{x \to a} \frac{y - b}{x - a} = \lim_{x \to a} \frac{f(x) - f(a)}{x - a} = m.$$

*In case the limit (1) exists, the **tangent**, or **tangent line**, to C at p is the line through p with slope m:*

$$(2) \qquad y - b = m(x - a).$$

*The number m, from (1), is also called the **slope of the curve** C at the point $(a, f(a))$.*

Example 1. Find the equation of the tangent line to the curve $y = x^2$ at the point (a, a^2).

Solution. We start by letting $f(x) \equiv x^2$ and evaluating the limit (1):

$$(3) \qquad \lim_{x \to a} \frac{f(x) - f(a)}{x - a} = \lim_{x \to a} \frac{x^2 - a^2}{x - a}.$$

If the functions ϕ and ψ are defined:

$$\begin{cases} \phi(x) \equiv \dfrac{x^2 - a^2}{x - a} = x + a \text{ with domain } \mathfrak{R} \setminus \{a\}, \\ \psi(x) \equiv x + a \text{ with domain } \mathfrak{R}, \end{cases}$$

then ϕ and ψ are identical on the domain of ϕ, that is, at all points except for a itself. Therefore the two limits

$$\lim_{x \to a} \phi(x) \quad \text{and} \quad \lim_{x \to a} \psi(x)$$

either both exist and are equal or both fail to exist. In other words, the problem of evaluating the limit (3) reduces to that of evaluating

$$(4) \qquad \lim_{x \to a} (x + a).$$

Finally, since ψ is a continuous function on $\mathfrak{R}$, $\lim_{x \to a} \psi(x) = \psi(a) = 2a$. We infer, therefore, that the curve $y = x^2$ has a tangent line L at the point (a, a^2), and the slope of L is $2a$. The equation of L is $(y - a^2) = 2a(x - a)$, or

$$(5) \qquad 2ax - y = a^2.$$

(Cf. Fig. 601-2.)

Example 2. Find the equation of the tangent line to the curve $y = 1/x$ at the point $(a, 1/a)$, $a \neq 0$.

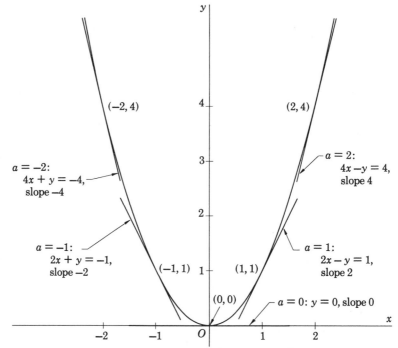

Tangent lines to the curve $y = x^2$

Figure 601-2

Solution. If $f(x) \equiv 1/x$, the limit (1) becomes

(6)
$$\lim_{x \to a} \frac{f(x) - f(a)}{x - a} = \lim_{x \to a} \frac{\dfrac{1}{x} - \dfrac{1}{a}}{x - a} = \lim_{x \to a} \frac{a - x}{ax(x - a)}.$$

Let the functions ϕ and ψ be defined:

(7)
$$\phi(x) \equiv \frac{a - x}{ax(x - a)} = -\frac{1}{ax} \text{ with domain } \mathfrak{R} \setminus \{0, a\},$$

(8)
$$\psi(x) \equiv -\frac{1}{ax} \text{ with domain } \mathfrak{R} \setminus \{0\}.$$

Then, as in the solution of Example 1, $\lim_{x \to a} \phi(x) = \lim_{x \to a} \psi(x)$, and since $\psi(x)$ is continuous at $x = a$, $\lim_{x \to a} \psi(x) = \psi(a) = -1/a^2$. Therefore the slope of the curve $C : y = 1/x$ at $(a, 1/a)$ is $-1/a^2$, and the equation of the tangent line is $(y - (1/a)) = (-1/a^2)(x - a)$, or

(9)
$$x + a^2 y = 2a.$$

(Cf. Fig. 601-3.)

The **normal,** or **normal line,** to a curve C at any point p of C at which C has a tangent line L is the line through p perpendicular (or orthogonal or normal) to L.

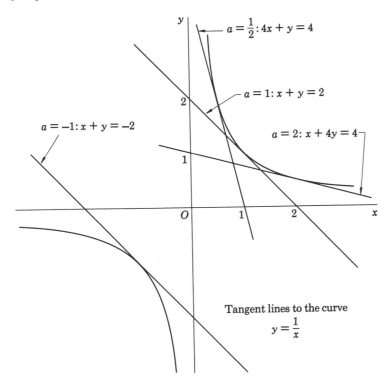

Tangent lines to the curve
$$y = \frac{1}{x}$$

Figure 601-3

Example 3. Find the equations of the normals to the curves of Examples 1 and 2 at general points of these curves.

Solution. For the curve $y = x^2$ of Example 1, for any point (a, a^2) other than the origin, the slope of the normal is $-1/2a$, and therefore the equation of the normal is $y - a^2 = (-1/2a)(x - a)$, or upon simplification,

$$(10) \qquad\qquad x + 2ay = a + 2a^3.$$

Equation (10) also gives the normal at the origin, when $a = 0$.

For the curve $y = 1/x$ of Example 2, the slope of the normal at $(a, 1/a)$ is a^2, and therefore the equation of the normal is $(y - (1/a)) = a^2(x - a)$, or

$$(11) \qquad\qquad a^3x - ay = a^4 - 1.$$

602   AVERAGE AND INSTANTANEOUS VELOCITY

Consider a particle p subject to *rectilinear motion*, that is, motion along a straight line L. Let t represent time measured in any uniform scale, with the moment at which $t = 0$ arbitrary but usually chosen on the basis of convenience, and let s be the directed distance of p measured along L from any convenient point O taken as origin and with a suitable direction having been assigned to L (cf. Fig. 602-1). Since any admissible value of t determines a position of p and hence a value of s,

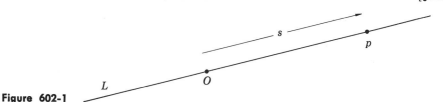

Figure 602-1

the variable s becomes a real-valued function of the real variable t. This function will be denoted elliptically $s(t)$.*

Example 1.   An object slides on a smooth inclined plane with its directed distance s from a point 0 given by the function $s(t) = -3t^2 + 12t + 5$. Draw a graph of this function, and interpret the result.

Solution.   For $-1 < t < 5$ the graph is shown in Figure 602-2, where for convenience different scales have been used on the two axes. If time $t = 0$ is interpreted as the starting time for the motion, it is evident from Figure 602-2, and the formulation $s(t) = -3(t - 2)^2 + 17$, that the object starts at a point 5 units above the "origin" for s, and rises to a maximum distance of 17 within 2 units of time. After $t = 2$ the object "falls" and continues to fall indefinitely.

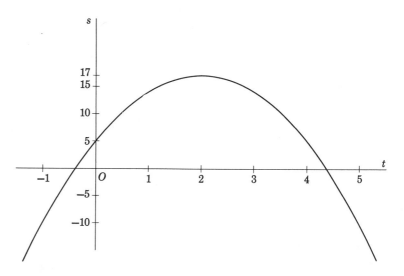

Figure 602-2

If a particle p moves rectilinearly, with directed distance s given as a function $s(t)$ of time t, over a time interval $[t_1, t_2]$, and if $s_1 \equiv s(t_1)$ and $s_2 \equiv s(t_2)$, then the **average velocity** of p over $[t_1, t_2]$ is defined

$$(1) \qquad\qquad \textbf{average velocity} \equiv \frac{s(t_2) - s(t_1)}{t_2 - t_1} = \frac{s_2 - s_1}{t_2 - t_1}.$$

*Strictly speaking, we should use two letters here, one letter, say s, for the variable representing directed distance and a distinct letter, say f, for the function defining s in terms of t: $s = f(t)$. It is partly for convenience and partly from convention in the applications of mathematics that we use the *same* letter s for both the dependent variable and the function. The elliptic notation $s(t)$ serves to distinguish between the function and the variable, and an unnecessary multiplicity of symbols is avoided. A similar double role is used below, and later in this book, for variables representing physical concepts, such as v for velocity, σ for speed, and a for acceleration.

In other words, the average velocity is the slope of the secant line to the graph of $s(t)$ through the two points (t_1, s_1) and (t_2, s_2) (cf. Fig. 602-3).

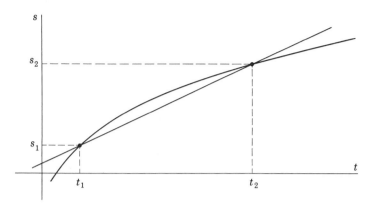

Figure 602-3

The problem now is to define what is meant by the **instantaneous velocity** of p for a certain value t_0 of t. To set the stage for this definition we consider average velocities over "small" time intervals "near" t_0. To be more precise, we consider the average velocity over time intervals of the form $[t_0, t]$, where $t > t_0$, and $[t, t_0]$, where $t < t_0$, and take a limit as $t \to t_0$. Since the formulas for average velocity over $[t_0, t]$ and $[t, t_0]$ reduce to the same expression:

$$\frac{s(t) - s(t_0)}{t - t_0} = \frac{s(t_0) - s(t)}{t_0 - t},$$

the limit desired requires only one formulation,

(2)   **instantaneous velocity** $\equiv \displaystyle\lim_{t \to t_0} \frac{s(t) - s(t_0)}{t - t_0}$.

Geometrically, the instantaneous velocity of p at time t_0 is equal to the slope of the *tangent line* to the graph of $s(t)$ at $t = t_0$ (assuming of course that the limit (2) exists), as indicated in Figure 602-4. The velocity v at time t_0 is denoted $v(t_0)$. Velocity v as a function of time t is denoted $v(t)$.

The **instantaneous speed** of a particle at any moment t is equal to the absolute value of its velocity at that moment, with the notation

(3)   **instantaneous speed** $= \sigma(t) \equiv |v(t)|$.

The single unmodified words *velocity* and *speed* will be used henceforth to mean *instantaneous velocity* and *instantaneous speed*, respectively.

Example 2. Find the (instantaneous) velocity of the object of Example 1 for an arbitrary time t_0 and for an arbitrary time t. Also write an expression for its speed at time t, and draw the graphs of both velocity and speed as functions of time t.

Solution. For the function $s(t) = -3t^2 + 12t + 5$, the formula (2) becomes

$$v(t_0) = \lim_{t \to t_0} \frac{(-3t^2 + 12t + 5) - (-3t_0^2 + 12t_0 + 5)}{t - t_0}$$

$$= \lim_{t \to t_0} \frac{-3(t^2 - t_0^2) + 12(t - t_0)}{t - t_0}.$$

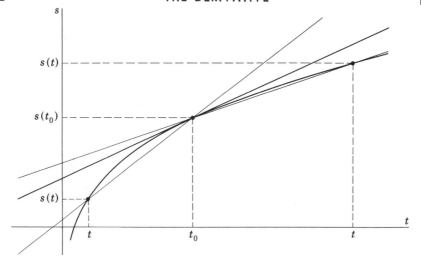

Figure 602-4

Since for $t \neq t_0$,

$$\frac{-3(t^2 - t_0^2) + 12(t - t_0)}{t - t_0} = -3(t + t_0) + 12,$$

and since the function $-3(t + t_0) + 12$ is everywhere continuous, the limit sought can be obtained by substitution:

$$\lim_{t \to t_0} [-3(t + t_0) + 12t] = -6t_0 + 12.$$

Therefore velocity as a function of time t is given by the formula

(4) $v(t) = -6t + 12.$

Speed is given by

(5) $\sigma(t) = |v(t)| = |-6t + 12| = 6|t - 2|.$

The graphs of $v(t)$ and $\sigma(t)$ are given in Figure 602-5.

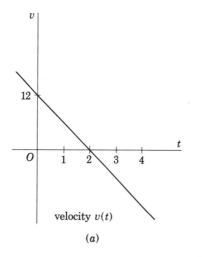

velocity $v(t)$

(a)

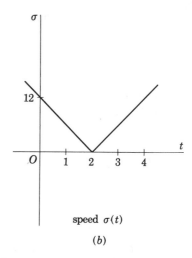

speed $\sigma(t)$

(b)

Figure 602-5

Reading from Figure 602-5, we can say that for time $t < 2$, the velocity is *positive* (this corresponds to motion *upward*), and for time $t > 2$, the velocity is *negative* (this corresponds to motion *downward*). At $t = 2$ the velocity is zero. From the graph of $\sigma(t)$ we can say that at $t = 2$ the speed is zero (the object is said to be *instantaneously at rest*), and that the further t is from 2 the faster the object is moving.

603 THE DERIVATIVE

In the preceding two sections we considered limits of the following type, where f is a given function:

(1)
$$\lim_{x \to a} \frac{f(x) - f(a)}{x - a}.$$

The number resulting from the evaluation of (1) depends on the value of a, and, of course, on the given function f. For instance, in Example 1, § 601, the original function $f(x)$ is the polynomial x^2, and the result of evaluating (1) is the number $2a$. In Example 2, § 602, the original function is the polynomial $-3t^2 + 12t + 5$, and the limit (1), with x and a replaced by t and t_0, respectively, is $-6t_0 + 12$. In the former case the result can be considered as the *function $2a$* of the *variable a*, and in the latter case the result can be considered as the *function $-6t_0 + 12$* of the *variable t_0*.

Our immediate objective now is to adjust the notation for the evaluation of the limit (1) in such a way that the result is displayed directly as a function of the variable x, where x denotes the point at which the limit is taken. One convenient shift in notation is to let the number a in (1) be replaced by the number x, and the number x in (1) be replaced by the number $x + h$, as shown in Figure 603-1. Then for purposes of the limit that is to replace (1), x denotes a *fixed* point and $x + h$ a *variable* point "approaching" x, or, in other words, h is a variable "approaching" 0. The limit (1), therefore, is replaced in the new notation by

(2)
$$\lim_{h \to 0} \frac{f(x + h) - f(x)}{(x + h) - h} = \lim_{h \to 0} \frac{f(x + h) - f(x)}{h}.$$

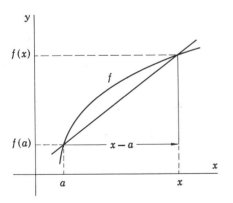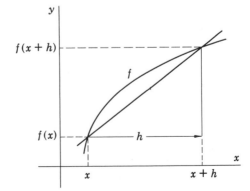

Figure 603-1

The function defined by (2) with domain consisting of all points x of the domain of f for which the limit (2) exists, in the finite sense, is called the **derivative** of f, and is denoted f' or Df. Its value at x is denoted $f'(x)$ or $Df(x)$:

$$(3) \qquad f'(x) = Df(x) \equiv \lim_{h \to 0} \frac{f(x+h) - f(x)}{h}.$$

The notation just introduced is also convenient for elliptic usage. For example, we can say in short that $f'(x)$ is the derivative of $f(x)$ or that $Df(x)$ is the derivative of $f(x)$. When an explicit expression represents a given function $f(x)$, the derivative $f'(x)$ is often written $(f(x))'$, as illustrated at the end of the solution of the following Example 1.

Example 1. Find the derivative of the function x^2 by use of formula (3), and check by comparing the result with that of Example 1, §601.

Solution. Formula (3) gives

$$\lim_{h \to 0} \frac{(x+h)^2 - x^2}{h} = \lim_{h \to 0} \frac{2xh + h^2}{h},$$

which, since only *nonzero* values of h are involved, is the same as

$$\lim_{h \to 0} (2x + h) = 2x + 0 = 2x,$$

the final evaluation by substitution being legitimate since the linear polynomial $2x + h$, as a function of h, is continuous everywhere, and in particular at $h = 0$. The function $2x$, as a function of the variable x, is the same as the result previously obtained, $2a$, regarded as a function of the variable a. The result obtained in this example can be expressed $Dx^2 = 2x$, or $(x^2)' = 2x$.

Example 2. Find the derivative of the function $-3t^2 + 12t + 5$, as a function of t, by adapting formula (3), and check by comparing the result with that of Example 2, §602.

Solution. With $f(t) \equiv -3t^2 + 12t + 5$, formula (3) becomes

$$\lim_{h \to 0} \frac{f(t+h) - f(t)}{h} = \lim_{h \to 0} \frac{-3(t+h)^2 + 12(t+h) + 5 - (-3t^2 + 12t + 5)}{h}$$

$$= \lim_{h \to 0} \frac{-6th - 3h^2 + 12h}{h},$$

and since only *nonzero* values of h are involved, this is the same as

$$\lim_{h \to 0} (-6t + 12 - 3h) = -6t + 12,$$

the final evaluation by substitution being legitimate by continuity at 0 of the linear polynominal $-6t + 12 - 3h$, as a function of h. The derivative $-6t + 12$ is the same as the velocity, as a function of t, obtained before.

If two variables x and y are associated by means of a functional relation, $y = f(x)$, then the derivative f' is also spoken of as **the derivative of y as a function of x,** or **the derivative of y with respect to x,** and is also written

$$(4) \qquad y' = Dy = D_x y = f' = Df.$$

The symbol D_x is used especially when it is important to emphasize that x is the independent variable.

A function f is said to be **differentiable**, or to **have a derivative, at a point** a of its domain if and only if its derivative f' exists there. A function that is differentiable at every point of its domain is **differentiable**. If f' is continuous (on a set A), then f is said to be **continuously differentiable** (on the set A). The process of obtaining the derivative of a function is called **differentiation.**

If the variables x and y are related by the equation $y = f(x)$ and if the function f is differentiable at a point x_1, then the value $f'(x_1)$ of its derivative f' at the point x_1 is also called the **instantaneous rate of change**, or simply the **rate of change**, of y with respect to x at the point x_1. If f is defined on a bounded closed interval $[x_1, x_2]$, and if $y_1 \equiv f(x_1)$ and $y_2 \equiv f(x_2)$, then the quotient $(y_2 - y_1)/(x_2 - x_1)$ is called the **average rate of change** of y with respect to x for the interval $[x_1, x_2]$. Formula (3), then, states that the instantaneous rate of change of y with respect to x at $x = x_1$ is the limit of the average rates of change of y with respect to x, as $h \to 0$, for intervals of the form $[x_1, x_1 + h]$ (if $h > 0$) and $[x_1 + h, x_1]$ (if $h < 0$).

The principal substance of §601 can be summarized: *If a function f is differentiable at a point a of its domain, then its graph has a tangent at the point $(a, f(a))$, and the slope of the tangent is the value of the derivative there, $f'(a)$.* In slightly different terms: *If y is a differentiable function of x, the slope of its graph at any point is equal to its derivative with respect to x at that point.* Slopes of tangent lines are instantaneous rates of change and slopes of secant lines are average rates of change.

In similar fashion, §602 can be summarized: *Velocity as a function of time is the derivative of directed distance with respect to time.* Instantaneous velocities are instantaneous rates of change (of distance with respect to time), and average velocities are average rates of change.

In future examples, in the evaluation of the limit $\lim\limits_{h \to 0} \dfrac{f(x + h) - f(x)}{h}$, it will be implicitly assumed that h is restricted to nonzero values for purposes of simplifying the fraction $[f(x + h) - f(x)]/h$, and for any simplified form of this fraction. It will also be implicitly assumed that $|h|$ is sufficiently small to ensure that $x + h$, as well as x, belongs to the domain of f.

Example 3. Find the derivative of $(2x - 3)/(x + 4)$, $x \neq -4$, by formula (3).

Solution. With $f(x) \equiv (2x - 3)/(x + 4)$, (3) becomes

$$\lim_{h \to 0} \frac{1}{h}\left(\frac{2x + 2h - 3}{x + h + 4} - \frac{2x - 3}{x + 4}\right) = \lim_{h \to 0} \frac{2h(x + 4) - h(2x - 3)}{h(x + h + 4)(x + 4)}$$

$$= \lim_{h \to 0} \frac{11}{(x + h + 4)(x + 4)} = \frac{11}{(x + 4)^2},$$

where the last equality holds by virtue of the continuity of the rational function of h, $11/(x + h + 4)(x + 4)$, at $h = 0$, provided $x \neq -4$.

Some limits of the form (3) can be evaluated by "rationalizing a numerator."

Example 4. Find the derivative of $\sqrt{x}$, for $x > 0$.

Solution. Formula (3) is

$$\lim_{h \to 0} \frac{\sqrt{x+h} - \sqrt{x}}{h} = \lim_{h \to 0} \frac{\sqrt{x+h} - \sqrt{x}}{h} \cdot \frac{\sqrt{x+h} + \sqrt{x}}{\sqrt{x+h} + \sqrt{x}}$$

$$= \lim_{h \to 0} \frac{(x+h) - x}{h(\sqrt{x+h} + \sqrt{x})} = \lim_{h \to 0} \frac{1}{\sqrt{x+h} + \sqrt{x}} = \frac{1}{2\sqrt{x}},$$

the last equality holding as a consequence of the continuity of the function $1/(\sqrt{x+h} + \sqrt{x})$ (as a function of h) at $h = 0$ (cf. Theorems III, IV, § 406). The result obtained in this example can be written

$$(5) \qquad\qquad (\sqrt{x})' = \frac{1}{2\sqrt{x}},$$

or

$$(6) \qquad\qquad (x^{\frac{1}{2}})' = \frac{1}{2}x^{-\frac{1}{2}}.$$

An alternative notation to that introduced earlier in this section is often convenient:

$$(7) \qquad\qquad \Delta x \equiv h, \quad \Delta y \equiv f(x+h) - f(x) = f(x + \Delta x) - f(x).$$

As in §402, *PCLA*, the Greek letter Δ is used in place of the Latin letter D to indicate that a *difference* is formed (cf. Fig. 603-2). The differences Δx and Δy are called **increments** of the variables x and y, respectively. The symbols Δx and Δy should always be used and interpreted as if they were single letters. (For example, Δx^2 means $(\Delta x)^2$.) The limit (3) can now be written

$$(8) \qquad f'(x) = Df(x) = \lim_{\Delta x \to 0} \frac{f(x + \Delta x) - f(x)}{\Delta x} = \lim_{\Delta x \to 0} \frac{\Delta y}{\Delta x}.$$

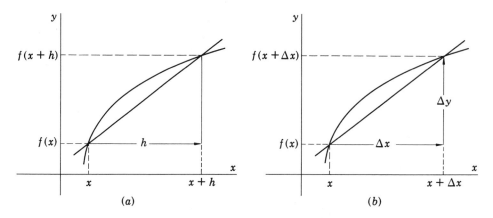

Figure 603-2

Example 5. Use the notation of (7) to find the derivative of $1/x$, $x \neq 0$.

Solution. With $y = f(x) = 1/x$, formula (8) becomes

$$(9) \qquad \lim_{\Delta x \to 0} \frac{\Delta y}{\Delta x} = \lim_{\Delta x \to 0} \frac{\dfrac{1}{x + \Delta x} - \dfrac{1}{x}}{\Delta x} = \lim_{\Delta x \to 0} - \frac{1}{x(x + \Delta x)} = -\frac{1}{x^2},$$

where the last equality holds since as a function of Δx the rational function $-1/x(x + \Delta x)$ is continuous at $\Delta x = 0$ for $x \neq 0$. The result just obtained can also be written

(10) $$\left(\frac{1}{x}\right)' = -\frac{1}{x^2},$$

or

(11) $$(x^{-1})' = -x^{-2}.$$

604   EXERCISES

In Exercises 1–4, find the slope of the tangent line to the given curve at the point corresponding to $x = a$ by means of formula (1), §601. Then write the equations of the tangent line and the normal line at this point. Indicate clearly the role played by continuity. Draw a graph.

1. $y = 5x^2 + 3x + 7$.

2. $y = 6x^2 - 4x - 9$.

3. $y = \dfrac{1}{x + 5}$.

4. $y = \dfrac{2}{x + 3}$.

In Exercises 5–8, find the instantaneous velocity of a particle moving along a straight line according to the given law, at time t_0, by evaluating the limit (2), §602. Then write expressions for both velocity and speed as functions of time t. Indicate clearly the role played by continuity. Draw graphs showing distance, velocity, and speed as functions of time t.

5. $s = -4t + 1$.

6. $s = 6t + 3$.

7. $s = -2t^2 + 8t$.

8. $s = -4t^2 + 7t + 3$.

In Exercises 9–16, find the slope or the velocity in the indicated exercise by using or adapting formula (3), §603.

9. Exercise 1.

10. Exercise 2.

11. Exercise 3.

12. Exercise 4.

13. Exercise 5.

14. Exercise 6.

15. Exercise 7.

16. Exercise 8.

In Exercises 17–25, find the derivative of the given function, whenever the derivative exists, by using or adapting formula (8), §603. Indicate clearly the role played by continuity.

17. $f(x) = 2x^2 + 9x - 10$.

18. $f(x) = 3x^2 - 8x + 2$.

19. $f(t) = -8t^2 - 5t + 8$.

20. $f(x) = \dfrac{3}{2x + 7}$.

21. $f(x) = \dfrac{2}{3x + 1}$.

22. $f(x) = \dfrac{2x + 5}{3x - 1}$.

23. $f(x) = \sqrt{x + 2}$.

24. $f(x) = \sqrt{x + 5}$.

25. $f(x) = \sqrt{2x + 3}$.

605   LAWS OF DERIVATIVES; POLYNOMIALS; HIGHER ORDERS

In this section we shall establish several important differentiation formulas, and introduce a new definition and related notation.

We start with the simplest of all functions, constants.

The derivative of any constant function c is the function that is identically zero.

(1) $$c' = Dc = 0.$$

Proof. With $f(x) \equiv c$, formula (3), § 603, is

$$\lim_{h\to 0} \frac{f(x+h) - f(x)}{h} = \lim_{h\to 0} \frac{c-c}{h} = \lim_{h\to 0} 0 = 0.$$

The identity function comes next:

The derivative of the identity function x is the constant function identically equal to 1:

(2) $$x' = Dx = 1.$$

Proof. With $f(x) \equiv x$, formula (3), § 603, is

$$\lim_{h\to 0} \frac{x+h-x}{h} = \lim_{h\to 0} \frac{h}{h} = \lim_{h\to 0} 1 = 1.$$

Derivatives of powers of x are given as follows:

If $f(x) \equiv x^n$, where n is a positive integer, then

(3) $$f'(x) = (x^n)' = nx^{n-1},$$

where, if $n = 1$, the function $nx^{n-1} = 1 \cdot x^0$ should be interpreted to be identically equal to 1, even when $x = 0$.

Proof. Since the case of $n = 1$ is given by (2), we shall assume that $n \geq 2$. With $f(x) \equiv x^n$, formula (3), § 603, is $\lim_{h\to 0} [(x+h)^n - x^n]/h$, which can be evaluated with the aid of the binomial theorem (Theorem XII, §307), *PCLA*):

(4) $$\lim_{h\to 0} \frac{x^n + nx^{n-1}h + \tfrac{1}{2}n(n-1)x^{n-2}h^2 + \cdots + h^n - x^n}{h}$$

$$= \lim_{h\to 0} (nx^{n-1} + \tfrac{1}{2}n(n-1)x^{n-2}h + \cdots + h^{n-1}),$$

where the dots $\cdots$ represent terms involving powers of h of degree at least 2. Since for any fixed x, the quantity in parentheses in the right-hand member of (4) is a polynomial in h, and hence continuous at $h = 0$, the limit can be evaluated by substitution of 0 for h, and formula (3) results.

NOTE. Example 4, §603, shows that formula (3) is valid in case $n = \tfrac{1}{2}$, for $x > 0$, and Example 5, §603, shows that formula (3) is also valid in case $n = -1$, for $x \neq 0$. We shall show in §619 that formula (3) is valid for *any* rational exponent n, for $x > 0$, and in §1111 that it is valid for any *real* exponent, for $x > 0$.

Example 1. Find the derivative of x^5.

Solution. With $n = 5$, formula (3) gives

$$(x^5)' = Dx^5 = 5x^4.$$

For any function that is the sum of two differentiable functions we have:

If $\phi = f + g$, and if f and g are differentiable at a point x, then ϕ is differentiable at x and the derivative of ϕ at x is the sum of the derivatives of f and g there:

(5) $$\phi'(x) = f'(x) + g'(x).$$

In short, the derivative of the sum is the sum of the derivatives:

(6) $$(f + g)' = f' + g',$$

(7) $$D(f + g) = Df + Dg.$$

Proof. We use the limit theorem (Theorem V, § 507) that states that the limit of the sum is the sum of the limits:

$$\lim_{h \to 0} \frac{\phi(x + h) - \phi(x)}{h} = \lim_{h \to 0} \frac{f(x + h) + g(x + h) - f(x) - g(x)}{h}$$

$$= \lim_{h \to 0} \left[\frac{f(x + h) - f(x)}{h} + \frac{g(x + h) - g(x)}{h} \right]$$

$$= \lim_{h \to 0} \frac{f(x + h) - f(x)}{h} + \lim_{h \to 0} \frac{g(x + h) - g(x)}{h} = f'(x) + g'(x).$$

Example 2. The derivative of $x^3 + x^4$ is $3x^2 + 4x^3$.

When a differentiable function is multiplied by a constant its derivative is multiplied by this same constant:

If $\phi = cf$, where c is a constant and f is differentiable at a point x, then ϕ is differentiable at x and

(8) $$\phi'(x) = cf'(x).$$

In short,

(9) $$(cf)' = cf',$$

(10) $$D(cf) = cDf.$$

If c is the number -1:

(11) $$(-f)' = -f'.$$

(12) $$D(-f) = -Df.$$

(Give proofs of (8)–(12) in Ex. 11, § 606.)

As a consequence of (6) and (11) we can say that *the derivative of the difference is the difference of the derivatives:*

(13) $$(f - g)' = f' - g',$$

(14) $$D(f - g) = Df - Dg.$$

Example 3. The derivative of $7x^3$ is $7 \cdot 3x^2 = 21x^2$. The derivative of $-18x^5 = -90x^4$. The derivative of $2x^5 - 8x$ is $10x^4 - 8$.

Since formula (6) can be extended by mathematical induction to any finite number of terms (cf. Ex. 12, § 606) and since any term of a polynomial can be differentiated by formulas (1), (3), and (8), we can now write down the derivative of any polynomial.

Example 4. The derivative of the polynomial

$$10x^6 - 8x^5 - 3x^4 + x^3 - 8x + 23$$

is the polynomial

$$60x^5 - 40x^4 - 12x^3 + 3x^2 - 8.$$

It is often possible to differentiate a function that is itself a derivative of a function f. In this case the result is called the **second derivative** of f, and if the original functional relation is written $y = f(x)$, the second derivative can be alternatively denoted

$$(15) \qquad f'' = D^2f = y'' = D^2y = D_x^2y,$$

or

$$(16) \qquad f''(x) = (f(x))'' = D^2f(x) = D_x^2f(x).$$

This process can be iterated to produce **third derivatives, fourth derivatives,** $\cdots$, and, in general **nth derivatives,** $n = 1, 2, \cdots$, denoted:

$$(17) \qquad f^{(n)} = D^nf = y^{(n)} = D^ny = D_x^ny,$$

or

$$(18) \qquad f^{(n)}(x) = (f(x))^{(n)} = D^nf(x) = D_x^nf(x).$$

An nth derivative is called an **nth order derivative** or a derivative of **order** n, and if $n > 1$, a derivative of **higher order.**

Example 5. If $f(x) = 10x^6 - 8x^5 - 3x^4 + x^3 - 8x + 23$,

$f'(x) = D(10x^6 - 8x^5 - 3x^4 + x^3 - 8x + 23) = 60x^5 - 40x^4 - 12x^3 + 3x^2 - 8,$

$f''(x) = D(60x^5 - 40x^4 - 12x^3 + 3x^2 - 8) = 300x^4 - 160x^3 - 36x^2 + 6x,$

$f'''(x) = D(300x^4 - 160x^3 - 36x^2 + 6x) = 1200x^3 - 480x^2 - 72x + 6,$

$f''''(x) = D(1200x^3 - 480x^2 - 72x + 6) = 3600x^2 - 960x - 72,$

$f^{(5)}(x) = D(3600x^2 - 960x - 72) = 7200x - 960,$

$f^{(6)}(x) = D(7200x - 960) = 7200,$

$f^{(n)}(x) = 0$ for $n \geq 7$.

For rectilinear motion the derivative of velocity with respect to time is called **acceleration.** Equivalently, acceleration can be defined as the second derivative of directed distance with respect to time. Acceleration as a function of time is customarily denoted $a(t)$, so that

$$(19) \qquad a(t) \equiv v'(t) = s''(t).$$

Example 6. For the function of Example 2, §602, $s(t) = -3t^2 + 12t + 5$,

$$\text{acceleration} = a(t) = (-6t + 12)' = -6.$$

606   EXERCISES

In Exercises 1–8, find the first derivative f' and the second derivative f'' of the given function f.

1. $f(x) = 4x^6 - 7x^3 + 1.$

2. $f(x) = 5x^3 + 18x - 17.$

3. $f(s) = 10s^5 - 16s^2 - 7.$

4. $f(t) = 8t^3 - 12t^2 - 24t.$

5. $f(u) = u^{10} + u^6 + u^2.$

6. $f(v) = v^{12} - v^8 - v.$

7. $f(y) = 2y^{16} - 4y^8 - 8y^4.$

8. $f(z) = 11z^7 + 5z^4 - 6z.$

In Exercises 9 and 10, find the nth order derivative $f^{(n)}$ of the given function, for $n \in \mathfrak{N}$.

9. $f(x) = x^4 + 6x^2 - 5x.$

10. $f(x) = x^5 - 2x^3 + 7.$

11. Prove formulas (8)–(12), §605.

12. Use mathematical induction to extend formula (6), §605, to an arbitrary number of terms.

13. If $f(x) = x^n, n \in \mathfrak{N}$, show that $f^{(n)}(x) = n!$

14. Prove that the set of all functions defined and differentiable on a fixed open interval I is a vector space.

15. For a fixed open interval I, let $\mho$ be the set of all functions f that are derivatives on I, that is, such that $g'(x) = f(x)$ for some function g on I. Prove that $\mho$ is a vector space.

In Exercises 16 and 17, show that the given function is differentiable on $\mathfrak{R}$, and find its derivative.

16. $x|x|.$

17. $|x|^3.$

607   DIFFERENTIABILITY AND CONTINUITY; PRODUCTS AND QUOTIENTS

Before deriving the next two fundamental differentiation formulas, we shall need the following theorem:

Theorem I.   *A function is continuous wherever it is differentiable.*

Proof.   Assume that f is differentiable at the point a; that is, that

(1)
$$\lim_{h \to 0} \frac{f(a + h) - f(a)}{h} = f'(a)$$

exists. We wish to prove that f is continuous at a by showing that

(2)
$$\lim_{x \to a} f(x) = f(a).$$

With the notational change of $h = x - a$, or $x = a + h$, (2) can be expressed as follows:

(3)
$$\lim_{h \to 0} f(a + h) = f(a).$$

In order to make use of (1) we first write $f(a + h)$, for $h \neq 0$, in the form

(4) $$f(a + h) = h \cdot \frac{f(a + h) - f(a)}{h} + f(a),$$

and use limit theorems from § 507:

(5) $$\lim_{h \to 0} f(a + h) = \lim_{h \to 0} h \cdot \lim_{h \to 0} \frac{f(a + h) - f(a)}{h} + f(a) = 0 \cdot f'(a) + f(a) = f(a),$$

and (3) is established as desired.

In terms of the notation Δx and Δy defined in (7), § 603, since $\Delta y = f(x + h) - f(x) = f(x + \Delta x) - f(x)$, continuity at the point x can be expressed as follows:

(6) $$\lim_{\Delta x \to 0} \Delta y = 0.$$

It will be shown in § 612 that the converse of the statement just established is false: *It is possible for a function to be continuous without being differentiable.* (Also cf. §624.)

We are now in a position to establish differentiation formulas for products and quotients:

Theorem II. *If $\phi = fg$, and if f and g are differentiable at a point x, then ϕ is differentiable at x and*

(7) $$\phi'(x) = f(x)g'(x) + g(x)f'(x).$$

In other words, the derivative of the product of two functions is the first function times the derivative of the second plus the second function times the derivative of the first:

(8) $$(fg)' = fg' + gf',$$

(9) $$D(fg) = fDg + gDf.$$

Proof. In order to evaluate the limit

(10) $$\lim_{h \to 0} \frac{f(x + h)g(x + h) - f(x)g(x)}{h},$$

we rewrite the numerator by adding and subtracting the quantity $f(x + h)g(x)$ (cf. Ex. 19, §608):

$$f(x + h)g(x + h) - f(x + h)g(x) + f(x + h)g(x) - f(x)g(x)$$
$$= f(x + h)[g(x + h) - g(x)] + g(x)[f(x + h) - f(x)].$$

Using this, and the fact that $\lim_{h \to 0} f(x + h) = f(x)$, which follows from the continuity of f at x, and limit theorems from §507, we can now evaluate the limit (10):

$$\lim_{h \to 0} \left[f(x + h) \frac{g(x + h) - g(x)}{h} + g(x) \frac{f(x + h) - f(x)}{h} \right]$$

$$= \lim_{h \to 0} f(x + h) \lim_{h \to 0} \frac{g(x + h) - g(x)}{h} + g(x) \lim_{h \to 0} \frac{f(x + h) - f(x)}{h}$$

$$= f(x)g'(x) + g(x)f'(x).$$

Example 1. Show that although the limit of a product is equal to the product of the limits, the *derivative* of a product is *not* equal to the product of the derivatives.

Solution. To show that a statement is *false* we construct a counterexample. Let $f(x) \equiv x^2$ and $g(x) \equiv x^3$. Then the derivative of the product is $(x^5)' = 5x^4$, whereas the product of the derivatives is $(2x)\cdot(3x^2) = 6x^3$, and $5x^4 \neq 6x^3$.

The formula for the derivative of the quotient of two differentiable functions is somewhat similar to that for a product, but is more complicated.

Theorem III. *If $\phi = f/g$, if f and g are differentiable at a point x, and if g is nonzero at x, $g(x) \neq 0$, then ϕ is differentiable at x and*

$$\phi'(x) = \frac{g(x)f'(x) - f(x)g'(x)}{(g(x))^2}. \tag{11}$$

In other words, the derivative of the quotient of two functions is the denominator times the derivative of the numerator minus the numerator times the derivative of the denominator, all divided by the square of the denominator:

$$\left(\frac{f}{g}\right)' = \frac{gf' - fg'}{g^2}, \tag{12}$$

$$D\left(\frac{f}{g}\right) = \frac{gDf - fDg}{g^2}. \tag{13}$$

Proof. The limit this time is made "manageable" by the addition and subtraction of the quantity $f(x)g(x)$ in the numerator:

$$\lim_{h \to 0} \frac{1}{h}\left[\frac{f(x+h)}{g(x+h)} - \frac{f(x)}{g(x)}\right] = \lim_{h \to 0}\frac{f(x+h)g(x) - f(x)g(x+h)}{hg(x+h)g(x)}$$

$$= \lim_{h \to 0} \frac{[f(x+h)g(x) - f(x)g(x)] - [f(x)g(x+h) - f(x)g(x)]}{hg(x+h)g(x)}$$

$$= \lim_{h \to 0}\left[\left(g(x)\frac{f(x+h) - f(x)}{h} - f(x)\frac{g(x+h) - g(x)}{h}\right)\frac{1}{g(x+h)g(x)}\right]$$

$$= [g(x)f'(x) - f(x)g'(x)]\cdot\frac{1}{g(x)g(x)}.$$

For the final equality the continuity of g at the point x is used. Throughout the proof, it is implicitly assumed that $g(x+h) \neq 0$. By the Corollary to Theorem VI, §406, this is a valid assumption if $|h|$ is sufficiently small.

Example 2. Find the derivative of $(2x - 3)/(x + 4)$, the function of Example 3, § 603, by means of formula (11).

Solution. With $f(x) = 2x - 3$ and $g(x) = x + 4$, formula (11) gives

$$\left(\frac{2x - 3}{x + 4}\right)' = \frac{(x + 4)(2x - 3)' - (2x - 3)(x + 4)'}{(x + 4)^2} = \frac{2(x + 4) - (2x - 3)}{(x + 4)^2} = \frac{11}{(x + 4)^2}.$$

608   EXERCISES

In Exercises 1–6, find the derivative of the given function by two methods: (*i*) expand first and then differentiate; (*ii*) differentiate the function as a product, according to Theorem II, § 607, and then expand and collect terms.

1. $(3x + 1)(2x + 5)$.

2. $(6x - 1)(5x - 3)$.

3. $x^2(x^3 + 4x + 1)$.

4. $x^3(x^2 - 5x + 1)$.

5. $(x^2 + 4)(3x^2 - 2)$.

6. $(4x^2 + 1)(5x^2 + 3)$.

In Exercises 7–12, find the derivative of the given function.

7. $\dfrac{3x + 1}{2x + 5}$.

8. $\dfrac{6x - 1}{5x - 3}$.

9. $\dfrac{x^2}{x^3 + 4x + 1}$.

10. $\dfrac{x^3}{x^2 - 5x + 1}$.

11. $\dfrac{x^2 + 4}{3x^2 - 2}$.

12. $\dfrac{4x^2 + 1}{5x^2 + 3}$.

In Exercises 13–16, use the formula $(\sqrt{x})' = 1/(2\sqrt{x})$ for finding the derivative of the given function.

13. $\sqrt{x}(x^2 + 4x - 7)$.

14. $\sqrt{x}(x^2 - 3x + 9)$.

15. $\dfrac{\sqrt{x}}{x - 3}$.

16. $\dfrac{\sqrt{x}}{x + 2}$.

In Exercises 17 and 18, use the formula $(\sqrt{x})' = 1/(2\sqrt{x})$ for finding the derivative of the given function. Interpret your result as an instance of formula (3), § 605, where the exponent is a certain fraction.

17. $x^{\frac{3}{2}} = x\sqrt{x}$.

18. $x^{\frac{5}{2}} = x^2\sqrt{x}$.

19. Prove Theorem II, § 607, by adding and subtracting the quantity $f(x)g(x + h)$ in the numerator of (10), § 607.

20. Show by a counterexample that the derivative of a quotient is not equal to the quotient of the derivatives.

21. Prove that the set of all functions defined and differentiable on a fixed open interval is an algebra. (Cf. Ex. 14, §606.)

22. Prove that the derivative of every polynomial is a polynomial and that the derivative of every rational function is a rational function.

23. Derive the following formulas that extend formula (7) of Theorem II, § 607:

(1) $(fgh)' = f'gh + fg'h + fgh'$,

(2) $(fg\phi\psi)' = f'g\phi\psi + fg'\phi\psi + fg\phi'\psi + fg\phi\psi'$.

Formulate a general rule for differentiating the product of n differentiable functions.

24. Use mathematical induction to prove $(x^n)' = nx^{n-1}$, for $n \in \mathfrak{N}$.

609   DIFFERENTIATION OF POWERS

If a differentiable function g is raised to a positive integral power, the resulting function is differentiable with a derivative given as follows:

Theorem. *If g is differentiable at the point x, if n is a positive integer, and if $\phi \equiv g^n$, then ϕ is differentiable at the point x, and*

(1) $$\phi'(x) = ng^{n-1}(x) \cdot g'(x).$$

That is, wherever g is differentiable:

(2) $$(g^n)' = ng^{n-1}g'.$$

In other terms, if u is a differentiable function of x,

(3) $$D_x(u^n) = nu^{n-1}D_x u.$$

Proof. It is possible to fashion a proof of this theorem similar to that given for formula (3), §605 $((x^n)' = nx^{n-1})$, based on the binomial theorem. For the sake of variety (and other reasons) we have chosen to give a proof by mathematical induction.

In the first place, formulas (1)–(3) are true when $n = 1$ (as in §605, we interpret the zeroth power u^0 of any quantity u to be identically equal to 1 even when the base u is equal to 0). We now assume that n is a positive integer for which formula (1) is valid and seek to establish the corresponding formula for the exponent $n + 1$:

(4) $$(g^{n+1}(x))' = (n + 1)g^n(x) \cdot g'(x).$$

We may write the power $g^{n+1}(x)$ as the product $g^n(x) \cdot g(x)$, and use formula (7), §607, for differentiating a product, together with formula (1), above, to obtain for the left-hand member of (4):

(5) $(g^n(x) \cdot g(x))' = g^n(x) \cdot g'(x) + g(x)[ng^{n-1}(x) \cdot g'(x)]$
$$= [g^n(x) + ng^n(x)]g'(x) = (n + 1)g^n(x) \cdot g'(x).$$

Since formula (1) implies formula (4), it follows that the set of positive integers for which formula (1) holds is an inductive set and is therefore equal to the set $\mathfrak{N}$ of *all* positive integers. This completes the proof.

Example 1. If $y = (2x^3 + 5x - 1)^7$, then

$$y' = 7(2x^3 + 5x - 1)^6(6x^2 + 5).$$

Example 2. If $y = (u^2 + 4)^2$, find $D_u y$.

Solution. $D_u y = ((u^2 + 4)^2)' = 2(u^2 + 4)(u^2 + 4)' = 4u(u^2 + 4)$, where primes indicate differentiation with respect to the variable u.

Example 3. Find the derivative of $[(2x - 3)/(x + 4)]^3$ by two methods.

First solution. Letting $u \equiv (2x - 3)/(x - 4)$ and using $D_x u = 11/(x + 4)^2$ from Example 3, §603, or Example 2, §607, we have

$$D_x\left(\frac{2x - 3}{x + 4}\right)^3 = 3\left(\frac{2x - 3}{x + 4}\right)^2 D_x \frac{2x - 3}{x + 4} = 33\frac{(2x - 3)^2}{(x + 4)^4}.$$

Second solution. Writing the function in the form of a quotient $(2x - 3)^3/(x + 4)^3$ gives

$$D_x \frac{(2x - 3)^3}{(x + 4)^3} = \frac{(x + 4)^3 \cdot 3(2x - 3)^2 \cdot 2 - (2x - 3)^3 \cdot 3(x + 4)^2 \cdot 1}{(x + 4)^6}$$

$$= \frac{(x + 4)^2(2x - 3)^2[6(x + 4) - 3(2x - 3)]}{(x + 4)^6} = 33\frac{(2x - 3)^2}{(x + 4)^4}.$$

610   COMPOSITE FUNCTIONS AND THE CHAIN RULE

The formula of the Theorem, §609, for the derivative of g^n, where n is a positive integer and g is differentiable at a point x, is a special case of a more general, and exceedingly useful, formula for differentiating a composite function $f \circ g$. In the case of g^n the function f is that given by the expression $f(u) \equiv u^n$, so that $f \circ g$ has the form

$$(1) \qquad\qquad\qquad f(g(x)) = (g(x))^n.$$

In terms of the functional notation (1), we notice that formula (2), §609, can be viewed as giving the derivative of $f \circ g$ as the product of the *two* derivatives f' and g', the first evaluated at $g(x)$ and the second at x:

$$(2) \qquad\qquad\qquad (f \circ g)'(x) = f'(g(x)) \cdot g'(x).$$

This is precisely the generalization we seek, and the one we shall now establish:

Theorem. Chain Rule.   *If ϕ is the composite function*

$$(3) \qquad\qquad\qquad \phi \equiv f \circ g,$$

where g is differentiable at the point x and f is differentiable at the point $g(x)$, then ϕ is differentiable at x and

$$(4) \qquad\qquad\qquad \phi'(x) = f'(g(x)) \cdot g'(x).$$

Formula (4) can also be written

$$(5) \qquad\qquad\qquad (f \circ g)' = (f' \circ g) \cdot g',$$

or, in terms of variables, where y is a function of u and u is a function of x:

$$(6) \qquad\qquad\qquad D_x y = D_u y \cdot D_x u,$$

where the points at which the derivatives are evaluated are implicitly understood from context.

Proof.   For the sake of clarity and in order to avoid confusion between constants and variables, we shall prove the theorem using the letter a in place of x for the fixed value of the independent variable at which the derivatives of ϕ and g are evaluated. In other words, we shall establish the formula

$$(7) \qquad\qquad\qquad \phi'(a) = f'(g(a)) \cdot g'(a),$$

under the assumptions that g is differentiable at a and that f is differentiable at $g(a)$.

We shall present the proof in two parts, depending on whether $g'(a)$ is nonzero or zero.

Case 1, $g'(a) \neq 0$. With the notation

(8) $$u \equiv g(a) \quad \text{and} \quad \Delta u \equiv g(a + \Delta x) - g(a),$$

(9) $$\lim_{\Delta x \to 0} \frac{\Delta u}{\Delta x} = \lim_{\Delta x \to 0} \frac{g(a + \Delta x) - g(a)}{\Delta x} = g'(a) \neq 0.$$

By Theorem XI, §507, there exists a deleted neighborhood D_0 of 0 such that for $\Delta x \in D_0$, $\Delta u / \Delta x$, and therefore Δu, is nonzero. With

(10) $$y \equiv \phi(a) = f(g(a)) = f(u)$$

and

(11) $$\Delta y \equiv \phi(a + \Delta x) - \phi(a) = f(g(a + \Delta x)) - f(g(a)),$$

we can write, for any $\Delta x \in D_0$,

(12) $$\frac{\Delta y}{\Delta x} = \frac{\Delta y}{\Delta u} \cdot \frac{\Delta u}{\Delta x},$$

and take limits (assuming for the moment that they exist):

(13) $$\lim_{\Delta x \to 0} \frac{\Delta y}{\Delta x} = \lim_{\Delta x \to 0} \frac{\Delta y}{\Delta u} \cdot \lim_{\Delta x \to 0} \frac{\Delta u}{\Delta x}.$$

Since the limit $\lim_{\Delta x \to 0} (\Delta u / \Delta x)$ exists and is equal to $g'(a)$ (as a consequence of the assumption that g is differentiable at the point a), all that remains, in order to establish (7), is to show that the limit $\lim_{\Delta x \to 0} (\Delta y / \Delta u)$ exists and is equal to $\lim_{\Delta u \to 0} (\Delta y / \Delta u)$:

(14) $$\lim_{\Delta x \to 0} \frac{\Delta y}{\Delta u} = f'(g(a)).$$

The general idea now is that since g is continuous at a, and hence $\lim_{\Delta x \to 0} \Delta u = 0$, and since $\lim_{\Delta u \to 0} \Delta y / \Delta u$ exists and is equal to $D_u y = f'(g(a))$, we can therefore conclude

(15) $$\lim_{\Delta x \to 0} \frac{\Delta y}{\Delta u} = \lim_{\Delta u \to 0} \frac{\Delta y}{\Delta u} = f'(g(a)).$$

Complete details are given in §1112, *CWAG.*

Case 2, $g'(a) = 0$. We wish to prove that $\phi'(a) = 0$. Since $\lim_{\Delta u \to 0} \Delta y / \Delta u$ exists as a finite limit, there must exist a positive number K such that $|\Delta y / \Delta u| < K$ for $|\Delta u|$ sufficiently small but nonzero (cf. Theorem VIII, §507). Therefore the inequality

(16) $$|\Delta y| \leq K |\Delta u|$$

must hold whenever $|\Delta u|$ is sufficiently small (whether zero or not). Since $\Delta u \to 0$ as $\Delta x \to 0$, we now know that (16) holds for all sufficiently small nonzero $|\Delta x|$, and hence

(17)
$$0 \leq \left|\frac{\Delta y}{\Delta x}\right| \leq K\left|\frac{\Delta u}{\Delta x}\right|,$$

Since both 0 and $K|\Delta u/\Delta x|$ have zero limits as $\Delta x \to 0$, it follows from Theorem IV, §507, that $|\Delta y/\Delta x|$ must also have a zero limit as $\Delta x \to 0$, and the proof is complete.

The chain rule extends to any finite number of functions. For example, for a function of a function of a function (y a function of u, u a function v, and v a function of x), formula (6) becomes:

(18)
$$D_x y = D_u y \cdot D_v u \cdot D_x v,$$

and for four functions it is

(19)
$$D_x y = D_u y \cdot D_v u \cdot D_w v \cdot D_x w.$$

It is from the appearance of formulas like (6), (18), and (19) — the individual factors being joined like links of a chain — that the name *chain rule* is derived. The derivation of (18) and (19) follows directly from (6). (Give the details in Ex. 11, §611.)

Example 1. Show that if g is a differentiable function with positive values, then the derivative of $\sqrt{g}$ is

(20)
$$(\sqrt{g})' = \frac{g'}{2\sqrt{g}}.$$

Use (20) to find the derivative of $\sqrt{x^2 + 1}$.

Solution. In the preceding Theorem let $f(x) \equiv \sqrt{x}$. Then $f(g(x)) = \sqrt{g(x)}$ and, by Example 4, §603, $f'(x) = 1/2\sqrt{x}$. Therefore formula (4) gives, for the derivative of $f \circ g$,

(21)
$$f'(g(x)) \cdot g'(x) = [1/2\sqrt{g(x)}] \cdot g'(x),$$

or (20). The derivative of the function $\sqrt{x^2 + 1}$ is given by letting $g(x) = x^2 + 1$ in (20) or (21):

(22)
$$D\sqrt{x^2 + 1} = \frac{D(x^2 + 1)}{2\sqrt{x^2 + 1}} = \frac{2x}{2\sqrt{x^2 + 1}} = \frac{x}{\sqrt{x^2 + 1}}.$$

Example 2. Differentiate $1/(x^2 + 1)$ in two ways.

First solution. Formula (11), § 607, for the derivative of a quotient, gives

(23)
$$\left(\frac{1}{x^2 + 1}\right)' = \frac{(x^2 + 1) \cdot 1' - 1(x^2 + 1)'}{(x^2 + 1)^2} = -\frac{2x}{(x^2 + 1)^2}.$$

Second solution. With $f(x) \equiv 1/x$ and $g(x) \equiv x^2 + 1$, the given function is the composite $f \circ g : 1/(x^2 + 1) = f(g(x))$. Since, by Example 5, § 603, $f'(x) = -1/x^2$, formula (4) gives

(24)
$$f(g(x)) \cdot g'(x) = \frac{-1}{(x^2 + 1)^2} \cdot 2x = -\frac{2x}{(x^2 + 1)^2}.$$

NOTE. Formula (20) of Example 1 and the second solution of Example 2 illustrate the fact that the formula of the Theorem, §609, which can be put in the form

(25)
$$(g^n(x))' = ng^{n-1}(x) \cdot g'(x),$$

is valid for the exponents $n = \frac{1}{2}$ and $n = -1$. (The proof for $n = -1$ is requested in Ex. 12, §611.) Extensions to rational exponents, and to real exponents in general, are given in §§619 and 1111, respectively.

Example 3. If $y = (u^2 + 4)^2$ and if $u = 1/(x^2 + 1)$, find $D_x y$.

First solution. Substitution gives $y = \left(\dfrac{1}{(x^2 + 1)^2} + 4\right)^2 = \dfrac{(4x^4 + 8x^2 + 5)^2}{(x^2 + 1)^4}$ and

therefore

$$D_x y = \frac{(x^2 + 1)^4 \cdot 2(4x^4 + 8x^2 + 5)(16x^3 + 16x) - (4x^4 + 8x^2 + 5)^2 \cdot 8x(x^2 + 1)^3}{(x^2 + 1)^8}$$

$$= \frac{8x(x^2 + 1)^3(4x^4 + 8x^2 + 5)(-1)}{(x^2 + 1)^8} = -\frac{8x(4x^4 + 8x^2 + 5)}{(x^2 + 1)^5}.$$

Second solution. By Example 2, §609, $D_u y = 4u(u^2 + 4)$, and by Example 2, above, $D_x u = -2x/(x^2 + 1)^2$. Therefore formula (6) gives

$$D_x y = D_u y \cdot D_x u = \frac{4}{x^2 + 1} \cdot \frac{4x^4 + 8x^2 + 5}{(x^2 + 1)^2} \cdot \frac{-2x}{(x^2 + 1)^2} = -\frac{8x(4x^4 + 8x^2 + 5)}{(x^2 + 1)^5}.$$

For a third solution see Example 2, §702.

611 EXERCISES

In Exercises 1–6, find the derivative of the given function f.

1. $f(x) = (6x + 5)^{10}$.   **2.** $f(x) = (10x - 3)^8$.

3. $f(x) = (5x^2 + 10x + 3)^6$.   **4.** $f(x) = (6x^2 + 4x - 5)^7$.

5. $f(u) = (4u^2 + 5)^9$.   **6.** $f(v) = (5v^2 + 8)^5$.

In Exercises 7–10, find the derivative of the given function by two methods, as illustrated in Example 3, §609.

7. $\left(\dfrac{3x + 4}{5x + 2}\right)^5$.   **8.** $\left(\dfrac{4x + 5}{2x + 3}\right)^6$.

9. $\left(\dfrac{x^2 + 2}{x^2 + 4}\right)^4$.   **10.** $\left(\dfrac{3x^2 + 1}{5x^2 + 1}\right)^3$.

11. Derive formulas (18) and (19), §610.

12. Prove (25), §610, for $n = -1$:

(1)
$$\left(\frac{1}{g(x)}\right)' = -\frac{g'(x)}{g^2(x)}.$$

In Exercises 13–16, use (20), §610, to find the derivative of the given function.

13. $\sqrt{3x^2 + 4}$.   **14.** $\sqrt{5x^2 - 2}$.

15. $\sqrt{x^2 + 10x + 30}$.   **16.** $\sqrt{4x^2 - 20x + 5}$.

In Exercises 17–20, find the derivative of the given function by two methods, as illustrated in Example 2, §610, making use of formula (1) of Exercise 12.

17. $\dfrac{1}{3x^2 + 4}$. **18.** $\dfrac{1}{5x^2 - 2}$. **19.** $\dfrac{1}{x^2 + 10x + 30}$. **20.** $\dfrac{1}{4x^2 - 20x + 5}$.

In Exercises 21–28, find the derivative of the given function f, and simplify your answer.

21. $f(x) = (2x + 3)^6(5x + 4)^7$.

22. $f(y) = (3y - 1)^5(7y + 2)^4$.

23. $f(s) = (s^2 + 3)^4(s^2 + 5)^6$.

24. $f(t) = (3t^2 + 2)^5(4t^2 + 1)^3$.

25. $f(u) = \dfrac{(2u + 3)^6}{(5u + 4)^7}$.

26. $f(v) = \dfrac{(3v - 1)^5}{(7v + 2)^4}$.

27. $f(r) = \dfrac{(r^2 + 3)^4}{(r^2 + 5)^6}$.

28. $f(z) = \dfrac{(3z^2 + 2)^5}{(4z^2 + 1)^3}$.

In Exercises 29–32, find the derivative of y with respect to x by two methods as illustrated in Example 3, §610.

29. $y = (2u + 3)^2$, $u = 4x^2 + 5$.

30. $y = (u^2 + 1)^3$, $u = 3x + 2$.

31. $y = (u + 4)^2$, $u = \dfrac{1}{5x + 6}$.

32. $y = \dfrac{1}{5u + 6}$, $u = (x + 4)^2$.

612   ONE-SIDED DERIVATIVES

If the values of h in the formation of the limit of the quotient $[f(x + h) - f(x)]/h$ are restricted either to positive numbers or to negative numbers, the result is a one-sided derivative of the function f, as follows:

(1)   **Right-hand derivative** at $x \equiv \lim\limits_{h \to 0+} \dfrac{f(x + h) - f(x)}{h}$,

(2)   **Left-hand derivative** at $x \equiv \lim\limits_{h \to 0-} \dfrac{f(x + h) - f(x)}{h}$.

If a function f is defined at a point x and at points on *one* side only of the point x, then the **derivative** of f at x is defined to be the relevant one-sided derivative.

Example 1.   Find the derivative of the function $x\sqrt{x} = x^{\frac{3}{2}}$ at $x = 0$.

Solution.   Since the domain of the function $f(x) \equiv x\sqrt{x}$ is implicitly assumed to be $[0, +\infty)$ a right-hand derivative is involved, defined

(3) $\lim\limits_{h \to 0+} \dfrac{f(h) - f(0)}{h} = \lim\limits_{h \to 0+} \dfrac{h\sqrt{h}}{h} = \lim\limits_{h \to 0+} \sqrt{h}$.

Since the function $\sqrt{h}$ is continuous at $h = 0$, the limit (3) is $\sqrt{0} = 0 : f'(0) = 0$.

If a function f is defined in a (complete) neighborhood of the point x, then it has a derivative there if and only if its two one-sided derivatives at that point exist and are equal; in case the two one-sided derivatives exist and are equal, the derivative at the point is equal to their common value. (Cf. Theorem III, §503.)   Consequently, a function defined in a neighborhood of a point and failing to have equal one-sided derivatives there cannot be differentiable at that point.

Example 2. Show that the function $|x|$ is not differentiable at $x = 0$, even though it is continuous there (cf. Theorem V(i), §401).

Solution. The one-sided derivatives of $|x|$ at $x = 0$ are

(4)   Right-hand derivative $= \lim_{h \to 0+} \dfrac{|h|}{h} = \lim_{h \to 0+} 1 = 1,$

(5)   Left-hand derivative $= \lim_{h \to 0-} \dfrac{|h|}{h} = \lim_{h \to 0-} (-1) = -1.$

Since $1 \neq -1$, $|x|$ is not differentiable at $x = 0$.

NOTE.   If $A = \{a_1, a_2, \cdots, a_n\}$ is an arbitrary finite set, then $|x - a_1| + |x - a_2| + \cdots + |x - a_n|$ is a function that is everywhere continuous, but nondifferentiable on A. The German mathematician K. W. T. Weierstrass (1815–1897) was the first to give an example of a function that is everywhere continuous and *nowhere* differentiable.

613   THE LAW OF THE MEAN

It should seem at least plausible that if f is a suitably well-behaved function on a bounded closed interval $[a, b]$, then there must be at least one tangent line to its graph, at some point c between a and b, that is parallel to the secant line joining the points $(a, f(a))$ and $(b, f(b))$ (cf. Fig. 613-1).   It is the purpose of this section to formulate with precision, and to establish, a statement concerning this question.

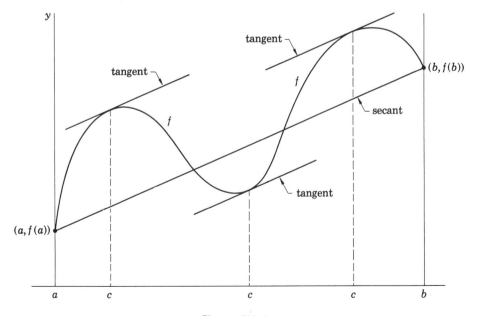

Figure 613-1

For simplicity we shall consider a special case, where the endpoints of the graph are on the x-axis, so that the secant line, and hence the tangent line sought, is *horizontal* and has zero slope. This special case is named after the French mathematician Michel Rolle (1652–1719).

Theorem I. Rolle's Theorem. *If the function f is continuous on the compact interval* $[a, b]$ *and differentiable in the open interval* (a, b), *and if* $f(a) = f(b) = 0$, *then there exists a number c between a and b,* $a < c < b$, *such that*

$$(1) \qquad\qquad f'(c) = 0.$$

Proof. There are three cases:

(*i*) $f(x) = 0$ *for all x between a and b:* In this case f is a constant, $f'(x) = 0$ for all x between a and b, and c can be chosen to be *any* interior point of the interval.

(*ii*) $f(x) > 0$ *for some x between a and b:* Since f is continuous on the compact interval $[a, b]$ it has a maximum value at some point $c \in [a, b]$ (cf. Theorem II, §414). Since this maximum value $f(c)$ is *positive*, $c \neq a$ and $c \neq b$, and hence $a < c < b$. Therefore $f'(c)$ exists. We shall show that $f'(c) = 0$ (cf. Fig. 613-2*a*), by proving that both inequalities $f'(c) > 0$ and $f'(c) < 0$ are impossible. In the former case $f'(c) > 0$, we consider the *right-hand* derivative at c (cf. Fig. 613-2*b*), and by Theorem XI, §507, infer from the positivity of the limit $\lim_{h\to 0+} [f(c + h) - f(c)]/h$ the existence of a positive number h less than $b - c$ (so that $c + h < b$) such that

$$(2) \qquad\qquad \frac{f(c + h) - f(c)}{h} > 0,$$

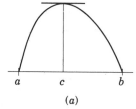 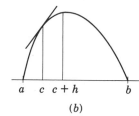 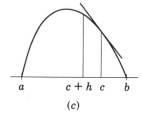

a c b	a c $c+h$ b	a $c+h$ c b
(*a*)	(*b*)	(*c*)

Figure   613-2

and hence $f(c + h) - f(c) > 0$ and $f(c + h) > f(c)$, in contradiction to the fact that $f(c)$ is the *maximum* value of f for points of $[a, b]$. Let us now assume that $f'(c) < 0$ and use the *left-hand* derivative at c (cf. Fig. 613-2*c*) to infer the existence of a *negative* number h such that $c + h > a$ and

$$(3) \qquad\qquad \frac{f(c + h) - f(c)}{h} < 0.$$

Since $h < 0$ we conclude from (3) that $f(c + h) > f(c)$, again a contradiction.

(*iii*) $f(x) < 0$ *for some x between a and b.* If $g \equiv -f$, then g satisfies the conditions of case (*ii*), and hence there exists a number c between a and b such that $g'(c) = 0$. Therefore $f'(c) = -g'(c) = 0$, and the proof is complete.

We now consider the general statement of the problem originally announced.

Theorem II. Law of the Mean (Mean Value Theorem for Derivatives). *If the function f is continuous on the compact interval [a, b] and differentiable in the open interval (a, b), then there exists a number c between a and b, a < c < b, such that*

(4)
$$f'(c) = \frac{f(b) - f(a)}{b - a}.$$

Proof. Let L denote the secant line L joining the points $(a, f(a))$ and $(b, f(b))$ (cf. Fig. 613-3). The idea of the proof is to express the vertical directed distance from L to the graph of f along the vertical line at the abscissa x, and then to make use of Rolle's theorem. Since the slope of L is $[f(b) - f(a)]/(b - a)$, and since L passes through the point $(b, f(b))$, L is the graph of the function

(5)
$$g(x) \equiv f(b) + \frac{f(b) - f(a)}{b - a} (x - b).$$

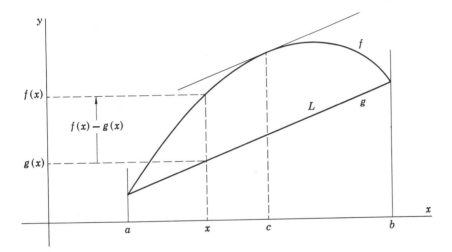

Figure 613-3

Therefore the vertical directed distance from the graph of g to the graph of f at the abscissa x is $f(x) - g(x)$, or

(6)
$$\phi(x) \equiv f(x) - f(b) - \frac{f(b) - f(a)}{b - a} (x - b).$$

Since the function $\phi(x)$ is a linear combination of the functions $f(x)$ and $x - b$, each of which is continuous on $[a, b]$ and differentiable in (a, b), and since $\phi(a) = \phi(b) = 0$, the function ϕ satisfies the conditions of Rolle's theorem and there must exist a number c between a and b such that

(7)
$$\phi'(c) = f'(c) - \frac{f(b) - f(a)}{b - a} = 0,$$

from which (4) follows, and the proof is complete.

Sometimes the formula (4) of the law of the mean is useful for the case $a > b$, and, if properly adjusted, for the case $a = b$ as well. The following statement is a generalization of Theorem II, and can be considered as an alternative form for the law of the mean:

Theorem III. *If f is continuous on an interval I (bounded or unbounded, open or closed or neither), if f is differentiable at every interior point of I, and if a and x are any two distinct points of I, then there exists a point ξ between a and x such that*

$$(8) \qquad\qquad f(x) = f(a) + f'(\xi)(x - a).$$

If f'(a) exists, then (8) holds for the case x = a = ξ as well.

Proof. If $x > a$, (8) follows from (4) with $x = b$ and $\xi = c$, since f is continuous on the closed interval $[a, x]$ and differentiable in (a, x). If $x < a$, (8) follows from (4) in a similar fashion, with a, b, and c replaced by x, a, and ξ, respectively. If $x = a = \xi$, (8) is satisfied trivially.

A third form of the law of the mean is the same as the preceding except for notation:

Theorem IV. *If f is continuous on an interval I (bounded or unbounded, open or closed or neither), if f is differentiable at every interior point of I, and if a and a + h are any two distinct points of I, then there exists a number θ such that $0 < \theta < 1$ and*

$$(9) \qquad\qquad f(a + h) = f(a) + f'(a + \theta h)h.$$

If f'(a) exists, then (9) holds for the case h = 0 as well.

Proof. In case $h \neq 0$, let $x = a + h$, use (8), and let $\theta \equiv (\xi - a)/h = (\xi - a)/(x - a)$. Then $0 < \theta < 1$ and $a + \theta h = \xi$. (Check these details.)

Example 1. Find values of c satisfying the requirements of Theorem I for the function $x(x + 1)(x - 2)$ and the interval $[a, b] = [-1, 2]$.

Solution. If $f(x) \equiv x^3 - x^2 - 2x$, $f'(x) = 3x^2 - 2x - 2$, and the roots of $3x^2 - 2x - 2 = 0$ are $c = \frac{1}{3}(1 \pm \sqrt{7})$. Since $-1 < \frac{1}{3}(1 - \sqrt{7}) < \frac{1}{3}(1 + \sqrt{7}) < 2$, either of these two values of c satisfies the requirements of Theorem I. (Cf. Fig. 614–1.)

Example 2. Write out explicitly the formulas (4) of Theorem II, (8) of Theorem III, and (9) of Theorem IV, for the quadratic function $\alpha x^2 + \beta x + \gamma$ and the interval $[a, b]$.

Solution. With $f(x) \equiv \alpha x^2 + \beta x + \gamma$, $f'(c) = 2\alpha c + \beta$ and

$$\frac{f(b) - f(a)}{b - a} = \frac{(\alpha b^2 + \beta b) - (\alpha a^2 + \beta a)}{b - a} = \alpha(a + b) + \beta.$$

Therefore equation (4) becomes $2\alpha c + \beta = \alpha(a + b) + \beta$, and $c = \frac{1}{2}(a + b)$. In other words, for any quadratic function f and any bounded closed interval I, the point at which the tangent line is parallel to the secant line for I is always $(c, f(c))$, where c is the midpoint of I. Formula (4) can be written, with $c = \frac{1}{2}(\alpha + b)$,

$$(10) \qquad\qquad 2\alpha \cdot \frac{a + b}{2} + \beta = \alpha(a + b) + \beta.$$

Similarly, formulas (8) and (9), respectively, become

(11) $$\alpha x^2 + \beta x + \gamma = \alpha a^2 + \beta a + \gamma + \left(2\alpha \frac{a+x}{2} + \beta\right)(x - a),$$

(12) $$\alpha(a + h)^2 + \beta(a + h) + \gamma = \alpha a^2 + \beta a + \gamma + [2\alpha(a + \tfrac{1}{2}h) + \beta]h.$$

614   MONOTONIC DIFFERENTIABLE FUNCTIONS

One of the simplest relationships between monotonic behavior of a function and the sign of its derivative is given in the theorem:

Theorem I. *If f is continuous on an interval I (bounded or unbounded, open or closed or neither), and if f is differentiable at least at every interior point of I, then f is increasing on I if and only if $f'(x) \geqq 0$ for every x of I at which $f'(x)$ is defined; f is decreasing on I if and only if $f'(x) \leqq 0$ for every x of I at which $f'(x)$ is defined.*

Proof. Assume first that $f'(x) \geqq 0$ at (at least) every interior point x of I. In order to prove that f is increasing on I, we shall assume the contrary, that there exist points a and b of I such at $a < b$ and $f(a) > f(b)$. By the law of the mean (Theorem II, §613), there exists a point c between a and b, and hence in the interior of I, such that $f'(c) = [f(b) - f(a)]/(b - a) < 0$. With this contradiction we conclude that f is increasing on I. In an exactly similar way it can be shown that if $f'(x) \leqq 0$ at every interior point of I, f must be decreasing on I.

To prove the converse (the "only if") part of the theorem, assume that f is increasing on I, and let c by any point of I at which $f'(c)$ exists. If c is *not* the right-hand endpoint of I, let h be any positive number such that $c + h \in I$. Then, since $f(c) \leqq f(c + h)$, $[f(c + h) - f(c)]/h \geqq 0$, and therefore, by the Corollary to Theorem III, §507,

(1) $$f'(c) = \lim_{h \to 0+} \frac{f(c + h) - f(c)}{h} \geqq 0.$$

If c *is* the right-hand endpoint of I, let h be any *negative* number such that $c + h \in I$. Then, since $f(c + h) \leqq f(c)$ and $h < 0$, $[f(c + h) - f(c)]/h \geqq 0$, and therefore, as above,

(2) $$f'(c) = \lim_{h \to 0-} \frac{f(c + h) - f(c)}{h} \geqq 0.$$

Finally, if f is decreasing on I, the argument just used, with the inequality symbols $\leqq$ and $\geqq$ reversed, proves that $f'(c) \leqq 0$.

A corollary of this theorem is destined for repeated use:

Theorem II. *If f is continuous on an interval I (bounded or unbounded, open or closed or neither), and if for every interior point x of I, $f'(x)$ exists and is equal to 0, then f is constant on I.*

First proof. By Theorem I, under the stated assumptions f is both increasing and decreasing, and hence constant, on I.

Second proof. Assume that $f'(x) = 0$ for every point x interior to I, and assume that f is *not* constant on I. Then there exist two points a and b of I such that $a < b$ and $f(a) \neq f(b)$. By the law of the mean (Theorem II, §613), there exists a point c between a and b, and hence in the interior of I, such that $f'(c) = [f(b) - f(a)]/(b - a) \neq 0$. (Contradiction.)

The case of *strict* increase or decrease is not quite so simple (cf. Example 1, below):

Theorem III. *If f is continuous on an interval I (bounded or unbounded, open or closed or neither), and if for every interior point x of I, $f'(x)$ exists and is positive ($f'(x) > 0$), then f is strictly increasing on I; if for every interior point x of I, $f'(x)$ exists and is negative ($f'(x) < 0$), then f is strictly decreasing on I.*

Proof. The details are the same as those of the first part of the proof of Theorem I except for inequality symbols. For example, if $f'(x) > 0$ for all interior points x, and if f were not *strictly* increasing on I, there would be points a and b of I such that $a < b$ and $f(a) \geq f(b)$, and hence an interior point c between a and b such that $f'(c) = [f(b) - f(a)]/(b - a) \leq 0$. (Contradiction.)

Example 1. Show that the converse of Theorem III is false.

Solution. The function x^3 is strictly increasing on $[-1, 1]$, but its derivative $3x^2$ vanishes at $x = 0$.

For problem work it will be convenient to have the following definition:

Definition. *Let f be a function with domain D and let I be an interval contained*

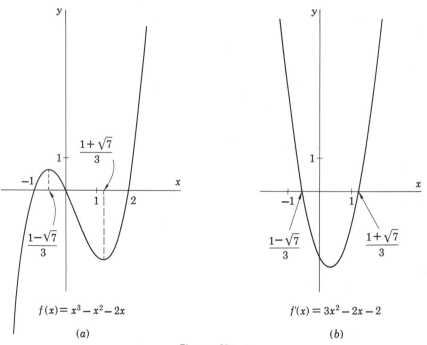

$$f(x) = x^3 - x^2 - 2x$$

$$(a)$$

$$f'(x) = 3x^2 - 2x - 2$$

$$(b)$$

Figure 614-1

*in D. Then I is a **maximal interval of monotonicity** of f if and only if (i) f is monotonic on I and (ii) whenever J is a proper superinterval of I, f fails to be monotonic on J.*

Similar definitions apply if the word *monotonicity* is replaced by *strict monotonocity, increase, strict increase, decrease,* or *strict decrease.*

Example 2. Find the maximal intervals of monotonicity of the function $x(x + 1)(x - 2)$.

Solution. With $f(x) \equiv x^3 - x^2 - 2x$,

$$(3) \qquad f'(x) = 3x^2 - 2x - 2 = 3\left(x - \frac{1 - \sqrt{7}}{3}\right)\left(x - \frac{1 + \sqrt{7}}{3}\right).$$

Since $f'(x) > 0$ if and only if $x < \frac{1}{3}(1 - \sqrt{7})$ or if $x > \frac{1}{3}(1 + \sqrt{7})$, maximal intervals of strict increase are $(-\infty, \frac{1}{3}(1 - \sqrt{7})]$ and $[\frac{1}{3}(1 + \sqrt{7}), +\infty)$ (cf. Fig. 614-1.) Since $f'(x) < 0$ if and only if $\frac{1}{3}(1 - \sqrt{7}) < x < \frac{1}{3}(1 + \sqrt{7})$, a maximal interval of strict decrease is $[\frac{1}{3}(1 - \sqrt{7}), \frac{1}{3}(1 + \sqrt{7})]$.

615   VERTICAL TANGENTS

The idea of a vertical tangent to the graph of a continuous function f at a point $(a, f(a))$ is the same as for a nonvertical tangent, except that the limit of $[f(a + h) - f(a)]/h$ is either $+\infty$ or $-\infty$ (cf. § 510):

$$(1) \qquad \lim_{h \to 0} \frac{f(a + h) - f(a)}{h} = +\infty \text{ or } -\infty.$$

In either case, the tangent line at $(a, f(a))$ is the line with equation $x = a$. Similar remarks apply to vertical tangents in case the associated infinite limits are one-sided limits. In case a graph is a composite of an "upper half" and a "lower half," as with $y^2 = x$ (cf. Example 5), then a vertical line is tangent to the composite graph at a point p if and only if it is tangent to each of the two constituent "halves" at p.

Example 1. Show that the y-axis is tangent to the curve $y = \sqrt[3]{x}$ at the origin (cf. Fig. 615-1).

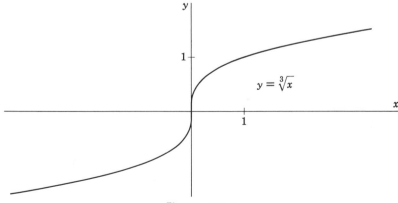

Figure 615-1

Solution. With $f(x) \equiv \sqrt[3]{x} = x^{\frac{1}{3}}$ and $a \equiv 0$, we evaluate the limit

(2) $$\lim_{h \to 0} \frac{f(0 + h) - f(0)}{h} = \lim_{h \to 0} \frac{h^{\frac{1}{3}}}{h} = \lim_{h \to 0} \frac{1}{h^{\frac{2}{3}}}.$$

Since $\lim_{h \to 0} h^{\frac{2}{3}} = 0$ (cf. Theorem VI, §411), it follows from Theorem I, §510, and the fact that $h^{\frac{2}{3}} \geqq 0$, that the limit (1) is $+\infty$. Therefore $y = \sqrt[3]{x}$ has a vertical tangent at $(0, 0)$, as was to be proved.

Example 2. Show that the y-axis is not tangent to the **semicubical parabola** $y = \sqrt[3]{x^2}$ at the origin (cf. Fig. 615-2a).

Solution   With $f(x) \equiv \sqrt[3]{x^2} = x^{\frac{2}{3}}$, the limit corresponding to (1) is

(3) $$\lim_{h \to 0} \frac{h^{\frac{2}{3}} - 0}{h} = \lim_{h \to 0} \frac{1}{h^{\frac{1}{3}}} = \infty.$$

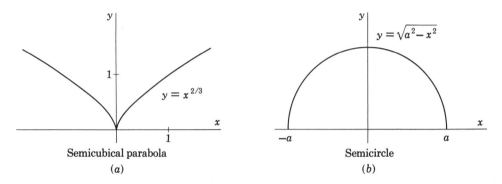

Semicubical parabola
(a)

Semicircle
(b)

Figure 615-2

However, the values of $1/h^{\frac{1}{3}}$ are *not* of one sign, and therefore neither limit $+\infty$ nor $-\infty$ is appropriate. The one-sided limits for this function at $(0, 0)$ are

(4) $$\lim_{h \to 0+} \frac{1}{h^{\frac{1}{3}}} = +\infty, \quad \lim_{h \to 0-} \frac{1}{h^{\frac{1}{3}}} = -\infty.$$

The origin is called a *cusp* of the curve $y = \sqrt[3]{x^2}$. (In general, if p is a point belonging to two curves C_1 and C_2 that have a common tangent at p and if the union $C_1 \cup C_2$ is a curve that does not possess a tangent at p, then p is a **cusp** of C. In the present example the curves C_1 and C_2 are given by $x^{\frac{2}{3}}, x \geqq 0$, and $x^{\frac{2}{3}}, x \leqq 0$.)

Example 3. Show that the semicircle $y = \sqrt{a^2 - x^2}$, $|x| \leqq a$, where $a > 0$, has vertical tangents at $x = a$ and at $x = -a$ (cf. Fig. 615-2b).

Solution. We give the details only for $x = a$. With $f(x) \equiv \sqrt{a^2 - x^2}$, we are led in this case to the one-sided limit

(5) $\lim_{h \to 0-} \dfrac{f(a + h) - f(a)}{h} = \lim_{h \to 0-} \dfrac{\sqrt{-2ah - h^2}}{h} = \lim_{h \to 0-} \dfrac{\sqrt{(-h)(2a + h)}}{-\sqrt{-h}\sqrt{-h}} = \lim_{h \to 0-} -\dfrac{\sqrt{2a + h}}{\sqrt{-h}}.$

Since $\lim_{h \to 0-} \sqrt{2a + h} = \sqrt{2a} > 0$, $\lim_{h \to 0-} \sqrt{-h} = 0$, and the values of $-\sqrt{2a + h}/\sqrt{-h}$ are all negative for $-a < h < 0$, it follows from Theorem I, §510, that the limit in (5) is $-\infty$.

Occasionally a vertical tangent can be identified by the behavior of a derivative evaluated near the point in question:

Theorem. *If f is defined and continuous on a one-sided neighborhood $N_{a+} = [a, a + \eta)$ or $N_{a-} = (a - \eta, a]$ of a, and differentiable in the interior $(a, a + \eta)$ or $(a - \eta, a)$, and if the appropriate one-sided limit*

$$(6) \qquad \lim_{x \to a+} f'(x) \quad \text{or} \quad \lim_{x \to a-} f'(x)$$

exists and is either $+\infty$ or $-\infty$, then the corresponding limit

$$(7) \qquad \lim_{h \to 0+} \frac{f(a + h) - f(a)}{h} \quad \text{or} \quad \lim_{h \to 0-} \frac{f(a + h) - f(a)}{h}$$

exists and is either $+\infty$ or $-\infty$ in agreement with the limit (6).

Proof. For definiteness we shall consider the case

$$(8) \qquad \lim_{x \to a+} f'(x) = +\infty.$$

By definition of the limit $+\infty$ (cf. §510), if p is an arbitrary positive number there exists a positive number δ less than or equal to η such that

$$(9) \qquad a < x < a + \delta \implies f'(x) > p.$$

We now let h be any number such that $0 < h < \delta$, and apply the law of the mean (Theorem II, §613) to the interval $[a, a + h]$. That is, there must exist a number c between a and $a + h$ such that

$$(10) \qquad f'(c) = \frac{f(a + h) - f(a)}{h}.$$

Since $a < c < a + h < a + \delta, f'(c) > p$, by (9), and consequently, from (10),

$$(11) \qquad \frac{f(a + h) - f(a)}{h} > p.$$

Therefore, $\lim_{h \to 0+} \dfrac{f(a + h) - f(a)}{h} = +\infty.$

Example 4. Prove that the y-axis is tangent to the graph of $y = \sqrt{x}, x \geqq 0$, at $(0, 0)$.

First solution. With $f(x) \equiv \sqrt{x} = x^{\frac{1}{2}}$, the limit (1) is

$$(12) \qquad \lim_{h \to 0+} \frac{f(0 + h) - f(0)}{h} = \lim_{h \to 0+} \frac{\sqrt{h}}{h} = \lim_{h \to 0+} \frac{1}{\sqrt{h}} = +\infty.$$

Furthermore, the function $\sqrt{x}$ is right-continuous at $x = 0$.

Second solution. Since $f'(x) = 1/2\sqrt{x}$ (cf. Example 4, § 603), and $\lim_{x \to 0+} 1/2\sqrt{x} = +\infty$, it follows from the preceding Theorem that $\lim_{x \to +0} \dfrac{f(0 + h) - f(0)}{h} = +\infty$.

Example 5. Prove that the y-axis is tangent to the graph of $y^2 = x$ at $(0, 0)$.

Solution. By Example 4 the *y*-axis is tangent to the curve $y = \sqrt{x}$ at $(0, 0)$, and by symmetry it is also tangent to the curve $y = -\sqrt{x}$ at $(0, 0)$. Therefore it is tangent to the union of these two curves at $(0, 0)$.

616   EXERCISES

A graph should accompany each of Exercises 1–26.

In Exercises 1–4, show that the given function is not differentiable at the specified point. Show that the function has distinct one-sided derivatives at this point, and find their values.

1. $2x + |x - 2|$, $x = 2$.

2. $x + 2|x - 1|$, $x = 1$.

3. $f(x) = \begin{cases} x^2, x \leq 1, \\ x^3, x > 1, \end{cases}$ $x = 1$.

4. $f(x) = \begin{cases} x^2, x < 2, \\ 6 - x, x \geq 2, \end{cases}$ $x = 2$.

In Exercises 5–8, find numbers c and θ in conformity with (4) and (9), § 613, for the given function f and interval $[a, b] = [a, + h]$.

5. $f(x) = x^2 - 2x$, $[1, 3]$.

6. $f(x) = 17 - x^2$, $[-1, 4]$.

7. $f(x) = x^3$, $[0, 2]$.

8. $f(x) = \dfrac{1}{x}$, $[1, 2]$.

In Exercises 9–16, find the maximal intervals of strict increase and of strict decrease for the given function. Justify your conclusion by relating monotonicity to the sign of a derivative.

9. $6x - x^2$.

10. $x^2 - 5x$.

11. $x^3 - 3x^2 - 9x$.

12. $9x^2 - x^3$.

13. $\dfrac{x}{x^2 + 9}$.

14. $\dfrac{x^2 + 4}{x}$.

15. $\dfrac{(x - 1)(x - 4)}{x} = x - 5 + \dfrac{4}{x}$.

16. $\dfrac{x - 1}{x^2} = \dfrac{1}{x} - \dfrac{1}{x^2}$.

In Exercises 17–20, show that the graph of the given function has a vertical tangent at the specified point, using the two methods illustrated in Example 4, §615.

17. $\sqrt{x - 1}$, $(1, 0)$. **18.** $\sqrt{1 - x}$, $(1, 0)$. **19.** $\sqrt{x - x^2}$, $(1, 0)$. **20.** $\sqrt{x - x^2}$, $(0, 0)$.

In Exercises 21 and 22, show that the graph of the given function has a cusp rather than a vertical tangent at the specified point.

21. $x^{\frac{2}{5}}$, $(0, 0)$.

22. $(x - 1)^{\frac{2}{3}}$, $(1, 0)$.

In Exercises 23–26, show that the graph of the given curve has a vertical tangent at the specified point. (Cf. Exs. 17–20.)

23. $y^2 = x - 1$, $(1, 0)$.

24. $y^2 = 1 - x$, $(1, 0)$.

25. $y^2 = x - x^2$, $(1, 0)$.

26. $y^2 = x - x^2$, $(0, 0)$.

617   THE INTERMEDIATE-VALUE PROPERTY FOR DERIVATIVES

Although there exist discontinuous derivatives (cf. H§1129, *CWAG*), every derivative shares with continuous functions the *intermediate-value property* (cf. Theorem II, §409) as we shall see in Theorem II, below. We start with a special case:

Theorem I. *If f is differentiable on a compact interval [a, b], and if f'(a) and f'(b) are nonzero and of opposite sign, then there exists a number c between a and b such that f'(c) = 0.*

Proof. We consider first the case where $f'(a) > 0$ and $f'(b) < 0$ (cf. Fig. 617-1).

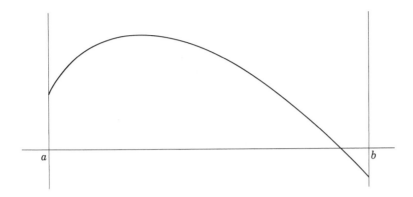

Figure 617-1

This means that neither $f(a)$ nor $f(b)$ can be the maximum value of f on $[a, b]$: (*i*) Since $\lim_{h \to 0+} [f(a + h) - f(a)]/h > 0$, there exists a positive number h such that $a + h < b$ and $[f(a + h) - f(a)]/h > 0$ (cf. Theorem XI, § 507), and hence $f(a + h) > f(a)$. (*ii*) Since $\lim_{h \to 0-} [f(b + h) - f(b)]/h < 0$, there exists a negative number h such that $b + h > a$ and $[f(b + h) - f(b)]/h < 0$ (cf. Theorem XI, § 507) and hence $f(b + h) > f(b)$. Therefore the maximum value of f on the bounded closed interval $[a, b]$ (cf. Theorem II, §414) must be attained at an *interior point c*. By the same argument as that used in the proof of Rolle's theorem (Theorem I, § 613), $f'(c) = 0$.

In case $f'(a) < 0$ and $f'(b) > 0$, we let $g \equiv -f$, and conclude from the preceding paragraph that there exists an interior point c such that $g'(c) = 0$, whence $f'(c) = -g'(c) = 0$.

We can now establish the **intermediate-value property** for derivatives:

Theorem II. *If f is differentiable on an interval I (bounded or unbounded, open or closed or neither), if a and b are any two points of I such that a < b and f'(a) ≠ f'(b), and if r is any number between f'(a) and f'(b), then there exists a number c between a and b such that f'(c) = r.*

Proof. Let $g(x) \equiv f(x) - rx$. Then $g'(x) = f'(x) - r$, $g'(a) = f'(a) - r$, and $g'(b) = f'(b) - r$. Since r is between $f'(a)$ and $f'(b)$, $g'(a)$ and $g'(b)$ have opposite signs and hence, by Theorem I, there exists a number c between a and b such that $g'(c) = 0$, or $f'(c) - r = 0$. Therefore $f'(c) = r$.

Example. Show that the signum function (Example 2, §115, *PCLA*) is not the derivative of any function.

Solution. Since the signum function has no values between the two values 0 and 1, it fails to have the intermediate-value property demanded by Theorem II.

As an immediate consequence of this theorem and Theorem III, § 614, we have:

Theorem III. *If f is continuous on an interval I (bounded or unbounded, open or closed or neither) and if f is differentiable with a nonzero derivative throughout the interior of I, then either f'(x) > 0 in the interior of I and f is strictly increasing on I or f'(x) < 0 in the interior of I and f is strictly decreasing on I.*

Proof. If there were two points interior to *I* at which *f'* had opposite signs, then the intermediate value of 0 would be assumed at some interior point, in contradiction to the assumption that *f'*(*x*) is never zero.

Theorem III gives a useful condition for the existence of the inverse of a function, by Theorem I, §410. And since a differentiable function is continuous, an extra dividend is the continuity of the inverse, by Theorem II, §410:

Theorem IV. *If f is continuous on an interval I and differentiable with a nonzero derivative throughout the interior of I, and if the interval J is the range of f, then the inverse function φ exists and is a strictly monotonic and continuous mapping of the interval J onto the interval I.*

618   DIFFERENTIABILITY OF INVERSE FUNCTIONS

Derivatives of inverse functions have a simple relationship; they are *reciprocals*. The precise statement completes Theorem IV, §617:

Theorem. *If f is differentiable with a nonzero derivative on an interval I, and if the interval J is the range of f, then the inverse function φ is differentiable with a non-zero derivative on J. If u is any point of I and v ≡ f(u), then*

$$(1) \qquad\qquad \phi'(v) = \frac{1}{f'(u)}, \quad f'(u) = \frac{1}{\phi'(v)}.$$

Proof. Let Δx be such that $u + \Delta x \in I$, and let $\Delta y \equiv f(u + \Delta x) - f(u)$ (cf. Fig. 618-1). Then formula (1) takes the form

$$(2) \qquad\qquad \lim_{\Delta y \to 0} \frac{\Delta x}{\Delta y} = \frac{1}{\lim\limits_{\Delta x \to 0} \dfrac{\Delta y}{\Delta x}}.$$

The *intuitive* idea is that since y is a continuous function of x, $\lim_{\Delta x \to 0} \Delta y = 0$, and since x is a continuous function of y, $\lim_{\Delta y \to 0} \Delta x = 0$, and therefore (2) follows from the limit theorem for quotients (Theorem XIII, § 507):

$$\lim_{\Delta y \to 0} \frac{\Delta x}{\Delta y} = \lim_{\Delta y \to 0} \frac{1}{\dfrac{\Delta y}{\Delta x}} = \frac{1}{\lim\limits_{\Delta y \to 0} \dfrac{\Delta y}{\Delta x}} = \frac{1}{\lim\limits_{\Delta x \to 0} \dfrac{\Delta y}{\Delta x}}.$$

The only detail that remains in order to make this proof completely rigorous is to show that if $\lim_{\Delta x \to 0} \Delta y / \Delta x$ exists and is equal to a number r, then $\lim_{\Delta y \to 0} \Delta y / \Delta x$ also exists and is equal to r:

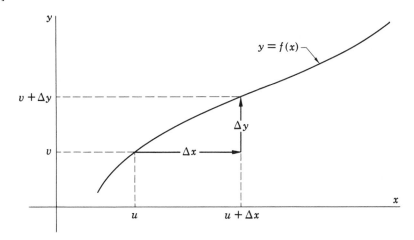

Figure 618-1

$$(3) \qquad \lim_{\Delta y \to 0} \frac{\Delta y}{\Delta x} = \lim_{\Delta x \to 0} \frac{\Delta y}{\Delta x} = r.$$

Accordingly, we assume:

$$(4) \qquad \forall \, \epsilon > 0, \exists \, \eta > 0 \ni \begin{Bmatrix} u + \Delta x \in I \\ 0 < |\Delta x| < \eta \end{Bmatrix} \Rightarrow \left| \frac{\Delta y}{\Delta x} - r \right| < \epsilon.$$

By the continuity of x as a function of y at the point v (Theorem IV, § 617), and the one-to-oneness of the mapping,

$$(5) \qquad \forall \, \eta > 0, \exists \, \delta > 0 \ni \begin{Bmatrix} v + \Delta y \in J \\ 0 < |\Delta y| < \delta \end{Bmatrix} \Rightarrow 0 < |\Delta x| < \eta.$$

In combination, (4) and (5) give:

$$(6) \qquad \forall \, \epsilon > 0, \exists \, \delta > 0 \ni \begin{Bmatrix} v + \Delta y \in J \\ 0 < |\Delta y| < \delta \end{Bmatrix} \Rightarrow \left| \frac{\Delta y}{\Delta x} - r \right| < \epsilon,$$

and therefore $\lim_{\Delta y \to 0} \Delta y / \Delta x = r$, as desired. This completes the proof.

In terms of the notation of variables x and y, formula (1) can be written

$$(7) \qquad D_y x = \frac{1}{D_x y}, \qquad D_x y = \frac{1}{D_y x}.$$

If a function f and its inverse f^{-1} are both expressed by means of the variable y as a function of x, then the preceding theorem states that not only the graphs of f and f^{-1}, but also tangent lines at corresponding points of these graphs, are symmetric with respect to the quadrant bisector $y = x$ (cf. Fig. 618-2).

Example 1. Use (1) to find the derivative of $\sqrt{x}$ for $x > 0$.

Solution. Writing $y = \sqrt{x}$, we can express the inverse function as a function of y by solving for x: $x = y^2$. Since $D_y x = 2y = 2\sqrt{x}$,

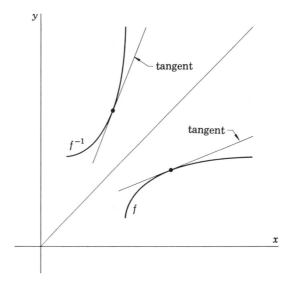

Figure 618-2

(8)
$$D_x y = \frac{1}{D_y x} = \frac{1}{2\sqrt{x}},$$

in agreement with Example 4, §603.

Example 2. Use (1) to find the derivative of $\sqrt[n]{x}$, for $x > 0$. Apply the resulting formula to the particular functions $\sqrt[3]{x}$ and $\sqrt[4]{x}$.

Solution. Writing $y = \sqrt[n]{x}$, we can express the inverse function as a function of y by solving for x: $x = y^n$. Since $D_y x = n y^{n-1} = n(\sqrt[n]{x})^{n-1} = n\sqrt[n]{x^{n-1}} = n x^{(n-1)/n}$,

(9)
$$D_x y = \frac{1}{D_y x} = \frac{1}{n x^{(n-1)/n}} = \frac{1}{n\sqrt[n]{x^{n-1}}}.$$

If $n = 3$ and $n = 4$, (9) gives

$$\left(\sqrt[3]{x}\right)' = \frac{1}{3x^{\frac{2}{3}}} = \frac{1}{3\sqrt[3]{x^2}}, \quad \left(\sqrt[4]{x}\right)' = \frac{1}{4x^{\frac{3}{4}}} = \frac{1}{4\sqrt[4]{x^3}}.$$

Example 3. Show that if both a function and its inverse are assumed to be differentiable then formula (1) can be derived from the formula for the derivative of a composite function

Solution. If ϕ is the inverse of f, then (cf. (7), §502, *PCLA*) for each x of the domain of f,

$$\phi(f(x)) = x,$$

and consequently (cf. (4), §610)

(10)
$$\phi'(f(x)) \cdot f'(x) = 1.$$

Letting $x = u$ and $f(u) = v$, (10) gives

(11)
$$\phi'(v) \cdot f'(u) = 1,$$

which is equivalent to (1).

619   DIFFERENTIATION OF RATIONAL POWERS

It has already been observed that the formula

(1) $$D_x(x^n) = nx^{n-1}$$

holds whenever n is a positive integer ((3), §605), $n = \frac{1}{2}$ (Example 4, §603), or $n = -1$ (Example 5, §603). We shall now show that this same formula is valid whenever n is *any* rational number, for appropriate values of x. In §1111 we shall establish (1) for *all real n* and $x > 0$.

Formula (1) holds whenever n is a negative integer and $x \neq 0$.

Proof. If n is a negative integer, let m be the positive integer $m \equiv -n$. Then the function $x^n = x^{-m} = 1/x^m$ can be differentiated as a quotient, when $x \neq 0$:

(2) $$D_x\left(\frac{1}{x^m}\right) = \frac{x^m \cdot D_x 1 - 1 \cdot D_x(x^m)}{(x^m)^2} = \frac{-mx^{m-1}}{x^{2m}} = -\frac{m}{x^{m+1}} = nx^{n-1}.$$

Formula (1) holds whenever n is the reciprocal of a positive integer and $x > 0$; formula (1) holds whenever n is the reciprocal of a positive odd integer and $x \neq 0$.

Proof. Let $n = 1/q$, where q is a positive integer (odd in case $x < 0$), and let $y = x^{1/q} = \sqrt[q]{x}$. Then $x = y^q$, $D_y x = qy^{q-1}$ and by (7), §618,

(3) $$D_x y = \frac{1}{D_y x} = \frac{1}{qy^{q-1}} = \frac{1}{q}(x^{\frac{1}{q}})^{1-q} = \frac{1}{q}x^{\frac{1}{q}-1},$$

which is (1) with $n = 1/q$.

Formula (1) holds whenever n is a rational number and $x > 0$; formula (1) holds whenever $n = p/q$ where p and q are integers and q is odd, and $x \neq 0$; if in either of the preceding two cases $n > 1$, formula (1) is also valid for $x = 0$.

Proof. Let $n = p/q$, where p and q are integers as specified, and let

(4) $$y = x^{p/q} = (\sqrt[q]{x})^p.$$

Then y can be expressed as the composite function

(5) $$y = u^p, \quad \text{where} \quad u = \sqrt[q]{x},$$

and hence by the chain rule (§610) and formulas already established,

(6) $$D_x y = D_u y \cdot D_x u = pu^{p-1} \cdot \frac{1}{q} x^{\frac{1}{q}-1} = \frac{p}{q}(x^{\frac{1}{q}})^{p-1} x^{\frac{1}{q}-1} = \frac{p}{q} x^{\frac{p}{q}-\frac{1}{q}+\frac{1}{q}-1},$$

which is (1) with $n = p/q$. Finally, if $n > 1$ and $x = 0$, $D_x(x^n)$ can be evaluated directly from the definition:

(7) $$D_x(x^n) \text{ at } x = 0 = \lim_{h \to 0} \frac{h^n - 0}{h} = \lim_{h \to 0} h^{n-1} = 0,$$

the last equality being valid by Theorem VI and Note 3, §411.

As far as the appropriate values of x are concerned we can summarize the preceding results by the simple statement that *formula (1) holds for rational n wherever it makes sense*.

By use of the chain rule (§ 610) we can extend the formulas (1)–(3) of the Theorem, § 609, to derivatives of rational powers g^n of a differentiable function g, whenever these formulas have meaning (for example, if n is a negative integer and $g(x) \neq 0$, or if n is rational and $g(x) > 0$):

(8) $$\text{If } \phi(x) = g^n(x), \; \phi'(x) = ng^{n-1}(x)g'(x),$$

(9) $$(g^n)' = ng^{n-1}g',$$

(10) $$D_x(u^n) = nu^{n-1}D_xu.$$

Example 1. $(x^{\frac{5}{4}})' = \dfrac{5}{4}x^{\frac{1}{4}} = \dfrac{5}{4}\sqrt[4]{x}, \; x \geq 0;$

$(x^{\frac{3}{8}})' = \dfrac{3}{8}x^{-\frac{5}{8}} = \dfrac{3}{8\sqrt[8]{x^5}}, \; x > 0;$

$(x^{\frac{2}{5}})' = \dfrac{2}{5}x^{-\frac{3}{5}} = \dfrac{2}{5\sqrt[5]{x^3}}, \; x \neq 0;$

$(x^{\frac{8}{5}})' = \dfrac{8}{5}x^{\frac{3}{5}} = \dfrac{8}{5}\sqrt[5]{x^3}; \; x \in \Re.$

Example 2. Differentiate $\sqrt[3]{x^3 + 5}$.

Solution. Writing the function in the form $(x^3 + 5)^{\frac{1}{3}}$, we have

$$((x^3 + 5)^{\frac{1}{3}})' = \frac{1}{3}(x^3 + 5)^{-\frac{2}{3}}(x^3 + 5)' = x^2/\sqrt[3]{(x^3 + 5)^2}.$$

Example 3. Differentiate $x/\sqrt{25 - x^2}$ in two ways, once as a quotient and once as a product.

First solution. Differentiating the function as a quotient gives

$$\left(\frac{x}{\sqrt{25 - x^2}}\right) = \frac{\sqrt{25 - x^2}\cdot x' - x((25 - x^2)^{\frac{1}{2}})'}{25 - x^2}$$

$$= \frac{\sqrt{25 - x^2} - x\cdot\frac{1}{2}(25 - x^2)^{-\frac{1}{2}}(-2x)}{25 - x^2} = \frac{25}{(25 - x^2)^{\frac{3}{2}}}.$$

Second solution. Differentiating the function as a product gives

$$(x\cdot(25 - x^2)^{-\frac{1}{2}})' = x\cdot((25 - x^2)^{-\frac{1}{2}})' + (25 - x^2)^{-\frac{1}{2}}\cdot x'$$

$$= x(-\tfrac{1}{2})(25 - x^2)^{-\frac{3}{2}}(-2x) + (25 - x^2)^{-\frac{1}{2}}$$

$$= (25 - x^2)^{-\frac{3}{2}}(x^2 + 25 - x^2) = 25/(25 - x^2)^{\frac{3}{2}}.$$

620 EXERCISES

In Exercises 1–16, find the derivative of the given function f.

1. $f(x) = \frac{2}{7}x^{\frac{7}{2}} - \frac{2}{5}x^{\frac{5}{2}} + \frac{2}{3}x^{\frac{3}{2}}.$ **2.** $f(x) = \frac{3}{7}x^{\frac{7}{3}} + \frac{3}{4}x^{\frac{4}{3}} - 3x^{\frac{1}{3}}.$

3. $f(r) = 6r^{\frac{5}{3}} - 8r^{-\frac{5}{4}}$.

4. $f(s) = 10s^{\frac{2}{5}} - 9s^{-\frac{5}{3}}$.

5. $f(y) = \sqrt{y} + \sqrt[4]{y} + \sqrt[6]{y}$.

6. $f(z) = \sqrt[3]{z^2} + \sqrt[5]{z^4} + \sqrt[7]{z^6}$.

7. $f(u) = 7u^{\frac{1}{3}} - 5u^{-\frac{2}{3}}$.

8. $f(v) = 3v^{\frac{2}{5}} - 2v^{-\frac{3}{5}}$.

9. $f(x) = \sqrt[4]{x^4 + 5}$.

10. $f(x) = \sqrt{3x^2 + 8}$.

11. $f(t) = (\sqrt{t} + 5)^8$.

12. $f(w) = (\sqrt[3]{w} - 4)^6$.

13. $f(r) = \sqrt{(9r^2 + 4)^3}$.

14. $f(s) = \sqrt{(5 - 2s^2)^5}$.

15. $f(u) = u\sqrt{9 - u^2}$.

16. $f(v) = v\sqrt{v^2 + 9}$.

In Exercises 17–20, find the derivative of the given function in two ways as suggested.

17. $\sqrt{3x} = (3x)^{\frac{1}{2}} = \sqrt{3}x^{\frac{1}{2}}$.

18. $\sqrt[3]{2x} = (2x)^{\frac{1}{3}} = \sqrt[3]{2}x^{\frac{1}{3}}$.

19. $x\sqrt[3]{4x} = (4x^4)^{\frac{1}{3}} = \sqrt[3]{4}x^{\frac{4}{3}}$.

20. $x\sqrt{5x} = (5x^3)^{\frac{1}{2}} = \sqrt{5}x^{\frac{3}{2}}$.

In Exercises 21–28, differentiate the given function in two ways, once as a quotient and once as a product.

21. $\dfrac{(2x + 5)^3}{(3x + 1)^2}$.

22. $\dfrac{(4x + 1)^2}{(5x + 3)^3}$.

23. $\dfrac{x^2 + 4}{(x^2 + 9)^3}$.

24. $\dfrac{x^2 + 5}{(x^2 + 2)^2}$.

25. $\dfrac{1}{\sqrt{x^2 + 4}}$.

26. $\dfrac{1}{\sqrt{9 - x^2}}$.

27. $\dfrac{x}{\sqrt{2x^2 + 3}}$.

28. $\dfrac{x}{\sqrt{3x^2 + 2}}$.

In Exercises 29–32, differentiate the given function in three ways, once as a power of a quotient, once as a quotient of powers, and once as a product of powers.

29. $\left(\dfrac{2x + 7}{5x + 1}\right)^4$.

30. $\left(\dfrac{3x + 2}{4x + 9}\right)^3$.

31. $\sqrt{\dfrac{x^2 + 4}{x^2 + 9}}$.

32. $\sqrt{\dfrac{9 - x^2}{4 - x^2}}$.

In Exercises 33–40, find the derivative of the given function, and simplify.

33. $(2x + 7)^4 \sqrt{8x + 1}$.

34. $(5x + 3)^6 \sqrt[3]{6x + 5}$.

35. $\sqrt{4x + 3} \sqrt[3]{3x + 4}$.

36. $\sqrt{x^2 + 4} \sqrt[3]{x^3 + 8}$.

37. $\dfrac{(2x + 7)^4}{\sqrt{8x + 1}}$.

38. $\dfrac{(5x + 3)^6}{\sqrt[3]{6x + 5}}$.

39. $\dfrac{\sqrt{4x + 3}}{\sqrt[3]{3x + 4}}$.

40. $\dfrac{\sqrt{x^2 + 4}}{\sqrt[3]{x^3 + 8}}$.

In Exercises 41–44, find the equations of the tangent line and normal line to the given curve at the specified point.

41. $y = (2x - 5)^{\frac{3}{2}}$, $(3, 1)$.

42. $y = (3x - 1)^{\frac{2}{3}}$, $(3, 4)$.

43. $y = \sqrt{2x^2 + 1}$, $(2, 3)$.

44. $y = \sqrt{20 - x^2}$, $(2, 4)$.

In Exercises 45–50, solve for y in terms of x and find $D_x y$. Solve for x in terms of y and find $D_y x$. Show that for corresponding points these derivatives are reciprocals. Draw graphs.

45. $3x + 2y = 12$.

46. $4x - 5y = 20$.

47. $x^2 - 3y + 5 = 0$.

48. $2x - y^2 = 8$.

49. $y^3 = x^5$.   **50.** $y^7 = x^4$.

In Exercises 51 and 52, find the derivative of the given function. (Cf. Ex. 23, §608.)

51. $x \cdot (3x + 1)^5 \cdot \sqrt{4x + 3}$.   **52.** $x \cdot (2x + 5)^6 \cdot \sqrt{6x + 1}$.

621   THE FORMULA FOR DIFFERENTIATING THE SINE FUNCTION

In §1117 an analytic treatment of the trigonometric functions is outlined, with reference to Chapter 19 and other portions of *CWAG* for complete details. For illustrative purposes we merely state without proof in this section a differentiation formula:

If $f(x) \equiv \sin x$, where $x \in \Re$, then f is everywhere differentiable, and $f'(x) = \cos x$:

(1) $D_x \sin x = \cos x$.

An immediate consequence of (1) and the chain rule is the following formula for differentiating $\sin u$, where u is a differentiable function of x:

(2) $D_x \sin u = \cos u \cdot D_x u$.

Proof.   With $y = \sin u$, $D_x y = D_u y \cdot D_x u = D_u \sin u \cdot D_x u = \cos u \cdot D_x u$.

Example 1.   Differentiate $\sin 3x$.

Solution.   With $u = 3x$, formula (2) gives $D_x(\sin 3x) = \cos 3x \cdot D_x(3x) = 3 \cos 3x$.

Example 2.   Differentiate $\sin x^2$.

Solution.   By (2), $(\sin x^2)' = (\cos x^2)(x^2)' = 2x \cos x^2$.

Example 3.   Differentiate $\sin \dfrac{1}{x}$, $x \neq 0$.

Solution.   By (2), $\left(\sin \dfrac{1}{x}\right)' = \left(\cos \dfrac{1}{x}\right)\left(\dfrac{1}{x}\right)' = -\dfrac{1}{x^2} \cos \dfrac{1}{x}$.

Example 4.   Differentiate $\sin^2 x$.

Solution.   We use the chain rule, but in this case the function under consideration is not the sine of another function, but the square of another function. With $u \equiv \sin x$ and $y = \sin^2 x = u^2$, we have $D_x y = D_u y \cdot D_x u = 2u \cdot \cos x = 2 \sin x \cos x$, or:

$$(\sin^2 x)' = 2 \cdot (\sin x) \cdot (\sin x)' = 2 \sin x \cos x.$$

Example 5.   Differentiate $\sin^2 3x$.

Solution.   This time we have a "function of a function of a function" and apply the chain rule with three "links." That is, $y = \sin^2 3x$ can be written:

$$y = u^2, \text{ where } u = \sin v \text{ and } v = 3x.$$

Then, by the chain rule (cf. (18), §610),

$$D_x y = D_u y \cdot D_v u \cdot D_x v = 2u \cdot \cos v \cdot 3 = 6 \sin 3x \cos 3x,$$

or

$$(\sin^2 3x)' = 2 \sin 3x(\sin 3x)' = 2 \sin 3x \cos 3x(3x)' = 6 \sin 3x \cos 3x.$$

622   THE DERIVATIVES OF THE OTHER TRIGONOMETRIC FUNCTIONS

As a consequence of formula (1), § 621, for differentiating $\sin x$ we can derive the formula for differentiating the cosine function:

If $f(x) \equiv \cos x$, where $x \in \mathfrak{R}$, then f is everywhere differentiable and $f'(x) = -\sin x$:

(1) $$D_x \cos x = -\sin x.$$

Proof. By use of the identities

(2) $$\sin\left(\tfrac{1}{2}\pi - x\right) = \cos x, \quad \cos\left(\tfrac{1}{2}\pi - x\right) = \sin x,$$

we can write $\cos x$ as a composite function:

(3) $$\cos x = \sin u, \quad \text{where} \quad u = \tfrac{1}{2}\pi - x,$$

and consequently

(4) $$D_x \cos x = D_x \sin u = D_u \sin u \cdot D_x u = \cos u \cdot (-1)$$
$$= -\cos u = -\cos\left(\tfrac{1}{2}\pi - x\right) = -\sin x.$$

Corresponding to (2), § 621, is the following:
If u is a differentiable function of x, then

(5) $$D_x \cos u = -\sin u \cdot D_x u.$$

Example 1.   Differentiate $\cos^5 (4x^2 + 1)$.

Solution. Since the function is the fifth power of $\cos (4x^2 + 1)$,
$(\cos^5 (4x^2 + 1))' = 5 \cos^4 (4x^2 + 1)(\cos (4x^2 + 1))' = -5 \cos^4 (4x^2 + 1) \sin (4x^2 + 1)(4x^2 + 1)'$
$= -40x \sin (4x^2 + 1) \cos^4 (4x^2 + 1).$

By use of the differentiation formulas for $\sin x$ and $\cos x$ we can derive differentiation formulas for the remaining four standard trigonometric functions, each of these formulas being valid wherever the functions concerned are defined. We give the formulas both in terms of functions of x and in terms of composite functions, that is, as functions of u where u is a differentiable function of x. We give proofs for $\tan x$ and $\sec x$, leaving the remaining details to Exercise 48, §623.

(6) $$D_x \tan x = \sec^2 x, \quad D_x \tan u = \sec^2 u \cdot D_x u,$$

(7) $$D_x \cot x = -\csc^2 x, \quad D_x \cot u = -\csc^2 u \cdot D_x u,$$

(8) $$D_x \sec x = \sec x \tan x, \quad D_x \sec u = \sec u \tan u \cdot D_x u,$$

(9) $$D_x \csc x = -\csc x \cot x, \quad D_x \csc u = -\csc u \cot u \cdot D_x u.$$

Proof of (6) for $\tan x$:   Write $\tan x = \sin x / \cos x$.   Then

$$D_x \frac{\sin x}{\cos x} = \frac{\cos x \, D_x \sin x - \sin x \, D_x \cos x}{\cos^2 x} = \frac{\cos^2 x - (-\sin^2 x)}{\cos^2 x}$$

$$= \frac{\sin^2 x + \cos^2 x}{\cos^2 x} = \frac{1}{\cos^2 x} = \sec^2 x.$$

Proof of (8) for sec *x:*   Write sec $x = 1/\cos x$.   Then

$$D_x \left(\frac{1}{\cos x} \right) = \frac{\cos x \cdot D_x 1 - 1 \cdot D_x \cos x}{\cos^2 x} = \frac{-(-\sin x)}{\cos^2 x}$$

$$= \frac{1}{\cos x} \cdot \frac{\sin x}{\cos x} = \sec x \tan x.$$

Example 2.   Differentiate $\tan^2 5x$.

Solution. $(\tan^2 5x)' = 2 \tan 5x (\tan 5x)' = 2 \tan 5x (\sec^2 5x) (5x)' = 10 \sec^2 5x \tan 5x.$

Example 3.   Differentiate $\sec^2 5x$.

First solution. $(\sec^2 5x)' = 2 \sec 5x (\sec 5x)'$
$$= 2 \sec 5x (\sec 5x \tan 5x)(5x)' = 10 \sec^2 5x \tan 5x.$$

Second solution. $(\sec^2 5x)' = (\tan^2 5x + 1)' = (\tan^2 5x)' = 10 \sec^2 5x \tan 5x$, from Example 2.

Formulas (2), § 621, and (5), above, provide a means of proving that the functions $\sin kx$ and $\cos kx$ are uniformly continuous on the interval $(-\infty, +\infty) = \Re$ (Theorem III, §301). We give the details for $\sin kx$ and leave those for $\cos kx$ to Exercise 47, §623.   Accordingly, we assume that k is any nonzero real number (the case where $k = 0$ is trivial), let $f(x) \equiv \sin kx$, and write out formula (8), §613, for the law of the mean, in the form $f(x_2) - f(x_1) = f'(\xi)(x_2 - x_1)$, or:

$$(10) \qquad\qquad \sin kx_2 - \sin kx_1 = k \cos k\xi \cdot (x_2 - x_1),$$

where x_1 and x_2 are any two real numbers and ξ is between x_1 and x_2 (equal to x_1 and x_2 if $x_1 = x_2$).   Applying absolute values to (10) gives

$$(11) \qquad\qquad |f(x_2) - f(x_1)| = |\sin kx_2 - \sin kx_1| \leq |k| \cdot |x_2 - x_1|.$$

If ϵ is an arbitrary positive number we have only to let $\delta \equiv \epsilon/|k|$ to obtain the implication

$$(12) \qquad\qquad |x_2 - x_1| < \delta \;\Rightarrow\; |f(x_2) - f(x_1)| < \epsilon,$$

which completes the proof.

Example 4.   Use the law of the mean to establish the inequality

$$(13) \qquad\qquad\qquad \sin x < x, \qquad x > 0.$$

Solution.   The law of the mean, formula (4), §613, with $a = 0$, $b = x$, and $f(x) = \sin x$, becomes

$$(14) \qquad\qquad \cos c = \frac{\sin x - \sin 0}{x - 0} = \frac{\sin x}{x}, \text{ where } 0 < c < x.$$

If $0 < x \leq 2\pi$ then $0 < c < 2\pi$, $\cos c < 1$, $(\sin x)/x < 1$, and $\sin x < x$. If $x > 2\pi$, then $\sin x \leq 1 < 2\pi < x$.

623   EXERCISES

In Exercises 1–36, find the derivative of the given function.

1. $\sin \pi x$.   **2.** $\cos 3\pi t$.   **3.** $\tan 2s$.   **4.** $\cot 4u$.

5. $\sec \frac{1}{2}\pi t$.   **6.** $\csc \frac{1}{3}\pi r$.   **7.** $\sin \sqrt{x}$.   **8.** $\cos \sqrt{t + 1}$.

9. $\sec \dfrac{t}{t + 1}$.   **10.** $\csc y^2$.   **11.** $\cot \dfrac{\pi}{u}$.   **12.** $\tan(r - 1)^2$.

13. $\sin^3 x$.   **14.** $\cot^4 u$.   **15.** $\sqrt{\cos t}$.   **16.** $\sec^3 s$.

17. $\sqrt{\csc v}$.   **18.** $\tan^2 w$.   **19.** $\cos^2 (3y - 1)$.   **20.** $\cot^3 4w$.

21. $\sin^3 2x$.   **22.** $\sqrt{\tan 6w}$.   **23.** $\sqrt{\sec 4t}$.   **24.** $\csc^2 5u$.

25. $x^3 \sin x$.   **26.** $x^2 \cos 2x$.   **27.** $\sqrt{t} \tan 4t$.   **28.** $u \sec u^2$.

29. $\sin 3x \cos 2x$.   **30.** $\sin^2 t \cos 4t$.   **31.** $\sin 2z \cos^2 3z$.   **32.** $\sin^2 2y \cos^2 5y$.

33. $\dfrac{1 - \cos x}{1 + \cos x}$.   **34.** $\dfrac{1 + \tan x}{1 - \tan x}$.   **35.** $\dfrac{\cos x - \sin x}{\cos x + \sin x}$.   **36.** $\dfrac{\cos x}{1 - \sin x}$.

In Exercises 37–40, write the equation of the tangent line to the given curve at the specified point.

37. $y = \sin 2x$, $(0, 0)$.   **38.** $y = \sin x$, $(\frac{1}{6}\pi, \frac{1}{2})$.

39. $y = \cos^2 \frac{1}{3}x$, $(\frac{1}{2}\pi, \frac{3}{4})$.   **40.** $y = \tan x$, $(\frac{1}{3}\pi, \sqrt{3})$.

In Exercises 41–44, find the second derivative of the given function.

41. $\sin^4 x$.   **42.** $\cos^3 x$.   **43.** $x^4 \cos x$.   **44.** $x^2 \sin x$.

In Exercises 45 and 46, use the law of the mean (§613) to establish the given inequality.

45. $\tan x > x$, $0 < x < \frac{1}{2}\pi$.

46. $\cos x < \frac{1}{2}\pi - x$, $0 < x < \frac{1}{2}\pi$.

47. Prove that $\cos kx$ is uniformly continuous on $(-\infty, +\infty)$.

48. Complete the derivation of formulas (6)–(9), §622.

624   COUNTEREXAMPLES

Any example is a counterexample to the statement that such an example is impossible. For instance, Weierstrass's celebrated example of a function that is everywhere continuous and nowhere differentiable (cf. the Note, §612) is a counterexample to the statement that every continuous function must be *somewhere* differentiable. The signum function (cf. the Example, §617), similarly, is a counterexample to the statement that every bounded monotonic function on a bounded closed interval (say) must be the derivative of some function there. Usually an isolated example is not called a counterexample unless there is at least some element of surprise or novelty. The most interesting counterexamples are never trivial, and often involve quite deep mathematics. For a discussion of this topic the reader is referred to the book by Bernard R. Gelbaum and the author entitled *Counterexamples in Analysis* (San Francisco, Holden-Day, Inc., 1964).

In this section we present two counterexamples based on the function $\sin (1/x)$, which possesses a discontinuity at the origin of an oscillatory nature (cf. IV, §407, and Figure 407-5). This function is useful as a means of pinpointing fallacies in certain statements that we might otherwise be tempted to accept. The statements made in the present section are established in H§1129, *CWAG*, where two further counterexamples, also based on the function $\sin (1/x)$, are described.

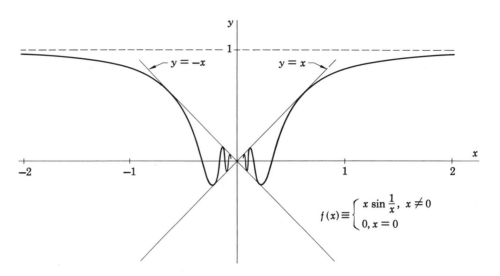

$$f(x) \equiv \begin{cases} x \sin\frac{1}{x}, & x \neq 0 \\ 0, & x = 0 \end{cases}$$

Figure 624-1

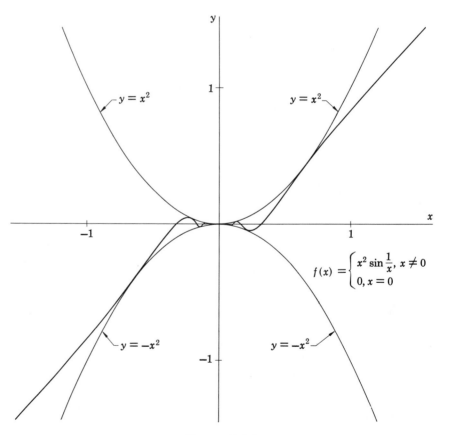

$$f(x) = \begin{cases} x^2 \sin\frac{1}{x}, & x \neq 0 \\ 0, & x = 0 \end{cases}$$

Figure 624-2

I. *A function f that is everywhere continuous, and a point at which f has no one-sided derivative in either the finite or infinite sense.*

The function

$$(1) \qquad f(x) \equiv \begin{cases} x \sin \dfrac{1}{x} & \text{if } x \neq 0, \\ 0 & \text{if } x = 0, \end{cases}$$

is everywhere continuous, but $f'(0)$ does not exist in any sense (finite or infinite or one-sided). (Cf. Fig. 624-1.)

II. *A function that is everywhere differentiable but whose derivative is not continuous.*

The function

$$(2) \qquad f(x) \equiv \begin{cases} x^2 \sin \dfrac{1}{x} & \text{if } x \neq 0, \\ 0 & \text{if } x = 0, \end{cases}$$

is everywhere continuous and, indeed, everywhere differentiable. However, its derivative $f'(x)$ is discontinuous at $x = 0$. (Cf. Fig. 624-2.)

7

Differentials and
Implicit Functions

701 DIFFERENTIALS

Let f be a differentiable function and let E be the domain of its derivative f'. Then the **differential** of f, denoted df, is the real-valued function with domain $E \times \mathfrak{R}$ whose value at the point (x, h) of $E \times \mathfrak{R}$ is denoted and defined:

$$(1) \qquad\qquad df(x, h) \equiv f'(x) \cdot h.$$

If the independent and dependent variables for the function f are labeled x and y, respectively, so that

$$(2) \qquad\qquad y = f(x),$$

and if the symbols dx and dy are defined:

$$(3) \qquad\qquad dx \equiv h, \quad dy \equiv df(x, h),$$

then formula (1) can be written

$$(4) \qquad\qquad dy = f'(x)dx.$$

Other notational variants of (1) and (4) are

$$(5) \qquad\qquad df = f'(x)dx,$$

$$(6) \qquad\qquad df(x) = f'(x)dx,$$

$$(7) \qquad\qquad dy = D_x\, y\, dx,$$

$$(8) \qquad\qquad df = D_x f\, dx,$$

$$(9) \qquad\qquad df(x) = D_x f(x)dx.$$

194

Example 1. The differential of the function $f(x) = x^3$ can be written

(10) $$df(x, h) = 3x^2h,$$

(11) $$df = df(x) = d(x^3) = 3x^2h = 3x^2dx,$$

or if we write $y = x^3$,

(12) $$dy = d(x^3) = 3x^2dx.$$

Since the domain of the differential for the function x^3 is the Cartesian plane $\Re \times \Re$, any real numbers can be substituted in (10) for x and h. For example, if $x = 5$ and $h = 10$ we have

(13) $$df(5, 10) = 3 \cdot 25 \cdot 10 = 750.$$

The symbol dx is called the **differential** of the independent variable x, and the symbol dy is called the **differential** of the dependent variable y. This differential notation is due to Leibniz. As we shall see, it is extremely useful in the more manipulative aspects of calculus.

Figure 701-1 illustrates the relationship among the quantities defined above. The reason that $df(x, h)$, or equivalently dy, is equal to the vertical side of the triangle T in Figure 701-1 whose horizontal base is $h = dx$ is that the slope of the tangent line at $(x, f(x))$ is equal simultaneously to $f'(x)$ and to the quotient of the vertical and horizontal sides of T. The result follows from (1) written in the form

(14) $$f'(x) = \frac{df(x, h)}{h} = \frac{dy}{dx}.$$

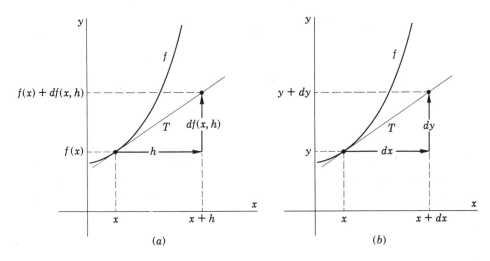

(a)   (b)

Figure 701-1

Equation (14), with its visual representation in Figure 701-1, displays an important basic relationship between differentials and derivatives:

Theorem. *If y is a differentiable function of x, $y = f(x)$, and if dy and dx are the differentials of the variables y and x, respectively, where dy is evaluated at the point* *x and dx ≠ 0, then the quotient of these differentials is equal to the derivative of y with respect to x evaluated at the point x:*

(15)
$$\frac{dy}{dx} = f'(x).$$

Example 2.   For the function $y = x^3$ of Example 1, we have from (12) or (15):

(16)
$$\frac{dy}{dx} = 3x^2.$$

If the differential *dx* is interpreted as an *increment* Δx, then the relationship of the *differential dy* to the *increment* Δy is shown in Figure 701-2.   We can say informally that *dy* is what the increment *would* be if we followed the *tangent line L* at *x* instead of the curve *C* itself.   The relationship between Δy and *dy* is discussed more fully in § 604.

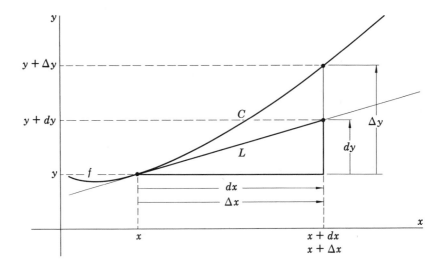

Figure 701-2

The differential notation of (5) and (6) lends itself in a natural way to the formulation of differential counterparts of formulas for differentiation.   To illustrate, formulas (1), (3), (7), (10), (12), and (14) of § 605 can be written, respectively:

(17)
$$dc = 0,$$

(18)
$$d(x^n) = nx^{n-1}dx,$$

(19)
$$d(f + g) = df + dg,$$

(20)
$$d(cf) = cdf,$$

(21)
$$d(-f) = -df,$$

(22)
$$d(f - g) = df - dg.$$

Formulas (9) and (13) of §607 can be written, respectively:

(23) $$d(fg) = f\,dg + g\,df,$$

(24) $$d\left(\frac{f}{g}\right) = \frac{g\,df - f\,dg}{g^2}.$$

Formula (2), §609, becomes

(25) $$d(g^n) = ng^{n-1}dg.$$

Formulas (1) and (2), §621, and (1) and (5)–(9), §622, can be written, respectively:

(26) $\quad d\sin x = \cos x\,dx,\qquad d\sin u = \cos u\,du,$

(27) $\quad d\cos x = -\sin x\,dx,\qquad d\cos u = -\sin u\,du,$

(28) $\quad d\tan x = \sec^2 x\,dx,\qquad d\tan u = \sec^2 u\,du,$

(29) $\quad d\cot x = -\csc^2 x\,dx,\qquad d\cot u = -\csc^2 u\,du,$

(30) $\quad d\sec x = \sec x\tan x\,dx,\qquad d\sec u = \sec u\tan u\,du,$

(31) $\quad d\csc x = -\csc x\cot x\,dx,\quad d\csc u = -\csc u\cot u\,du.$

We shall verify only one of the formulas (17)–(31), and leave the rest to the student in Exercise 37, §703. Formula (19), to be specific, states that

$$(f+g)'\,dx = f'\,dx + g'\,dx,$$

which is true for any real number dx, since by (7), §605, $(f+g)' = f' + g'$.
Since division of (5) and (6) by any nonzero dx gives

(32) $$\frac{df}{dx} = \frac{df(x)}{dx} = f'(x),$$

the symbol $d/dx = \dfrac{d}{dx}$ is often taken to be synonymous with the symbol D_x, or in case the variable x is understood from context, with the symbol D. Thus, for example, formulas (18) and (26) can be written, respectively:

(33) $$\frac{d}{dx}(x^n) = nx^{n-1},$$

(34) $$\frac{d}{dx}\sin x = \cos x.$$

In keeping with the notation d/dx for D, we can symbolize the operators for higher order derivatives (cf. §605) thus:

(35) $$D^2 = \frac{d^2}{dx^2},\quad D^3 = \frac{d^3}{dx^3},\cdots,\quad D^n = \frac{d^n}{dx^n}.$$

For example, second order derivatives can be written

(36) $$\frac{d^2y}{dx^2},\ \frac{d^2f}{dx^2},\ \frac{d^2f(x)}{dx^2},\ \frac{d^2}{dx^2}f(x),\cdots,$$

as well as

(37) $$\frac{d}{dx}\left(\frac{dy}{dx}\right), \quad \frac{d}{dx}\left(\frac{df}{dx}\right), \quad \frac{d}{dx}\left(\frac{d}{dx}(f(x))\right) = \frac{d}{dx}(f'(x)), \cdots,$$

and in general, nth order derivatives can be written

(38) $$\frac{d^ny}{dx^n}, \quad \frac{d^nf}{dx^n}, \quad \frac{d^nf(x)}{dx^n}, \quad \frac{d^n}{dx^n}f(x), \cdots.$$

Example 3. If f is the function $y = f(x) \equiv x^3$ of Examples 1 and 2, then the second derivative of x^3 can be written

(39) $$\frac{d^2y}{dx^2} = \frac{d}{dx}\left(\frac{dy}{dx}\right) = \frac{d^2}{dx^2}(x^3) = \frac{d}{dx}(3x^2) = 6x.$$

Example 4. Since the independent variable may be denoted by any convenient letter,

$$d(t^5) = 5t^4\, dt,$$

$$d(u^4 + 3u^2 - 5) = (4u^3 + 6u)du,$$

$$d(\sqrt{y^2 + 1}) = (y/\sqrt{y^2 + 1})dy = y\, dy/\sqrt{y^2 + 1}.$$

702   IDENTITY, INVERSE, AND COMPOSITE FUNCTIONS

The differential notation introduced in §701 is used in two quite distinct ways. If x and y denote independent and dependent variables, respectively, the differential dx of x represents an arbitrary real number thought of as a new independent variable, whereas dy is the product of dx and the value of the derivative of y with respect to x at a particular value of x. It is to be expected, then, that we might be concerned lest there arise on occasion a possible confusion between the two symbols dy and dx that have such a similar appearance. It turns out (to put it quite crudely and in an oversimplified way) that if such confusion of notation does occur, it doesn't really matter. In a sense, the differential notation is almost "foolproof," and can even "cover up" for careless oversight! It is our purpose now to discuss this notational phenomenon.

Theorem I. *If $y = f(x)$, where f is the identity function*

(1) $$y = x,$$

then the values of the differential of y are identically equal to those of the differential of x:

(2) $$dy = dx.$$

Proof. Since in this case $f'(x) = 1$ for all x, formula (4), §701, reduces to (2), above.

Formula (2) can be viewed geometrically quite easily. If $f(x) = x$, the graph of $y = f(x)$ is the straight line $y = x$, and at every point this line is its own tangent. Therefore, in Figures 701-1 and 701-2 the triangle T is an isosceles right triangle, and the line L is a line of slope 1.

Theorem II. *If $x = \phi(y)$ is a differentiable function in a certain interval, if $\phi'(y)$ $\neq 0$ in this interval, and if dy and dx denote the differentials of the independent variable y and the dependent variable x, respectively, related by definition by the equation*

$$(3) \qquad\qquad dx \equiv \phi'(y)dy,$$

then if $y = f(x)$ denotes the inverse function of $x = \phi(y)$, these same differentials are also related by equation (4), § 701:

$$(4) \qquad\qquad dy = f'(x)dx.$$

Proof. By the Theorem, §618, D_xy and D_yx are reciprocals (and nonzero) and therefore (3) can be written $dx = D_yx \cdot dy = dy/D_xy$. Multiplication by the nonzero quantity D_xy gives $D_xy \cdot dx = dy$ or, since $D_xy = f'(x)$, formula (4).

The geometrical counterpart of Figure 701-2, for formulas (3) and (4), is shown in Figure 702-1.

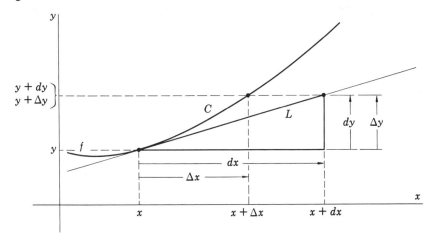

Figure 702-1

Example 1. Illustrate Theorem II for the function $y = x^2$, $x > 0$.

Solution. The inverse function ϕ of $y = x^2$ is given by $x = \sqrt{y}$, for $y > 0$, and formula (3) is

$$dx = \frac{1}{2\sqrt{y}}dy.$$

Consequently, $dx = \dfrac{1}{2x} dy$, whence $2x\, dx = dy$, and formula (4) is valid since $f(x) = x^2$ and $f'(x) = 2x$.

Theorem III. *If $y = f(x)$ is a differentiable function of the variable x, if x is a differentiable function of the variable t, and if x and y are both regarded as dependent variables, depending on the independent variable t, then their differentials,*

$$(5) \qquad\qquad dy \equiv D_ty \cdot dt, \qquad dx \equiv D_tx \cdot dt,$$

are related by equation (4), §701:

(6) $$dy = f'(x)dx.$$

Proof. Substitution of (5) into (6) shows that what we wish to prove is

$$D_t y \cdot dt = f'(x)D_t x\, dt,$$

and this is true by virtue of the chain rule, §610:

$$D_t y = D_x y D_t x = f'(x)D_t x.$$

The principal substance of Theorems II and III can be distilled to the simple statement that equation (15), §701, or equivalently

(7) $$\frac{dy}{dx} = D_x y,$$

which is true by definition when (*i*) *x is the independent variable*, is also true when (*ii*) *y is the independent variable* and also when (*iii*) *x and y are both dependent on a third variable.*

The facts just recorded permit us to write the chain rule $D_x y = D_u y \cdot D_x u$ in a form using differentials, which is particularly easy to remember:

(8) $$\frac{dy}{dx} = \frac{dy}{du} \cdot \frac{du}{dx}.$$

Extensions of more "links" have corresponding formulations. For example, the chain rule with three factors, $D_x y = D_u y \cdot D_v u \cdot D_x v$ becomes

(9) $$\frac{dy}{dx} = \frac{dy}{du} \cdot \frac{du}{dv} \cdot \frac{dv}{dx}.$$

These formulas are deceptively simple in appearance because of the apparent "cancellation" of the factor *du* in (8) and the factors *du* and *dv* in (9).

Example 2. Use differentials to find the derivative of the function $\left(\dfrac{1}{(x^2+1)^2} + 4\right)^2$ of Example 3, §610.

Solution. We let $y \equiv (u+4)^2$ and $u \equiv (x^2+1)^{-2}$, and write

$$\frac{dy}{du} = 2(u+4), \quad \frac{du}{dx} = \frac{-4x}{(x^2+1)^3}$$

and multiply to obtain

$$\frac{dy}{dx} = \frac{dy}{du}\frac{du}{dx} = \frac{-8x}{(x^2+1)^3}\left(\frac{1}{(x^2+1)^2} + 4\right) = -\frac{8x(4x^4 + 8x^2 + 5)}{(x^2+1)^5}.$$

An alternative solution is given by letting $y = (u^2+4)^2$ and $u = 1/(x^2+1)$, as in the second solution of Example 3, §610.

The manipulative details in a problem like the present one are frequently carried through by use of the principle just illustrated but without explicit introduction of new variables, thus:

$$d\left(\frac{1}{(x^2+1)^2}+4\right)^2 = 2\left(\frac{1}{(x^2+1)^2}+4\right)d\left(\frac{1}{(x^2+1)^2}+4\right)$$

$$= 2\frac{4x^4+8x^2+5}{(x^2+1)^2}\,d((x^2+1)^{-2}+4)$$

$$= 2\frac{4x^4+8x^2+5}{(x^2+1)^2}(-2)(x^2+1)^{-3}d(x^2) = \frac{-8x(4x^4+8x^2+5)dx}{(x^2+1)^5}.$$

Example 3. Find the differential of the function $\dfrac{(4x^2+1)^2}{(x^2+2)^3}$ by techniques that employ differentials.

First solution.

$$d\frac{(4x^2+1)^2}{(x^2+2)^3} = \frac{(x^2+2)^3d(4x^2+1)^2-(4x^2+1)^2d(x^2+2)^3}{(x^2+2)^6}$$

$$= \frac{(x^2+2)^3\cdot2(4x^2+1)d(4x^2)-(4x^2+1)^2\cdot3(x^2+2)^2d(x^2)}{(x^2+2)^6}$$

$$= \frac{2x(-4x^2+13)(4x^2+1)}{(x^2+2)^4}\,dx.$$

Second solution. $d((4x^2+1)^2(x^2+2)^{-3})$

$$= (x^2+2)^{-3}\,d(4x^2+1)^2+(4x^2+1)^2\,d(x^2+2)^{-3}$$

$$= (x^2+2)^{-3}\cdot2(4x^2+1)\cdot8x\,dx+(4x^2+1)^2(-3)(x^2+2)^{-4}\cdot2x\,dx$$

$$= 2x(-4x^2+13)(4x^2+1)(x^2+2)^{-4}dx.$$

703 EXERCISES

In Exercises 1–12, write the differential of the given function. Then express the derivative of the function as the quotient of two differentials.

1. $y = 5x^2$.   **2.** $y = t^3$.   **3.** $u = s^2 + s$.

4. $v = r^2 + r^{-2}$.   **5.** $w = \sqrt{v}$.   **6.** $z = y^{\frac{7}{3}}$.

7. $y = \sqrt{4x^2+9}$.   **8.** $v = \sqrt{4-9u^2}$.   **9.** $x = \sin t^2$.

10. $y = \cos\dfrac{1}{t}$.   **11.** $u = \sin^3 5z$.   **12.** $v = \tan^2 y^3$.

In Exercises 13–18, find the indicated higher order derivative.

13. $\dfrac{d^2y}{dx^2}$, $y = x^n$.   **14.** $\dfrac{d^2x}{dt^2}$, $x = t \sin 2t$.

15. $\dfrac{d^3}{dt^3}(\sin t^2)$.   **16.** $\dfrac{d^3}{dx^3}(\sin^2 x)$.

17. $\dfrac{d^n}{dx^n}\left(\dfrac{1}{x}\right)$.   **18.** $\dfrac{d^n}{dy^n}\left(\dfrac{1}{\sqrt{y}}\right)$.

In Exercises 19–22, illustrate Theorem II, §702, if the variables are related by the given equation.

19. $2x - 5y = 1$.   **20.** $4y - 3x = 2$.

21. $y = x^3$.   **22.** $x = y^2$.

In Exercises 23–26, illustrate Theroem III, §702, by means of the given functions.

23. $y = x^3, x = t^2$.   **24.** $y = 5x^2, x = 3t + 2$.

25. $y = \sqrt{x}, x = t^2 + 4$.   **26.** $y = \sqrt[3]{x}, x = t^3 + 1$.

In Exercises 27–30, find $\dfrac{dy}{dx}$ by use of (9), §702, for the given functions.

27. $y = u^8, u = 2v + 1, v = \dfrac{1}{x}$.   **28.** $y = \sqrt{u}, u = 9v + 4, v = x^2$.

29. $y = u^2, u = \sin v, v = 3x$.   **30.** $y = u^3, u = \cos v, v = 2x$.

In Exercises 31–36, find the differential of the given function by techniques that employ differentials, as illustrated in Example 3, §702.

31. $(2x + 5)^4(6x - 1)^3$.   **32.** $u\sqrt{u^2 + a^2}$.

33. $\dfrac{v}{\sqrt{v^2 + a^2}}$.   **34.** $\dfrac{(2y + 5)^4}{(6y - 1)^3}$.

35. $\sin^4 5t^2$.   **36.** $\sin(\alpha^2 + 1)^4$.

37. Verify a representative selection from the formulas (17)–(31), §701.

704   APPROXIMATIONS BY DIFFERENTIALS

It appears from Figure 701-2 that if dx is regarded as an increment Δx in the variable x, and if $|dx|$ is "small," then dy and Δy are "approximately equal." More precisely, this means that the difference $\Delta y - dy$ is a "small" fraction of Δx in the following sense:

$$(1) \qquad \lim_{\Delta x \to 0} \frac{\Delta y - dy}{\Delta x} = \lim_{dx \to 0} \frac{\Delta y - dy}{dx} = 0.$$

To prove (1), we evaluate the limit involved, making use of the fact that $dy = f'(x)dx = f'(x)\Delta x$:

$$\lim_{\Delta x \to 0}\left[\frac{\Delta y}{\Delta x} - \frac{dy}{\Delta x}\right] = \lim_{\Delta x \to 0}\frac{\Delta y}{\Delta x} - \lim_{\Delta x \to 0}\frac{f'(x)\Delta x}{\Delta x} = f'(x) - f'(x) = 0.$$

If we express the fraction $(\Delta y - dy)/\Delta x$ as a function of $h = \Delta x = dx$ (considering the point x to be fixed),

$$(2) \quad \eta(h) \equiv \frac{\Delta y - dy}{\Delta x} = \frac{f(x + h) - f(x) - f'(x) \cdot h}{h} = \frac{f(x + h) - f(x)}{h} - f'(x),$$

then the function $\eta(h)$ is an **infinitesimal** in the sense that

$$(3) \qquad \lim_{h \to 0} \eta(h) = 0.$$

In other words,

(4) $$\Delta y = dy + \eta(\Delta x)\Delta x,$$

where the function $\eta(\Delta x)$ is an infinitesimal.

In case $f'(x) \neq 0$, the statement that Δy and dy are approximately equal can also be expressed

(5) $$\lim_{\Delta x \to 0} \frac{\Delta y}{dy} = 1,$$

since (5) can be written

$$\lim_{\Delta x \to 0} \frac{\Delta y}{dy} = \lim_{\Delta x \to 0} \frac{\Delta y/\Delta x}{dy/dx} = \frac{\lim_{\Delta x \to 0}(\Delta y/\Delta x)}{f'(x)} = \frac{f'(x)}{f'(x)} = 1.$$

In practice, whenever f' can be determined readily, dy is usually easier to compute than Δy, and is often a useful approximation for Δy. When dy is used in this fashion as an approximation for Δy, it is possible to measure the accuracy of this approximation. Means for accomplishing this accuracy measurement are discussed in §1207, *CWAG*, and are omitted here.

Example 1. For the function $y = x^3$, $dy = 3x^2 dx = 3x^2\,\Delta x$, and

$$\Delta y = (x + \Delta x)^3 - x^3 = 3x^2\,\Delta x + 3x\,\Delta x^2 + \Delta x^3.$$

Equation (1) becomes

$$\lim_{\Delta x \to 0} \frac{3x\,\Delta x^2 + \Delta x^3}{\Delta x} = \lim_{\Delta x \to 0}(3x\,\Delta x + \Delta x^2) = 0,$$

and the function $\eta(h)$ of (2) is

$$\eta(h) = \frac{3x\,h^2 + h^3}{h} = 3xh + h^2.$$

Equation (4) assumes the form

$$3x^2\,\Delta x + 3x\,\Delta x^2 + \Delta x^3 = 3x^2\,\Delta x + (3x\,\Delta x + \Delta x^2)\,\Delta x.$$

If $x \neq 0$, equation (5) is

$$\lim_{\Delta x \to 0} \frac{3x^2\,\Delta x + 3x\,\Delta x^2 + \Delta x^3}{3x^2\,\Delta x} = \lim_{\Delta x \to 0}\left[1 + \frac{\Delta x}{x} + \frac{\Delta x^2}{3x^2}\right] = 1.$$

The statement that dy is a good approximation to Δy for small $|\Delta x|$, in this instance, says that $3x^2\,\Delta x$ is a good approximation to $3x^2\,\Delta x + 3x\,\Delta x^2 + \Delta x^3$ for small $|\Delta x|$.

Differential approximations are often convenient for giving "linear approximations" to functions. To be specific, if the function f is differentiable at the point x, if $f(x)$ and $f'(x)$ are known or can be determined, and if $|h|$ is small, then with $\Delta y \equiv f(x + h) - f(x)$,

$$f(x + h) = f(x) + \Delta y,$$

and since $dy = f'(x) \cdot h$ is a "good approximation" to Δy, $f(x) + f'(x) \cdot h$ is a "good approximation" to $f(x) + \Delta y$. In other words:

A good approximation to $f(x + h)$, for small $|h|$, is $f(x) + f'(x) \cdot h$, in the sense that

(6) $$\lim_{h \to 0} \frac{f(x + h) - [f(x) + f'(x)h]}{h} = 0.$$

Since, for fixed x and variable h, $f(x) + f'(x) \cdot h$ is linear,

(7) $$f(x) + f'(x)h$$

is called a **linear approximation** to $f(x + h)$, regarded as a function of h.

Example 2. The linear approximation (7) to the function $(x + h)^3$ is $x^3 + 3x^2 \cdot h$. The linear approximation to the function $(1 + h)^3$ is $1 + 3h$.

Example 3. Find the linear approximation (7) to the function $\sqrt{1 + h}$.

Solution. With $f(x) \equiv \sqrt{x}$, the linear approximation (7) to $\sqrt{x + h}$, as a function of h, is $f(x) + f'(x) \cdot h = \sqrt{x} + \dfrac{1}{2\sqrt{x}} h$. With $x = 1$, this becomes $1 + \frac{1}{2} h$.

Example 4. Use Example 3 to find an approximation to $\sqrt{23}$, considering 23 as "near" 25.

Solution. Write $\sqrt{23} = \sqrt{25 \cdot \frac{23}{25}} = 5 \sqrt{\frac{23}{25}} = 5 \sqrt{1 - \frac{2}{25}}$. Approximating $\sqrt{1 + h}$ by $1 + \frac{1}{2} h$, with $h = -\frac{2}{25}$, we have $\sqrt{23}$ approximated by $5[1 - \frac{1}{2} \cdot \frac{2}{25}] = 5(1 - 0.04) = 4.8$. (To four decimal places, $\sqrt{23} = 4.7958$.)

Example 5. Estimate $\sqrt{2}$, considering 1.96 as "near" 2.

Solution. We start by writing

$$\sqrt{2} = \sqrt{1.96 \frac{2}{1.96}} = 1.4 \sqrt{1 + \frac{0.04}{1.96}},$$

then approximate $\sqrt{1 + h}$ by $1 + \frac{1}{2}h$, with $h = 0.04/1.96$, to obtain as an approximation to $\sqrt{2}$:

$$1.4\left(1 + \frac{0.02}{1.96}\right) = 1.4 + \frac{0.02}{1.4} = 1.4 + \frac{1}{70},$$

or, to four decimal places: 1.4143. (To four decimal places $\sqrt{2} = 1.4142$.)

705   EXERCISES

In Exercises 1–8, evaluate dy and Δy for the given function and the specified values of x and of $dx = \Delta x$.

1. $y = x^2$, $x = 10$, $\Delta x = 0.1$.   **2.** $y = x^2$, $x = 10$, $\Delta x = -0.1$.

3. $y = x^3$, $x = 2$, $\Delta x = -0.1$.   **4.** $y = x^3$, $x = 1$, $\Delta x = 0.01$.

5. $y = \dfrac{1}{x}$, $x = 5$, $\Delta x = 0.02$.   **6.** $y = \dfrac{1}{x}$, $x = 10$, $\Delta x = -0.04$.

7. $y = \sqrt{x}$, $x = 4$, $\Delta x = -0.39$.   **8.** $y = \sqrt{x}$, $x = 100$, $\Delta x = 2.01$.

In Exercises 9–12, write out the limit statements (1) and (5), §704, and write an explicit expression for $\eta(h)$ of (2), §704, for the given function.

9. $y = x^2$.   **10.** $y = x^3$.   **11.** $y = \dfrac{1}{x}$.   **12.** $y = \sqrt{x}$.

In Exercises 13–16, use differentials to obtain the given linear expression in h as a linear approximation to the given function of h, for small values of $|h|$.

13. $\sqrt[3]{1 + h} : 1 + \dfrac{1}{3}h$.

14. $\dfrac{1}{\sqrt{1 + h}} : 1 - \dfrac{1}{2}h$.

15. $\dfrac{1}{1 + h} : 1 - h$.

16. $(1 + h)^n : 1 + nh$.

In Exercises 17–22, estimate the given number to the specified number of decimal places by means of differentials, making use of the specified approximation. (The actual value to the stated number of decimal places is given in parentheses.)

17. $\sqrt{83}$ to 4 decimal places, 83 near 81. (9.1104)

18. $\sqrt[3]{61}$ to 4 decimal places, 61 near 64. (3.9365)

19. $\sqrt[3]{2}$ to 3 decimal places, 2 near $2.197 = 1.3^3$. (1.260)

20. $\sqrt{3}$ to 5 decimal places, 3 near $2.9929 = 1.73^2$. (1.73205)

21. $\frac{1}{254} = 254^{-1}$ to 6 decimal places, 254 near 250. (0.003937)

22. $\dfrac{1}{\sqrt{142}} = 142^{-\frac{1}{2}}$ to 6 decimal places, 142 near 144. (0.083918)

23. Use differentials to estimate the total area of a sidewalk one yard wide surrounding a square enclosure one mile on each side. How does this estimate compare with the true area? Illustrate with a figure. *Suggestion:* Consider the approximate change in the values of the function x^2 if x increases from 1760 yards to 1762 yards.

24. Use differentials to estimate the total area between two concentric circles of radii 5 inches and 5.04 inches. How does this estimate compare with the true area? (Cf. Ex. 23.)

25. A solid cylindrical shaft of diameter 1 inch and length 18 inches is put on a lathe and reduced to a diameter of 0.97 inches. Use differentials to estimate the volume of the material removed. (Cf. Ex. 24.)

26. A solid cube each of whose edges is 8 inches long is given a coat of paint one one-thousandth of an inch thick. Use differentials to estimate the volume of the coat of paint. (Cf. Ex. 23.)

27. A spherical balloon leaks gas and reduces in size from a radius of 10 feet to a radius of 9 feet and 11 inches. Use differentials to estimate the total volume of gas that has thus escaped. (Cf. Ex. 24.)

706 FUNCTIONS DEFINED IMPLICITLY

It is often desirable or necessary to treat functions that are not given by any explicit expression, but instead are defined by or involved in an equation relating two variables. For example, it may be convenient to study properties of the function

$y = \sqrt{25 - x^2}$ by means of the equation $x^2 + y^2 = 25$ (cf. Example 1). On the other hand, the inverse function of $y = x^5 + x$, *defined* by the equation $y^5 + y = x$ (cf. Example 2) cannot be given a simple explicit formulation.

A basic fact of the greatest importance is that when a variable y is defined by an equation in x and y as a function of the variable x, then this equation, considered as an equation in x alone, is an *identity*. For example, in the equation $x^2 + y^2 = 25$, when $\sqrt{25 - x^2}$ is substituted for y, the resulting equation in x is the identity

$$x^2 + (25 - x^2) = 25.$$

Similarly, if $y = \phi(x)$ is the function defined by the equation $y^5 + y = x$, then the equation

$$\phi^5(x) + \phi(x) = x$$

is true for all x by definition. We shall use the expression "is defined by" to mean "satisfies identically." Whenever a function is defined by an equation in any manner other than by an explicit formulation, we say that the function is **defined implicitly,** and that the function is an **implicit function.**

Derivatives of implicit functions can usually be found by the chain rule, as illustrated in the Examples given below. This process is called **implicit differentiation.**

Example 1. Find the equation of the tangent to the circle $x^2 + y^2 = 25$ at the point $(3, 4)$ by implicit differentiation.

Solution. Since $(3, 4)$ lies on the upper semicircle of $x^2 + y^2 = 25$, consider $y = f(x)$ as the function whose graph is that upper semicircle (cf. Fig. 706-1). (The explicit expression for $f(x)$ is $\sqrt{25 - x^2}$.) Then since the two sides of the equation $x^2 + y^2 = 25$ are identically equal as functions of x, so are their derivatives with respect to x:

(1) $$D_x(x^2) + D_x(y^2) = D_x 25.$$

This reduces, by the chain rule applied to the second term, to the equation

(2) $$2x + 2y \, D_x y = 0.$$

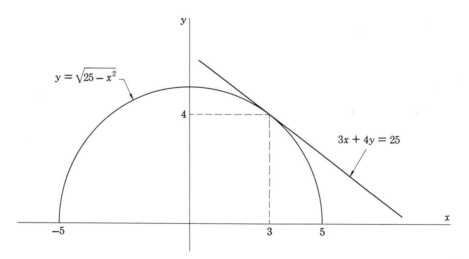

Figure 706-1

Therefore $D_x y = -x/y = -3/4$ at the point in question, and the equation of the tangent is $(y - 4) = -\frac{3}{4}(x - 3)$, or $3x + 4y = 25$.

Example 2.   Find $D_x y$ if $y^5 + y = x$.

Solution.   Implicit differentiation gives $D_x(y^5) + D_x y = (5y^4 + 1)D_x y = 1$, or

(3) $D_x y = 1/(5y^4 + 1)$.

The graph is shown in Figure 706-2.

If primes are used to indicate differentiation with respect to x, then the implicit differentiation of this example takes the form

$$(y^5)' + y' = x', \quad (5y^4 + 1)y' = 1, \quad \text{and} \quad y' = 1/(5y^4 + 1)$$

with (3) resulting as before.

Example 3.   Find $D_x y$ if $2x^3 y^2 - 5xy^4 + 3 = 0$.

Solution.   With primes indicating differentiation with respect to x, we have

$$2(x^3 y^2)' - 5(xy^4)' = 2[x^3(y^2)' + y^2(x^3)'] - 5[x(y^4)' + y^4 x'] = 0,$$
$$2(x^3 \cdot 2yy' + y^2 \cdot 3x^2) - 5(x \cdot 4y^3 y' + y^4) = (4x^3 y - 20xy^3)y' + (6x^2 y^2 - 5y^4) = 0,$$

and therefore

$$y' = D_x y = -\frac{6x^2 y^2 - 5y^4}{4x^3 y - 20xy^3} = \frac{y(5y^2 - 6x^2)}{4x(x^2 - 5y^2)},$$

wherever the denominator is nonzero.

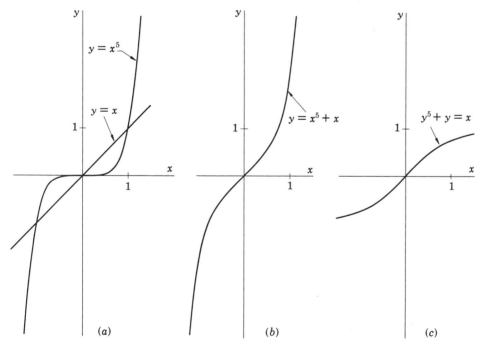

$y = x^5$

$y = x$

$y = x^5 + x$

$y^5 + y = x$

(a)   (b)   (c)

Figure 706-2

707   THE USE OF DIFFERENTIALS

Derivatives of implicitly defined functions can often be obtained readily by the use of differentials. In forming the differential of a function $f(y)$ of a variable y, where y is in turn considered to be a function of an independent variable x, one should bear in mind the import of Theorem III, § 702. The differential $df(y)$ is expressed in terms of f' and dy by exactly the same formula as would be the case if y were an independent variable:

$$df(y) = f'(y)dy.$$

Example 1. Use differentials to solve Example 1, § 706.

Solution. From $x^2 + y^2 = 25$ we have $2x\, dx + 2y\, dy = 0$, $y\, dy = -x\, dx$, or

$$\frac{dy}{dx} = -\frac{x}{y} = -\frac{3}{4}$$

at the point in question. The remaining details are unchanged.

Example 2. Use differentials to solve Example 2, § 706.

Solution. If $y^5 + y = x$, then $5y^4\, dy + dy = dx$, or $dy/dx = 1/(5y^4 + 1)$.

Example 3. Use differentials to solve Example 3, § 706.

Solution. If $2x^3y^2 - 5xy^4 + 3 = 0$, then

$$2(x^3d(y^2) + y^2d(x^3)) - 5(xd(y^4) + y^4dx) = 0,$$
$$2(2x^3y\, dy + 3x^2y^2dx) - 5(4xy^3dy + y^4dx) = (4x^3y - 20xy^3)dy + (6x^2y^2 - 5y^4)dx = 0,$$

and therefore

$$\frac{dy}{dx} = -\frac{6x^2y^2 - 5y^4}{4x^3y - 20xy^3} = \frac{y(5y^2 - 6x^2)}{4x(x^2 - 5y^2)}.$$

708   SECOND-ORDER DERIVATIVES

If y is defined implicitly as a function of x, its higher order derivatives can be found by implicit differentiation. The details are often facilitated by denoting derivatives with primes, and substituting after differentiation, as illustrated below. Often the result can be simplified by use of the original defining equation. We shall limit ourselves in this section to derivatives of order 2. Derivatives of order higher than 2 are treated in H§1219, *CWAG*.

Example 1. If y is defined as a function of x by the equation $x^2 + y^2 = 25$, find the second derivative of y with respect to x by implicit differentiation.

Solution. As in Example 1, § 706, or Example 1, § 707, we find the first derivative:

(1) $$y' = -\frac{x}{y}.$$

Differentiating (1), we have

(2) $$y'' = -\left(\frac{x}{y}\right)' = -\frac{yx' - xy'}{y^2} = \frac{xy' - y}{y^2}$$

and therefore, upon substitution from (1) and use of the equation $x^2 + y^2 = 25$,

(3)
$$y'' = \frac{x(-x/y) - y}{y^2} = -\frac{x^2 + y^2}{y^3} = -\frac{25}{y^3}.$$

In terms of x this can be written

(4)
$$\frac{d^2}{dx^2}\sqrt{25 - x^2} = -25(25 - x^2)^{-\frac{3}{2}}.$$

Example 2. Find d^2y/dx^2 if $y^5 + y = x$.

Solution. As in Example 2, §706, or Example 2, §707,

(5)
$$y' = \frac{1}{5y^4 + 1} = (5y^4 + 1)^{-1}.$$

Therefore

$$y'' = (-1)(5y^4 + 1)^{-2}(20y^3) \cdot y' = -20y^3(5y^4 + 1)^{-3}.$$

Example 3. Find d^2y/dx^2 if $3x^2 + xy + 2y^2 = 1$.

Solution. Implicit differentiation, with primes indicating differentiation with respect to x, gives

$$(3x^2 + xy + 2y^2)' = 6x + y + xy' + 4yy' = 0,$$

or

(6)
$$y' = -\frac{6x + y}{x + 4y}.$$

Differentiation once more, followed by substitution from (6), gives

$$y'' = \frac{(x + 4y)(-6 - y') + (6x + y)(1 + 4y')}{(x + 4y)^2}$$

$$= \frac{(x + 4y)\left(-6 + \frac{6x + y}{x + 4y}\right) + (6x + y)\left(1 - \frac{24x + 4y}{x + 4y}\right)}{(x + 4y)^2}$$

$$= (x + 4y)^{-3}[-23y(x + 4y) - 23x(6x + y)]$$

$$= -46(3x^2 + xy + 2y^2)(x + 4y)^{-3} = -46(x + 4y)^{-3},$$

where the final simplification follows from the original defining equation.

709   EXERCISES

In Exercises 1–6, find the derivative with respect to x of the given function, expressed in terms of x, y, and y', where y is a differentiable function of x and $y' \equiv D_x y = dy/dx$.

1. x^2y^3.

2. $\dfrac{x^2}{y^3}$.

3. $\sqrt{2x + y^2}$.

4. $\sin(x^2 + y^2)$.

5. $\cos\sqrt{xy}$.

6. $\tan^2(2x + 3y)$.

In Exercises 7–10, by means of implicit differentiation, find $D_x y = dy/dx$ by the following two methods: (*i*) using either primes or the symbol D_x, (*ii*) using differentials.

7. $xy + y^2 = 2$.

8. $3x^2y + xy^2 = x + y$.

9. $x^3 + y^3 = xy$.

10. $x^2y^2 = \sqrt{x} + \sqrt{y}$.

In Exercises 11–18, find $D_x y = dy/dx$ by implicit differentiation.

11. $3x^2 + 8xy - y^2 = 4$.

12. $5x^2 - 2xy + 7y^2 = 8$.

13. $x^3 - 4xy^2 - 2y^3 - 5y = 0$.

14. $2x^3 + 3x^2y - y^3 + 6x = 1$.

15. $x + \sqrt{xy} + \sqrt{x + y} = 1$.

16. $\sqrt[3]{x} + \sqrt[3]{y} + \sqrt[3]{x + y} = 1$.

17. $\sin xy = x + y$.

18. $\tan(x^2 + y^2) = 2xy$.

In Exercises 19–24, find the equation of the tangent line to the given curve at the specified point.

19. $x^2 + 2xy + 7y^2 = 7$; $(0, 1)$.

20. $x^2 - 2xy - 5y^2 = 1$; $(3, -2)$.

21. $2(x^3 + y^3) = 9xy$; $(1, 2)$.

22. $x^2y + xy^2 = 6$; $(2, 1)$.

23. $y = 4\sin\left(\frac{1}{18}\pi(x + y)\right)$; $(1, 2)$.

24. $y = \tan\left(\frac{1}{8}\pi xy\right)$; $(2, 1)$.

In Exercises 25–30, find $D_x^2 y = d^2y/dx^2$ by implicit differentiation, and simplify by use of the defining equation.

25. $x^2 - xy + y^2 = 5$.

26. $x^2 + xy - y^2 = 5$.

27. $x^2 + 2xy - 5y^2 = 6$.

28. $x^2 - 2xy + 5y^2 = 6$.

29. $x^3 + 5y^3 = 4$.

30. $x^3 + x^2y + y^3 = 4$.

31. Show that the equation of the tangent line to the parabola $y^2 = 4cx$ at the point (x_1, y_1) can be written in the form $y_1y = 2c(x + x_1)$.

32. Show that the equation of the tangent line to the ellipse $\dfrac{x^2}{a^2} + \dfrac{y^2}{b^2} = 1$ at the point (x_1, y_1) can be written $\dfrac{x_1x}{a^2} + \dfrac{y_1y}{b^2} = 1$.

33. Show that the equation of the tangent line to the hyperbola $\dfrac{x^2}{a^2} - \dfrac{y^2}{b^2} = 1$ $\left(\text{or } \dfrac{y^2}{a^2} - \dfrac{x^2}{b^2} = 1\right)$ at the point (x_1, y_1) can be written $\dfrac{x_1x}{a^2} - \dfrac{y_1y}{b^2} = 1$ $\left(\text{or } \dfrac{y_1y}{a^2} - \dfrac{x_1x}{b^2} = 1\right)$.

34. Prove the *reflection property* of parabolas: For any point p on a parabola C, the tangent line to C at p makes equal acute angles with the following two lines through p: (*i*) the line through p that passes through the focus f of C, (*ii*) the line through p that is parallel to the axis of C. *Hints:* Let the parabola C have the equation $y^2 = 4cx$, where $c > 0$, and let p be (x_1, y_1). If q is the point where the tangent to C at p meets the x-axis, the problem reduces to showing that the triangle qfp is isosceles, with $qf = fp$. (Cf. Ex. 31.)

35. Prove the *reflection property* of ellipses: For any point p on an ellipse C, the tangent line to C at p makes equal acute angles with the two lines through p that pass respectively through the two foci of C. *Hints:* If the equation of the ellipse is that of Ex. 32, then with the aid of the equation of the tangent line to C at p, from Ex. 32, and the formula for the distance between a line and a point (Theorem II, §413, *PCLA*), the problem is reduced to establishing

$$\frac{\left|\dfrac{cx_1}{a^2} - 1\right|\Big/\sqrt{\dfrac{x_1^2}{a^4} + \dfrac{y_1^2}{b^4}}}{\sqrt{(x_1 - c)^2 + y_1^2}} = \frac{\left|\dfrac{-cx_1}{a^2} - 1\right|\Big/\sqrt{\dfrac{x_1^2}{a^4} + \dfrac{y_1^2}{b^4}}}{\sqrt{(x_1 + c)^2 + y_1^2}}.$$

36. Prove the *reflection property* of hyperbolas: For any point p on a hyperbola C, the tangent line to C at p makes equal acute angles with the two lines through p that pass respectively through the two foci of C. *Hint:* See Ex. 35.

710   CURVES DEFINED PARAMETRICALLY

Let x and y be expressed as differentiable functions of a third variable t, called a **parameter,** for values of t in an interval I (cf. (6), §411, *PCLA*):

$$(1) \qquad\qquad x = f(t), \qquad y = g(t), \qquad t \in I.$$

If the derivatives $f'(t)$ and $g'(t)$ never vanish simultaneously for the same t,

$$(2) \qquad\qquad (f'(t))^2 + (g'(t))^2 > 0,$$

then the set of points (x, y) corresponding to $t \in I$,

$$(3) \qquad\qquad \{(x, y) \mid x = f(t), y = g(t), t \in I\},$$

is called a **regular curve.** The parameter t can be thought of as representing *time.* (For a further discussion of curves, see Chapter 1, *SCC*, especially §108, *SCC*.)

If, for a subinterval J of I, $f'(t) \neq 0$, then (Theorem III, §617) x is a strictly monotonic function of t, and distinct values of t give distinct values of x for $t \in J$ (cf. Fig. 710-1*a*). If $g'(t) \neq 0$ over a subinterval of I, then y is a strictly monotonic function of t, and distinct values of t give distinct values of y, when t is restricted to the subinterval (cf. Fig. 710-1*b*). In other cases (cf. Example 3, below) two distinct values of t may give the *same* point (x, y), and the curve may "cross itself."

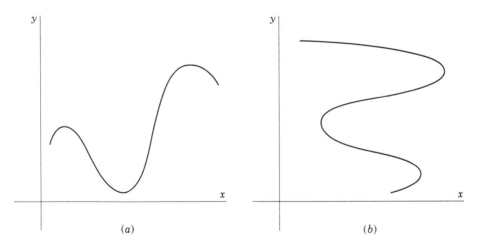

(a) (b)

Figure 710-1

At a point $(a, b) = (f(t_0), g(t_0))$ such that $f'(t) \neq 0$ for t in a neighborhood of t_0, t is a differentiable function of x, by the Theorem, §618, with derivative

$$(4) \qquad\qquad \frac{dt}{dx} = \frac{1}{dx/dt} = \frac{1}{f'(t_0)}.$$

Therefore, by the chain rule, y is a differentiable function of x, with derivative

$$(5) \qquad\qquad \frac{dy}{dx} = \frac{dy}{dt}\cdot\frac{dt}{dx} = \frac{dy/dt}{dx/dt} = \frac{g'(t_0)}{f'(t_0)}.$$

The (nonvertical) tangent line at such a point is given by the equation

(6)
$$y - b = \frac{g'(t_0)}{f'(t_0)}(x - a).$$

The formula $dy/dx = g'(t_0)/f'(t_0)$ can be easily remembered by the use of differentials

(7)
$$\frac{dy}{dx} = \frac{D_t y\, dt}{D_t x\, dt} = \frac{D_t y}{D_t x} = \frac{g'(t_0)}{f'(t_0)}.$$

Similarly, if $g'(t) \neq 0$ for t in a neighborhood of t_0, t is a differentiable function of y, and the derivative of x with respect to y is given

(8)
$$\frac{dx}{dy} = \frac{dx}{dt}\cdot\frac{dt}{dy} = \frac{dx/dt}{dy/dt} = \frac{f'(t_0)}{g'(t_0)}.$$

Thus, the (nonhorizontal) tangent line at such a point is given by the equation

(9)
$$x - a = \frac{f'(t_0)}{g'(t_0)}(y - b).$$

From (6) and (9) we see that horizontal tangents occur where $g'(t) = dy/dt = 0$, and vertical tangents occur where $f'(t) = dx/dt = 0$.

In the following three examples, and in some future exercises, a request is made for a *discussion* of a curve. Such a discussion should be interpreted to include a determination of the extent to which the curve is regular, points at which there are horizontal or vertical tangents, an equation of the tangent line at a general point, symmetry properties if they exist, and, when feasible, an elimination of the parameter to produce an equation in x and y.

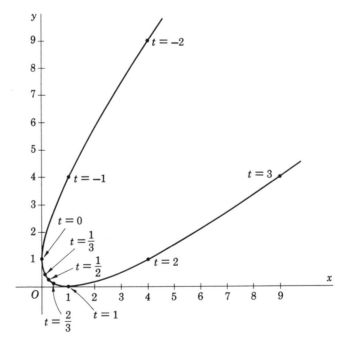

Figure 710-2

Example 1.   Sketch and discuss the curve $x = t^2$, $y = (t - 1)^2$, $t \in \mathcal{R}$.

Solution.   We differentiate, and get

(10) $$\frac{dx}{dt} = 2t, \quad \frac{dy}{dt} = 2(t - 1), \quad \frac{dy}{dx} = \frac{t - 1}{t} \text{ if } t \neq 0.$$

Since $dx/dt = 0$ if and only if $t = 0$ and $dy/dt = 0$ if and only if $t = 1$, there is no point at which *both* $dx/dt = 0$ *and* $dy/dt = 0$, and the curve is a regular curve everywhere. There is exactly one horizontal tangent, at the point $(1, 0)$ where $t = 1$, and exactly one vertical tangent, at the point $(0, 1)$ where $t = 0$. If $t_0 \neq 0$ the equation of the tangent line at the point corresponding to $t = t_0$ is

(11) $$y - (t_0 - 1)^2 = \frac{t_0 - 1}{t_0} (x - t_0^2).$$

The equation of the tangent line at $(0, 1)$ (corresponding to $t = 0$) is $x = 0$. Elimination of t can be achieved through the equation $x - y = 2t - 1$, so that substitution of $t = (x - y + 1)/2$ into the equation $x = t^2$ gives $x = [(x - y + 1)/2]^2$, or

(12) $$x^2 - 2xy + y^2 - 2x - 2y + 1 = 0.$$

Since (12) is unchanged if x and y are interchanged, the curve is symmetric with respect to the line $x = y$. Graphing (cf. Fig. 710-2) is facilitated by a table of values:

t	-3	-2	-1	0	$\frac{1}{3}$	$\frac{1}{2}$	$\frac{2}{3}$	1	2	3	4
x	9	4	1	0	$\frac{1}{9}$	$\frac{1}{4}$	$\frac{4}{9}$	1	4	9	16
y	16	9	4	1	$\frac{4}{9}$	$\frac{1}{4}$	$\frac{1}{9}$	0	1	4	9
slope	$\frac{4}{3}$	$\frac{3}{2}$	2	none	-2	-1	$-\frac{1}{2}$	0	$\frac{1}{2}$	$\frac{2}{3}$	$\frac{3}{4}$

(Cf. Ex. 26, §604, *PCLA*.)

Example 2.   Sketch and discuss the semicubical parabola $x = t^2$, $y = t^3$, $t \in \mathcal{R}$.

Solution.   Differentiation gives

(13) $$\frac{dx}{dt} = 2t, \quad \frac{dy}{dt} = 3t^2, \quad \frac{dy}{dx} = \tfrac{3}{2}t.$$

The curve is regular except at the point $(0, 0)$ corresponding to $t = 0$. At any other point, corresponding to $t = t_0 \neq 0$, the equation of the tangent line is

(14) $$y - t_0^3 = \tfrac{3}{2} t_0(x - t_0^2).$$

There is no tangent line at the origin, which is called a *cusp* of the curve. (Cf. Fig. 710-3a.) Since a change in sign in t changes the point (x, y) into the point $(x, -y)$, the graph is symmetric with respect to the x-axis. Elimination of t gives the equation $x^3 = y^2$, or $x = y^{\frac{2}{3}}$.

Example 3.   Sketch and discuss the curve $x = 4 - t^2$, $y = 4t - t^3$.

Solution.   Differentiation gives

(15) $$\frac{dx}{dt} = -2t, \quad \frac{dy}{dt} = 4 - 3t^2, \quad \frac{dy}{dx} = \frac{3t^2 - 4}{2t} \text{ if } t \neq 0.$$

The curve is a regular curve everywhere. There are two horizontal tangents at the points $(\frac{8}{3}, \pm\frac{16}{9}\sqrt{3})$ that correspond to $t = \pm\frac{2}{3}\sqrt{3}$, and one vertical tangent at the point $(4, 0)$ that corresponds to $t = 0$. There is one "double point," $(0, 0)$, that corresponds to two distinct

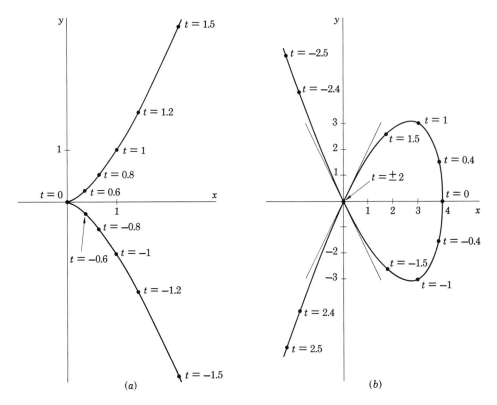

Figure 710-3

values of $t : t = \pm 2$. At this double point the two tangent lines have slopes of ± 2. (Cf. Fig. 710-3b.) The equation of the tangent line at the point corresponding to $t = t_0 \neq 0$ is

$$(16) \qquad y - 4t_0 + t_0^3 = \frac{3t_0^2 - 4}{2t_0}(x - 4 + t_0^2).$$

Since a change in sign in t changes the point (x, y) into the point $(x, -y)$ the graph is symmetric with respect to the x-axis. Elimination of t through the relationship $y = tx$ gives

$$(17) \qquad y^2 = x^2(4 - x).$$

The following is a table of values for the graph (Fig. 710-3b):

t	$\cdots$	-1	0	1	$\frac{2}{3}\sqrt{3}$	$\frac{3}{2}$	2	3	4
x	$\cdots$	3	4	3	$\frac{8}{3} = 2.67$	$\frac{7}{4}$	0	-5	-12
y	$\cdots$	-3	0	-3	$\frac{16}{9}\sqrt{3} = 3.08$	$\frac{21}{8}$	0	-15	-48
slope	$\cdots$	$\frac{1}{2}$	none	$-\frac{1}{2}$	0	$\frac{11}{12}$	2	$\frac{23}{6}$	$\frac{11}{2}$

Example 4. Find the slope of the tangent line at each point of the **cycloid**

$$(18) \qquad x = a\theta - a\sin\theta, \quad y = a - a\cos\theta, a > 0, \theta \in \Re,$$

which is the locus of a point on the circumference of a circle of radius a "rolling" along the x-axis (cf. Fig. 710-4). (We assume here the formula $a\theta$ for the length of an arc of a circle of radius a that subtends an angle of θ radians at the center of the circle; cf. §107, *SCC*.)

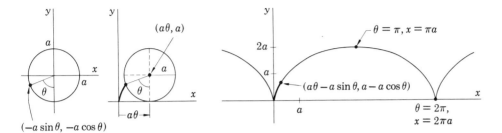

Figure 710-4

Solution: Formula (7) gives

(19) $$\frac{dy}{dx} = \frac{a \sin \theta}{a(1 - \cos \theta)} = \frac{\sin \theta}{1 - \cos \theta} = \frac{2 \sin \tfrac{1}{2}\theta \cos \tfrac{1}{2}\theta}{2 \sin^2 \tfrac{1}{2}\theta} = \cot \tfrac{1}{2}\theta,$$

for all values of θ except for integral multiples of 2π, which correspond to cusps. At all points except the cusps the curve is regular. The horizontal line $y = 2a$ is tangent at all points corresponding to $\theta = (2n + 1)\pi$, $n \in \mathcal{I}$. At any regular point the equation of the tangent line is

(20) $$y - a + a \cos \theta = \frac{\sin \theta}{1 - \cos \theta} (x - a\theta + a \sin \theta).$$

The curve is symmetric with respect to every vertical $x = na\pi$, $n \in \mathcal{I}$. It is impractical to attempt to eliminate the parameter θ and thus to obtain an equation for the cycloid (18) in terms of x and y alone.

711   SECOND-ORDER DERIVATIVES

If x and y are related by means of a parameter t, $x = f(t)$, $y = g(t)$, second-order derivatives can be determined much as in the manner of §708 for functions defined implicitly. A helpful technique in finding d^2y/dx^2 is to label dy/dx by some other letter, say z, and to use

(1) $$\frac{d^2y}{dx^2} = \frac{dz}{dx} = \frac{dz/dt}{dx/dt} = \frac{1}{dx/dt}\frac{d}{dt}\left(\frac{dy}{dx}\right) = \frac{1}{f'(t)}\frac{d}{dt}\left(\frac{g'(t)}{f'(t)}\right)$$
$$= \frac{1}{f'(t)}\frac{f'(t)g''(t) - g'(t)f''(t)}{(f'(t))^2} = \frac{f'g'' - g'f''}{(f')^3},$$

where it is assumed of course that $f'(t) \neq 0$, that is, that the point is not one where the curve has a vertical tangent. *In practice* it is usually better to use the *principles* involved in (1) rather than the formula itself. For derivatives of order higher than the second, see H §1219, *CWAG*.

Example 1.   Find d^2y/dx^2 if $x = t^2$, $y = (t - 1)^2$ (cf. Example 1, §710).

Solution.   We start with $z = dy/dx$:

(2) $$z = \frac{dy}{dx} = \frac{dy/dt}{dx/dt} = \frac{2(t - 1)}{2t} = \frac{t - 1}{t}, \quad t \neq 0.$$

We now write

$$(3) \qquad \frac{d^2y}{dx^2} = \frac{dz}{dx} = \frac{\dfrac{dz}{dt}}{\dfrac{dx}{dt}} = \frac{\dfrac{d}{dt}\left(\dfrac{t-1}{t}\right)}{\dfrac{d}{dt}(t^2)} = \frac{\dfrac{1}{t^2}}{2t} = \frac{1}{2t^3}, \quad t \neq 0.$$

Example 2. Find d^2y/dx^2 if $x = 4 - t^2$, $y = 4t - t^3$ (cf. Example 3, §710).

Solution. The first derivative $z = dy/dx$ is

$$(4) \qquad z = \frac{dy}{dx} = \frac{dy/dt}{dx/dt} = \frac{4 - 3t^2}{-2t} = \frac{3t^2 - 4}{2t}, \quad t \neq 0.$$

A second differentiation gives

$$(5) \qquad \frac{d^2y}{dx^2} = \frac{dz}{dx} = \frac{\dfrac{dz}{dt}}{\dfrac{dx}{dt}} = \frac{\dfrac{3t^2 + 4}{2t^2}}{-2t} = -\frac{3t^2 + 4}{4t^3}, \quad t \neq 0.$$

Example 3. Find d^2y/dx^2 for the cycloid of Example 4, §710.

Solution. Since $z = dy/dx = \sin\theta/(1 - \cos\theta)$,

$$(6) \qquad \frac{d^2y}{dx^2} = \frac{\dfrac{dz}{d\theta}}{\dfrac{dx}{d\theta}} = \frac{\dfrac{-1}{1 - \cos\theta}}{a(1 - \cos\theta)} = \frac{-1}{a(1 - \cos\theta)^2} = \frac{-1}{4a \sin^4 \tfrac{1}{2}\theta}.$$

712 THE GENERALIZED LAW OF THE MEAN

The following generalized form of the law of the mean (§613) will be needed later (§1302):

Theorem. Generalized Law of the Mean (Generalized Mean Value Theorem for Derivatives). *If f and g are continuous on an interval I and differentiable at every interior point of I, if f' is nonzero throughout the interior of I, and if a and b are any two distinct points of I, then there exists a point ξ between a and b such that*

$$(1) \qquad \frac{g'(\xi)}{f'(\xi)} = \frac{g(b) - g(a)}{f(b) - f(a)}.$$

Proof. Our first comment is that since f' is nonzero throughout the interior of an interval containing the points a and b, it must follow that the denominator on the right in (1) is nonzero, by the law of the mean in the form of Theorem III, §613. for the function f. Therefore the formula (1) we are attempting to establish at least exists. We shall now show that it is true.

The *picture* to have in mind for motivation is similar to Figure 613-1, used in conjunction with the proof of the law of the mean of §613, and is given in Figure 712-1. We use the parameter t and consider the curve C: $x = f(t)$, $y = g(t)$. The case where $a < b$ and where $f'(t) > 0$ is represented in Figure 712-1, although the results will not be dependent on these assumptions. The straight line L through the two points $(f(a), g(a))$ and $(f(b), g(b))$ is the graph of the function of x:

$$(2) \qquad\qquad g(b) + \frac{g(b) - g(a)}{f(b) - f(a)}(x - f(b)),$$

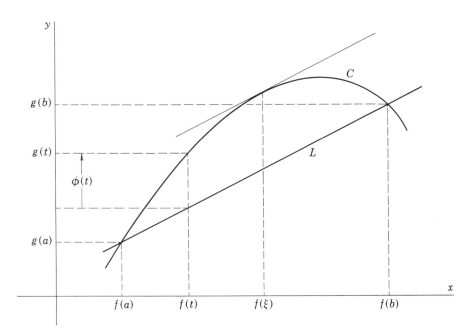

Figure 712-1

and therefore, for any t of the interval $[a, b]$, the directed vertical distance from L to C is given by the function

$$(3) \qquad\qquad \phi(t) \equiv g(t) - g(b) - \frac{g(b) - g(a)}{f(b) - f(a)}(f(t) - f(b)).$$

We now define the function $\phi(t)$ by (3) in every case (whether $a > b$ or $a < b$, and whether f' is positive or negative). It is easy to verify that ϕ is continuous for $a \leqq t \leqq b$, or for $b \leqq t \leqq a$, and is differentiable between a and b, and that $\phi(a) = \phi(b) = 0$, by direct substitution. Therefore, by the law of the mean in the form of Theorem III, §613, there must be a point ξ between a and b where $\phi'(\xi) = (\phi(b) - \phi(a))/(b - a) = 0$:

$$(4) \qquad\qquad \phi'(\xi) = g'(\xi) - \frac{g(b) - g(a)}{f(b) - f(a)}f'(\xi) = 0.$$

After division by $f'(\xi)$, (1) follows.

The law of the mean, Theorem II, §613, can be obtained from the generalized law of the mean, except for notation, by considering the special case of (1) given by $f(x) = x$ and $a < b$.

Example. Find a number ξ satisfying (1) for the functions $f(t) = 4 - t^2$, $g(t) = 4t - t^3$ of Example 3, §710, for the interval $0 \leqq t \leqq 3$.

Solution. We verify first that the conditions of the preceding Theorem are satisfied, with $a = 0$, $b = 3$, and $I = [0, 3]$. In particular, we note that $f'(t) = -2t$ is nonzero throughout the interior $(0, 3)$ of I. Formula (1) takes the form

$$(5) \qquad \frac{4 - 3\xi^2}{-2\xi} = \frac{(12 - 27) - 0}{(4 - 9) - 4},$$

which simplifies to the quadratic equation

$$(6) \qquad 9\xi^2 - 10\xi - 12 = 0.$$

Of the two roots of (6), one is an interior point of I:

$$(7) \qquad 0 < \frac{5 + \sqrt{133}}{9} < 3.$$

The number in the center of (7) is the number ξ sought.

713   EXERCISES

In Exercises 1–16, sketch and discuss the curve. Determine where the curve is regular, the location of horizontal and vertical tangent lines, an equation of the tangent line at a general point, and symmetry properties. Find an equation of the curve in terms of x and y alone.

1. $x = 3t - 3$, $y = -2t + 4$.

2. $x = 3t^2 - 6$, $y = -2t^2 + 6$.

3. $x = 2t$, $y = t^2$.

4. $x = 1 - t^2$, $y = 3t$.

5. $x = t^2 + 1$, $y = \dfrac{1}{t^2 + 1}$.

6. $x = t - \dfrac{1}{t}$, $y = \dfrac{t}{t^2 - 1}$ $(t^2 \neq 0, 1)$.

7. $x = t^6$, $y = t^4$.

8. $x = t^3 + 1$, $y = t^2$.

9. $x = t^2 + t$, $y = t^2 - t$.

10. $x = t^2 + 1$, $y = t - t^2$.

11. $x = t^2 - 1$, $y = t^3 - t$.

12. $x = 3t - t^3$, $y = 3 - t^2$.

13. $x = \cos t$, $y = \sin t$.

14. $x = \cos t$, $y = \sin^2 t$.

15. $x = \dfrac{2}{1 + t^2}$, $y = \dfrac{2t}{1 + t^2}$.

16. $x = \dfrac{2t}{1 + t^2}$, $y = \dfrac{2t^2}{1 + t^2}$.

In Exercises 17–32, find $\dfrac{d^2y}{dx^2}$ in terms of t, for the indicated exercise.

17. Exercise 1.

18. Exercise 2.

19. Exercise 3.

20. Exercise 4.

21. Exercise 5.

22. Exercise 6.

23. Exercise 7.

24. Exercise 8.

25. Exercise 9.

26. Exercise 10.

27. Exercise 11.

28. Exercise 12.

29. Exercise 13.

30. Exercise 14.

31. Exercise 15.

32. Exercise 16.

In Exercises 33–36, find a number ξ satisfying (1), §712, for the functions $x = f(t)$ and $y = g(t)$ of the specified exercise and the given values of a and b.

33. Exercise 5; $a = 0$, $b = \sqrt{3}$.

34. Exercise 8; $a = 1$, $b = 2$.

35. Exercise 9; $a = 0$, $b = b$.

36. Exercise 15; $a = 0$, $b = 1$.

37. Show that the ellipse $\dfrac{x^2}{a^2} + \dfrac{y^2}{b^2} = 1$ can be prescribed by the parametric equations

$$\begin{cases} x = a \cos \theta, \\ y = b \sin \theta, \end{cases}$$

where $0 \leqq \theta < 2\pi$.

38. A projectile shot from near the earth's surface and moving in a vertical plane over comparatively short distances follows approximately a trajectory given by the equations

(1) $x = v_0\, t \cos \alpha, \quad y = -16t^2 + v_0\, t \sin \alpha,$

where t is elapsed time in seconds, x is distance in feet measured horizontally, y is distance in feet measured vertically, v_0 is the initial firing velocity in feet per second, and α is the inclination of the gun muzzle. Sketch the trajectory for the following data: (*i*) $\cos \alpha = 3/\sqrt{10}$, $\sin \alpha = 1/\sqrt{10}$, $v_0 = 320\sqrt{10}$, (*ii*) $\cos \alpha = 1/\sqrt{2}$, $\sin \alpha = 1/\sqrt{2}$, $v_0 = 480\sqrt{2}$, (*iii*) $\cos \alpha = 1/\sqrt{10}$, $\sin \alpha = 3/\sqrt{10}$, $v_0 = 640\sqrt{10}$. (Cf. Ex. 29, §1205.)

39. A **hypocycloid of four cusps** is the locus of a point on the circumference of a circle of radius $\tfrac{1}{4}a$ rolling inside and along the circumference of a fixed circle of radius a. With the aid of Figure 713-1, show that the equations of a hypercycloid of four cusps can be written in the form $x = \tfrac{1}{4}a(3 \cos \theta + \cos 3\theta)$, $y = \tfrac{1}{4}a(3 \sin \theta - \sin 3\theta)$, or equivalently (cf. Exs. 11 and 12, §702, *PCLA*),

(2) $x = a \cos^3 \theta, \qquad y = a \sin^3 \theta.$

Show that an equation for (2) in terms of x and y alone is

(3) $x^{\frac{2}{3}} + y^{\frac{2}{3}} = a^{\frac{2}{3}}.$

Find the first and second derivatives of y with respect to x in terms of the parameter θ.

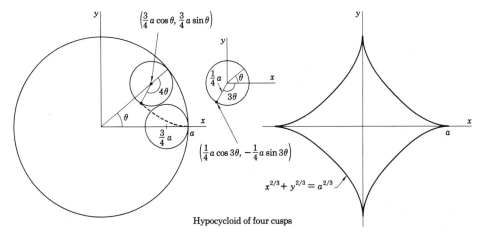

Hypocycloid of four cusps

Figure 713-1

8

Extrema and Related Rates

801 GLOBAL EXTREMA*

In §401 the two opposing concepts of global and local properties were introduced. Our principal attention since that time has been drawn to such local properties as limits, derivatives, and differentials. With the topic of extrema we have occasion once more to focus our thoughts on the global aspects of the subject.

All functions concerned with extrema will be assumed to be real-valued.

Definition I. *Let f be a (real-valued) function with domain D. A number M is the global maximum value, or the global maximum, of f if and only if there exists a point c of D such that*

$$(1) \qquad\qquad x \in D \implies f(x) \leqq f(c) = M.$$

A number m is the global minimum value, or the global minimum, of f if and only if there exists a point d of D such that

$$(2) \qquad\qquad x \in D \implies f(x) \geqq f(d) = m.$$

A global extreme value, or global extremum, of f is either a global maximum or a global minimum of f. The global maximum of f for a subset A of D is the global maximum of the restriction of f to A, with similar definitions holding for global minima and extrema, for a subset A of D. The adjective strict, applied to any of the preceding extrema, means that the implied inequality, $\leqq$ or $\geqq$, becomes a strict inequality, $<$ or $>$, whenever $x \neq c$ or $x \neq d$.

*The word *absolute* is often used in place of *global*, when applied to extrema.

NOTE. If, in the preceding definition, the word *global* is omitted at any stage, the interpretation should be unaffected. For example, the maximum of a function f on a subset A of its domain is the same as its global maximum there.

As a convenience in the formulation of statements concerning extrema, we introduce a definition:

Definition II. *A **critical point** of a function f of a real variable is a point ξ of the domain of f at which the derivative of f either does not exist or is equal to 0:*

(3) $f'(\xi)$ *does not exist or* $f'(\xi) = 0.$

If f is considered as a function of the variable x, then any critical point of f is also called a **critical value** *of the variable x.*

Our first theorem applies to extrema on *intervals*.

Theorem I. *If a function f has an extremum on an interval I (bounded or unbounded, open or closed or neither) and if this extremum occurs at a point ξ of I, then ξ is either an endpoint of I or a critical point of f.*

Proof. Assume that f has an extreme value on I at ξ, and that ξ is neither an endpoint of I nor a critical point of f. Then ξ must be an interior point of I and $f'(\xi)$ must exist and be different from 0: $f'(\xi) \neq 0$. There are two main cases, (i) $f(\xi)$ is a *maximum value* of f on I and (ii) $f(\xi)$ is a *minimum value* of f on I. We give the details for case (i) and leave case (ii) to Exercise 15, §802. The details for case (i) are given in part (ii) of the proof of Theorem I, §613. The idea is that if $f'(\xi) > 0$, then there must be a point $\xi + h$ to the *right* of ξ where $f(\xi + h) > f(\xi)$ (contradiction), and if $f'(\xi) < 0$, then there must be a point $\xi + h$ to the *left* of ξ where $f(\xi + h) > f(\xi)$ (contradiction).

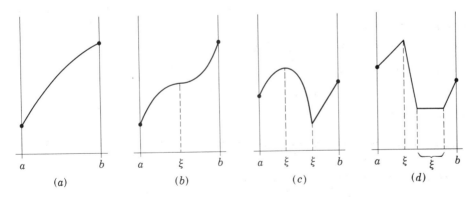

Figure 801-1

Figure 801-1 shows some of the possibilities where I is a compact interval $[a, b]$, and f is continuous. There may be *no* critical points (Fig. 801-1*a*), there may be *exactly one* critical point (Fig. 801-1*b*), there may be more than one critical point but only finitely many such (Fig. 801-1*c*), or there may be infinitely many critical points (Fig. 801-1d),   Figure 801-1b shows that *a critical point need not correspond to an extremum.*

An immediate consequence of Theorem I is the following test for extrema on a compact interval:

Theorem II.   Critical-point Test for Extrema. *Assume that f is continuous on the compact interval $I = [a, b]$, and let the maximum and minimum values of f on I be denoted by M and m, respectively. If f has no critical points between a and b, then its extrema are given by*

(4)
$$\begin{cases} M = \max (f(a), f(b)), \\ m = \min (f(a), f(b)). \end{cases}$$

If f has exactly one critical point ξ between a and b, then

(5)
$$\begin{cases} M = \max (f(a), f(b), f(\xi)), \\ m = \min (f(a), f(b), f(\xi)). \end{cases}$$

More generally, if the critical points of f in the open interval (a, b) form a finite set $\{\xi_1, \xi_2, \cdots, \xi_n\}$, then

(6)
$$\begin{cases} M = \max (f(a), f(b), f(\xi_1), \cdots, f(\xi_n)), \\ m = \min (f(a), f(b), f(\xi_1), \cdots, f(\xi_n)). \end{cases}$$

Example 1.   Find the extrema of the function $x^2 - 5x$ on the interval $[1, 2]$.

Solution.   The only critical value of x for the function $x^2 - 5x$ is the root $\frac{5}{2}$ of the equation $2x - 5 = 0$, and since $\frac{5}{2} \notin (1, 2)$, the maximum value of $f(x) = x^2 - 5x$ on $[1, 2]$ is $\max (f(1), f(2)) = \max(-4, -6) = -4$, and the minimum value is $\min(-4, -6) = -6$. (Cf. Fig. 801-2a.)

Example 2.   Find the extrema of the function $x^3 - x$ on the interval $[-1, 2]$.

Solution.   The critical values of x for the function $x^3 - x$ are the roots of the equation $3x^2 - 1 = 0$: $x = \pm \frac{1}{3}\sqrt{3} = \pm 0.58$ (to two decimal places).   Since both of these points belong to the interval $I \equiv [-1, 2]$, the maximum value of the function $f(x) \equiv x^3 - x$ on I is

$$M = \max (f(-1), f(-\tfrac{1}{3}\sqrt{3}), f(\tfrac{1}{3}\sqrt{3}), f(2)) = \max(0, \tfrac{2}{9}\sqrt{3}, -\tfrac{2}{9}\sqrt{3}, 6) = 6,$$

and the minimum value is

$$m = \min(0, \tfrac{2}{9}\sqrt{3}, -\tfrac{2}{9}\sqrt{3}, 6) = -\tfrac{2}{9}\sqrt{3}.$$

(Cf. Fig. 801-2b.)

Example 3.   Find the extrema of the functions $f(x) \equiv |x - 1| + |x - 2|$ and $g(x) \equiv 2|x - 1| + |x - 2|$ on the interval $[0, 3]$.

Solution.   The functions f and g can be described:
$$f(x) = \begin{cases} -2x + 3, 0 \le x \le 1, \\ 1, \quad 1 \le x \le 2, \\ 2x - 3, 2 \le x \le 3, \end{cases} g(x) = \begin{cases} -3x + 4, 0 \le x \le 1, \\ x, \quad 1 \le x \le 2, \\ 3x - 4, 2 \le x \le 3. \end{cases}$$

(Cf. Fig. 801-2c, d.)   The critical points of f are therefore all points of the interval $[1, 2]$ ($f'(1)$ and $f'(2)$ do not exist, and $f'(x) = 0$ for $1 < x < 2$), and the critical points of g are 1 and 2 where $g'(x)$ does not exist.   The extrema of f and g are thus

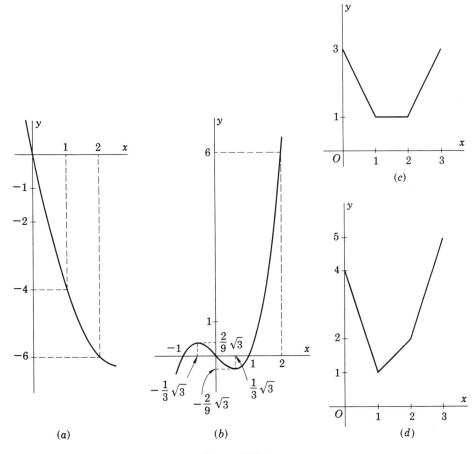

Figure 801-2

maximum of $f = \max (f(0), 1, f(3)) = \max(3, 1, 3) = 3,$
minimum of $f = \min (f(0), 1, f(3)) = \min (3, 1, 3) = 1,$
maximum of $g = \max (g(0), g(1), g(2), g(3)) = \max (4, 1, 2, 5) = 5,$
minimum of $g = \min (g(0), g(1), g(2), g(3)) = \min(4, 1, 2, 5) = 1.$

802 EXERCISES

In Exercises 1–14, find all critical points ξ of the given function on the specified interval. Then find the global extrema for the given function on this interval. A graph should accompany each of these exercises.

1. x^2, $[-1, 4]$.

2. x^3, $[-2, 1]$.

3. $x - \dfrac{4}{x}$, $[1, 3]$.

4. $x + \dfrac{4}{x}$, $[1, 3]$.

5. $x^2 - 2x$, $[1, 3]$.

6. $4x - x^2$, $[0, 3]$.

7. $x^3 - 12x$, $[1, 3]$.

8. $\dfrac{x}{x^2 + 9}$, $[2, 4]$.

9. $\dfrac{16}{x^2 - 9}$, $[5, 7]$.

10. $|x| - |x - 1|$, $[-1, 2]$.

11. $2|x| - |x - 1|$, $[-1, 2]$.

12. $|x| - 2|x - 1|$, $[-1, 2]$.

13. $f(x) \equiv \begin{cases} x^2, x < 0, \\ x^3, x \geq 0, \end{cases} \; [-1, 1]$.

14. $f(x) \equiv \begin{cases} x^2, x < 0, \\ x, \; x \geq 0, \end{cases} \; [-1, 1]$.

15. Give the details in the proof of Theorem I, §801, for case (*ii*), where $f(\xi)$ is a minimum value of f on I.

16. If f is a step-function on an interval I, prove that every point of I is a critical point of f.

17. Prove that every step-function has a global maximum and a global minimum on every subinterval of its domain.

18. Prove that every point of discontinuity in the domain of a function is a critical point of the function. Show by counterexample that the converse is false: it is possible for a function to be continuous at a critical point.

19. Prove that a function possessing both a global maximum and a global minimum is bounded. Show by counterexample that a bounded function may possess neither a global maximum nor a global minimum.

20. Prove that a function monotonic on a compact interval has both a global maximum and a global minimum there. Show by counterexample that a function monotonic on an interval that is not bounded and closed may fail to have global extrema there.

803   LOCAL EXTREMA*

Definition. *If c is a point of the domain D of a function f, then f(c) is a **local maximum value** or a **local maximum**, of f, if and only if there exists a neighborhood N_c of c such that f(c) is the maximum value of f on $D \cap N_c$:*

$$(1) \qquad\qquad x \in D \cap N_c \; \Rightarrow \; f(x) \leq f(c).$$

*A similar definition applies to a **local minimum value**, or a **local minimum**, of f, with the inequality $\leq$ of (1) being replaced by $\geq$. A **local extreme value**, or **local extremum** of f is either a local maximum or a local minimum of f. The adjective **strict**, applied to any of the preceding extrema, means that the implied inequality, $\leq$ or $\geq$, is a strict inequality, $<$ or $>$, whenever $x \neq c$. (Cf. Fig. 803-1.)*

It follows immediately that any global extremum for a function f must be a local extremum. In many cases it follows that the problem of determining *global* extrema may be reduced to that of determining *local* extrema (proof of the following theorem is left as an exercise for the reader):

Theorem I. *If a function f has a global maximum M and only a finite number of local maxima at the points $c_1, c_2, \cdots, c_j$, then*

$$(2) \qquad\qquad M = \max \left(f(c_1), f(c_2), \cdots, f(c_j) \right).$$

*The word *relative* is often used in place of *local*, when applied to extrema.

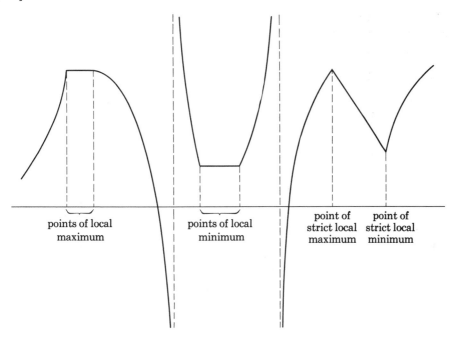

Figure 803-1

If a function f has a global minimum m and only a finite number of local minima at the points $(d_1, d_2, \cdots, d_k)$, then

$$(3) \qquad\qquad m = \min\ (f(d_1), f(d_2), \cdots, f(d_k)).$$

Critical points are related to local extrema in a simple fashion:

Theorem II. *If f is a function whose domain contains a neighborhood of the point ξ and if $f(\xi)$ is a local extremum of f, then ξ is a critical point of f.*

Proof. This follows directly by application of the same ideas as those used in the proof of Theorem I, §801.

The following theorem is a consequence of the two preceding:

Theorem III. *If f is a function whose domain is the union of a finite number of disjoint intervals $I_1, I_2, \cdots, I_n$, and if f has a global extremum and only a finite number of critical points, then f has only a finite number of local extrema, and formula (2) or (3) of Theorem I is applicable.*

Proof. Any point ξ at which the function f has a local extremum must be either an endpoint of one of the intervals $I_1, I_2, \cdots, I_n$, or an interior point of one of these intervals and hence, by Theorem II, a critical point of f. Since there are only finitely many intervals in $\{I_1, I_2, \cdots, I_n\}$ and, by assumption, only finitely many critical points of f, there can be only finitely many local extrema. The conclusion now follows from Theorem I.

In succeeding sections we shall develop methods for testing for local extrema.

Theorem III can often be used to locate global extrema. This usually amounts to individual examination of values of the function under consideration at critical points and endpoints of intervals.

Example 1. The function $f(x) \equiv x + \dfrac{1}{x}$ with domain $\mathcal{P} = (0, +\infty)$ has no global maximum since it is unbounded above. Since $f'(x) = 1 - (1/x^2)$, f has a single critical point at $x = 1$. Therefore, if f has a global minimum it must be at $x = 1$. To see that $f(1) = 2$ is a global minimum we establish the inequality

(4) $f(x) - f(1) = x + \dfrac{1}{x} - 2 = \dfrac{x^2 - 2x + 1}{x} = \dfrac{(x-1)^2}{x} \geqq 0.$

(Cf. Fig. 803-2a.)

Example 2. The function $x + \dfrac{1}{x}$ with domain $\mathcal{R} \setminus \{0\}$ has no global maximum since it is unbounded above, and it has no global minimum since it is unbounded below. It has a local minimum of 2 at $x = 1$, and a local maximum of -2 at $x = -1$. (Cf. Fig. 803-2b.)

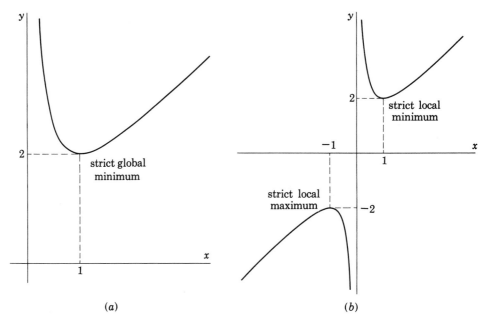

$$(a) \qquad\qquad\qquad\qquad (b)$$

Figure 803-2

Example 3. Find the global extrema of the function $f(x) \equiv \dfrac{\sqrt{x}}{x + a}$, $a > 0$, on the interval $[0, +\infty)$.

Solution. Since $f(0) = 0$ and $f(x) > 0$ for $x > 0$, f has a global minimum of 0 at $x = 0$. If f has a global maximum value it must be attained at an interior point of the interval $[0, +\infty)$ and hence at a critical point of f. We equate to 0 the derivative,

$$f'(x) = (x + a)^{-2}\left[\frac{x + a}{2\sqrt{x}} - \sqrt{x}\right],$$

and solve the resulting equation:

(5) $$\frac{x+a}{2\sqrt{x}} = \sqrt{x}, \qquad x + a = 2x, \qquad x = a.$$

Proving that $f(a) = \sqrt{a}/2a$ is a global maximum of f is equivalent to establishing the inequality $f(x) \leqq f(a)$, for $x \geqq 0$. This inequality is equivalent to the following in turn:

(6) $$\frac{\sqrt{x}}{x+a} \leqq \frac{\sqrt{a}}{2a}, \qquad \frac{x}{(x+a)^2} \leqq \frac{1}{4a}, \qquad 4ax \leqq x^2 + 2ax + a^2.$$

Since the last inequality of (6) is equivalent to $x^2 - 2ax + a^2 = (x - a)^2 \geqq 0$, we have the conclusion sought. (Cf. Fig. 803-3.)

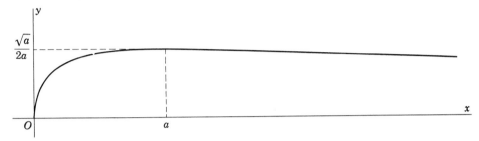

Figure 803-3

804   THE FIRST DERIVATIVE TEST; POINTS OF INFLECTION

The following test is often convenient for determining whether a differentiable function has a local extreme value at a critical point.

Theorem I. First Derivative Test. *If f is a function whose domain contains a neighborhood N_c of the point c, defined*

(1) $$N_c \equiv (c - \delta, c + \delta) = \{x \mid |x - c| < \delta\},$$

where $\delta > 0$, if f is continuous in N_c, and if $f'(x)$ exists for all x in the deleted neighborhood $N_c \setminus \{c\}$ of c and satisfies there the inequalities

(2) $$\begin{cases} c - \delta < x < c \implies f'(x) > 0, \\ c < x < c + \delta \implies f'(x) < 0, \end{cases}$$

then $f(c)$ is a strict local maximum of f. If the inequalities on the right in (2) are reversed,

(3) $$\begin{cases} c - \delta < x < c \implies f'(x) < 0, \\ c < x < c + \delta \implies f'(x) > 0, \end{cases}$$

then $f(c)$ is a strict local minimum of f. (Cf. Fig. 804-1.)

Proof. We give the details for the implications (2) and a local maximum, leaving those for (3) and a local minimum to the reader. By Theorem III, §614, f is strictly increasing on the half-open interval $(c - \delta, c]$ and strictly decreasing on the half-open interval $[c, c + \delta)$, and therefore $0 < |x - c| < \delta \Rightarrow f(x) < f(c)$.

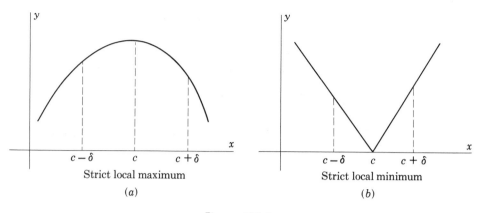

Strict local maximum

(a)

Strict local minimum

(b)

Figure 804-1

Example 1. If $f(x) = x^3 - x$ on $(-\infty, +\infty)$ (cf. Example 2, §801, and Fig. 801-2), then $f'(x) = 3x^2 - 1$ and the two critical points of f are $\pm 1/\sqrt{3} = \pm\frac{1}{3}\sqrt{3}$. Since $f'(x)$ can be written $f'(x) = 3(x + \frac{1}{3}\sqrt{3})(x - \frac{1}{3}\sqrt{3})$, the derivative f' has the pattern of signs shown in Figure 804-2. As x changes from $x < -\frac{1}{3}\sqrt{3}$ to $x > -\frac{1}{3}\sqrt{3}$, $f'(x)$ changes from positive to negative, and by Theorem I the function f has a strict local maximum at the critical point $-\frac{1}{3}\sqrt{3}$. Similarly, as x changes from $x < \frac{1}{3}\sqrt{3}$ to $x > \frac{1}{3}\sqrt{3}$, $f'(x)$ changes from negative to positive, and the function f has a strict local minimum at the critical point $\frac{1}{3}\sqrt{3}$. Since f is unbounded above and below, neither of these local extrema is a global extremum.

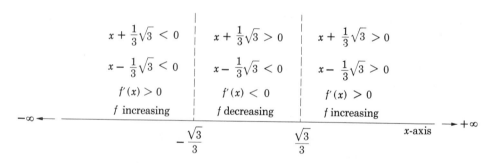

Figure 804-2

On some occasions when the implications (2) or (3) are difficult to establish, the following simplified variant of Theorem I is useful:

Theorem II. *If f is a differentiable function whose domain contains an open interval I, if there is exactly one point c of I where f' vanishes: $f'(c) = 0$, and if there exist points a and b of I such that $a < c < b$ and*

$$(4) \qquad\qquad f'(a) > 0, \quad f'(b) < 0,$$

then $f(c)$ is a strict local maximum of f. If the inequalities of (4) are replaced by

$$(5) \qquad\qquad f'(a) < 0, \quad f'(b) > 0,$$

then $f(c)$ is a strict local minimum of f. (Cf. Fig. 804-3.)

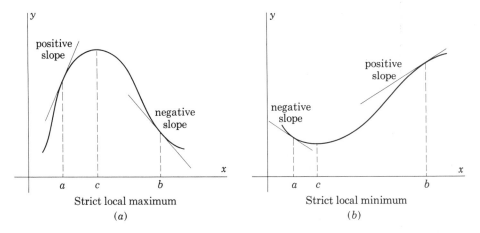

Figure 804-3

Proof. We prove the part associated with (4) and leave the second part to the reader. If $f'(x) = 0$ only for $x = c$, in the interval I, then $f'(x)$ must be of constant sign in the interval consisting of the points of I that lie to the left of c (Theorem III, §617). Since $f'(a) > 0$ and a is a point of I lying to the left of c, $f'(x) > 0$ for *all* points of I such that $x < c$. Similarly, $f'(x)$ must be of constant sign to the right of c, for $x \in I$, and since $f'(b) < 0$ and $b > c$, $f'(x) < 0$ for *all* points x of I such that $x > c$. Therefore the implications (2) are satisfied, and the conclusion follows from that of Theorem I.

Example 2. Since the domain of the function $x^3 - x$ of Example 1 is an open interval containing its two critical points, the inequalities displayed in Figure 804-2 can be replaced by the simpler table

x	-1	$-\frac{1}{3}\sqrt{3}$	0	$\frac{1}{3}\sqrt{3}$	1
$f'(x) = 3x^2 - 1$	$+$	0	$-$	0	$+$

The entries -1, 0, and 1 of the first row of this table are chosen as convenient numbers satisfying the inequalities $-1 < -\frac{1}{3}\sqrt{3} < 0 < \frac{1}{3}\sqrt{3} < 1$. The fact that $f(-\frac{1}{3}\sqrt{3})$ is a strict local maximum follows from Theorem II applied to the interval $(-\infty, \frac{1}{3}\sqrt{3})$, and the fact that $f(\frac{1}{3}\sqrt{3})$ is a strict local minimum follows from Theorem II applied to the interval $(-\frac{1}{3}\sqrt{3}, +\infty)$.

Example 3. The point $x = 1$ is the unique point of the interval $I = (0, +\infty)$ at which the derivative $1 - (1/x^2)$ of the function $f(x) \equiv x + (1/x)$ of Example 1, §803, vanishes. We can therefore apply Theorem II by choosing $a \equiv \frac{1}{2}$ and $b \equiv 2$ (for example), obtaining

$$f'(a) = -3 < 0, f'(b) = \tfrac{3}{4} > 0.$$

By inequalities (5), $f(1) = 2$ is a strict local minimum of f.

The following theorem concerns a situation that resembles those of the last two theorems but is at the same time quite different:

Theorem III. *If f is a function whose domain contains a neighborhood N_c of the point c, defined*

$$N_c \equiv (c - \delta, c + \delta) = \{ x \mid |x - c| < \delta \},$$

where $\delta > 0$, if f is continuous in N_c, and if $f'(x)$ exists and is of one sign (either always positive or always negative) in the deleted neighborhood $N_c \setminus \{c\}$ of c, then f is strictly monotonic on N_c and has neither a local maximum nor a local minimum at c. (Cf. Fig. 804-4.)

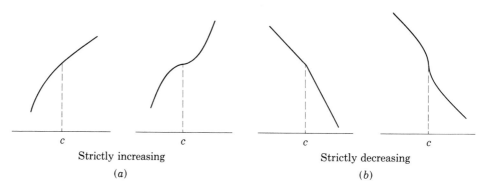

Strictly increasing   Strictly decreasing

(a)   (b)

Figure 804-4

Proof. By Theorem III, §614, f is either strictly increasing or strictly decreasing on both of the two intervals $(c - \delta, c]$ and $[c, c + \delta)$, and therefore f is strictly monotonic on their union $(c - \delta, c] \cup [c, c + \delta) = N_c$.

In case $f'(c) = 0$ and $f(c)$ is *not* an extremum of f, the usual situation normally occurring is that the point $(c, f(c))$ is a point of inflection of the graph of f, according to the definition:

Definition. *If f is a function whose domain contains a neighborhood of the point c, then the point $(c, f(c))$ is a **point of inflection**, or **inflection point** of the graph C of f if and only if the tangent to C at $(c, f(c))$ exists and crosses C there. For the case of a nonvertical tangent, since the tangent line to C at $(c, f(c))$ is the graph of the function $f(c) + f'(c)(x - c)$, this means that $f'(c)$ exists and the function*

(6) $$g(x) \equiv f(x) - f(c) - f'(c)(x - c)$$

changes sign at c: there exists a neighborhood $(c - \delta, c + \delta)$ of c such that either

(7) $$0 < h < \delta \;\Rightarrow\; g(c - h) < 0 \text{ and } g(c + h) > 0,$$

or

(8) $$0 < h < \delta \;\Rightarrow\; g(c - h) > 0 \text{ and } g(c + h) < 0.$$

(Cf. Fig. 804-5a.) If the graph C of the function f has a vertical tangent at $(c, f(c))$, then $(c, f(c))$ is automatically a point of inflection of C. (Cf. Fig. 804-5b.)

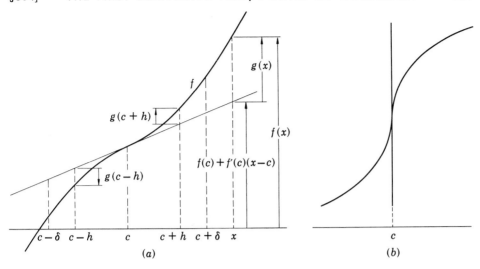

Figure 804-5

Corresponding to Theorem I for extrema is the following theorem for points of inflection:

Theorem IV. *If a function f is differentiable in a neighborhood N_c of a point c, if $f'(c) = 0$, and if $f'(x)$ is of constant sign (either always positive or always negative) for x in the deleted neighborhood $N_c \setminus \{c\}$ of c, then $(c, f(c))$ is a point of inflection of the graph of f.*

Proof. Under the assumptions stated, the function $g(x)$, of (6), simplifies to

$$(9) \qquad\qquad g(x) \equiv f(x) - f(c),$$

and since by Theorem III, f is strictly monotonic on N_c, g must be strictly monotonic on N_c and zero at the midpoint c. Therefore g must change sign, and either (7) or (8) must be true. (Cf. Fig. 804-6.)

Example 4. The origin is a point of inflection of the graph of $f(x) = \sqrt[3]{x}$, but not of the semicubical parabola $f(x) = \sqrt[3]{x^2}$. (Cf. Example 2, §615.)

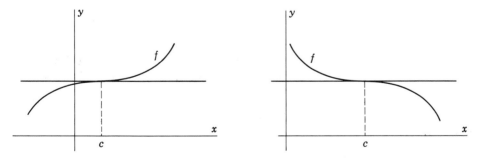

Figure 804-6

Example 5. The origin is a point of inflection of the graph of $f(x) = x^{2n+1}$, where n is any positive integer, since $x = 0$ is the unique point where $f'(x) = (2n + 1)x^{2n}$ vanishes, and $x \neq 0 \Rightarrow f'(x) > 0$. (Cf. Fig. 804-7a.)

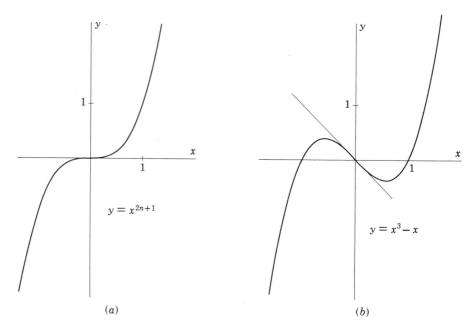

$y = x^{2n+1}$

(a)

$y = x^3 - x$

(b)

Figure 804-7

Example 6. The origin is a point of inflection of the function $f(x) \equiv x^3 - x$, since the function $g(x)$ of (6) becomes

$$g(x) = (x^3 - x) - 0 - (-1)(x - 0) = x^3,$$

and $g(x) = x^3$ changes sign at $x = 0$ (from $g(x) < 0$ for $x < 0$ to $g(x) > 0$ for $x > 0$). (Cf. Fig. 804-7b.)

NOTE. Points of inflection are taken up again, and studied more thoroughly, in §901.

805 EXERCISES

A graph should accompany each of Exercises 1–30.

In Exercises 1–6, find the global extrema for the given function on the specified interval. Justify your conclusion by use of inequalities in the manner of Examples 1 and 3, §803.

1. $x^2 - 6x + 3$, $\mathcal{R}$.

2. $7 + 10x - x^2$, $\mathcal{R}$.

3. $x + \dfrac{9}{x}$, $(0, +\infty)$.

4. $x^2 + \dfrac{16}{x^2}$, $(0, +\infty)$.

5. $\dfrac{x}{x^2 + 9}$, $[0, +\infty)$.

6. $\dfrac{x}{x^2 + 4}$, $[0, +\infty)$.

In Exercises 7–30, test the given function for local extrema at all critical points in the specified interval. Use Theorem I or Theorem II, §804, to identify extrema and Theorem IV, §804, to identify points of inflection.

7. $x^2 + 12x - 5$, $\Re$.

8. $6 - 7x - x^2$, $\Re$.

9. $x^3 - 6x^2 + 9x + 5$, $\Re$.

10. $16 + 24x + 3x^2 - x^3$, $\Re$.

11. $5 - 3x + 3x^2 - x^3$, $\Re$.

12. $x^3 + 6x^3 + 12x + 10$, $\Re$.

13. $(1 - x)^5$, $(-\infty, +\infty)$.

14. $(x + 3)^4$, $(-\infty, +\infty)$.

15. $(x^2 - 1)^2$, $(-\infty, +\infty)$.

16. $4x^3 - 3x^4$, $(-\infty, +\infty)$.

17. $\dfrac{x - 1}{x^2}$, $(0, +\infty)$.

18. $\dfrac{x}{(x - 1)^2}$, $(-\infty, 1)$.

19. $\left(1 - \dfrac{1}{x}\right)^2$, $(0, +\infty)$.

20. $\dfrac{(x - 2)(x - 6)}{x^2}$, $(0, +\infty)$.

21. $x\sqrt{8 - x^2}$, $(0, 2\sqrt{2})$.

22. $\dfrac{\sqrt{x}}{x^2 + 12}$, $(0, +\infty)$.

23. $\sqrt[5]{x^2}$, $(-\infty, +\infty)$.

24. $\sqrt{x} - \sqrt[4]{x}$, $(0, +\infty)$.

25. $|x|$, $(-\infty, +\infty)$.

26. $\sqrt{|x|}$, $(-\infty, +\infty)$.

27. $\dfrac{1}{|x| + 1}$, $(-\infty, +\infty)$.

28. $\dfrac{x}{|x| + 1}$, $(-\infty, +\infty)$.

29. $x \tan x$, $(-\tfrac{1}{2}\pi, \tfrac{1}{2}\pi)$.

30. $x \sin^2 x$, $(-\tfrac{1}{2}\pi, \tfrac{1}{2}\pi)$.

31. Prove that the function x^{2n}, $n \in \Re$, with domain $\Re$, has a strict global minimum at $x = 0$.

32. State and prove a simplified variant of Theorem IV, §804, by analogy with Theorem II, §804.

806   CONCAVITY AND THE SECOND DERIVATIVE TEST

The idea of *concavity* of a curve is closely related to that of a point of inflection. In a sense, these two notions are diametrically opposed. At a point of inflection the tangent crosses a curve; at a point where concavity is defined the tangent does *not* cross the curve, but instead remains on one side of it. The exact definition follows:

Definition. *If f is a function whose domain contains a neighborhood of the point c, then the graph C of f is **concave up** (or has **concavity upward**) at $(c, f(c))$ if and only if C has a nonvertical tangent at $(c, f(c))$ that lies below C for all x in some deleted neighborhood of c. The curve C is **concave down** (or has **concavity downward**) at $(c, f(c))$ if and only if C has a nonvertical tangent at $(c, f(c))$ that lies above C for all x in some deleted neighborhood of c. Since the tangent line to C at $(c, f(c))$ is the graph of the function $f(c) + f'(c)(x - c)$, these two definitions mean that if*

(1) $g(x) \equiv f(x) - f(c) - f'(c)(x - c)$,

then there exists a deleted neighborhood

(2) $$D_c \equiv \{x \mid 0 < |x - c| < \delta\}$$

of c such that for concavity upward or for concavity downward, respectively, we have:

(3)   *Concavity upward:* $x \in D_c \implies g(x) > 0,$

(4)   *Concavity downward:* $x \in D_c \implies g(x) < 0.$

(*Cf.* Fig. *806-1.*)

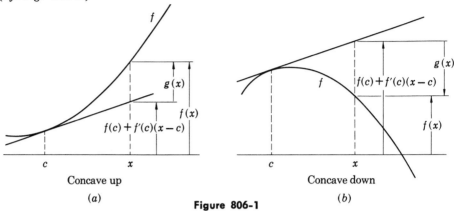

Concave up   Concave down

(*a*)   **Figure 806-1**   (*b*)

The simplest conditions guaranteeing concavity upward or downward involve the second derivative:

Theorem I. *If f is differentiable in a neighborhood of the point c, and if $f''(c)$ exists and is positive, then the graph of f is concave up at $(c, f(c))$; if $f''(c)$ exists and is negative, then the graph of f is concave down at $(c, f(c))$.*

Proof. We give the details on the basis of the assumption $f''(c) > 0$; those for the case $f''(c) < 0$ are entirely similar and will be omitted. Our assumptions, if expressed in terms of the function g of (1), take the form that g is differentiable in a neighborhood of c, that $g''(c)$ exists, and

(5) $$g(c) = 0, \quad g'(c) = 0, \quad g''(c) > 0.$$

For convenience and ease of visualization we define the function

(6) $$\phi(x) \equiv g'(x),$$

for x in the neighborhood of c where $g'(x)$ exists. Then, from (5),

(7) $$\phi(c) = 0, \phi'(c) > 0.$$

Since $\phi'(c)$ is defined as the limit

(8) $$\phi'(c) = \lim_{h \to 0} \frac{\phi(c + h) - \phi(c)}{h} = \lim_{h \to 0} \frac{\phi(c + h)}{h},$$

and since this limit is *positive*, we know from Theorem XI, § 507, that there must exist a deleted neighborhood $D_c = \{x \mid 0 < |x - c| < \delta\}$ of c such that

(9) $$c + h \in D_c \implies \frac{\phi(c + h)}{h} > 0,$$

and therefore,

(10)
$$\begin{cases} c - \delta < x < c \implies \phi(x) < 0, \\ c < x < c + \delta \implies \phi(x) > 0. \end{cases}$$

If $\phi(x)$ is replaced by $g'(x)$, the implications (10) tell us (cf. Theorem III, §614) that g is strictly decreasing on $(c - \delta, c]$ and strictly increasing on $[c, c + \delta)$. Finally, since $g(c) = 0$, this implies that $g(x)$ must be *positive* in both $(c - \delta, c)$ and $(c, c + \delta)$, and the proof is complete.

A corollary of Theorem I that is useful in the study of extrema is now a ready dividend:

Theorem II.   Second Derivative Test. *If f is differentiable in a neighborhood of the point c, if $f'(c) = 0$, and if $f''(c)$ exists and is nonzero, then $f(c)$ is a strict local extremum of f; if $f''(c) > 0$, $f(c)$ is a strict local minimum, and if $f''(c) < 0$, $f(c)$ is a strict local maximum.*

Proof.   Under the stated assumptions, if $f''(c) > 0$, the function g of (1) is

(11)
$$g(x) = f(x) - f(c),$$

and since $g(x)$ is positive in some deleted neighborhood D_c of c, $f(x)$ must be greater than $f(c)$ for $x \in D_c$. The case $f''(c) < 0$ is similar.

NOTE.   If we merely know that f is differentiable in a neighborhood of a point c, that $f'(c) = 0$, and that $f''(c) = 0$, then nothing can be inferred regarding the extremal nature of $f(c)$, as shown in Example 1, below.

Example 1.   Show that each of the three functions

$$x^4, \qquad -x^4, \qquad x^3$$

satisfies the conditions $f'(0) = f''(0) = 0$, that x^4 has a strict global minimum at $x = 0$, that $-x^4$ has a strict global maximum at $x = 0$, and that the origin is a point of inflection of the graph of $y = x^3$. (Cf. Fig. 806-2.)

Solution.   Verifying the conditions $f'(0) = f''(0) = 0$ is elementary. Furthermore, $x \neq 0 \implies x^4 > 0$ and $x \neq 0 \implies -x^4 < 0$. Finally, the origin is a point of inflection of the graph of $y = x^3$, by Example 5, §804. It should be noted that x^4 is everywhere concave up, and that $-x^4$ is everywhere concave down, even though at $x = 0$ each function has a vanishing second derivative.

Example 2.   Find the values of x for which the graph of the function $f(x) \equiv x + \dfrac{1}{x}$ of Example 2, §803, is concave up, and those for which it is concave down. Also apply the second derivative test (Theorem II) to the function at its critical points $x = \pm 1$.

Solution.   Since $f'(x) = 1 - (1/x^2)$ and $f''(x) = 2/x^3$, $f''(x) > 0$ when $x > 0$ and $f''(x) < 0$ when $x < 0$. Therefore the graph of f is concave up when $x > 0$ and concave down when $x < 0$. Since $f'(1) = 0$ and $f''(1) > 0$, the function f has a strict local minimum value of $f(1) = 2$ at $x = 1$, and since $f'(-1) = 0$ and $f''(-1) < 0$, the function f has a strict local maximum value of $f(-1) = -2$ at $x = -1$. (Cf. Fig. 803-2b.)

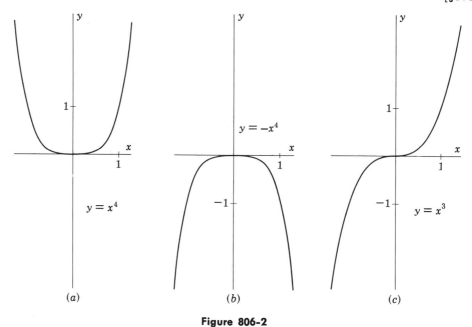

Figure 806-2

Example 3. Show that the graph of the function

$$f(x) \equiv 2x^2 + x|x| = \begin{cases} 3x^2 \text{ if } x \geqq 0, \\ x^2 \text{ if } x \leqq 0, \end{cases}$$

is everywhere concave up even though at $x = 0$ the second derivative of f does not exist. (Cf. Fig. 806-3.)

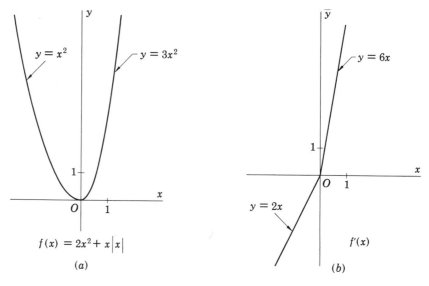

Figure 806-3

Solution. If $x > 0$, $f''(x) = 6 > 0$, and if $x < 0$, $f''(x) = 2 > 0$. Therefore the graph of *f* is concave up at every point except possibly at $x = 0$. Since

$$f'(x) = 4x + 2|x| = \begin{cases} 6x \text{ if } x \geq 0, \\ 2x \text{ if } x \leq 0, \end{cases}$$

the graph of *f* has a horizontal tangent at the origin, and since $x \neq 0 \Rightarrow f(x) > 0$, the graph of *f* lies above the *x*-axis at every point but the origin, and is therefore concave up at the origin. However, since the one-sided derivatives of *f'* at the origin are distinct, $f''(0)$ does not exist. The function $f(x)$ has a strict absolute minimum at $x = 0$.

We conclude this section with two theorems that embody the principles of Theorem I in a more global setting.

Theorem III. *Assume that f is continuously differentiable on an interval I and that $f''(x)$ exists and is of one sign (either always positive or always negative) throughout the interior of I. If c is any point of I, then the graph C of f remains on one side of the tangent line at c. More precisely, if ϕ is the linear function $f(c) + f'(c)(x - c)$ whose graph is the tangent to C at $(c, f(c))$, then if $f''(x) > 0$,*

(12) $$x \in I \setminus \{c\} \implies f(x) > \phi(x),$$

and if $f''(x) < 0$,

(13) $$x \in I \setminus \{c\} \implies f(x) < \phi(x).$$

(Cf. Fig. 806-4.)

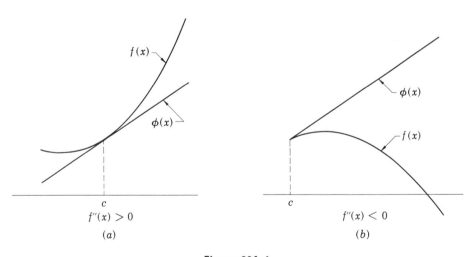

$$f(x)$$

$$\phi(x)$$

$$c$$
$$f''(x) > 0$$
$$(a)$$

$$\phi(x)$$

$$f(x)$$

$$c$$
$$f''(x) < 0$$
$$(b)$$

Figure 806-4

Proof. We give the details for the case $f''(x) > 0$ and leave those for $f''(x) < 0$ to the reader. Under the stated assumptions, let $g(x) \equiv f(x) - \phi(x)$. Then *g* is continuously differentiable on *I*, and since ϕ is linear, $\phi''(x) = 0$ and $g''(x) = f''(x) > 0$ throughout the interior of *I*. Furthermore, $g'(c) = f'(c) - \phi'(c) = 0$. As a consequence of the inequality $g''(x) > 0$ for x in the interior of I, and the continuity of g' on I, g' is a strictly increasing function on the interval I (cf. Theorem III, §614). Since $g'(c) = 0$, $g'(x) < 0$ for all x of I that lie to the left of c and $g'(x) > 0$ for all x of I that lie to the right of c. This means that g is strictly decreasing on $(-\infty, c] \cap I$ and strictly increasing on $[c, +\infty) \cap I$. Consequently, since $g(c) = 0$, $g(x) > 0$ for $x \in I \setminus \{c\}$, and (12) follows.

Theorem IV. *Assume that f is continuous on an interval I, that $f'(x)$ and $f''(x)$ exist at every interior point x of I, and that $f''(x)$ is of one sign (either always positive or always negative) throughout the interior of I. If $[a, b]$ is any bounded closed sub-interval of I, then the portion of the graph C of f for points between a and b lies on one side of the secant line joining $(a, f(a))$ and $(b, f(b))$. More precisely, if ψ is the linear function whose graph is the secant line joining $(a, f(a))$ and $(b, f(b))$, then if $f''(x) > 0$,*

(14) $$a < x < b \implies f(x) < \psi(x),$$

and if $f''(x) < 0$,

(15) $$a < x < b \implies f(x) > \psi(x).$$

(Cf. Fig. 806-5.)

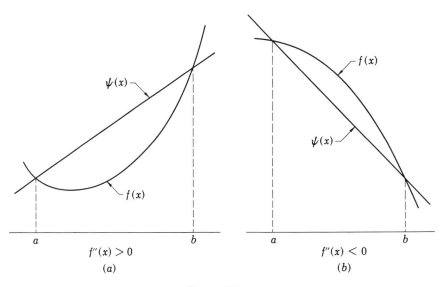

Figure 806-5

Proof. As with Theorem III we give the details only for the case $f''(x) > 0$. Under the stated assumptions, let $h(x) \equiv \psi(x) - f(x)$. Then h is continuous on I, $h'(x)$ and $h''(x)$ exist in the interior of I, and since ψ is linear, $\psi''(x) = 0$ and $h''(x) = -f''(x) < 0$. As a consequence of the inequality $h''(x) < 0$, h' is a strictly decreasing function in the interior of I and therefore in the open interval (a, b). By Rolle's theorem (§613), since h is continuous on $[a, b]$ and $h(a) = h(b) = 0$, there

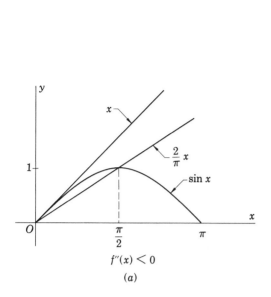

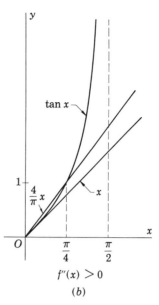

Figure 806-6

exists a point ξ between a and b such that $h'(\xi) = 0$. Since h' is strictly decreasing on (a, b), $h'(x) > 0$ for $a < x < \xi$ and $h'(x) < 0$ for $\xi < x < b$. Therefore h is strictly increasing on $[a, \xi]$ and strictly decreasing on $[\xi, b]$. Conclusion (14) now follows from the vanishing of $h(a)$ and $h(b)$.

Example 4. If $f(x) = \sin x$ and $I = [0, \pi]$, then $f'(x) = \cos x$ and $f''(x) = -\sin x < 0$ for $0 < x < \pi$. With $c = 0$ $a = 0$, and $b = \frac{1}{2}\pi$, (13) and (15) give the inequalities

$$\text{(16)} \qquad \sin x < x \text{ for } 0 < x < \pi, \qquad \sin x > \frac{2}{\pi}x \text{ for } 0 < x < \frac{\pi}{2}.$$

(Cf. Example 4, §622, and Fig. 806-6a.)   If $f(x) = \tan x$ and $I = [0, \frac{1}{2}\pi)$, then $f'(x) = \sec^2 x$ and $f''(x) = 2 \sec^2 x \tan x > 0$ for $0 < x < \frac{1}{2}\pi$. With $c = 0$, $a = 0$, and $b = \frac{1}{4}\pi$, (12) and (14) give the inequalities

$$\text{(17)} \qquad \tan x > x \text{ for } 0 < x < \frac{1}{2}\pi, \qquad \tan x < \frac{4}{\pi}x \text{ for } 0 < x < \frac{\pi}{4}.$$

(Cf. Ex. 45, §623, and Fig. 806-6b.)

807   OPEN-ENDED INTERVALS; SUBSTITUTION TECHNIQUES

Let I be an interval that is not a bounded closed interval $[a, b]$. That is, assume that either I is a bounded interval that fails to contain at least one of its endpoints (I is either half-open or open), or I is an unbounded interval. If f is a function that is continuous on I, then f may or may not be bounded, and even if f is bounded on I it may fail to have a global maximum value on I or it may fail to have a global minimum value on I. (Cf. Examples 1 and 2, §414.) On the other hand, f *may* have a global maximum or a global minimum, or both, on I, and it may be important to find these global extrema. One of the most useful simple tests is the following:

Theorem I. *If f is continuous on an interval I and differentiable in its interior, if $f'(x) = 0$ at exactly one point $x = c$ interior to I, and if $f(c)$ is a local extremum of f, then $f(c)$ is a strict global extremum for the restriction of f to the interval I.*

Proof. Assume for definiteness that f has a local *maximum* at the interior point c of I. Since c is the *only* interior point of I at which f' vanishes, the function f must be strictly monotonic on the part of I that lies on either side of the point c (cf. Theorem III, §617). Therefore f must be strictly increasing to the left of c and strictly decreasing to the right of c, and $f(c)$ is a strict global maximum for the restriction of f to I, as claimed.

Example 1. The function $f(x) \equiv x + \dfrac{1}{x}$ with domain $\mathcal{P} = (0, +\infty)$ (cf. Example 1, §803) has exactly one critical point, $x = 1$, in the open interval $\mathcal{P}$. Since f has a local minimum at $x = 1$ (cf. Example 2, §806), f has a strict global minimum there.

Another simple principle permits the location of global extrema with a minimum of test machinery. We state this principle in two parts in the following two theorems. We prove the first and leave the second to the reader.

Theorem II. *If f is differentiable on an interval I, if $f'(x) = 0$ at exactly one point $x = c$ of I, and if there exist points a and b of I such that $a < c < b$ and*

$$(1) \qquad\qquad f(c) < \begin{cases} f(a), \\ f(b), \end{cases}$$

then $f(c)$ is a strict global minimum for the restriction of f to the interval I. (Cf. Fig. 807-1a.)

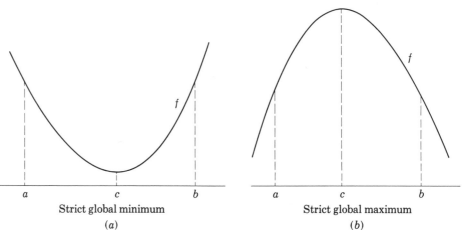

Strict global minimum
(a)

Strict global maximum
(b)

Figure 807-1

Proof. As in the proof of Theorem I, the function f must be strictly monotonic on each side of the point c in the interval I. But this means, since $f(c) < f(a)$, that f is strictly decreasing to the left of c, and since $f(c) < f(b)$ that f is strictly increasing to the right of c. Consequently, $f(c)$ is a strict global minimum for the restriction of f to I, as claimed.

Theorem III.   *Under the assumptions of Theorem II, except that (1) is replaced by*

(2)
$$f(c) > \begin{cases} f(a), \\ f(b), \end{cases}$$

$f(c)$ is a strict global maximum for the restriction of f to the interval I. (Cf. Fig. 807-1b.)

Example 2.   Let $f(x) \equiv \dfrac{x}{9 + x^2}$, with domain $I \equiv [0, +\infty)$. Then $f'(x) = \dfrac{9 - x^2}{(9 + x^2)^2}$, and $c = 3$ is the unique point of the interval I at which $f'(x)$ vanishes. Since $1 < 3 < 9$ and

$$f(3) = \tfrac{1}{6} > \begin{cases} f(1) = \tfrac{1}{10}, \\ f(9) = \tfrac{1}{10}, \end{cases}$$

the function f has a strict global maximum of $\tfrac{1}{6}$ at $x = 3$. (Cf. Fig. 807-2.)

If the second derivative of a function is readily obtained, the following theorem is frequently helpful:

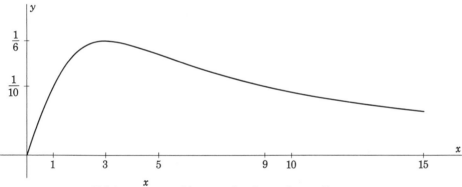

$f(x) = \dfrac{x}{9 + x^2}$, with unequal scales on the coordinate axes

Figure 807-2

Theorem IV.   *If $f''(x)$ exists and is of constant sign in an interval I and if ξ is a point of I that is a critical point of f, then f has a strict global extremum at ξ for the interval I; if $f''(x) > 0$ in I, $f(\xi)$ is a strict global minimum, and if $f''(x) < 0$ in I, $f(\xi)$ is a strict global maximum.*

Proof.   We give the details only on the assumption that $f''(x) > 0$ in I. Accordingly, the function f' is strictly increasing in I, and since $f'(\xi) = 0$, $f'(x) < 0$ for $x < \xi$ in I and $f'(x) > 0$ for $x > \xi$ in I. Consequently, the function f is strictly decreasing for $x \leq \xi$ in I and strictly increasing for $x \geq \xi$ in I, and $f(\xi)$ must be a strict global minimum for f for the interval I.

Example 3. The function $f(x) \equiv x + \dfrac{1}{x}$ with domain $\mathcal{P} = (0, +\infty)$ (cf. Example 1, §803, and Example 1, above) has first derivative $f'(x) = 1 - (1/x^2)$ and second derivative $f''(x) = 2/x^3$. Since $f''(x) > 0$ for $x > 0$ and $f'(1) = 0$, $f(1) = 2$ is a strict global minimum for f.

The details of determining global extrema can often be simplified by the procedure of removing radicals by squaring, eliminating constant factors or terms, taking reciprocals, and making substitutions. The general underlying principle is to restrict these steps to those involving strictly *monotonic* functions (for example, *squaring* is legitimate for nonnegative quantities since the squaring function x^2 is strictly increasing for $x \geq 0$). Also, when changes are made that involve *decreasing* substitutions maxima and minima may be interchanged (for example, if a positive-valued function is replaced by its *reciprocal*, maxima and minima are interchanged since the reciprocal function $1/x$ is strictly decreasing for positive x). Rather than pursue a detailed discussion of these substitution techniques, we shall indicate the type of simplification possible by means of an example.

Example 4. Find the values of x on the interval $[1, 2]$ for which the function

$$f(x) \equiv \frac{17x}{50\sqrt{x^4 + 2x^2 + 2}}$$

assumes its extreme values.

Solution. The value of x that maximizes (or minimizes) the function f is the same as that which maximizes (minimizes) the function $x/\sqrt{x^4 + 2x^2 + 2}$ or, more simply, $x^2/(x^4 + 2x^2 + 2)$. This will be the same as the value of x that minimizes (maximizes) the reciprocal $(x^4 + 2x^2 + 2)/x^2 = x^2 + 2 + 2x^{-2}$, or, with the constant term 2 subtracted, $x^2 + 2x^{-2}$. Let us now substitute $t = x^2$, and seek the value of t (with $1 \leq t \leq 4$) that minimizes (maximizes) the function $g(t) \equiv t + 2t^{-1}$. Since $g'(t) = 1 - 2t^{-2}$, $t = \sqrt{2}$ is the single critical value of t in the interval $[1, 4]$, and since $g(\sqrt{2}) = 2\sqrt{2} < g(4) = 4\frac{1}{2}$ and $g(\sqrt{2}) < g(1) < g(4)$, the function g is minimized on the interval $[1, 4]$ by $t = \sqrt{2}$ and maximized by $t = 4$. Therefore the original function f is maximized on the interval $[1, 2]$ by $x = \sqrt[4]{2}$ and minimized by $x = 2$.

808 EXERCISES

A graph should accompany each of the following exercises.

In Exercises 1–9, find the points at which the graph of the given function is concave up, and the points at which the graph is concave down. Assume a domain consisting of all real numbers at which the formula defining the function has meaning.

1. $3x^2 + 4x$.

2. $10 - x - 2x^2$.

3. $x^3 - 15x - 4$.

4. $2 + 18x - x^3$.

5. $x^4 - 4x^3$.

6. $x^4 - 8x^3 + 18x^2$.

7. $x^2 + \dfrac{8}{x}$.

8. $x + \dfrac{4}{x^2}$.

9. $\dfrac{1}{x} - \dfrac{2}{x^2}$.

In Exercises 10–18, find all local suprema for the given interval, with the aid of the second derivative test (Theorem II, §806).

10. $x^2 - 10x + 30$, $(-\infty, +\infty)$.

11. $5 + 12x - 3x^2$, $(-\infty, +\infty)$.

12. $10 - 24x + 9x^2 - x^3$, $(-\infty, +\infty)$.

13. $2x^3 - 9x^2 + 21x - 3$, $(-\infty, +\infty)$.

14. $2x^2 + x^4$, $(-\infty, +\infty)$.

15. $1 - x^2 - x^6$, $(-\infty, +\infty)$.

16. $x^2 + \dfrac{6}{x}$, $(0, +\infty)$.

17. $x + \dfrac{6}{x^2}$, $(0, +\infty)$.

18. $\dfrac{1}{x} - \dfrac{2}{x^2}$, $(0, +\infty)$.

In Exercises 19–24, establish the given inequality for $x \geq 0$ and $x \neq 1$ by relating the graph of the given function to the tangent line at the point $(1, 1)$.

19. $\sqrt{x} < \frac{1}{2}(x + 1)$.

20. $\sqrt[n]{x} < (x + n - 1)/n$.

21. $x^{\frac{2}{3}} < \frac{2}{3}x + \frac{1}{3}$.

22. $x^{\frac{3}{2}} > \frac{3}{2}x - \frac{1}{2}$.

23. $x^r < rx + (1 - r)$, r rational, $0 < r < 1$. **24.** $x^r > rx - (r - 1)$, r rational, $r > 1$.

In Exercises 25–27, use Theorem I, §807, to show that the local extremum requested in the indicated preceding Exercise of this section is a global extremum of the given function for the specified interval.

25. Exercise 16.   **26.** Exercise 17.   **27.** Exercise 18.

In Exercises 28–30, use Theorem II or Theorem III, §807, to find a global extremum (and to establish its global nature) for the given function on the specified interval.

28. $x + \sqrt{1 - x}$, $(-\infty, 1]$.   **29.** $\dfrac{(x - 9)^2}{36 - x^2}$, $(-3, 6)$.   **30.** $\dfrac{x}{x^4 + 48}$, $(0, +\infty)$.

In Exercises 31–33, use Theorem IV, §807, to find a global extremum (and to establish its global nature) for the given function on the specified interval.

31. $3x^2 - x^3$, $(1, +\infty)$.   **32.** $x^3 + \dfrac{48}{x}$, $(0, +\infty)$.   **33.** $\sqrt{x} - 2x^2$, $(0, +\infty)$.

In Exercises 34 and 35, maximize or minimize the given function on the specified interval by minimizing or maximizing its square. Justify this procedure.

34. $x\sqrt{1 - x}$, $(0, 1)$.

35. $x\sqrt{2 - x^2}$, $(0, \sqrt{2})$.

In Exercises 36 and 37, maximize or minimize the given function on the specified interval by minimizing or maximizing its reciprocal. Justify this procedure.

36. $\dfrac{x}{x^2 + 1}$, $(0, +\infty)$.

37. $\dfrac{1}{(x - 1)(7 - x)}$, $(1, 7)$.

809 THE EXTENDED LAW OF THE MEAN

If a function f is differentiable at a point a, then the equation of the tangent line to the graph of f at the point $(a, f(a))$ is $y - f(a) = f'(a)(x - a)$, which is the graph of the polynomial

$$(1) \qquad p(x) = f(a) + f'(a)(x - a).$$

(It should be noted that, except for notation. this is precisely the linear approxima-tion obtained by use of differentials in (7), §704.)

The law of the mean, in the form of (8), §613, provides the following formula for $f(x)$ itself:

$$(2) \qquad f(x) = f(a) + f'(\xi)(x - a),$$

where ξ is between a and x ($\xi = a = x$ in case $a = x$). In other words, the law of the mean states that $f(x)$ can be represented by an expression that resembles the approxi-mating polynomial (1) of at most the first degree, differing from it only by the sub-stitution of ξ for a in the coefficient of the last term.

Consider now the case of a function f that is differentiable in a neighborhood of the point a and has a second derivative $f''(a)$ at a. Let us define a polynomial $p(x)$ of degree at most 2 that has the following three properties at a:

$$(3) \qquad p(a) = f(a), \quad p'(a) = f'(a), \quad p''(a) = f''(a).$$

It is reasonable to think of $p(x)$ as the polynomial of degree at most 2 that best ap-proximates the function $f(x)$ near the point a. We shall now find an explicit form for $p(x)$.

If $p(x) = c_0 + c_1 x + c_2 x^2$, then $p(x)$ can be expressed in terms of powers of $x - a$, by expansion as follows, since $p(x) = p((x - a) + a)$:

$$(4) \quad \begin{aligned} p(x) &= c_0 + c_1[(x - a) + a] + c_2[(x - a) + a]^2 \\ &= [c_0 + c_1 a + c_2 a^2] + [c_1 + 2c_2 a](x - a) + c_2(x - a)^2 \\ &= p_0 + p_1(x - a) + p_2(x - a)^2, \end{aligned}$$

where $p_0 \equiv c_0 + c_1 a + c_2 a^2$, $p_1 \equiv c_1 + 2c_2 a$, and $p_2 \equiv c_2$. By differentiating (4), and using (3), we obtain:

$$(5) \qquad \begin{aligned} p'(x) &= p_1 + 2p_2(x - a), \quad p'(a) = f'(a) = p_1, \\ p''(x) &= 2p_2, \quad p''(a) = f''(a) = 2p_2, \end{aligned}$$

and since $p(a) = f(a) = p_0$, the polynomial $p(x)$ can be expressed as follows:

$$(6) \qquad p(x) = f(a) + f'(a)(x - a) + \tfrac{1}{2}f''(a)(x - a)^2.$$

It is not altogether unreasonable to expect that if f has a second-order derivative $f''(x)$ for x near a, then $f(x)$ can be represented by an expression that resembles the approximating polynomial (6) of degree at most 2, differing from it only by the sub-stitution of a quantity ξ for a in the coefficient of the last term. Our objective now is to show that this is indeed the case. In fact, we shall establish the following general theorem, which extends the preceding discussion to an arbitrary positive integer n:

Theorem I. Extended Law of the Mean (Mean Value Theorem for Derivatives).
*If $f, f', \cdots, f^{(n-1)}$ are continuous on an interval I, if $f^{(n)}$ exists at every interior
point of I, and if x and a are any two distinct points of I, then there exists a point
ξ between a and x such that*

(7) $f(x) = f(a) + f'(a)(x - a) + \dfrac{f''(a)}{2!}(x - a)^2 + \cdots$

$$+ \frac{f^{(n-1)}(a)}{(n - 1)!}(x - a)^{n-1} + \frac{f^{(n)}(\xi)}{n!}(x - a)^n.$$

If $f^{(n)}(a)$ exists, then (1) holds for the case $x = a = \xi$ as well.

Proof. If $a \neq x$, let the constant K be defined by the equation

(8) $f(x) = f(a) + f'(a)(x - a) + \dfrac{f''(a)}{2!}(x - a)^2 + \cdots$

$$+ \frac{f^{(n-1)}(a)}{(n - 1)!}(x - a)^{n-1} + \frac{K}{n!}(x - a)^n,$$

and define a function $\phi(t)$ by replacing a by t in (8) and subtracting the term $f(x)$:

(9) $\phi(t) \equiv f(t) - f(x) + f'(t)(x - t) + \dfrac{f''(t)}{2!}(x - t)^2 + \cdots$

$$+ \frac{f^{(n-1)}(t)}{(n - 1)!}(x - t)^{n-1} + \frac{K}{n!}(x - t)^n.$$

This function $\phi(t)$, for the interval I, satisfies the conditions of Theorem III, §613
(with f replaced by ϕ): $\phi(t)$ is continuous on I and $\phi'(t)$ exists at every interior point of
I. In addition, $\phi(a) = 0$ by (8), and $\phi(x) = 0$ by substitution. Therefore there exists
a point ξ between a and x such that $\phi(x) = \phi(a) + \phi'(\xi)(x - a)$, or $\phi'(\xi)(x - a) = 0$,
whence $\phi'(\xi) = 0$:

(10) $\phi'(\xi) = f'(\xi) - f'(\xi) + f''(\xi)(x - \xi) - f''(\xi)(x - \xi) + \cdots$

$$+ \frac{f^{(n)}(\xi)}{(n - 1)!}(x - \xi)^{n-1} - \frac{K}{(n - 1)!}(x - \xi)^{n-1}$$

$$= \frac{1}{(n - 1)!}(f^{(n)}(\xi) - K)(x - \xi)^{n-1} = 0,$$

and therefore $K = f^{(n)}(\xi)$, and (7) follows from (8). If $x = a = \xi$, (7) is satisfied
trivially.

The extended law of the mean is also called **Taylor's Formula with a Remainder**
(cf. §1105, *SCC*).

Corresponding to Theorem IV, §613, is the following form of the extended law
of the mean:

Theorem II. *If $f, f', \cdots, f^{(n-1)}$ are continuous on an interval I, if $f^{(n)}$ exists at every
interior point of I, and if a and $a + h$ are any two distinct points of I, then there exists
a number θ such that $0 < \theta < 1$ and*

(11) $f(a + h) = f(a) + f'(a)h + \dfrac{f''(a)}{2!}h^2 + \cdots + \dfrac{f^{(n-1)}(a)}{(n - 1)!}h^{n-1} + \dfrac{f^{(n)}(a + \theta h)}{n!}h^n.$

If $f^{(n)}(a)$ exists, then (11) *holds for the case $h = 0$ as well.*

Proof. In case $h \neq 0$, let $x = a + h$, use (7), and let $\theta \equiv (\xi - a)/h = (\xi - a)/(x - a)$. Then $0 < \theta < 1$ and $a + \theta h = \xi$.

A useful extension of the second derivative text for extrema (Theorem II, §806) is now possible:

Theorem III. *Let f be a function which, in some neighborhood of the point c, is defined and has derivatives $f', f'', \cdots, f^{(n-1)}$ of order $\leq n - 1$, where $n > 1$. If $f'(c) = f''(c) = \cdots = f^{(n-1)}(c) = 0$, and if $f^{(n)}(c)$ exists and is nonzero, then (i) if n is even, f has a strict local extremum at c, which is a maximum if $f^{(n)}(c) < 0$ and a minimum if $f^{(n)}(c) > 0$, and (ii) if n is odd, the point $(c, f(c))$ is a point of inflection of the graph of f, and $f(c)$ is not a local extremum of f.*

Proof. Owing to the vanishing of the derivatives of order $< n - 1$ at the point c, the extended law of the mean (Theorem I) provides the formula

$$(12) \qquad f(x) - f(c) = \frac{f^{(n-1)}(\xi)}{(n-1)!} (x - c)^{n-1},$$

where x is in a suitably restricted deleted neighborhood of c, and ξ is between c and x. The proof resolves itself into determining what happens to the sign of the right-hand member of (12) as x changes from $x < c$ to $x > c$, according to the various possibilities for the sign of $f^{(n)}(c)$ and whether n is even or odd. We give the details for the case $f^{(n)}(c) < 0$, and leave those for $f^{(n)}(c) > 0$ to Exercise 9, §810. If $g(x) \equiv f^{(n-1)}(x)$, then $g(c) = 0$, and

$$(13) \qquad f^{(n)}(c) = g'(c) = \lim_{h \to 0} \frac{g(c + h) - g(c)}{h} = \lim_{h \to 0} \frac{g(c + h)}{h} < 0,$$

and by Theorem XI, §507, there exists a positive number δ such that

$$(14) \qquad \begin{cases} -\delta < h < 0 \implies \dfrac{g(c + h)}{h} < 0 \text{ and } g(c + h) > 0, \\[2mm] 0 < h < \delta \implies \dfrac{g(c + h)}{h} < 0 \text{ and } g(c + h) < 0. \end{cases}$$

Consequently, the values of the function $f^{(n-1)}$ change from positive to negative as x changes from $x < c$ to $x > c$. Therefore, if n is even, the right-hand member of (12) is negative whether $x < c$ or $x > c$, whence $f(x) < f(c)$ for x in a deleted neighborhood of c, and $f(c)$ is a strict local maximum value of f. If n is odd, the right-hand member of (12) is positive for $x < c$ and negative for $x > c$, so that the graph of f crosses the tangent line at $(c, f(c))$, the point $(c, f(c))$ is a point of inflection of the graph of f, and $f(c)$ is neither a local maximum nor a local minimum of f.

Example 1. Use the extended law of the mean to establish the inequalities

$$(15) \qquad x - \tfrac{1}{6} x^3 < \sin x < x, \text{ for } x > 0.$$

Solution. The inequality $\sin x < x$ was proved in Example 4, §622. We now write out formula (7) for $f(x) = \sin x$, $x > 0$, $a = 0$, and $n = 3$:

$$(16) \quad \sin x = \sin 0 + \cos 0 \cdot (x - 0) - \frac{\sin 0}{2!}(x - 0)^2 - \frac{\cos \xi}{3!}(x - 0)^3$$

$$= x - \tfrac{1}{6}(\cos \xi)x^3,$$

where $0 < \xi < x$. If $0 < x \leqq 2\pi$, then $0 < \xi < 2\pi$, $\cos \xi < 1$, $-\frac{1}{6}\cos \xi > -\frac{1}{6}$, and $\sin x = x - \frac{1}{6}(\cos \xi)x^3 > x - \frac{1}{6}x^3$. If $x > 2\pi$, then $x > 6$, $x^2 > 36$, $\frac{1}{6}x^2 > 6$, and $\frac{1}{6}x^3 > 6x$. Consequently, $x - \frac{1}{6}x^3 < x - 6x = -5x < -1 \leqq \sin x$, and (15) is established.

Example 2. Prove that $x^5 \sin x$ has a strict local minimum at $x = 0$.

First solution. With $f(x) \equiv x^5 \sin x$, we have $f'(x) = x^5 \cos x + 5x^4 \sin x$, $f''(x) = -x^5 \sin x + 10x^4 \cos x + 15x^3 \sin x$, $f'''(x) = -x^5 \cos x - 15x^4 \sin x + 55x^3 \cos x + 45x^2 \sin x$, $f''''(x) = x^5 \sin x - 20x^4 \cos x - 115x^3 \sin x + 210x^2 \cos x + 90x \sin x$, $f^{(5)}(x) = x^5 \cos x + 25x^4 \sin x - 195x^3 \cos x - 555x^2 \sin x + 510x \cos x + 90 \sin x$, and $f^{6)}(x) = -x^5 \sin x + 30x^4 \cos x + 295x^3 \sin x - 1140x^2 \cos x - 1620x \sin x + 600 \cos x$. Therefore $f'(0) = f''(0) = \cdots = f^{(5)}(0) = 0$ and $f^{6)}(0) = 600 > 0$, and the desired result follows from Theorem III.

Second solution. The function $x^5 \sin x$ is even, for $0 < x < \pi$ it is positive-valued, and at $x = 0$ its value is 0.

810   EXERCISES

1. Write out formula (7), §809, for $n = 1, 2, 3$, and 4.

2. Write out formula (11), §809, for $n = 1, 2, 3$, and 4.

In Exercises 3–6, use the extended law of the mean to establish the given identity.

3. $\cos x > 1 - \frac{1}{2}x^2$, $x > 0$.   **4.** $\sec x > 1 + \frac{1}{2}x^2$, $0 < x < \frac{1}{2}\pi$.

5. $\tan x > x + \frac{1}{3}x^3$, $0 < x < \frac{1}{2}\pi$.   **6.** $\cos x < 1 - \frac{1}{2}x^2 + \frac{1}{24}x^4$, $x > 0$.

7. If r is a rational number between 0 and 1, use Theorem I, §809, with $a = 0$ and $n = 2$, to establish the inequality

(1) $$(1 + x)^r < 1 + rx, x \geqq -1, x \neq 0.$$

From (1) infer the following, where n is a positive integer:

(2) $$\sqrt[n]{1 + x} < 1 + \frac{x}{n}, x \geqq -1, x \neq 0.$$

(Cf. Exs. 20, 23, §808.)

8. If r is a rational number greater than 1, use Theorem I, §809, with $a = 0$ and $n = 2$, to establish the inequality

(3) $$(1 + x)^r > 1 + rx, x \geqq -1, x \neq 0.$$

(Cf. Ex. 24, §808.)

9. Complete the details in the proof of Theorem III, § 809, for the case $f^{(n)}(c) > 0$.

811   APPLIED PROBLEMS

Most applied problems concerned with extrema are problems in which the object sought is a *global* extremum of a function, or at least a global extremum of the restriction of a function to an interval. When it is easy to express the quantity to be extremized as a function of a single variable, the methods developed in the preceding sections of this chapter are applicable. In most cases it is not necessary to obtain a second derivative, and frequently the principles stated in § 807 make it unnecessary to apply the first derivative test of § 804.

Examples 5 and 6 illustrate methods of introducing *two* variables, with a relationship between them that permits the *elimination* of one. In a stated problem it is often helpful to sketch not only a figure illustrating the problem itself (with appropriate labeling) but also a figure giving the graph of the function of a single variable that is to be maximized or minimized.

Example 1. From the four corners of a rectangle 2 feet by 3 feet are cut small squares of equal size. If the side flaps remaining are folded through a right angle to form an open tray, what is the maximum possible resulting volume? (Cf. Fig. 811-1.)

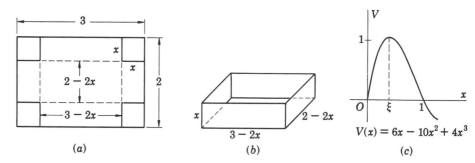

Figure 811-1

Solution. If the length of each side of the squares cut from the rectangle is x feet, then the physical limitations of the problem impose the inequalities

(1) $0 \leq x \leq 1$.

The volume of the tray is $x(3 - 2x)(2 - 2x)$ cubic feet, or

(2) $V(x) = 6x - 10x^2 + 4x^3$.

Since $V(0) = V(1) = 0$, since $V(x) > 0$ for $0 < x < 1$, and since $V(x)$ is everywhere continuous, we examine the critical values of x for $V(x)$ by equating to zero its derivative:

(3) $V'(x) = 6 - 20x + 12x^2 = 0$.

Of the two roots of (3) exactly one belongs to the interval $[0, 1]$:

(4) $\xi = \frac{1}{6}(5 - \sqrt{7}) = 0.39$ (to two decimal places).

By Theorem III, §806, the maximum value of $V(x)$ for $0 \leq x \leq 1$ is $V(\xi)$. The value of $V(\xi)$ is $(10 + 7\sqrt{7})/27 = 1.06$ cubic feet (to two decimal places).

Example 2. A man has 24 feet of fencing with which he wishes to construct a rectangular playpen for his child. If he makes use of a wall of his house for one side of the playpen, what dimensions will give the maximum enclosed area?

Solution. If the length of the edge of the rectangle at right angles to the house is x feet, then the other dimension is $24 - 2x$ feet and the enclosed area is $x(24 - 2x)$ square feet, or

$$(5) \qquad\qquad A(x) = 24x - 2x^2.$$

(Cf. Fig. 811-2.)   The variable x is restricted by the inequalities $0 \leq x \leq 12$. Since $A'(x) = 24 - 4x = 0$ if and only if $x = 6$, since $A(0) = 0$, $A(6) > 0$, and $A(12) = 0$, the global maximum of $A(x)$ for $0 \leq x \leq 12$ is given by $x = 6$, and the dimensions of the playpen area are 6 feet and 12 feet. The maximum enclosed area is 72 square feet.

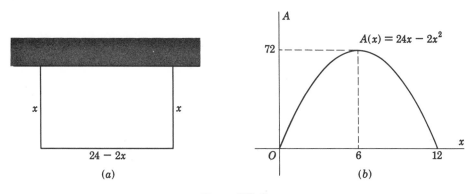

$$(a) \qquad\qquad\qquad\qquad (b)$$

Figure 811-2

Example 3.   The man of Example 2 has decided to make use of a corner of his house, which contains an inset rectangle 4 feet by 10 feet, as shown in Figure 811-3a.   What dimensions of a rectangular playpen will give the maximum enclosed area?

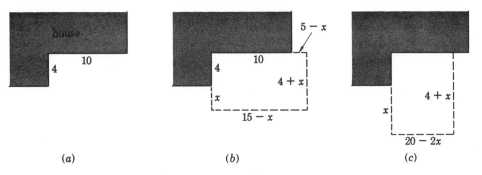

$$(a) \qquad\qquad\qquad (b) \qquad\qquad\qquad (c)$$

Figure 811-3

Solution.   If x is the length of the extension indicated in Figure 811-3b, then the other portions of the playpen area have the lengths indicated. (For example, the piece of length $5 - x$ can be obtained as follows. Label it y and add up the pieces that give the total length of 24 feet: $x + (4 + x) + y + (10 + y) = 24$, or $2x + 2y = 10$, and $y = 5 - x$.) The enclosed area, in square feet, is therefore

$$(6) \qquad\qquad A(x) = (4 + x)(15 - x) = 60 + 11x - x^2.$$

The problem is to maximize $A(x)$ on the interval $0 \leq x \leq 5$. Since the graph of $A(x)$ is a parabola opening downward with vertex at $x = 5\frac{1}{2}$ (where $A'(x) = 0$), the maximum value of $A(x)$ on $[0, 5]$ is given by the right-hand endpoint $x = 5$. Therefore the playpen does *not* extend beyond the 10-foot piece of wall. On the other hand, it does not fall *short* of making full use of the 10-foot piece, as is seen from Figure 811-3*c*. In this last case, with the notation indicated in Figure 811-3*c*, the area is

$$(4 + x)(20 - 2x) = 80 + 12x + 2x^2$$

whose maximum value for $20 - 2x \leq 10$, or $x \geq 5$, is given by $x = 5$ for reasons similar to those given above. Combining these two results, we have $x = 5$, and the dimensions of the playpen are 9 feet and 10 feet. The maximum enclosed area is 90 square feet, as compared with 72 square feet in Example 2.

Example 4. A man is on a small island in a lake having a nearby shoreline that extends in a straight line for a considerable distance. The man wishes to go as quickly as possible to a certain point on the shore, and he has available to him a rowboat. If he can walk faster than he can row, what course should he steer?

Solution. We set up a coordinate system so that the x-axis lies along the shoreline, with the island at the point $(0, a)$, $a > 0$, and with the shoreline objective at $(b, 0)$, $b \geq 0$, the units being miles. (Cf. Fig. 811-4*a*.) If the man can row at the rate of r miles an hour and walk at the rate of w miles an hour, with $r < w$, then since, for uniform rectilinear motion, distance is equal to rate times time, the total time necessary if he rows directly for the point $(x, 0)$, $0 \leq x \leq b$, and then walks from $(x, 0)$ to $(b, 0)$, is

$$(7) \qquad t(x) = \frac{\sqrt{x^2 + a^2}}{r} + \frac{b - x}{w}.$$

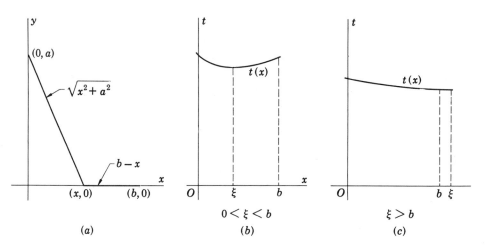

$$0 < \xi < b \qquad\qquad \xi > b$$
$$(a) \qquad\qquad (b) \qquad\qquad (c)$$

Figure 811-4

We wish to minimize the function $t(x)$ subject to the inequality $0 \leq x \leq b$. We start by examining the critical points of $t(x)$ by equating to zero its derivative:

$$(8) \qquad t'(x) = \frac{x}{r\sqrt{x^2 + a^2}} - \frac{1}{w} = 0.$$

Solving (8) for x gives the unique critical value ξ of x on the interval $(0, +\infty)$:

$$(9) \qquad \xi = \frac{ar}{\sqrt{w^2 - r^2}}.$$

There are now two cases, depending on whether or not the point ξ of (9) belongs to the interval $[0, b]$. The case where $0 < \xi < b$ is illustrated in Figure 811-4b. The case where $\xi > b$ is illustrated in Figure 811-4c. In either case, since

(10)
$$t''(x) = \frac{a^2}{r(x^2 + a^2)^{3/2}} > 0,$$

the graph of $t(x)$ is everywhere concave up, and consequently, by Theorem IV, §807, the function $t(x)$ has a strict global minimum at ξ for the interval $[0, +\infty)$. If $0 < \xi \leq b$, then $t(x)$ has a strict global minimum at ξ for the interval $[0, b]$. If $\xi > b$, since $t(x)$ is strictly decreasing on $[0, b]$, $t(x)$ must have a strict global minimum at b for the interval $[0, b]$. In any case, then, the global minimum of $t(x)$ for $0 \leq x \leq b$ is attained at the point

(11)
$$\min (b, \xi) = \min (b, ar/\sqrt{w^2 - r^2}).$$

(Cf. Exs. 8–9, §812.)

Example 5. What are the most economical dimensions of a tin can?

Solution. We interpret this question to mean: "What are the base radius and altitude of a right circular cylinder of given volume and minimum total surface area?" As indicated in Figure 811-5a, we let the base radius and altitude be denoted by r and h, respectively. If V is the given volume, then $\pi r^2 h = V$, or, if we denote by C the constant $C = V/\pi$,

(12)
$$r^2 h = C.$$

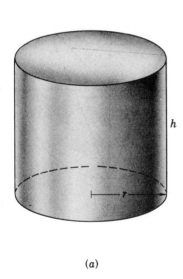

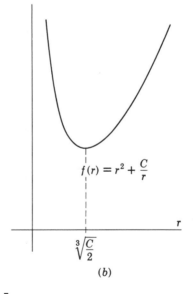

$$f(r) = r^2 + \frac{C}{r}$$

$$\sqrt[3]{\frac{C}{2}}$$

(a)   (b)

Figure 811-5

We wish to minimize the total surface area $2\pi r^2 + 2\pi rh$ (cf. §112, *SCC*) or, equivalently, since 2π is a positive constant factor (cf. Example 4, §807):

(13)
$$\text{Minimize: } r^2 + rh.$$

Solving (12) for h in terms of r (we *could* solve for r in terms of h, but solving for h is simpler) gives the following function of r to be minimized:

(14)
$$\text{Minimize: } f(r) \equiv r^2 + \frac{C}{r}, \; 0 < r < +\infty.$$

Since

(15) $$f'(r) = 2r - \frac{C}{r^2} \quad \text{and} \quad f''(r) = 2 + \frac{2C}{r^3},$$

$f''(r) > 0$ for $r > 0$, and $f'(r) = 0$ for $r = \sqrt[3]{C/2}$. Consequently (Theorem IV, § 807) $f(r)$ has a strict global minimum at $r = \sqrt[3]{C/2}$. Therefore, for this same value of r, $h = C/r^2 = \sqrt[3]{4C} = 2r$. We conclude that most economical dimensions of a tin can are those for which the altitude is equal to the diameter of the base.

Example 6.   Find the maximum possible volume for a right circular cone inscribed in a sphere of radius a.

Solution.   For convenience we orient the cone with vertical axis and vertex down, as shown in Figure 811-6. With the notation of that figure, with (x, y) located in the first quadrant, the volume of the inscribed cone is equal to $\frac{1}{3}\pi x^2(y + a)$, where x and y satisfy the equation $x^2 + y^2 = a^2$ (cf. Example 2, §206). Solving for x^2 in terms of y gives the following function to be maximized, for $0 \leq y \leq a$:

(16) $$V(y) = \tfrac{1}{3}\pi(a^2 - y^2)(a + y) = \tfrac{1}{3}\pi(a^3 + a^2 y - ay^2 - y^3).$$

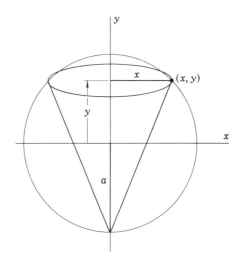

Figure 811-6

Differentiation gives

(17) $$V'(y) = \tfrac{1}{3}\pi(a^2 - 2ay - 3y^2), \quad V''(y) = \tfrac{1}{3}\pi(-2a - 6y).$$

Solving the equation $V'(y) = 0$ gives two roots, $y = -a$ and $y = \tfrac{1}{3}a$, only the latter of which belongs to the interval $[0, a]$. Since $V''(y) < 0$ throughout this interval, $V(y)$ has a strict global maximum at $y = \tfrac{1}{3}a$, by Theorem IV, §807.   The altitude of the cone of maximum volume is $a + y = \tfrac{4}{3}a$, and the base radius is $(a^2 - y^2)^{\frac{1}{2}} = \tfrac{2}{3}\sqrt{2}\, a$. The maximum volume is $\tfrac{1}{3}\pi \cdot \tfrac{8}{9}a^2 \cdot \tfrac{4}{3}\, a = \tfrac{32}{81}\pi a^3$.

Example 7.   Two hallways in a hotel meet at right angles. If these hallways are 8 feet and 12 feet wide, respectively, and if the ceilings are 10 feet high, how long a slim pole can be carried around the turn from one hallway to the other?

Solution.   We first solve the problem for a pole lying on the floor. In the notation of Figure 811-7*a* we seek a *minimum* for the expression 8 csc θ + 12 sec θ as a function of θ:

(18) $$f(\theta) \equiv 8 \csc \theta + 12 \sec \theta, 0 < \theta < \tfrac{1}{2}\pi.$$

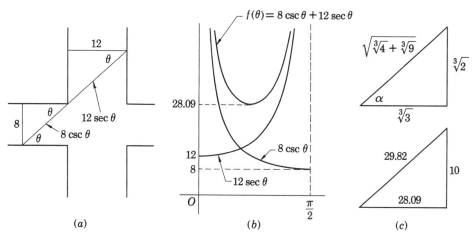

Figure 811-7

The function $f(\theta)$ has the limits

(19) $$\lim_{\theta \to 0+} f(\theta) = +\infty, \ \lim_{\theta \to \frac{1}{2}\pi -} f(\theta) = +\infty$$

(cf. Fig. 811-7*b*), and a single critical point in $(0, \tfrac{1}{2}\pi)$ got by equating to zero its derivative:

(20) $$f'(\theta) = -8 \csc \theta \cot \theta + 12 \sec \theta \tan \theta = 0,$$

which is equivalent to 2 cos $\theta/\sin^2 \theta$ = 3 sin $\theta/\cos^2 \theta$, or tan^3 $\theta = \tfrac{2}{3}$, giving

(21) $$\tan \theta = \sqrt[3]{\frac{2}{3}} = \frac{\sqrt[3]{2}}{\sqrt[3]{3}}.$$

Therefore (cf. Theorem II, § 807), if α is the acute angle whose tangent is $\sqrt[3]{\tfrac{2}{3}}$, $\theta = \alpha$ gives the global minimum for $f(\theta)$ on $(0, \tfrac{1}{2}\pi)$. The length of the longest *horizontal* pole that can turn the corner can now be computed (cf. Fig. 811-7*c*):

$$8 \csc \theta + 12 \sec \theta = \sqrt{\sqrt[3]{4} + \sqrt[3]{9}} \left(\frac{8}{\sqrt[3]{2}} + \frac{12}{\sqrt[3]{3}} \right) = 4(\sqrt[3]{4} + \sqrt[3]{9})^{\frac{3}{2}}$$

$$= 4 \cdot 3.6675^{\frac{3}{2}} \text{ (approximately)} = 28.09 \text{ feet (to two decimal places)}.$$

Finally, the longest pole that can turn the corner is one such that if one end is on the floor and the other end on the ceiling, then its orthogonal projection onto a horizontal plane has length 28.09 feet (approximately). In other words, the length L sought is (cf. Fig. 811-7c):

$$L = \sqrt{28.09^2 + 10^2} \text{ (approximately)} = 29.82 \text{ feet (to two decimal places)}.$$

Example 8.   A bus company in a certain city is required to operate at least 100 busses regularly, and owns 120 in good condition. To operate any bus costs the company \$32 per day, aside from certain invariant overhead expenses. An economist has made a study which reveals that if 100 busses are operated, an average of 496 people ride each bus per day, and that (within the limitations imposed by the number of busses owned by the company) each additional bus beyond 100 reduces the average number of people using each bus per day by 3. If the fare is 25 cents per ride, how many busses should the company operate?

Solution. If n is the number of busses beyond 100, so that $100 + n$ is the total number of busses being operated, the total number of people using the busses per day is

$$(22) \qquad N = (496 - 3n)(100 + n) = 49600 + 196n - 3n^2,$$

and the total gross income from fares is, in dollars,

$$(23) \qquad 0.25N = 12400 + 49n - 0.75n^2.$$

Since the cost of operating $100 + n$ busses is $32(100 + n) = 3200 + 32n$ dollars, the profit is $(12400 + 49n - 0.75n^2) - (3200 + 32n)$, or, in dollars,

$$(24) \qquad p(n) = 9200 + 17n - 0.75n^2.$$

We wish to find the integer n satisfying the inequalities $0 \leq n \leq 20$ that gives the largest possible value for the function $p(n)$. Since for the range $\Re$ of all real numbers the graph of the function $p(x) = 9200 + 17x - 0.75x^2$ is a parabola that is everywhere concave down and possesses a vertex at the point ξ where $p'(\xi) = 0$:

$$(25) \qquad p'(\xi) = 17 - 1.5\xi = 0, \xi = \tfrac{34}{3} = 11\tfrac{1}{3}$$

and since the graph of $y = p(x)$ has the vertical axis of symmetry $x = 11\tfrac{1}{3}$, it follows that the integer n that maximizes $p(x)$ must be the integer nearest $11\tfrac{1}{3}$. With $n = 11$, then, the company should operate 111 busses for maximum profit. If the company owned 108 busses in good condition, the problem would reduce to an endpoint maximum, with 108 as the solution (and similarly with any number between 100 and 111).

812   EXERCISES

Each of the following exercises should be accompanied by an argument validating the conclusion.

1. Solve Example 1, §811, if the rectangle is 3 feet by 8 feet.

2. Solve Example 1, §811, if the rectangle is 5 feet by 8 feet.

3. Find the maximum area of a rectangle with sides parallel to the coordinate axes inscribed in the triangle with vertices $(0, 0)$, $(a, 0)$, and $(0, b)$, where $a > 0$ and $b > 0$.

4. Prove that a triangle of maximum area inscribed in a circle must be equilateral.

5. The man of Example 2, §811, has decided to construct his child's playpen so that the enclosed area is equal to 72 square feet. What is the minimum amount of fencing that he must purchase?

6. Solve Example 3, §811, if the length of fencing is 30 feet. (The inset rectangle is still 4 feet by 10 feet.)

7. Solve Example 3, §811, if the length of fencing is 12 feet.

8. Solve Example 4, §811, if the man can row at the rate of 3 miles per hour and walk at the rate of 5 miles per hour, and if the island is 4 miles from shore and his objective is 7 miles along the shore from the point of the shore nearest the island.

9. Solve Example 4, §811, if the man can row at the rate of 2 miles per hour and walk at the rate of 4 miles per hour, and if the island is 7 miles from shore and his objective is 4 miles along the shore from the point of the shore nearest the island.

10. A horizontal straight wire of length $3a$ is regarded as consisting of three portions each of length a. The two end pieces are bent upward about the points of trisection through equal angles θ to form the two slanting sides of the trapezoid illustrated in Figure 812-1a.   Find θ if the area of this trapezoid is a maximum.

11. The sides and bottom of a trough are to be made from a 6-foot by 10-foot rectangular piece of galvanized sheet iron by folding up two 2-foot by 10-foot rectangular portions along lines parallel to the 10-foot sides, as indicated in Figure 812-1b.   The trough thus produced has a cross section that is a trapezoid of the type illustrated in Figure 812-1a.   Assuming that material is available for forming the ends, find the maximum volume that the trough can contain.

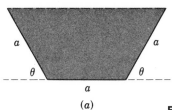

(a)

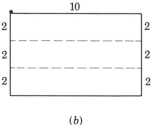

(b)

Figure 812-1

12. A square sheet of glass 8 feet on each side is being moved from a vertical closet 1 foot wide into a corridor, as indicated in Figure 812-2a.   Prove that if the corridor is at least 5 feet 3 inches wide the sheet of glass can be moved completely into the corridor, but that if the corridor is at most 5 feet 2 inches wide this is impossible.   Ignore the thickness of the glass.

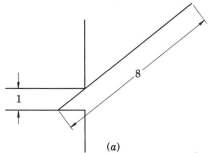

(a)

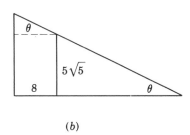

(b)

Figure 812-2

13. A thin wall $5\sqrt{5}$ feet (approximately 11 feet 2 inches) high stands on level ground 8 feet from a tall building.   How long is the shortest ladder that can simultaneously touch the building, the ground, and the top of the wall? *Suggestion:* Use trigonometry (cf. Fig. 812-2b).

14. A truck has a top speed of 60 miles per hour and, when traveling at the rate of x miles per hour, consumes gasoline at the rate of $\dfrac{1}{200}\left(\dfrac{400}{x} + x\right)$ gallons per mile. This truck is to be taken on a 200-mile trip by the owner, who receives no compensation for driving.   What is the most economical speed?

15. The truck owner in Exercise 14 has decided to hire a driver for the truck trip of 200 miles.   If gasoline costs 30 cents per gallon and if the owner pays the driver 2 dollars per hour, the total cost is $\dfrac{30}{100}\left(\dfrac{400}{x} + x\right) + 2\left(\dfrac{200}{x}\right)$ dollars. (Why?) What is the most economical speed?

16. The truck owner in Exercise 14 finds that he must send a crew of men costing a total of at least 5 dollars per hour. What is the most economical speed?

17. A candy manufacturer is planning on mass-producing a new packaged candy product, and an efficiency expert has estimated that if the price per package is x cents, the profit is given by a formula of the type

$$\text{Profit} = K\left(\frac{x-7}{x^2} - 0.01\right),$$

where $K > 0$, for $x > 7$. Find the value of x that maximizes the profit.

18. The manufacturer, in Exercise 17, has decided to market his new product at a price per package that is an integral multiple of 10 cents. What price gives him maximum profit under this added condition?

19. The manufacturer, in Exercise 17, is dissatisfied with the recommendations of his first adviser and hires a second, who produces the formula

$$\text{Profit} = K\left(\frac{x-15}{x^2} - 0.02\right),$$

where $K > 0$, for $x > 15$. Why does the manufacturer feel justified in dispensing with the services of the second "expert"?

20. A farmer has a house and a barn on the same side of a straight river flowing through his property. He wishes to construct a path consisting of two straight portions, one connecting his house with a point p on the river and one connecting his barn with the point p. Where should the point p be located for the total length of his path to be a minimum?

21. Find the point on the parabola $y^2 = x$ that is nearest the point $(-1, 5)$.

22. Find the point on the hyperbola $2xy = 1$ that is nearest the point $(\frac{3}{4}, 0)$.

23. A rectangle with sides parallel to the coordinate axes is inscribed in the triangle with vertices $(2, 0)$, $(-2, 0)$, and $(0, 6)$. Find the maximum possible area of this rectangle if it is at least twice as long as it is wide.

24. From a rectangular piece of plywood 3 feet by 4 feet are cut two square pieces with sides parallel to the sides of the original piece. Find the maximum sum of the areas of the two square pieces.

25. An estimate of the value of a certain quantity being measured is to be determined from n measurements $x_1, x_2, \cdots, x_n$. The **least squares** estimate is the number x that minimizes the sum of squares

$$S(x) \equiv (x - x_1)^2 + (x - x_2)^2 + \cdots + (x - x_n)^2.$$

Show that the least squares estimate is the arithmetic mean of the measurements,

$$x = \frac{x_1 + x_2 + \cdots + x_n}{n}.$$

26. In Exercise 38 §713, let d be the horizontal distance between the point at which the projectile is fired and the point where it strikes the earth's surface, assumed to be level. Find the value of α that maximizes this distance.

813   IMPLICIT FUNCTIONS AND EXTREMA

On occasion it is difficult or awkward to express a quantity to be extremized as an explicit function of a single variable. In such an event it is often feasible to permit the pertinent variables to remain related by an equation, and to obtain the relevant derivatives by implicit differentiation. The method of implicit differentiation often leads easily to relationships among the variables in question.

Example 1. Find the most economical dimensions of a tin can (Example 5, §811) by implicit differentiation.

Solution. As in the solution of Example 5, §811, the problem reduces to that of minimizing the function

$$(1) \qquad\qquad r^2 + rh,$$

where r and h are positive, subject to the condition that r^2h is equal to a given positive constant C:

$$(2) \qquad\qquad r^2h = C.$$

If we were to solve (2) for h in terms of r and substitute the result in (1) we should obtain a function of the form $r^2 + (C/r)$ which is readily shown to have a global minimum for exactly one positive value of r. Our problem now is simply that of establishing a relationship between r and h that corresponds to the global minimum of $r^2 + rh$. We return to equations (1) and (2), and let h be regarded as a function of r, defined implicitly by (2). We differentiate (1) and (2) with respect to r, and set *both* derivatives equal to 0 (that of (1) because $r^2 + rh$ is assumed to have an extreme value at an interior point r of $(0, +\infty)$, and that of (2) because r^2h is a constant):

$$(3) \qquad\qquad 2r + h + rh' = 0,$$

$$(4) \qquad\qquad 2rh + r^2h' = 0,$$

where h' denotes the derivative of h with respect to r. Division of (4) by r gives $rh' = -2h$, and therefore, from (3), $2r + h - 2h = 0$, or

$$(5) \qquad\qquad h = 2r.$$

Therefore a tin can of most economical dimensions must have its altitude equal to its base diameter.

Example 2. Find the maximum volume of a right circular cylinder inscribed in a given right circular cone, assuming the cylinder and cone have coincident axes of symmetry.

Solution. Let R and H denote the base radius and altitude, respectively, of the given cone, and denote by r and h the base radius and altitude, respectively, of the inscribed cylinder (cf. Fig. 813-1a). We choose coordinate axes so that the given cone is generated by revolving about the y-axis the line having x-intercept R and y-intercept H. Since the equation of this line is $(x/R) + (y/H) = 1$ (cf. Example 3, §407, *PCLA*), r and h are related by the equation

$$(6) \qquad\qquad \frac{r}{R} + \frac{h}{H} = 1.$$

Since the volume of the inscribed cylinder is πr^2h, we have the problem of minimizing the function

$$(7) \qquad\qquad r^2h.$$

(The positive constant π is omitted for convenience.) Equation (6) defines h as a differentiable function of r that is positive-valued for $0 < r < R$ and zero at the endpoint R of the interval $[0, R]$ (cf. Fig. 813-1a). The resulting expression r^2h in (7), as a function of r, is also differentiable on $[0, R]$, positive in the interior, and equal to zero at both endpoints (cf. Fig. 813-1b). Therefore r^2h has a global maximum for a value of r between 0 and R, at which point $(r^2h)'$, the derivative with respect to r, must vanish. As in the solution of Example 1 we have two equations

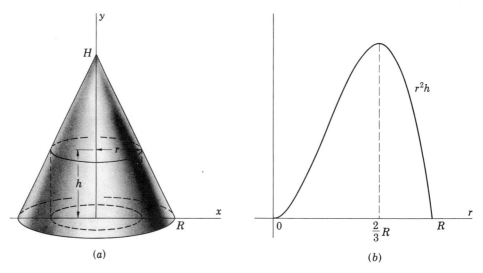

Figure 813-1

$$(8) \qquad \frac{1}{R} + \frac{h'}{H} = 0,$$

$$(9) \qquad 2rh + r^2h' = 0.$$

Elimination of $h' = -\dfrac{H}{R} = -2\dfrac{h}{r}$ gives $\dfrac{r}{R} = 2\dfrac{h}{H}$, and therefore, from (6), $3\dfrac{h}{H} = 1$, $\dfrac{h}{H} = \dfrac{1}{3}$,

and $\dfrac{r}{R} = \dfrac{2}{3}$. In other words, the cylinder of maximum volume is given by $r = \dfrac{2}{3}R$ and

$h = \dfrac{1}{3}H$.

814   EXERCISES

Each of the following exercises should be accompanied by an argument validating the conclusion.

1. Show that the relative dimensions of a right circular cylinder whose volume is maximized for a given total surface area are the same as those of Example 5, §811.

2. Show that two positive numbers with a given sum and a maximum product must be equal. Infer that a rectangle of given perimeter and maximum area is a square.

3. Show that two positive numbers with a given product and a minimum sum must be equal. Infer that a rectangle of given area and minimum perimeter is a square.

4. Find the rectangle of maximum area that can be inscribed in the ellipse

$$\frac{x^2}{a^2} + \frac{y^2}{b^2} = 1,$$

assuming that the sides of the rectangle are parallel to the coordinate axes.

5. A rectangular field is surrounded by a fence and is subdivided into three rectangular areas by two fences parallel to the ends of the field. If the total area of the field is 3200 square yards, find the dimensions that minimize the total length of fencing.

6. Solve Exercise 5 in case unrestricted use can be made of a long straight vertical cliff in place of fencing along one side of the field.

7. A wire of fixed length is bent so that it encloses a plane region that is the union of a rectangle and a half-disk, the diameter of the half-disk being a side of the rectangle. Find the relative dimensions of this rectangle if the area of the region enclosed by the wire is a maximum.

8. An open-top box with a square base and containing 32 cubic feet is to be constructed of material costing a uniform amount per square foot for the four sides and the base. Find the dimensions for minimum total cost.

9. Solve Exercise 8 if the volume of the box is 48 cubic feet and the material for the base costs 50 percent more per square foot than that for the sides.

10. A line through a fixed point (x_1, y_1), where x_1 and y_1 are positive, has intercepts $(a, 0)$ and $(0, b)$, where a and b are positive. Find the minimum possible area for the triangle with vertices $(0, 0)$, $(a, 0)$, and $(0, b)$.

11. Find a relationship between the base radius r and the altitude h of a right circular cone of given volume if the lateral surface area $\pi r \sqrt{r^2 + h^2}$ is a minimum.

12. Find the base radius r and altitude h of a right circular cone of maximum volume and given slant height $\sqrt{r^2 + h^2} = a > 0$.

13. Let $A : (0, a)$ and $B : (0, b)$, where $0 < a < b$, designate two distinct points on the positive half of the y-axis, let $X : (x, 0)$, where $x > 0$, designate a point on the positive half of the x-axis, and let $O : (0, 0)$ designate the origin. If α and β are the positive acute angles OXA and OXB, respectively, find the value of x that maximizes the difference angle $\beta - \alpha = AXB$. *Suggestion:* Letting primes indicate differentiation with respect to the variable x, write $(\beta - \alpha)' = 0$ in the form $\beta' = \alpha'$, and from the equations $\cot \alpha = x/a$ and $\cot \beta = x/b$ obtain $-\alpha' \csc^2 \alpha = 1/a$ and $-\beta' \csc^2 \beta = 1/b$.

14. A publisher is drawing up plans for the page-format of a new book. Each page is to contain 40 square inches of printed material, and is to include side margins of $1\frac{1}{4}$ inches each and top and bottom margins of 2 inches each. What page dimensions minimize the amount of paper used?

15. The strength of a beam of rectangular cross section is proportional to the (horizontal) breadth and to the square of the (vertical) depth. What are the dimensions of the cross section of a rectangular beam of maximum strength that can be cut from a right circular cylindrical log of radius 9 inches?

16. The "stiffness" of a beam of rectangular cross section is proportional to the (horizontal) breadth and to the cube of the (vertical) depth. What are the dimensions of the cross section of a rectangular beam of maximum stiffness that can be cut from a right circular cylindrical log of radius 9 inches?

17. A right circular cone is circumscribed about a sphere of radius $a > 0$. Find the base radius r and altitude h of the cone if its volume is a minimum.

18. Find the minimum volume of a right circular cone circumscribed about a given right circular cylinder, assuming the cylinder and cone have coincident axes of symmetry.

815 RELATED RATES

Often when two (or more) quantities are considered to be varying as functions of time, and when these quantities are related by an equation, their time rates of change (derivatives with respect to time) become related by an equation obtained from the original equation by implicit differentiation. These time rates of change are then called **related rates.**

A word of caution is in order: When particular values of related variables are to be substituted for these variables, such substitutions should always be made *after* the rates of change (derivatives) of these variables have been determined in general.

In this section primes will be used to indicate time rates of change, that is, derivatives with respect to time.

Example 1. A ship is sailing due east at a speed of 18 miles per hour, while a second ship is sailing due north at a speed of 24 miles per hour. At 2:00 P.M. the second ship is 120 miles directly south of the first ship. What is their relative velocity (rate of change of the distance separating them) at 3:00 P.M.? What is it at midnight? How close do they come to each other, and at what time are they closest?

Solution. Choose a coordinate system so that the first ship is sailing to the right on the *x*-axis and the second ship is sailing upward on the *y*-axis, and let t represent time in hours measured from 2:00 P.M. At time t, then, the first ship has coordinates $(18t, 0)$ and the second ship has coordinates $(0, 24t - 120)$. If z is the (positive) distance between the ships at time t, then

$$(1) \qquad z^2 = (18t)^2 + (24t - 120)^2 = 36(25t^2 - 160t + 400).$$

By implicit differentiation, $2zz' = 36(50t - 160)$, whence

$$(2) \qquad z' = \frac{30(5t - 16)}{\sqrt{25t^2 - 160t + 400}}.$$

The time 3:00 P.M. corresponds to $t = 1$, and therefore the relative velocity of the two ships at that time is

$$z' = \frac{30(-11)}{\sqrt{265}} = -\frac{66}{53}\sqrt{265} = -20.27.$$

miles per hour (to two decimal places). The negative sign indicates that the distance between the ships is *decreasing*. At midnight $t = 10$, and

$$z' = \frac{30 \cdot 34}{\sqrt{1300}} = \frac{102}{13}\sqrt{13} = 28.29$$

miles per hour (to two decimal places). The minimum distance is obtained by setting $z' = 0$, which gives $t = \frac{16}{5}$. In other words, the ships are closest at 5:12 P.M., and their closest distance at that time is $z = 6\sqrt{144} = 72$ miles.

Example 2. A conical tank with vertical axis of symmetry, open at the top and with vertex at the bottom, has base radius 3 feet and altitude 8 feet. If water is flowing into the tank at the rate of 12 cubic feet per minute, how fast is the level rising when the water is 6 feet deep?

Solution. We take a coordinate system with origin at the vertex of the cone and *y*-axis coinciding with the axis of symmetry (cf. Fig. 815-1*a*). The surface of the cone is generated

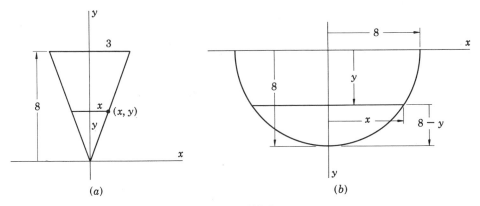

Figure 815-1

by revolving about the *y*-axis the line $y = \frac{8}{3}x$. When the depth is *y* feet, therefore, the base radius of the cone of water in the tank is $x = \frac{3}{8}y$, and the volume of water is

$$(3) \qquad\qquad V = V(y) = \frac{1}{3}\pi x^2 y = \frac{1}{3}\pi\left(\frac{3}{8}y\right)^2 y = \frac{3\pi}{64}y^3.$$

Since the rate of change of *V* is 12 cubic feet per minute, we have by implicit differentiation of (3) with respect to time,

$$(4) \qquad\qquad 12 = V' = \frac{9\pi}{64}y^2 y' = \frac{9\pi}{64}\cdot 36y' = \frac{81\pi}{16}y'$$

cubic feet per minute, and therefore

$$(5) \qquad y' = \frac{64}{27\pi} \text{ feet per minute} = \frac{256}{9\pi} \text{ inches per minute} = 9.05 \text{ inches per minute}$$

(to two decimal places).

Example 3. A hemispherical tank with vertical axis of symmetry, open at the top, has radius equal to 8 feet. If water is flowing into the tank at the rate of 12 cubic feet per minute, how fast is the level rising when the water is 6 feet deep?

Solution. For convenience, this time we choose a coordinate system with origin at the center of the sphere of which the tank forms half, with the *y*-axis oriented positively downward, and consider the hemisphere as produced by revolving about the *y*-axis the quarter circle given by $x^2 + y^2 = 64$ in the first quadrant (cf. Fig. 815-1*b*). We shall need a formula for the volume of water in the tank of depth $8 - y$. By Theorem II, §206, with an interchange of the variables *x* and *y*, this volume is equal to

$$(6) \quad V = V(y) = \pi \int_y^8 (64 - z^2)dz = \pi\left[64(8 - y) - \frac{512 - y^3}{3}\right] = \frac{1}{3}\pi(1024 - 192y + y^3)$$

cubic feet. Differentiating implicitly with respect to time, and then substituting $y = 2$, we have

$$(7) \qquad\qquad 12 = V' = -\pi(64 - y^2)y' = -60\pi y'$$

cubic feet per minute, and therefore

(8) $y' = -\dfrac{1}{5\pi}$ feet per minute $= -\dfrac{12}{5\pi}$ inches per minute $= -0.76$ inches per minute

(to two decimal places). The negative sign means that y is *decreasing*, and the water level is *rising*.

Example 4. A launch is being towed toward a pier by means of a cable passing over a pulley on the edge of the pier and then extending to the rear axle of a truck (cf. Fig. 815-2). Assume that the cable extends in a straight line from the prow of the launch to the pulley and horizontally in a straight line from the pulley to the truck, that the pulley is 25 feet vertically above the point of attachment to the launch, and that the truck is moving at the rate of 3 miles per hour. How fast is the launch moving when it is 60 feet from the pier?

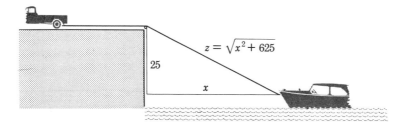

Figure 815-2

Solution. If x is the horizontal distance between the launch and the pier and if z is the length of the cable between the launch and the pulley,

(9) $z^2 = x^2 + 625,$

and therefore differentiation with respect to time gives $2zz' = 2xx'$, and therefore

(10) $x' = \dfrac{z}{x} z'.$

Since the ratio z/x is independent of the units used, it is immaterial whether we convert distances to miles, or whether we convert rates to feet per minute. For convenience we shall leave the units as prescribed, and substitute:

$$x' = \frac{\sqrt{x^2 + 625}}{x}(-3) = \frac{\sqrt{4225}}{60}(-3) = -\frac{65}{60} \cdot 3 = -3.25$$

miles per hour. It should be noted that formula (10) should not be taken literally for small values of x. For example, the limit statement $\lim\limits_{x \to 0+} \dfrac{\sqrt{x^2 + 625}}{x} = +\infty$ would mean that the speed of the launch would exceed the speed of light before it crashes into the pier!

816   EXERCISES

In the following exercises all rates of change are implicitly assumed to be time rates of change. Primes indicate differentiation with respect to time t. The formula $4\pi r^2$ for the surface area of a sphere of radius r, used in Exercises 12 and 13, is derived in Example 3, §112, *SCC*.

  1. If $z = xy^2 - y^3$, and if $x' = 5$ and $y' = -2$, find z' when $x = 3$ and $y = 1$.

  2. If $x' = 8$, find y' at the point $(2, 1)$ of the curve $x^2 + xy + y^2 = 7$.

3. In the conical tank of Example 2, §815, how fast is the water level rising when the water is $\frac{1}{2}$ inch deep? (The water is still flowing in at the rate of 12 cubic feet per minute.)

4. A steady supply of seed grain is running down a chute and falling onto the top of a conical pile whose altitude remains equal to one-third of the diameter of the base circle. If the grain is falling at the rate of 1 cubic foot per second, at what rate is the altitude increasing when the altitude is equal to 4 feet?

5. A trough 10 feet long has cross sections that are equilateral triangles with vertical axes of symmetry and vertices at the bottom. Water is flowing into the trough at a constant rate of R cubic feet per minute. Find R if the water level is rising at the rate of 3 inches per minute when the depth is 18 inches.

6. A ladder 8 feet long is leaning against a vertical wall. If the bottom of the ladder is slipping at the rate of 2 feet per minute, how fast is the top of the ladder falling when it is 5 feet from the floor?

7. In a right triangle the sides a and b that intersect at right angles are changing in such a way that the hypotenuse is of constant length. If the rate of change of side a is $a' = 3$ inches per minute, find the rate of change of side b when $a = 4$ feet and $b = 6$ feet.

8. An airplane is flying a horizontal straight-line course at a height of 5 miles, and passes directly over a certain courthouse. If the speed of the airplane is 260 miles per hour, what is the rate of change of the straight-line distance between the courthouse and the airplane at the moment when the airplane has traveled 12 miles from the point directly above the courthouse?

9. Between noon and 1:00 P.M. of a certain day one man is driving east on an east–west highway at a uniform rate of 75 miles per hour, and a second man is driving north on a north–south highway at a uniform rate of 50 miles per hour. At noon the first man is 3 miles west of the intersection of the two highways, and the second man is 4 miles north of this intersection. At this moment what is the rate of change of the distance between the two drivers? Are they approaching each other or separating? At what time are they nearest? How rapidly are they separating at 1:00 P.M.?

10. A boy 5 feet tall is walking at the rate of 3 feet per second and passes directly below a street light 20 feet above the ground. At what rate is his shadow lengthening 6 seconds after he has passed under the light?

11. The volume of a cube is increasing at the rate of 12 cubic inches per second. At what rate is the total surface area (6 squares) increasing when the surface area is 54 square inches?

12. A spherical balloon is being inflated at the rate of 40 cubic feet per minute. At what rate is the radius r changing when $r = 5$? At what rate is the surface area changing at this moment?

13. A spherical snowball is melting in such a way that the rate of change of its volume is proportional to its surface area. Show that the rate of change of its radius is constant.

14. A hemispherical tank with vertical axis of symmetry, open at the top, has radius equal to 10 feet. If water is flowing into the tank at a constant rate R and if the water level is rising at the rate of 1 inch per minute when the depth is 6 feet, find R.

15. Under ideal conditions, at constant temperature a gas obeys the law $pv = c$, where p and v represent pressure and volume and c is a constant. Under these "isothermal" conditions the volume of a certain gas is increasing at the rate of 3 cubic feet per minute at an instant when $p = 8$ pounds per square inch and $v = 700$ cubic feet. Find the rate of change of p at this instant.

16. An airplane is flying east on a horizontal course 1200 feet directly above an east–west highway, and a car is moving north on a north–south highway. If the speeds of the plane and the car are 300 feet per second and 100 feet per second, respectively, and if at noon the plane is 2000 feet due west of a point directly over the point of intersection of the two highways while the car is 1000 feet south of this point of intersection, at what time are the plane and car closest?

17. In Exercise 16, what is the rate of change of the distance between the plane and the car at 6 seconds after noon? At 10 seconds after noon?

9

Curve Sketching

901 POINTS OF INFLECTION

In § 804 a point $(c, f(c))$ was defined to be a *point of inflection* of the graph C of f if and only if the tangent to C at $(c, f(c))$ exists and crosses C there. If the tangent is nonvertical at a point of inflection $(c, f(c))$, $f'(c)$ exists and the function

$$(1) \qquad\qquad g(x) \equiv f(x) - f(c) - f'(c)(x - c)$$

changes sign at c. Theorem IV, §804, states a sufficient condition for a point $(c, f(c))$ to be a point of inflection of C, this condition involving the *first* derivative of f evaluated near the point c, and the additional assumption that C has a *horizontal* tangent at $(c, f(c))$. Again, Theorem III, § 809, states another sufficient condition for the point $(c, f(c))$ to be a point of inflection of C, the condition this time involving higher order derivatives of f all evaluated at c, and again with the assumption of a horizontal tangent.

In this section we shall formulate sufficient conditions similar to those of §§ 804 and 809, but applicable whenever the graph of f has a nonvertical tangent at $(c, f(c))$.

Corresponding to Theorem IV, §804, we have:

Theorem I. *If a function f is differentiable in a neighborhood $(c - \delta, c + \delta)$ of a point c, and if the function*

$$(2) \qquad\qquad\qquad f'(x) - f'(c)$$

is of constant sign (either always positive or always negative) for x in the deleted neighborhood $\{x \mid 0 < |x - c| < \delta\}$ of c, then $(c, f(c))$ is a point of inflection of the graph of f.

Proof. Under the assumptions stated, the function $g(x)$, of (1), since $g'(x) = f'(x) - f'(c)$, is strictly monotonic on $(c - \delta, c + \delta)$ and zero at the midpoint (cf. the proof of Theorem IV, §804). Therefore $g(x)$ changes sign at c.

A condition involving the second derivative of f can be formulated:

Theorem II. *If a function f is differentiable in a neighborhood of a point c, if $f''(x)$ exists in a deleted neighborhood D_c of c, and if $f''(x)$ changes sign at c ($f''(x) > 0$ for x in D_c and on one side of c, and $f''(x) < 0$ for x in D_c and on the other side of c), then $(c, f(c))$ is a point of inflection of the graph of f.*

Proof. If $g(x)$ is the function (1), for $x \in D_c \cup \{c\}$, and if $\phi(x) \equiv g'(x) = f'(x) - f'(c)$, then $\phi'(x) = g''(x) = f''(x)$. Therefore, from the assumptions of Theorem II, ϕ is strictly decreasing on one side of c and strictly increasing on the other, and equal to 0 at c. Consequently, $\phi(x)$ must be of constant sign for x in D_c, and the result follows from Theorem I.

NOTE 1. Under the assumptions of Theorem II, if $f''(c)$ exists, $f''(c) = 0$, since by the argument presented in the preceding proof the function ϕ has a local extremum at c, and hence (Theorem II, §803) $\phi'(c) = f''(c) = 0$. Examples 2 and 3 below show that the conditions of Theorem II may be satisfied while $f''(c)$ fails to exist. The example $f(x) = x^4$ shows that the second derivative of f may vanish at a point c ($c = 0$) such that $(c, f(c))$ is *not* a point of inflection of the graph of f.

Example 1. Show that the graph of every cubic polynomial $f(x) = ax^3 + bx^2 + cx + d$, $a \neq 0$, has exactly one point of inflection.

Solution. Since $f'(x) = 3ax^2 + 2bx + c$ and $f''(x) = 6ax + 2b$, the second derivative vanishes at exactly one point, $x = -b/3a$. Since $f''(x)$ is defined everywhere, the point $(-b/3a, f(-b/3a))$ is the only *possible* point of inflection. Furthermore, since $f''(x) = 6a(x + (b/3a))$, $f''(x)$ changes sign at $x = -b/3a$, and $(-b/3a, f(-b/3a))$ *is* a point of inflection of the graph of f.

Example 2. Show that the graph of the function $x^{\frac{5}{3}}$, $x \in \mathcal{R}$, has a point of inflection at $x = 0$, even though its second derivative does not exist there. (Cf. Fig. 901-1a.)

Solution. With $f(x) \equiv x^{\frac{5}{3}}, f'(x) = \frac{5}{3}x^{\frac{2}{3}}$ for all x, and $f''(x) = \frac{10}{9}x^{-\frac{1}{3}}$ for $x \neq 0$. Since $\sqrt[3]{x}$ changes sign at $x = 0$, the conditions of Theorem II are satisfied at the point 0.

Example 3. Show that the graph of the function $x|x|$, $x \in \mathcal{R}$, has a point of inflection at $x = 0$ even though its second derivative does not exist there. (Cf. Fig. 901-1b.)

Solution. Since $f(x) \equiv x|x|$ can be expressed

$$(3) \qquad\qquad f(x) = \begin{cases} x^2, x \geqq 0, \\ -x^2, x \leqq 0, \end{cases}$$

its first and second derivatives can be written

$$(4) \qquad f'(x) = \begin{cases} 2x, x \geqq 0, \\ -2x, x \leqq 0, \end{cases} \qquad f''(x) = \begin{cases} 2, x > 0, \\ -2, x < 0. \end{cases}$$

The conditions of Theorem II are satisfied at the point $x = 0$.

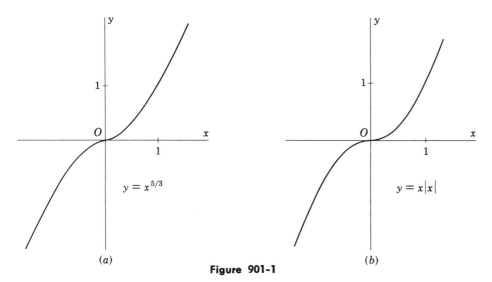

Figure 901-1

Corresponding to Theorem III, § 809, is the following:

Theorem III. *Let f be a function which, in some neighborhood of the point c, is defined and has derivatives $f', f'', \cdots, f^{(n-1)}$ of order less than or equal to $n-1$, where $n > 1$. If $f^{(k)}(c) = 0$ for every integer k such that $1 < k < n$, and if $f^{(n)}(c)$ exists and is nonzero, then the point $(c, f(c))$ is a point of inflection of the graph of f if and only if n is odd.*

Proof. If g is defined by (1), then g satisfies the conditions of Theorem III, § 809, and in addition, $g(c) = 0$. From the conclusions of that theorem we infer that if n is odd, $g(x)$ changes sign at $x = c$, and if n is even, $g(x)$ does not change sign at $x = c$. This is the conclusion sought.

Example 4. If $f(x) \equiv ax + x^n$, $x \in \Re$, where n is an integer greater than 1, then the graph of f has a point of inflection at $x = 0$ if and only if n is odd.

NOTE 2. Location of points of inflection, particularly when this is accompanied by sketching the tangent lines at the points of inflection, is often a helpful aid in sketching the graph of a function.

Example 5. Find the values of x for which the function $f(x) \equiv x^4 - 2x^3 - 12x^2 + 13$ is concave up, and those for which it is concave down. Find the relative extrema of the function and the points of inflection of its graph. Sketch the graph of f.

Solution. The first derivative,

(5) $$f'(x) = 2x(2x^2 - 3x - 12),$$

vanishes at the points $x = 0, \frac{1}{4}(3 \pm \sqrt{105})$, or 0, 3.31, and -1.81 (to two decimal places). The corresponding values of f are $f(0) = 13$ and (to the nearest integer) $f(3.31) = -71$ and $f(-1.81) = -4$. The second derivative,

(6) $$f''(x) = 12(x^2 - x - 2) = 12(x - 2)(x + 1),$$

changes sign at $x = -1$ and at $x = 2$. Therefore $(-1, f(-1)) = (-1, 4)$ and $(2, f(2)) = (2, -35)$ are points of inflection of the graph of f. At these points the slopes of the graph are $f'(-1) = 14$ and $f'(2) = -40$, respectively. Since $f''(x) > 0$ if $x < -1$ or if $x > 2$, the graph is concave up if $x < -1$ or if $x > 2$. Similarly, the graph is concave down if $-1 < x < 2$. The function f has a strict local maximum at $x = 0$, by the second derivative test (§806). It has a strict local minima at $x = \frac{1}{4}(3 \pm \sqrt{105})$. Since $f(\frac{1}{4}(3 + \sqrt{105})) < f(\frac{1}{4}(3 - \sqrt{105}))$, and since $\lim_{x \to -\infty} f(x) = \lim_{x \to +\infty} f(x) = +\infty$, f has no global maximum, and $f(\frac{1}{4}(3 + \sqrt{105}))$ is the global minimum of f. The graph of f, together with the tangent lines at the points of inflection, is shown in Figure 901-2. The following table, used in the plotting of the graph, is most readily computed (as are the local minima of f) by synthetic substitution:

x	-3	-2	-1	0	1	2	3	4	5
$f(x)$	40	-3	4	13	0	-35	-68	-51	81
$f'(x)$	-90	-8	14	0	-26	-40	-18	64	230

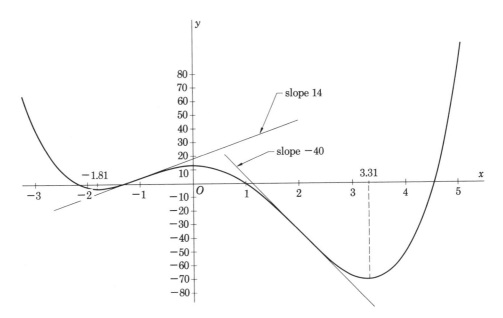

Figure 901-2

902   EXERCISES

In Exercises 1–9, identify the points of inflection of the graph in the exercise of §808 that bears the same number.

In Exercises 10 and 11, find the points of inflection of the graph of the given function with domain $\mathfrak{R}$, where $a > 0$. Then draw an accurate graph of the function for the specified value of a, showing symmetry, asymptotes, extreme points, and points of inflection. Draw the tangent line at each point of inflection. Use equal units on the two coordinate axes.

10. $y = \dfrac{a^2}{x^2 + a^2};\ a = \sqrt{3}.$ **11.** $y = \dfrac{x}{x^2 + a^2};\ a = \dfrac{1}{\sqrt{3}}.$

In Exercises 12–14, draw an accurate graph of the given function for the specified interval, showing asymptotes, extreme points, and points of inflection. Draw the tangent line at each point of inflection. Use equal units on the two coordinate axes.

12. $\dfrac{2x - 1}{x^2},\ (0, +\infty).$ **13.** $\dfrac{x^2 - 3}{x^2 + 3},\ (-\infty, +\infty).$ **14.** $\dfrac{6x}{x^3 + 4},\ (0, +\infty).$

In Exercises 15–17, show that the origin is a point of inflection of the graph of the given function, with domain $\mathfrak{R}$.

15. $x^{\frac{7}{5}}.$ **16.** $x^{\frac{5}{7}}.$ **17.** $x^3|x|.$

In Exercises 18–20, show that the origin is not a point of inflection of the graph of the given function, with domain $\mathfrak{R}$.

18. $x^{\frac{6}{5}}.$ **19.** $x^{\frac{4}{5}}.$ **20.** $x^2|x|.$

903 POLYNOMIALS IN FACTORED FORM

The principal basic facts needed for sketching the general shape of the graph of a polynomial in factored form are given in the theorem:

Theorem I.   *If $f(x)$ is a polynomial, and if*

(1) $$f(x) = (x - c)^n \phi(x),$$

where n is a positive integer and $\phi(x)$ is a polynomial such that $\phi(c) \neq 0$, then (i) if $n = 1$, the graph of $f(x)$ crosses the x-axis with a slope equal to $\phi(c)$; (ii) if n is even, $f'(c) = 0$ and $f(c)$ is a strict local extremum, being a maximum or a minimum according as $\phi(c)$ is negative or positive; (iii) if n is odd and greater than 1, $f'(c) = 0$ and $(c, 0)$ is a point of inflection for the graph of $f(x)$. (Cf. Fig. 903-1.)

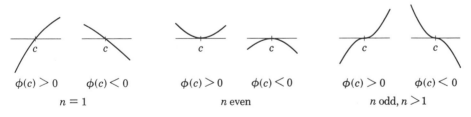

$\phi(c) > 0$ $\phi(c) < 0$ $\phi(c) > 0$ $\phi(c) < 0$ $\phi(c) > 0$ $\phi(c) < 0$

$n = 1$ n even n odd, $n > 1$

Figure 903-1

Proof.   *(i)*: If $n = 1$, then $f(x) = (x - c)\phi(x)$, $f'(x) = \phi(x) + (x - c)\phi'(c)$, and $f'(c) = \phi(c) \neq 0$. Therefore $f'(x) \neq 0$ for x in a neighborhood of c, and $f(x)$ is strictly monotonic in this neighborhood, and $f(c) = 0$. Therefore the graph of $f(x)$ crosses the x-axis at $x = c$ with slope $\phi(c)$.

(ii) and (iii): If $n > 1$, then $f'(x) = n(x - c)^{n-1}\phi(x) + (x - c)^n\phi'(x)$, and $f'(c) = 0$. If N_c is a neighborhood of c in which $\phi(x) \neq 0$, then for each x in the corresponding deleted neighborhood $D_c \equiv N_c \setminus \{c\}$, the sign of $f(x) = (x - c)^n\phi(x)$ is the same as that of $(x - c)^n\phi(c)$. If n is even, this sign is constant, being positive if $\phi(c)$ is positive and negative if $\phi(c)$ is negative. If n is odd, $f(x)$ changes sign at c. This completes the proof.

In practice, if a polynomial is *completely* factored as far as real linear factors are concerned,

$$(2) \qquad f(x) = (x - c_1)^{n_1}(x - c_2)^{n_2}\cdots(x - c_m)^{n_m}\phi(x),$$

where $\phi(x)$ is never zero for real x, then the graph of $f(x)$ can be pieced together by use of Theorem I. It is usually simplest to start with the *largest* real root and proceed to the left.

Example 1. Sketch a crude graph of $f(x) = 2(x - 1)^3(x - 3)(x - 5)^2$, showing the general shape only.

Solution. Since $f(x) > 0$ for $x > 5$, part (ii) of Theorem I states that the local behavior of $f(x)$ for x near 5 is that indicated in Figure 903-2a. Since $f(x) > 0$ for $3 < x < 5$, part (i) of Theorem I states that the local behavior of $f(x)$ for x near 3 is that indicated in Figure 903-2b. Since $f(x) < 0$ for $1 < x < 3$, part (iii) of Theorem I states that the local behavior of $f(x)$ for x near 1 is that indicated in Figure 903-2c. Combining parts (a), (b), and (c), we have the sketch shown in Figure 903-2d.

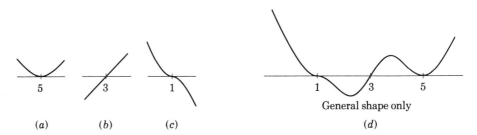

| (a) | (b) | (c) | | (d) |

General shape only

Figure 903-2

It is sometimes necessary to sketch the graph of an equation of the form $y^2 = f(x)$, where $f(x)$ is a polynomial. Such a graph is always symmetric with respect to the x-axis, and is real for precisely those values of x for which $f(x) \geq 0$. It is helpful, therefore, to sketch first the graph of the polynomial $y = f(x)$ itself. A fairly detailed description of this type of graphical problem is given in §1504, *CWAG*. We shall content ourselves with a discussion of a single illustrative example.

Example 2. Sketch a crude graph of $y^2 = 2(x - 1)^3(x - 3)(x - 5)^2$, showing the general shape only. (Cf. Example 1.)

Solution. The most helpful first step is to examine the graph of $y = 2(x - 1)^3(x - 3)(x - 5)^2$, in Figure 903-2. From this it is clear that the present graph contains no points for $1 < x < 3$, and has x-intercepts at $x = 1$, 3, and 5. The general shape near $x = 5$ is that of $y^2 = 2\cdot64\cdot2(x - 5)^2$, or $y^2 = k^2(x - 5)^2$, or $y = \pm k(x - 5)$, as shown in Figure

903-3*a*. The general shape near $x = 3$ is that of $y^2 = 2 \cdot 8(x - 3) \cdot 4 = k^2(x - 3)$ (cf. Fig. 903-3*b*). The general shape near $x = 1$ is that of $y^2 = 2(x - 1)^3(-2) \cdot 16 = -k^2(x - 3)^3$ (cf. Fig. 903-3*c*). Pieced together, these give the total graph shown in Figure 903-3*d*.

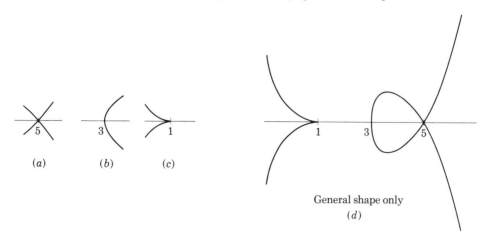

(*a*)   (*b*)   (*c*)

General shape only
(*d*)

Figure 903-3

904   GRAPHICAL SOLUTIONS OF INEQUALITIES

An inequality involving a single real variable can often be solved most easily with the aid of the graphs of the two members of the inequality. For example, the values of x that satisfy the inequality

(1) $f(x) \leqq 0$

are those for which points of the graph of the equation $y = f(x)$ lie on or below the x-axis. In like fashion, the solution set of the inequality

(2) $f(x) > g(x)$

consists of all points x such that the corresponding point $(x, f(x))$ lies above the point $(x, g(x))$.

Example 1.   Use graphical means to solve the inequality $x^2 - 2x < 8$.

Solution. The given inequality is equivalent to the inequality $x^2 - 2x - 8 = (x - 4)(x + 2) < 0$. Since the graph of the function $(x - 4)(x + 2)$ is a parabola opening up and crossing the x-axis at the points -2 and 4, the desired solution set is the open interval $(-2, 4)$. (Cf. Fig. 904 -1*a*.)

Example 2.   Use graphical means to solve the inequality $2|x - 2| \geqq |x| + 1$.

Solution. Graphing separately the two functions $f(x) \equiv 2|x - 2|$ and $g(x) \equiv |x| + 1$ (cf. Fig. 904 -1*b*) shows that we must obtain the two points of intersection of

$$\begin{cases} y = 2(2 - x), \\ y = x + 1, \end{cases} \quad \text{and} \quad \begin{cases} y = 2(x - 2), \\ y = x + 1. \end{cases}$$

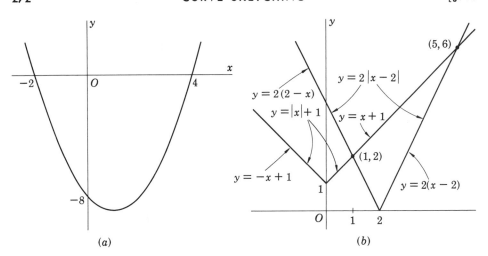

Figure 904-1

Since these points of intersection are (1, 2) and (5, 6), respectively, the values of x satisfying the given inequality are those where the graph of f lies above or intersects the graph of g. Consequently they are those such that $x \leq 1$ and those such that $x \geq 5$. In other words, the solution set is

$$\{x \mid 2|x - 2| \geq |x| + 1\} = (-\infty, 1] \cup [5, +\infty).$$

905 LOCAL BEHAVIOR AND DOMINANT TERMS

If a function ϕ is defined as the sum (or difference) of two other functions f and g, the graph of ϕ can often be obtained by graphing f and g separately, and then combining their graphs by adding (or subtracting) ordinates for various abscissas. This method of graphing is called **composition of ordinates.**

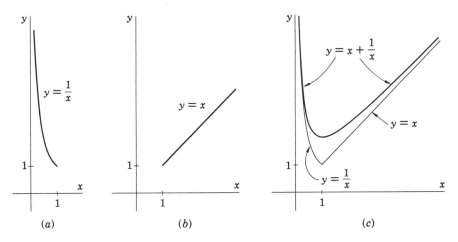

Figure 905-1

Sometimes, if "pieces" of a graph can be sketched, then the entire graph can be inferred. This principle was used in the discussion of Examples 1 and 2, §903. This same principle is applicable in case a function is defined as the sum (or difference) of two functions, each of which is numerically small in a portion of the graph where the other function is not numerically small.

Example. The function $x + \dfrac{1}{x}, x \in \mathcal{P}$, is approximately equal to $\dfrac{1}{x}$ for small positive x (cf. Fig. 905-1a) and approximately equal to x for large positive x (cf. Fig. 905-1b). Combining these two portions we have the total graph of Figure 905-1c.

906   EXERCISES

In Exercises 1–8, sketch a crude graph of the given function $f(x)$, showing the general shape only.

1. $x(x - 1)^2$.
2. $(x + 1)^3(x - 2)$.
3. $(x + 1)(x - 1)^3$.
4. $x(x - 1)^2(x - 4)^3$.
5. $(x + 1)^2(x - 1)^3(x - 2)$.
6. $(x + 1)(x - 1)^4(x - 3)^2$.
7. $x^4(x - 1)(x - 4)^2$.
8. $(x + 2)(x - 2)^2(x - 3)^4$.

In Exercises 9–16, sketch a crude graph of the equation $y^2 = f(x)$, where $f(x)$ is the function of the indicated preceding exercise, showing the general shape only.

9. Exercise 1.
10. Exercise 2.
11. Exercise 3.
12. Exercise 4.
13. Exercise 5.
14. Exercise 6.
15. Exercise 7.
16. Exercise 8.

In Exercises 17–24, find the solution set of the given inequality by graphical methods.

17. $x^2 < 3x$.
18. $x^2 - 1 \geqq x + 1$.
19. $x^3 \leqq -x^2$.
20. $x^2 > x^3$.
21. $|x| > x - 1$.
22. $|x + 1| \leqq \frac{1}{2}x$.
23. $|x + 3| \geqq 2|x|$.
24. $|x| < 2|x + 3|$.

In Exercises 25–28, use the principle of composition of ordinates to sketch the graph of the given function.

25. $|x| + |x - 1|$.
26. $|x| - |x - 1|$.
27. $\sin 2\theta + 2 \sin \theta$.
28. $\sin 2\theta + 2 \cos \theta$.

In Exercises 29–34, sketch the graph of the given equation by combining suitable local graphs, for the given values of x.

29. $x^2 + \dfrac{1}{x}, x \in \mathcal{P}$.
30. $x^2 - \dfrac{1}{x}, x \in \mathcal{P}$.
31. $y = x(x - 1)^2, x \in \mathcal{R}$.
32. $y = x(x - 1)(x - 2), x \in \mathcal{R}$.
33. $y^2 = x(x - 1)^2, x \in \mathcal{R}$.
34. $y^2 = x(x - 1)(x - 2), x \in \mathcal{R}$.

10

The Fundamental Theorem
of Calculus

1001 STRICT POSITIVITY OF THE INTEGRAL FOR CONTINUOUS FUNCTIONS

It was proved in §111 that the definite integral $\int_a^b$ is a positive linear functional on the space $\mathfrak{D}$ of functions integrable on $[a, b]$. This means that $\int_a^b$ is a linear functional distinct from the zero functional and such that if f is nonnegative on $[a, b]$ and $f \in \mathfrak{D}$ then $\int_a^b f \geqq 0$. If we restrict ourselves to the subspace $\mathfrak{U}$ of functions that are *continuous* (and hence uniformly continuous) on $[a, b]$ we can say more. The following theorem can be interpreted as stating that in the presence of *continuity*, positivity of the linear functional $\int_a^b$ becomes *strict positivity:*

Theorem. * *If f and g are real-valued functions that are continuous on a compact interval $[a, b]$, then*

(1) $$(f \geqq 0) \wedge (f \neq 0) \Rightarrow \int_a^b f > 0,$$

(2) $$(f \leqq g) \wedge (f \neq g) \Rightarrow \int_a^b f < \int_a^b g.$$

Proof. By Theorem VI, §406, if c is a point of $[a, b]$ where $f(c) > 0$, there exist a positive number η and a neighborhood N_c of c such that

(3) $$x \in [a, b] \cap N_c \Rightarrow f(x) > \eta.$$

---

*We recall that 0 represents both the zero number and the zero function, that $f \leqq g$ means that $f(x) \leqq g(x)$ for all $x \in [a, b]$, and that $f \neq g$ means that f and g are not the same function (i.e., not identically equal). (Cf §§101, 504, *PCLA*.)

If we define the step-function s:

(4)
$$s(x) \equiv \begin{cases} \eta \text{ if } x \in [a, b] \cap N_c, \\ 0 \text{ if } x \in [a, b] \setminus N_c \end{cases}$$

(cf. Fig. 1001-1), then $\int_a^b s > 0$, and if f is nonnegative on $[a, b]$, f and s are related by the inequality $f \geqq s$, and therefore, by Theorem I, §111, $\int_a^b f \geqq \int_a^b s > 0$, and (4) is proved. The implication (2) follows from (1) by linearity of $\int_a^b$ and the fact that $(f \leqq g) \wedge (f \neq g)$ is equivalent to $(g - f \geqq 0) \wedge (g - f \neq 0)$:

$$\int_a^b g - \int_a^b f = \int_a^b (g - f) > 0.$$

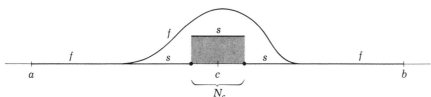

Figure 1001-1

1002 THE MEAN VALUE THEOREM FOR INTEGRALS

The **average** or **arithmetic mean** of two numbers a_1 and a_2 is defined to be half their sum, $\frac{1}{2}(a_1 + a_2)$. More generally, the **average** or **arithmetic mean** of n numbers a_1, $a_2, \cdots, a_n$ is defined by the formula

(1)
$$AM(a_1, a_2, \cdots, a_n) \equiv \frac{a_1 + a_2 + \cdots + a_n}{n},$$

where AM is an abbreviation for "arithmetic mean."

A similar definition holds for any function f integrable on a compact interval $[a, b]$. The **average** or **arithmetic mean** of f on $[a, b]$ is given by

(2)
$$AM(f) \equiv \frac{1}{b - a} \int_a^b f.$$

If the function f is *continuous* on the interval $[a, b]$, then its arithmetic mean (2) is given by an actual *value* of the function. For this reason, the arithmetic mean of a function continuous on a compact interval is also called its **mean value.** The existence of this mean value is established in the following theorem:

Theorem.   Mean Value Theorem for Integrals.* *If f is continuous on the compact interval $[a, b]$, then there exists a point c between a and b, $a < c < b$, such that*

(3)
$$f(c) = \frac{1}{b - a} \int_a^b f.$$

---

*This theorem is also known as the *First Mean Value Theorem for Integrals*. (Cf. Ex. 14, H§2210, *CWAG*, for the *Second Mean Value Theorem for Integrals*.)

Proof. There are two cases. (*i*) If f is a constant k, then (3) is true for *all* c: $k = [1/(b - a)] \int_a^b k = [1/(b - a)] \cdot k(b - a)$. (*ii*) If f is not a constant, then its minimum value m and its maximum value M are unequal: $m < M$. Letting m and M now denote the corresponding constant functions, as well as numbers, we have the following inequalities:

(4) $$(m \leq f) \wedge (m \neq f), \quad (f \leq M) \wedge (f \neq M).$$

Consequently, by (2), §1001, $m(b - a) = \int_a^b m < \int_a^b f < \int_a^b M = M(b - a)$, or:

(5) $$m < \frac{1}{b - a} \int_a^b f < M.$$

Since $v \equiv [1/(b - a)] \int_a^b f$ is a number between the two values $m = f(x_1)$ and $M = f(x_2)$ of the continuous function f, by the intermediate-value property for continuous functions (Theorem II, §409) the number v is a value of f, assumed for some point c between x_1 and x_2.

NOTE 1. For a function f continuous on an interval $[a, b]$ and possessing nonnegative values there, the mean value theorem with equation (3) written in the form

(6) $$\int_a^b f = (b - a)f(c)$$

can be interpreted as stating that the area of the ordinate set of f is equal to the area of a rectangle with base $[a, b]$ and altitude equal to the value $f(c)$ of f for some interior point c of $[a, b]$. (Cf. Fig. 1002-1.)

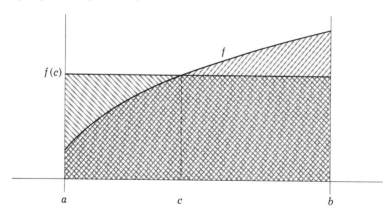

Figure 1002-1

Example 1. Find the arithmetic mean of the function $f(x) = x^2 + 2x$ on the interval $[a, b] = [2, 5]$, and find an interior point c of this interval satisfying (3).

Solution. The arithmetic mean of the function f is given by (2):

$$AM(f) = \frac{1}{5 - 2} \int_2^5 (x^2 + 2x)dx = \frac{1}{3}\left(\frac{125 - 8}{3} + 25 - 4\right) = 20.$$

Equation (3) becomes $c^2 + 2c = 20$, whose roots are $-1 \pm \sqrt{21}$. Since only one of these roots, $-1 + \sqrt{21}$, is a point of the interval $[2, 5]$, we have $c = \sqrt{21} - 1 = 3.58$ (to 2 decimal places).

Example 2. Find the arithmetic mean of the signum function $f(x) = \text{sgn } x$ (cf. Example 2, §115, *PCLA*) on the interval $[a, b] = [-1, 2]$, and show that there is no point c of this interval satisfying (3).

Solution. The arithmetic mean of the function f is given by (2):

$$\text{AM}(f) = \frac{1}{2 - (-1)} \int_{-1}^{2} \text{sgn } x \, dx = \frac{1}{3} \int_{-1}^{0} -1 \, dx + \frac{1}{3} \int_{0}^{2} 1 \, dx = \frac{1}{3}.$$

For no real number c is the value $\text{sgn } c$ of the signum function equal to $\frac{1}{3}$.

Note 2. Example 2 demonstrates that the condition of continuity in the mean value theorem for integrals cannot be omitted.

1003 INDEFINITE INTEGRALS AND THEIR CONTINUITY

Before progressing further we extend the definition of the symbol $\int_a^b$ to cases where a is not less than b:

Definition I. *If f is integrable on the compact interval $[b, a]$, where $b < a$, then*

(1)
$$\int_{a}^{b} f = \int_{a}^{b} f(x)dx \equiv -\int_{b}^{a} f.$$

If f is defined at the point a, then

(2)
$$\int_{a}^{a} f = \int_{a}^{a} f(x)dx \equiv 0.$$

As a consequence of this definition we can express the additivity of the definite integral on adjacent intervals (§113) as follows:

Theorem I. *If f is integrable on a compact interval I that contains the three points a, b, and c, whether these points are distinct or not and regardless of the order relation among them, then:*

(3)
$$\int_{a}^{c} f = \int_{a}^{b} f + \int_{b}^{c} f.$$

Proof. By Theorem III, §112, all three integrals in (3) *exist*. The problem is to establish the *equality*. The proof can be divided into three cases (*i*) $a < c$, (*ii*) $a = c$, and (*iii*) $a > c$.

Proof of (*i*): If $b < a$, then $b < a < c$ and by Theorem II, §113, $\int_b^c f = \int_b^a f + \int_a^c f$, and therefore $\int_a^c f = -\int_b^a f + \int_b^c f$, and by Definition I, (3) follows. If $b = a$, then (3) reduces to $\int_a^c f = \int_a^a f + \int_a^c f = 0 + \int_a^c f$. If $a < b < c$, (3) is the formula of Theorem II, §113. If $b = c$, (3) reduces to $\int_a^b f = \int_a^b f + 0$. If $b > c$, then $a < c < b$ and by Theorem II, §113, $\int_a^b f = \int_a^c f + \int_c^b f$, and hence $\int_a^c f = \int_a^b f - \int_c^b f$, and (3) follows from Definition I.

Proof of (*ii*): If $a = c$, formula (3) reduces to $\int_a^b f + \int_b^a f = 0$, or $\int_a^b f = -\int_b^a f$, which is always true, whether $a < b$, $a = b$, or $a > b$.

Proof of (iii): If $a > c$, we know from part (*i*) that $\int_c^a f = \int_c^b f + \int_b^a f$, or $-\int_b^a f = -\int_b^c f - \int_c^b f$. Since $\int_a^c f = -\int_c^a f$, $\int_a^b f = -\int_b^a f$, and $\int_b^c f = -\int_c^b f$ for all numbers a, b, c, (3) results and the proof is complete.

The formula resulting from subtraction of the term $\int_a^b f$ or the term $\int_b^c f$ of (3) is used so much that we include it in a corollary to Theorem I:

Corollary.   *Under the conditions of Theorem I,*

(4)
$$\int_a^c f - \int_a^b f = \int_b^c f, \quad \int_a^c f - \int_b^c f = \int_a^b f.$$

Formula (3) can be extended by mathematical induction to any finite number of terms:

(5)
$$\int_{a_1}^{a_n} f = \int_{a_1}^{a_2} f + \int_{a_2}^{a_3} f + \cdots + \int_{a_{n-1}}^{a_n} f,$$

where a_1, a_2, $\cdots$, a_n are any n points of a compact interval on which f is integrable.

NOTE 1.   With the aid of the preceding Definition I, Theorem VI, §114, can be extended to permit arbitrary values of a and b as follows (give a proof in Ex. 17, §1004): *If n is a nonnegative integer and if a and b are real numbers, then*

(6)
$$\int_a^b x^n \, dx = \frac{b^{n+1} - a^{n+1}}{n + 1}.$$

The inequality established in the following theorem will be useful later:

Theorem II.   *If f is integrable on every compact subinterval of an interval I, and if a and b are any two points of I, then*

(7)
$$\left| \int_a^b f \right| \leqq \left| \int_a^b |f| \right|,$$

or equivalently,

(8)
$$\left| \int_a^b f(x)dx \right| \leqq \left| \int_a^b |f(x)|dx \right|.$$

Proof.   If $a < b$, (7) and (8) are true by Theorem V, §114. If $a = b$, (7) and (8) become $0 = 0$. If $a > b$, then $\left|\int_a^b f\right| = \left|\int_b^a f\right| \leqq \int_b^a |f| = \left|-\int_b^a |f|\right| = \left|\int_a^b |f|\right|$.

We now define the concept of *indefinite integral*, and draw an immediate inference:

Definition II.   *A function Φ is called an* **indefinite integral*** *of a function f on an*

---

*There is no universal agreement on the definition of an indefinite integral. Some authors define an indefinite integral of f by the formula $\Phi(x) = \int_a^x f$, without the constant γ. Others define an indefinite integral of f to be any function whose derivative exists at every point x of I and is equal there to $f(x)$. According to this last form of the definition an indefinite integral is synonymous with a *primitive* or *antiderivative*, as defined in §1005. As will be seen presently, our definition is a compromise between these two alternative forms, and for continuous functions f, it becomes equivalent to the second.

interval I if and only if f is integrable on every compact subinterval of I, and there exist a point a of I and a constant γ such that

$$(9) \qquad x \in I \implies \Phi(x) = \int_a^x f + \gamma = \int_a^x f(t)dt + \gamma.$$

NOTE 2. In the last part of (9) the "variable of integration" has been denoted by a letter other than x in order that the same symbol will not be used twice with two distinct meanings in the same formula.

Theorem III. *If Φ and Ψ are any two indefinite integrals of a function f on an interval I, then Φ and Ψ differ by a constant there; that is, there exists a constant C such that*

$$(10) \qquad x \in I \implies \Phi(x) = \Psi(x) + C.$$

Proof. Let $\Phi(x) \equiv \int_a^x f + \gamma_1$ and $\Psi(x) \equiv \int_b^x f + \gamma_2$. Then $\Phi(x) - \Psi(x) = \int_a^x f - \int_b^x f + \gamma_1 - \gamma_2 = \int_a^b f + \gamma_1 - \gamma_2$ by the Corollary to Theorem I. Let $C \equiv \int_a^b f + \gamma_1 - \gamma_2$.

Example 1. Let $f(x) \equiv x^2$, $x \in \Re$. Then

$$\Phi(x) \equiv \int_0^x t^2\, dt + 17 = \frac{x^3 - 0^3}{3} + 17 = \frac{1}{3}x^3 + 17$$

and

$$\Psi(x) \equiv \int_6^x t^2\, dt - 31 = \frac{x^3 - 216}{3} - 31 = \frac{1}{3}x^3 - 103$$

are indefinite intervals of f on $\Re$. They differ by the constant 120: $\Phi(x) - \Psi(x) = 120$.

Example 2. Find an indefinite integral for the bracket function $f(x) \equiv [x]$ (cf. Example 3, §115, *PCLA*) on the interval $[0, 3]$.

Solution. The simplest indefinite integral of f is $\Phi(x) \equiv \int_0^x [t]dt$, which is given as follows:

$$(11) \qquad \Phi(x) = \begin{cases} \int_0^x 0\, dt = 0, \text{ if } 0 \leqq x \leqq 1, \\ \int_0^1 0\, dt + \int_1^x 1\, dt = x - 1, \text{ if } 1 \leqq x \leqq 2, \\ \int_1^2 1\, dt + \int_2^x 2\, dt = 2x - 3, \text{ if } 2 \leqq x \leqq 3. \end{cases}$$

(Cf. Fig. 1003-1.) Any other indefinite integral Ψ is obtained by adding a constant to Φ.

A deeper fact about indefinite integrals is the following:

Theorem IV. *If f is integrable on every compact subinterval of an interval I, and if Φ is any indefinite integral of f on I, then Φ is continuous on I.*

Proof. Let c be any point of I. We shall prove that Φ, defined by (9), is continuous at c if c is an interior point of I. (The cases where c is an endpoint of I do not differ from this case in any essential way.) Accordingly, let η be a positive number such that the closed interval $[c - \eta, c + \eta]$ is a subinterval of I. Since f is integrable

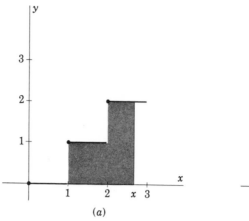
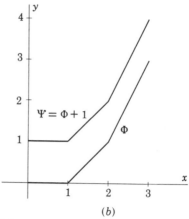

(a) (b)

Figure 1003-1

on $[c - \eta, c + \eta]$, f is bounded there (Theorem II, §105) and there exists a positive number K such that $|x - c| \leqq \eta \Rightarrow |f(x)| \leqq K$. If ϵ is an arbitrary positive number we now seek a positive number δ such that

(12) $x \in I$ and $|x - c| < \delta \implies |\Phi(x) - \Phi(c)| < \epsilon.$

Such a number δ is provided by the formula

(13) $\delta \equiv \min\left(\eta, \dfrac{\epsilon}{K}\right),$

since for this δ, $|x - c| < \delta$ implies $|x - c| < \eta$, and consequently, by Theorems I and II,

(14) $|\Phi(x) - \Phi(c)| = \left|\int_a^x f - \int_a^c f\right| = \left|\int_c^x f\right| \leqq \left|\int_c^x |f|\right| \leqq \left|\int_c^x K\right|$

$$= K|x - c| < K\delta \leqq K(\epsilon/K) = \epsilon.$$

Example 3. Although the restriction of the bracket function to the interval $[0, 3]$ is discontinuous at $x = 1, 2$, and 3, its indefinite integral Φ of Example 2 is continuous on $[0, 3]$. Let us observe, however, that Φ is not differentiable at the points 1 and 2.

1004 EXERCISES

In Exercises 1 and 2, find the arithmetic mean of the given function f on the specified interval $[a, b]$, and find an interior point c of this interval satisfying (3), §1002.

  1. x^2, $[-2, 4]$.   **2.** x^3, $[1, 5]$.

In Exercises 3 and 4, find the arithmetic mean of the given function f on the specified interval $[a, b]$, and show that there is no point c of this interval satisfying (3), §1002.

  3. $[x]$, $[0, 2]$.   **4.** sgn $x + [x]$, $[-1, 1]$.

In Exercises 5–8, evaluate the integral.

  5. $\displaystyle\int_7^7 [x]dx.$ **6.** $\displaystyle\int_3^0 [x]dx.$

7. $\displaystyle\int_5^2 x^2\,dx.$ **8.** $\displaystyle\int_7^1 (x^2 - 15x)dx.$

In Exercises 9 and 10, verify (3), §1003, for the given function f and the specified numbers a, b, and c.

9. x^2; $a = 2, b = 1, c = 3.$ **10.** $[x]$; $a = 4, b = 3, c = 1.$

In Exercises 11 and 12, verify the inequality $\left|\displaystyle\int_a^b f\right| \leqq \left|\displaystyle\int_a^b |f|\right|$ for the given function and the specified numbers a and b.

11. x^3 ; $a = 2, b = -4.$ **12.** $[x]$; $a = 3, b = -2.$

In Exercises 13–16, find an indefinite integral for the given function on the interval $(-\infty, +\infty)$.

13. $x^3.$ **14.** $3x^2 - 8x^3.$

15. $\operatorname{sgn} x.$ **16.** $|x|.$

17. Establish formula (6) of Note 1, §1003.

1005   DIFFERENTIABILITY; PRIMITIVES AND ANTIDERIVATIVES

Examples 2 and 3, §1003, show that an indefinite integral Φ of a function f, although Φ is everywhere continuous, may fail to be differentiable, at least at certain points. The following theorem shows that Φ is differentiable wherever f is *continuous*, and therefore establishes our first fundamental relationship between definite integrals and derivatives*:

Theorem I. *If f is integrable on every compact subinterval of an interval I and continuous at the point c of I, and if Φ is any indefinite integral of f on I, then Φ is differentiable at c and its derivative there is equal to the value of f there:*

(1) $$\Phi'(c) = f(c).$$

Proof. Let $\Phi(x)$ be defined by the formula

(2) $$\Phi(x) \equiv \int_a^x f + \gamma = \int_a^x f(t)\,dt + \gamma,$$

where $a \in I$. We wish to prove that

(3) $$\lim_{h \to 0} \frac{\Phi(c + h) - \Phi(c)}{h} = \lim_{h \to 0} \frac{\int_a^{c+h} f - \int_a^c f}{h} = f(c),$$

or, equivalently, that

(4) $$\lim_{h \to 0} \frac{1}{h} \int_c^{c+h} f = f(c), \quad \text{or} \quad \lim_{h \to 0} \frac{1}{h} \int_c^{c+h} f(x)dx = f(c),$$

*Theorem I is sometimes called the *First Form of the Fundamental Theorem of Calculus.*

where it is implicitly assumed that h is such that $c + h \in I$. Since $\int_c^{c+h} f(c) = hf(c)$, or $\frac{1}{h}\int_c^{c+h} f(c)\,dx = f(c)$, (4) can be expressed in the form

$$(5) \qquad \lim_{h \to 0} \frac{1}{h} \int_c^{c+h} [f(x) - f(c)]dx = 0.$$

We now use the continuity of f at c: If ϵ is an arbitrary positive number, we choose $\delta > 0$ such that

$$(6) \qquad x \in I \text{ and } |x - c| < \delta \;\Rightarrow\; |f(x) - f(c)| < \tfrac{1}{2}\epsilon.$$

Consequently, $0 < |h| < \delta$ and $c + h \in I$ imply, by Theorem II, §1003,

$$(7) \qquad \left| \frac{1}{h} \int_c^{c+h} [f(x) - f(c)]dx \right| \leq \frac{1}{|h|} \left| \int_c^{c+h} |f(x) - f(c)|\,dx \right|$$

$$\leq \frac{1}{|h|} \left| \int_c^{c+h} \tfrac{1}{2}\epsilon \right| = \frac{1}{|h|} \cdot \tfrac{1}{2}\epsilon \cdot |h| < \epsilon,$$

and the proof is complete.

Example 1. If f is the bracket function restricted to the interval $[0, 3]$ and if Φ is the indefinite integral of Example 2, §1003, then Φ is differentiable wherever f is continuous, that is, for $0 \leq x < 1, 1 < x < 2$, and $2 < x < 3$, and

$$\Phi'(x) = \begin{cases} 0 = [x] \text{ if } 0 \leq x < 1, \\ 1 = [x] \text{ if } 1 < x < 2, \\ 2 = [x] \text{ if } 2 < x < 3. \end{cases}$$

At the point $x = 3$, Φ is differentiable but its derivative there is

$$\Phi'(3) = 2 \neq [3].$$

A notion closely related to that of an *indefinite integral* of a function f on an interval is that of *primitive* or *antiderivative* of a function f on an interval:

Definition. *A function F is called a **primitive** or an **antiderivative** of a function f on an interval I if and only if f is defined on I, and F is differentiable at every point x of I and its derivative is equal there to the value of f at x:*

$$(8) \qquad F'(x) = f(x).$$

In brief, F is a primitive or antiderivative of f on I if and only if f is the derivative of F on I.

Two primitives of a function f on an interval I are related much as two indefinite integrals are:

Theorem II. *If F and G are any two primitives of a function f on an interval I, then F and G differ by a constant there; that is, there exists a constant C such that*

$$(9) \qquad x \in I \;\Rightarrow\; F(x) = G(x) + C.$$

Proof. Define the function $H(x) \equiv F(x) - G(x)$. Then at every point x of I,

(10) $$H'(x) = F'(x) - G'(x) = f(x) - f(x) = 0.$$

By Theorem II, §614, $H(x)$ is a constant C:

(11) $$H(x) = F(x) - G(x) = C,$$

and (9) follows.

We are now in a position to establish a sequence of five short theorems, each concerned with a function continuous on an interval.

Theorem III. *Every function continuous on an interval has an indefinite integral there.*

Proof. If f is continuous on an interval I, then $\int_a^x f$ exists for all points a and x of I. (Cf. §307.)

Theorem IV. *Every indefinite integral of a function f continuous on an interval is a primitive of f there.*

Proof. This follows immediately from Theorem I.

Theorem V. *Every function continuous on an interval has a primitive there.*

Proof. This follows from Theorems III and IV.

Theorem VI. *Every primitive of a function f continuous on an interval is an indefinite integral of f there.*

Proof. If F is an arbitrary primitive of a continuous function f on an interval I, let $a \in I$ and $\Phi(x) \equiv \int_a^x f$, for $x \in I$. Then the indefinite integral Φ of f is a primitive of f, by Theorem IV, and by Theorem II there exists a constant γ such that $F = \Phi + \gamma$, and F is an indefinite integral of f on I.

Theorem VII. *If a function f is continuous on an interval I, then the class of indefinite integrals of f on I is identical with the class of primitives of f on I.*

Proof. This is a restatement of Theorems IV and VI.

Example 2. The function x^3 is continuous on the interval $(-\infty, +\infty)$. An indefinite integral of x^3 there is

(12) $$\Phi(x) \equiv \int_0^x t^3 \, dt = \frac{x^4 - 0^4}{4} = \frac{x^4}{4}.$$

Therefore the most general indefinite integral of x^3, as well as the most general primitive of x^3, has the form

(13) $$F(x) = \frac{x^4}{4} + C,$$

where C is a constant.

NOTE. In general (in the absence of continuity) an indefinite integral of a function is not necessarily a primitive of that function. For example, the function Φ of Example 2, §1003, is an indefinite integral of the function $f(x) \equiv [x]$, restricted to the interval [0, 3], but since it fails to be differentiable at the points 1 and 2 it is not a primitive of f. In fact, the function f of Example 2, §1003, is an example of a function which, though it has an indefinite integral, has no primitive. To see that f can have no primitive we have only to observe that it fails to have the intermediate-value property possessed by every derivative. (Cf. the Example, §617.) In Exercise 1, H §1610, *CWAG*, is given an example of a function with a primitive but no indefinite integral.

Example 3. Find the derivative of the function $F(x) \equiv \int_x^b f(t)dt$, where f is continuous on an interval I, and x and $b \in I$.

Solution. Since $F(x) = -\int_b^x f(t)dt$, and the derivative of the function $\int_b^x f(t)dt$, is $f(x)$, the derivative of the function F at the point x is $-f(x)$.

1006 THE SYMBOL $\int$

In this section we shall assume that f is a function that is continuous on an interval I. By Theorem VII, §1005, the class of indefinite integrals of f on I is identical with the class of primitives of f on I. We shall now introduce symbols for the general members of these two equal classes.

The symbol $\int$ of integration, without the limits of integration that are attached when a definite integral is under consideration as in the notation $\int_a^b$, is used to indicate a general member of the class of all indefinite integrals of f, as follows:

(1) $\int f$ = a general indefinite integral of f.

Another way of expressing (1) is

(2) $\{\int f\}$ = the class of all indefinite integrals of f.

In practice, the general indefinite integral of a function f is expressed in terms of the independent variable. Thus, if this variable is denoted x and if a is a point of the interval I, we can write

(3) $$\int f(x)dx \equiv \int_a^x f(t)dt + C,$$

where C is an arbitrary constant. For brevity the general indefinite integral $\int f(x)dx$ is called **the indefinite integral** of the function f. The use of the words *the indefinite integral of* f, then, is similar to the use of the words *the variable x*, to refer to the general member of a certain class.

In a similar fashion, by Theorem II, §1005, if F is any particular primitive of f on I, the general primitive of f can be written with the aid of an arbitrary constant C:

(4) $F + C$ = a general primitive of f.

Alternatively, corresponding to (2):

(5) $\{F + C\}$ = the class of all primitives of f.

With the elliptic notation of $F(x)$ for the function F whose value at x is $F(x)$, we can write (4) in the form

(6) $F(x) + C$ = a general primitive of $f(x)$.

Theorem VII, §1005, states that the two classes of (2) and (5) are identical. This usually takes a form involving the independent variable, as in (3) and (6):

$$(7) \qquad\qquad \int f(x)dx = F(x) + C.$$

The precise meaning of (7) is that it is the conjunction of the following two statements, where F is any particular primitive of f: (*i*) Every indefinite integral of the function $f(x)$ has the form $F(x) + C$, where C is a constant. (*ii*) Every function of the form $F(x) + C$ is an indefinite integral of $f(x)$.

The process of determining the class of all indefinite integrals of a given function f is called **indefinite integration,** or simply **integration** if there is no likelihood of confusion with the process of determining a *definite* integral. To **integrate** a function f means to determine all indefinite integrals of f. If f is continuous on an interval I, the problem of integrating f reduces, by (7), to the problem of finding a primitive F of f. Any formula providing a primitive for a continuous function on an interval is called an **integration formula.** The general constant C appearing in any integration formula (7) is called the **constant of integration.** The function f in the expression $\int f$ or $\int f(x)dx$ is called the **integrand,** and the variable x in $\int f(x)dx$ is called the variable of integration. It should be noted that whereas the variable of integration in a *definite* integral is a dummy variable (cf. §102), that is

$$(8) \qquad\qquad \int_a^b f(x)dx = \int_a^b f(t)dt = \int_a^b f(u)du = \cdots,$$

the variable of integration in an *indefinite* integral is *not*:

$$(9) \qquad\qquad \int f(x)dx \neq \int f(t)dt \neq \int f(u)du \neq \cdots.$$

NOTE.   For continuous functions the two operations of differentiation and integration can be considered as *inverse operations:* if a continuous function f is integrated and the integral is then differentiated, the result is the original function f; on the other hand, if a function F has a continuous derivative f, then F is an indefinite integral of f.

The indefinite integral of the constant function 1 is written alternatively $\int dx$ or $\int 1\ dx$ and is equal to $x + C$:

$$(10) \qquad\qquad \int dx = \int 1\ dx = x + C.$$

The indefinite integral of the reciprocal of a function and the indefinite integral of the quotient of two functions are written, similarly,

$$(11) \qquad\qquad \int \frac{dx}{g(x)} \equiv \int \frac{1}{g(x)}\ dx, \qquad \int \frac{f(x)dx}{g(x)} \equiv \int \frac{f(x)}{g(x)}\ dx.$$

Notation analogous to (10) and (11) applies to definite integrals, thus:

$$(12) \quad \int_a^b dx \equiv \int_a^b 1\, dx = b - a, \quad \int_a^b \frac{dx}{g(x)} \equiv \int_a^b \frac{1}{g(x)}\, dx, \quad \int_a^b \frac{f(x)dx}{g(x)} \equiv \int_a^b \frac{f(x)}{g(x)}\, dx.$$

In future examples and exercises, the instruction *integrate f* will often be expressed in other ways, such as: *evaluate the integral* $\int f(x)dx$, *integrate:* $\int f(x)dx$, or *perform the indicated integration:* $\int f(x)dx$.

Example 1.   The result of Example 2, §1005, can be written

$$(13) \qquad \int x^3\, dx = \frac{x^4}{4} + C.$$

Example 2.   If n is any nonnegative integer, since the function x^n is continuous on the interval $(-\infty, +\infty)$ and since the derivative of the function $\dfrac{x^{n+1}}{n+1}$ is equal to x^n, $\dfrac{x^{n+1}}{n+1}$ is a primitive of x^n on $\Re$ and

$$(14) \qquad \int x^n\, dx = \frac{x^{n+1}}{n+1} + C.$$

Example 3.   Integrate: $\int x^7\, dx$.

Solution.   By (14), $\int x^7\, dx = \dfrac{x^8}{8} + C$. The domain is assumed to be $\Re = (-\infty, +\infty)$.

1007   THE FUNDAMENTAL THEOREM OF CALCULUS

We have arrived at the place where we can bring together in a particularly definitive manner the two main processes of calculus, that of *integration* which is a global concept, and that of *differentiation* which is a local concept (cf. the opening paragraph of §401)   The principal practical dividend issuing from this statement uniting integration and differentiation, known as the *fundamental theorem of calculus,* is a means of using the limiting procedures and formulas of the *derivative* as an aid in obtaining evaluations for the *definite,* or *Riemann, integral.* This is a technique that was unknown at the time of the ancient Greeks, and became available only with the invention of calculus by Newton and Leibniz in the seventeenth century. It is a technique that brings within easy reach of the college freshman today problems that taxed the genius of Archimedes in the third century B.C. We shall exploit the power of the following theorem throughout the remainder of this book:

Theorem.*   **Fundamental Theorem of Calculus.**   *If f is integrable on every compact subinterval of an interval I, if F is continuous on I and differentiable in the interior of I with $F'(x) = f(x)$ at every interior point x of I, then for any two points a and b of I,*

$$(1) \qquad \int_a^b f = \int_a^b f(x)dx = F(b) - F(a).$$

Proof.   The case $a = b$ is trivial, and the case $a > b$ can be deduced from the case $a < b$ by a change of sign in each member of (1). We assume now that $a < b$. Since

---

*This theorem is sometimes called the *Second Form of the Fundamental Theorem of Calculus.*

f is integrable on the interval $[a, b]$, we may use the fact, as given in the Theorem of §514, that $\int_a^b f$ is equal to the limit of a sum of the form $\sum f(x_i)\Delta x_i$. If ϵ is an arbitrary positive number, let δ be a positive number such that whenever $\mathfrak{N} = \{a_0, a_1, a_2, \cdots, a_n\}$ is a net on $[a, b]$ of norm $|\mathfrak{N}|$ less than δ, and $x_i \in [a_{i-1}, a_i]$ for $i = 1, 2, \cdots, n$, then

$$(2) \qquad \left| \sum_{i=1}^n f(x_i)\Delta x_i - \int_a^b f \right| < \epsilon.$$

Now let $\mathfrak{N}$ be any net with norm less than δ, and write the difference $F(b) - F(a)$ in the following form:

$$(3) \qquad F(b) - F(a) = [F(a_1) - F(a_0)] + [F(a_2) - F(a_1)] + \cdots + [F(a_n) + F(a_{n-1})].$$

By the law of the mean for derivatives (Theorem II, §613) each term in the sum (3) can be written

$$(4) \qquad F(a_i) - F(a_{i-1}) = F'(x_i)(a_i - a_{i-1}) = f(x_i)\,\Delta x_i,$$

where $x_i \in (a_{i-1}, a_i)$, for $i = 1, 2, \cdots, n$. Therefore the sum (3) is one of the approximating sums for $\int_a^b f$, and we have, as a consequence, from (2):

$$(5) \qquad \left| F(b) - F(a) - \int_a^b f \right| < \epsilon.$$

Since ϵ is an arbitrary positive number and the quantity on the left of (5) is a non-negative *constant*, this constant must be zero, and formula (1) is established.

The fundamental theorem of calculus has two corollaries, of which the first is immediate. We give two proofs for Corollary II, of which the second is independent of the fundamental theorem of calculus.

Corollary I. *If f is integrable on the interval $[a, b]$ and if f has a primitive on $[a, b]$, then formula (1) holds for every primitive F of f on $[a, b]$.*

Corollary II. *If f is continuous on an interval I and if F is any primitive of f on I, then formula (1) holds for any two points a and b of I.*

First proof. If f is continuous on I, then f is integrable on every bounded closed subinterval of I and the conditions of the fundamental theorem of calculus are satisfied. (The function F is continuous since it is differentiable.)

Second proof. If f satisfies the conditions stated and if $\Phi(x) \equiv \int_a^x f$, then Φ is a primitive of f on I (Theorem IV, §1005). Therefore, by Theorem II, §1005, Φ and F differ by a constant C:

$$(6) \qquad \Phi(x) = \int_a^x f = F(x) + C, \, x \in I.$$

Substituting both a and b for x in (6), we obtain the two equations

$$(7) \qquad \begin{cases} \Phi(a) = 0 = F(a) + C, \\ \Phi(b) = \int_a^b f = F(b) + C. \end{cases}$$

Subtracting the first equation of (7) from the second gives $\int_a^b f = F(b) - F(a)$, or (1).

Notational Note. It is often convenient in specific problems to denote a difference of the form $F(b) - F(a)$ thus:

(8)
$$F(x)\Big|_a^b \equiv F(b) - F(a).$$

With this notation, formula (1) of the fundamental theorem of calculus can be written:

(9)
$$\int_a^b f = \int_a^b f(x)dx = F(x)\Big|_a^b.$$

In many practical problems the primitive $F(x)$ may consist of several terms, or of relatively complicated parts. In such an event square brackets may be more convenient than the vertical bar, and (9) can be written thus:

(10)
$$\int_a^b f = \int_a^b f(x)dx = \Big[F(x) \Big]_a^b.$$

Formulas (9) and (10) can also be written in terms of the indefinite integral symbol, as it is expressed in the formula $\int f(x)\, dx = F(x) + C$ of (7), §1006, as follows:

(11)
$$\int_a^b f(x)\, dx = \int f(x)\, dx \Big|_a^b = \Big[\int f(x)\, dx \Big]_a^b.$$

Example 1. Formula (6) of Note 1, §1003, now has the following simple derivation (cf. Example 2, §1006):

(12)
$$\int_a^b x^n dx = \frac{x^{n+1}}{n+1}\Big|_a^b = \frac{b^{n+1}}{n+1} - \frac{a^{n+1}}{n+1} = \frac{b^{n+1} - a^{n+1}}{n+1}.$$

Example 2. Since $D_x(x - \cos 2x) = 1 + 2\sin 2x$,

$$\int_0^{\frac{\pi}{2}} (1 + 2\sin 2x)dx = \Big[x - \cos 2x \Big]_0^{\frac{\pi}{2}} = \Big(\frac{\pi}{2} - \cos\pi \Big) - (0 - \cos 0) = \frac{1}{2}(\pi + 4).$$

Example 3. Show that the mean value theorems for derivatives and integrals (Theorem II, §613, and the Theorem, §1002), in case all functions concerned are continuous, differ only in notation.

Solution. If the functions f and F are continuous on the interval $[a, b]$, and if $F'(x) = f(x)$ there, then Theorem II, §613, asserts the existence of a number c between a and b such that

(13)
$$f(c) = \frac{F(b) - F(a)}{b - a}.$$

On the other hand, by formula (1) of the fundamental theorem of calculus, $F(b) - F(a) = \int_a^b f$, and (13) becomes formula (3), §1002, of the Theorem, §1002.

1008 EXERCISES

In Exercises 1–4, verify Theorem I, §1005, at each point of continuity of the integrand (cf. Exs. 13–16, §1004).

1. $\displaystyle\int_2^x t^3\,dt.$

2. $\displaystyle\int_1^x (3u^2 - 8u^3)du.$

3. $\displaystyle\int_0^x \operatorname{sgn} r\,dr.$

4. $\displaystyle\int_0^x |s|\,ds.$

In Exercises 5 and 6, find the derivative of the function defined by the integral (cf. Example 3, §1005).

5. $\displaystyle\int_x^{-1} (w^3 - w^4)dw.$

6. $\displaystyle\int_x^{10} (5z^2 - 7z)dz.$

In Exercises 7 and 8, show that the given function is integrable on every compact interval, but that it has no primitive on the interval $(-\infty, +\infty)$.

7. $\operatorname{sgn} x.$

8. $[x].$

In Exercises 9–12, find $\int f(x)dx$ for the given function $f(x)$.

9. $x^8.$

10. $x^{10}.$

11. $x^6.$

12. $x^{11}.$

In Exercises 13–20, use the given differentiation formula to evaluate the given definite integral.

13. $D_x (3x + 5)^8 = 24(3x + 5)^7;\ \displaystyle\int_0^1 24(3r + 5)^7\,dr.$

14. $D_x (5x - 4)^7 = 35(5x - 4)^6;\ \displaystyle\int_1^3 35(5s - 4)^6\,ds.$

15. $D_x \dfrac{1}{4x - 1} = -\dfrac{4}{(4x - 1)^2};\ \displaystyle\int_1^2 -\dfrac{4dw}{(4w - 1)^2}.$

16. $D_x \dfrac{1}{x^2 + 4} = -\dfrac{2x}{(x^2 + 4)^2};\ \displaystyle\int_2^4 -\dfrac{2ydy}{(y^2 + 4)^2}.$

17. $D_x \sqrt{4x + 3} = \dfrac{2}{\sqrt{4x + 3}};\ \displaystyle\int_1^3 \dfrac{2dx}{\sqrt{4x + 3}}.$

18. $D_x \sqrt{x^2 + 5} = \dfrac{x}{\sqrt{x^2 + 5}};\ \displaystyle\int_2^5 \dfrac{u\,du}{\sqrt{u^2 + 5}}.$

19. $D_x \sin^3 2x = 6 \sin^2 2x \cos 2x;\ \displaystyle\int_{\frac{\pi}{12}}^{\frac{\pi}{4}} 6 \sin^2 2z \cos 2z\,dz.$

20. $D_x \sec^2 3x = 6 \sec^2 3x \tan 3x;\ \displaystyle\int_0^{\frac{\pi}{9}} 6 \sec^2 3t \cos 3t\,dt.$

In Exercises 21–23, use the given differentiation formula as a means of evaluating the given limit. (Cf. the Example, §514, and Exs. 1–4, §516.)

21. $D_x \left(\frac{2}{3} x^{\frac{3}{2}} \right) = \sqrt{x}; \quad \lim\limits_{n \to +\infty} \frac{1}{n\sqrt{n}} \left[\sqrt{1} + \sqrt{2} + \cdots + \sqrt{n} \right].$

22. $D_x \left(-\frac{1}{x+1} \right) = \frac{1}{(x+1)^2}; \quad \lim\limits_{n \to +\infty} n \left[\frac{1}{(1+n)^2} + \frac{1}{(2+n)^2} + \cdots + \frac{1}{(n+n)^2} \right].$

23. $D_x \sqrt{x^2 + 1} = \frac{x}{\sqrt{x^2 + 1}}; \quad \lim\limits_{n \to +\infty} \frac{1}{n} \left[\frac{1}{\sqrt{1^2 + n^2}} + \frac{2}{\sqrt{2^2 + n^2}} + \cdots + \frac{n}{\sqrt{n^2 + n^2}} \right].$

1009 SOME INTEGRATION FORMULAS

In this section *all functions under consideration will be assumed to be continuous on an interval.*

Integration formulas are of two principal types, (*i*) where the integral sign $\int$ appears only once and there is a constant of integration C, and (*ii*) where the integral sign $\int$ appears more than once and there is no constant of integration.

The first type of integration formula (*i*) has the form of (7), § 1006,

$$(1) \qquad \int f(x)\, dx = F(x) + C,$$

and is exemplified by formula (14) of Example 2, §1006,

$$(2) \qquad \int x^n\, dx = \frac{x^{n+1}}{n+1} + C, \quad n \in \mathfrak{N} \cup \{0\}, x \in \mathfrak{R}.$$

The meaning of such a formula, where f is continuous on an interval, has already been explained: The function F is a primitive of f, or in other words, f is the derivative of F. Verification of (1) is equivalent to verification of the equation $F'(x) = f(x)$ on the interval in question.

The second type of integration formula (*ii*) is exemplified by

$$(3) \qquad \int (f + g) = \int f + \int g, \text{ or } \int [f(x) + g(x)] dx = \int f(x) dx + \int g(x) dx.$$

Either equation in (3) should be interpreted as expressing the equality of two classes. More precisely, (3) states that every function H whose derivative is $f + g$ must be equal to the sum of two functions F and G whose derivatives are f and g, respectively, and conversely, whenever F and G are functions whose derivatives are f and g, respectively, the derivative of their sum $F + G$ must be $f + g$. Having stated what. (3) *means*, let us proceed to show that it is *true*. In the first place, if H is an arbitrary primitive of $f + g$, let ϕ and ψ be arbitrary primitives of f and g, respectively: $\phi' = f$ and $\psi' = g$. Then since $(\phi + \psi)' = \phi' + \psi'$ (cf. formula (6), § 605), the two functions H and $\phi + \psi$ have the same derivative on the interval in question. Therefore, by Theorem II, §1005, H and $\phi + \psi$ differ by a constant C: $H = \phi + \psi + C$. Consequently, if we let $F \equiv \phi$ and $G \equiv \psi + C$, H is the sum of two functions F and G whose derivatives are f and g, respectively. Finally, if F and G are primitives of f and g, respectively, their sum $F + G$ must be a primitive of $f + g$ (again using (6), §605), and the proof of (3) is complete.

Since any differentiation formula gives rise to an integration formula, we can assemble now a list of such integration formulas, making use of differentiation formulas from §§605, 619, 621, and 622. Proofs of the formulas in the following list are left for the student to complete in Exercise 31, §1010. The domain is assumed to be an unspecified interval I where the functions involved are continuous, except for formula II, where particulars are included. For additional details on formula II, see the Note, below.

Integration Formulas.

I. $\int c \, dx = cx + C$, where c is a constant.

II. $\int x^n \, dx = \dfrac{x^{n+1}}{n+1} + C, \quad n \in \mathfrak{N} \cup \{0\}, \quad x \in \mathfrak{R},$
$$\text{or } n \in \mathfrak{Q}, \quad x > 0. \quad \text{(Cf. the Note, below.)}$$

III. $\int (f + g) = \int f + \int g$, or $\int [f(x) + g(x)] dx = \int f(x) dx + \int g(x) dx.$

IV. $\int cf = c \int f$, or $\int cf(x) dx = c \int f(x) dx$, where c is any nonzero constant.

IVa. $\int -f = -\int f$, or $\int -f(x) dx = -\int f(x) dx.$

V. $\int \sin x \, dx = -\cos x + C.$

VI. $\int \cos x \, dx = \sin x + C.$

VII. $\int \sec^2 x \, dx = \tan x + C.$

VIII. $\int \csc^2 x \, dx = -\cot x + C.$

IX. $\int \sec x \tan x \, dx = \sec x + C.$

X. $\int \csc x \cot x \, dx = -\csc x + C.$

NOTE. Formula II is also valid for other values of n and ranges for x, as explained in §619. The general principle is that II holds whenever it "makes sense." To be specific, II is true for the following cases in addition to those already specified: (i) n a positive rational number, $x \geq 0$; (ii) n a positive rational number of the form $n = p/q$ where q is odd, $x \in \mathfrak{R}$; (iii) n a rational number of the form $n = p/q$ where q is odd, $x < 0$. In §1111 it will be shown that if n is *any* real number different from -1, formula II is valid for $x > 0$. In §1115 the integration formula for the case $n = -1$, $\int \dfrac{dx}{x}$, is discussed.

Example 1. $\int 7\,dx = 7x + C, \int 7x^4\,dx = 7\int x^4\,dx = 7\left(\dfrac{x^5}{5} + C_1\right) = \dfrac{7x^5}{5} + C,$

where the constant of integration C is equal to 7 times the constant of integration C_1.

Example 2. $\int (5 - 6x + 3x^7)dx = \int 5\,dx - 6\int x\,dx + 3\int x^7\,dx$

$$= 5x - 3x^2 + \tfrac{3}{8}x^8 + C.$$

Example 3. $\displaystyle\int_1^3 (5x - x^2)dx = \left[\dfrac{5x^2}{2} - \dfrac{x^3}{3}\right]_1^3 = \left[\dfrac{45}{2} - 9\right] - \left[\dfrac{5}{2} - \dfrac{1}{3}\right] = 11\tfrac{1}{3}.$

Example 4. $\displaystyle\int_0^{\frac{\pi}{3}} \sec x \tan x\,dx = \sec x \Big|_0^{\frac{\pi}{3}} = 2 - 1 = 1.$

Example 5. Find the area under the arch of the graph $y = \sin x$, for $0 \leq x \leq \pi$.

Solution. We interpret the question to mean "Find the area of the ordinate set of $y = \sin x$, for $0 \leq x \leq \pi$." This area is equal to the integral

$$\int_0^\pi \sin x\,dx = -\cos x \Big|_0^\pi = -(-1) - (-1) = 2.$$

The negative sign before $\cos x$ in the final evaluation can be most easily handled by reversing the order of substitutions, thus:

$$-\cos x \Big|_0^\pi = \cos x \Big|_\pi^0 = 1 - (-1) = 2.$$

1010   EXERCISES

In Exercises 1–20, perform the indicated integration.

1. $\displaystyle\int dx.$

2. $\displaystyle\int (6x + 8)dx.$

3. $\displaystyle\int (-2r^3 + 5r^2)dr.$

4. $\displaystyle\int (18s^5 - 16s^3)ds.$

5. $\displaystyle\int \dfrac{dw}{w^2}.$

6. $\displaystyle\int \left(\dfrac{3}{z^2} - \dfrac{5}{z^3}\right)dz.$

7. $\displaystyle\int \dfrac{u^2 - 1}{u^2}\,du.$

8. $\displaystyle\int \dfrac{v^3 + 2v - 3}{v^3}\,dv.$

9. $\displaystyle\int \sqrt{x}\,dx.$

10. $\displaystyle\int x\sqrt{x}\,dx.$

11. $\displaystyle\int \sqrt{u}(3u + 4)du.$

12. $\displaystyle\int \dfrac{3v + 4}{\sqrt{v}}\,dv.$

13. $\displaystyle\int (3\sqrt{w} + 4\sqrt[3]{w})dw.$

14. $\displaystyle\int (5\sqrt[3]{z^2} - 7\sqrt[4]{z^3})dz.$

15. $\displaystyle\int \sin r \, dr.$

16. $\displaystyle\int \cos s \, ds.$

17. $\displaystyle\int 3 \csc u \cot u \, du.$

18. $\displaystyle\int 6 \csc^2 v \, dv.$

19. $\displaystyle\int 5 \sec^2 w \, dw.$

20. $\displaystyle\int 2 \sec z \tan z \, dz.$

In Exercises 21–30, evaluate the definite integral.

21. $\displaystyle\int_1^4 x(x+2)dx.$

22. $\displaystyle\int_1^5 x^2(x-3)dx.$

23. $\displaystyle\int_1^4 3\sqrt{u} \, du.$

24. $\displaystyle\int_1^8 4\sqrt[3]{v} \, dv.$

25. $\displaystyle\int_2^3 \frac{dw}{w^3}.$

26. $\displaystyle\int_4^5 \frac{dz}{z^2}.$

27. $\displaystyle\int_{\frac{\pi}{6}}^{\frac{\pi}{2}} \cos t \, dt.$

28. $\displaystyle\int_0^{\frac{\pi}{3}} \sin r \, dr.$

29. $\displaystyle\int_{\frac{\pi}{6}}^{\frac{\pi}{3}} \sec^2 s \, ds.$

30. $\displaystyle\int_0^{\frac{\pi}{4}} \sec y \tan y \, dy.$

31. Complete the proofs of the formulas I–X, §1009.

1011 INTEGRATION BY SUBSTITUTION

The three equivalent formulas (8)–(10), §619, have the following forms when expressed as (equivalent) integration formulas, where it is assumed that $u = g(x)$ has a continuous derivative on an interval I, and that the values of n are rational and different from -1, and such as to make meaningful the powers of $g(x)$ involved:

(1) $$\int g^n(x)g'(x)dx = \frac{g^{n+1}(x)}{n+1} + C,$$

(2) $$\int g^n g' = \frac{g^{n+1}}{n+1} + C,$$

(3) $$\int u^n D_x u \, dx = \frac{u^{n+1}}{n+1} + C.$$

Each of the formulas (1)–(3) can be verified directly by differentiation of the right-hand member (with respect to the variable x).

Let us look now at formula (3), and compare it with that of II, §1009, with the letter u being used for the variable of integration instead of x:

(4) $$\int u^n \, du = \frac{u^{n+1}}{n+1} + C.$$

If we recall the definition (§701) of the differential of u when u is considered as a function of x:

(5) $$du = D_x u \, dx,$$

we have what *appears* to be a pair of formulas, (3) and (4), that are identical except for the substitution of du for $D_x u \, dx$. It is important, however, to appreciate that these two formulas are *not* the same, since the independent variable on both sides of (3) is x and that of the two members of (4) is u. We illustrate the distinction by an example.

Example 1. If $u = (x^2 + 1)$ and $n = \frac{1}{2}$, formula (3) becomes

(6) $$\int \sqrt{x^2 + 1} \cdot 2x \cdot dx = \tfrac{2}{3}(x^2 + 1)^{\frac{3}{2}} + C,$$

while (4) is

(7) $$\int \sqrt{u} \, du = \tfrac{2}{3}u^{\frac{3}{2}} + C.$$

To verify (6) we differentiate both members with respect to x: $\sqrt{x^2 + 1} \cdot 2x = \tfrac{2}{3} \cdot \tfrac{3}{2}(x^2 + 1)^{\frac{1}{2}} \cdot 2x$, and to verify (7) we differentiate both members with respect to u: $\sqrt{u} = \tfrac{2}{3} \cdot \tfrac{3}{2}u^{\frac{1}{2}}$.

Until the present discussion the symbol dx associated with the integral sign, as in $\int f(x)dx$, has been merely a *symbol* with no apparent relation to a *differential* which it resembles in outward appearance. It now appears that this use of the differential symbol is particularly apt and appropriate, since the dx in (3) seems to "behave" as if it were a differential by means of the "substitution" (5), which leads to the relatively simple form of (4). The point of all this is that *if* we write down the integral on the left-hand side of (3), and then group together by a sort of "associative law" the last two parts that look like "factors," thus:

(8) $$(u^n D_x u)dx = u^n(D_x u \, dx),$$

and then "act" as though the quantity $D_x u \, dx$ were the same as the differential du, proceeding next to integrate the resulting expression $\int u^n \, du$ *as if* u were the variable of integration by means of formula (4), *then*, when we are through, if we reinterpret the result with u once more the function of x with which we started, *the final result is correct!* This is a truly remarkable fact, and one that we shall exploit in several varying contexts repeatedly and rewardingly. It is this fortunate circumstance that is the reason for the universal use of the Leibniz differential notation in integration.

Let us look at two more examples in order to begin to develop a technique of integration by use of formula (3).

Example 2. Find a primitive of the function $(5x + 3)^{10}$.

Solution. Any primitive of $(5x + 3)^{10}$ has the form

(9) $$\int (5x + 3)^{10} \, dx,$$

or if $u = (5x + 3)$, $\int u^{10} \, dx$. Since $D_x u = 5$, the left-hand member of formula (3) can be written $\int u^{10} \cdot 5 \cdot dx = \int u^{10} du$. The integral (9) can be transformed into a form closer to $\int u^{10} du$ by multiplying and dividing by 5, and factoring the *constant* $\frac{1}{5}$ according to IV, §1009:

(10) $$\int (5x + 3)^{10}dx = \int \tfrac{1}{5}(5x + 3)^{10} \cdot 5 \cdot dx = \tfrac{1}{5}\int u^{10}du = \tfrac{1}{5} \cdot \frac{u^{11}}{11} + C = \frac{(5x + 3)^{11}}{55} + C.$$

That $(5x + 3)^{11}/55$ is a primitive of $(5x + 3)^{10}$ can be verified by differentiation.

In practice, the actual steps following the substitution $u = 5x + 3$ are usually carried through without explicit use of the variable u, and the multiplication and division by 5 is done simultaneously before the integral and within the integrand, thus:

$$(11) \quad \int (5x + 3)^{10} dx = \frac{1}{5} \int (5x + 3)^{10} \cdot 5 \, dx = \frac{1}{5} \int (5x + 3)^{10} d(5x + 3) = \frac{(5x + 3)^{11}}{55} + C.$$

Notational Note. It is sometimes convenient in an integration by substitution to indicate within a formula the substitution that is being made. For this purpose the following notation is convenient:

$$\left[F(u) \right]^{u=\phi(x)} = F(u) \Big|^{u=\phi(x)} \equiv F(\phi(x)),$$

or with an indefinite integral:

$$\left[\int f(u) du \right]^{u=\phi(x)} = \int f(u) du \Big|^{u=\phi(x)} \equiv F(\phi(x)) + C,$$

where F is an arbitrary primitive of f. Thus, equation (10) could be written

$$\int (5x + 3)^{10} \, dx = \frac{1}{5} \int u^{10} \, du \Big|^{u=5x+3} = \frac{1}{5} \cdot \frac{u^{11}}{11} \Big|^{u=5x+3} + C = \frac{(5x + 3)^{11}}{55} + C.$$

Example 3. Evaluate $\int x\sqrt{x^2 + 1} \, dx$.

Solution. We multiply by $\frac{1}{2}$ before the integral sign and by 2 in the integrand, and rearrange factors to obtain the integral (6) of Example 1:

$$\int x\sqrt{x^2 + 1} \, dx = \frac{1}{2} \int \sqrt{x^2 + 1} \, 2x \, dx = \frac{1}{2} \int (x^2 + 1)^{\frac{1}{2}} \, d(x^2 + 1)$$
$$= \frac{1}{2} \cdot \frac{(x^2 + 1)^{\frac{3}{2}}}{\frac{3}{2}} + C = \frac{1}{3}(x^2 + 1)^{\frac{3}{2}} + C.$$

Example 4. Evaluate $\displaystyle\int_0^5 \frac{dx}{\sqrt{3x + 1}}$.

Solution. We use an exponent $-\frac{1}{2}$ and factors $\frac{1}{3}$ and 3:

$$\frac{1}{3} \int_0^5 (3x + 1)^{-\frac{1}{2}} \, 3 \, dx = \frac{1}{3} \int_0^5 (3x + 1)^{-\frac{1}{2}} \, d(3x + 1) = \frac{1}{3} \frac{(3x + 1)^{\frac{1}{2}}}{\frac{1}{2}} \Big|_0^5 = \frac{2}{3}(\sqrt{16} - \sqrt{1}) = 2.$$

Example 5. Integrate: $\int \sin^3 5x \cos 5x \, dx$.

Solution. If we write $u = \sin 5x$, then $D_x u = 5 \cos 5x$. We multiply by $\frac{1}{5}$ and 5:

$$\frac{1}{5} \int \sin^3 5x \cdot (5 \cos 5x \, dx) = \frac{1}{5} \int \sin^3 5x \, d(\sin 5x) = \frac{\sin^4 5x}{20} + C.$$

The principle of the use of a differential in integration discussed in the preceding paragraphs of this section is applicable to formulas from §§621 and 622, corresponding to V–X, §1009. In the following formulas, u is assumed to be a continuously differentiable function of x, and the symbol du is a substitute for $D_x u \, dx$:

$$(12) \quad \int \sin u \, D_x u \, dx = \int \sin u \, du = -\cos u + C,$$

$$(13) \quad \int \cos u \, D_x u \, dx = \int \cos u \, du = \sin u + C,$$

(14) $\int \sec^2 u \; D_x u \; dx = \int \sec^2 u \; du = \tan u + C,$

(15) $\int \csc^2 u \; D_x u \; dx = \int \csc^2 u \; du = -\cot u + C,$

(16) $\int \sec u \tan u \; D_x u \; dx = \int \sec u \tan u \; du = \sec u + C,$

(17) $\int \csc u \cot u \; D_x u \; dx = \int \csc u \cot u \; du = -\csc u + C.$

Example 6. Integrate: $\int \sec^2 7x \; dx.$

Solution. With $u = 7x$, $D_x u = 7$, and we multiply by $\frac{1}{7}$ and 7 to write the given integral:

$$\tfrac{1}{7} \int \sec^2 u \; D_x u \; dx = \tfrac{1}{7} \int \sec^2 7x \; d(7x) = \tfrac{1}{7} \tan 7x + C.$$

Example 7. Find the volume obtained by revolving about the y-axis the quarter-disk

$$\{(x, y) \mid x^2 + y^2 \leqq a^2, \; 0 \leqq x \leqq a, \; 0 \leqq y \leqq a\},$$

using the method of cylindrical shells.

Solution. By formula (13), §208, the desired volume is

$$2\pi \int_0^a x\sqrt{a^2 - x^2} \; dx = -\pi \int_0^a (a^2 - x^2)^{\frac{1}{2}} \; d(a^2 - x^2)$$

$$= -\pi \frac{(a^2 - x^2)^{\frac{3}{2}}}{\frac{3}{2}} \Big|_0^a = -\frac{2\pi}{3}(0 - a^3) = \frac{2}{3}\pi a^3.$$

All of the preceding formulas of this section that make use of the differential $du = D_x u \; dx$ are only specific instances of a more general formula:

Theorem I. *If u is a continuously differentiable function of the variable x on an interval I and if the range of u is contained in an interval J of continuity of the function f, then*

(18) $\int f(u(x))u'(x)dx = \int f(u(x))du(x) = \int f(u)du,$

where the symbol du(x) is a substitute for u'(x)dx, and the final integral $\int f(u)du$ is to be interpreted to mean F(u(x)) + C, where F is any primitive of f on J.

Proof. The problem is to show that $F(u(x)) + C$ is a primitive of $f(u(x))u'(x)$ on I. But this is a consequence of the chain rule (§ 610):

(19) $D_x(F(u(x))) = F'(u(x)) \cdot D_x u(x) = f(u(x)) \cdot u'(x).$

On frequent occasions the technique of integration by substitution prescribed by Theorem I is carried out in reverse. That is, the integral given to be evaluated plays the role of the final integral $\int f(u)du$ of (18), and the one resulting from a substitution is the first integral $\int f(u(x))u'(x)dx$. We state the appropriate alternative form of the preceding theorem, with the roles of the variables x and u reversed:

Theorem II. *Let x and u be variables such that u is a continuously differentiable function u(x) of x with a nonzero derivative u'(x), on an interval I and with range an interval J, and such that x is a continuously differentiable function x(u) of u on J with range I. If the function f is continuous on the interval I, then*

(20) $\int f(x)dx = \int f(x(u))dx(u) = \int f(x(u))x'(u)du,$

where the symbol $dx(u)$ is a substitute for $x'(u)du$, and the final integral $\int f(x(u))x'(u)du$ is to be interpreted to mean $\Phi(u(x)) + C$, where Φ is any primitive of $(f \circ x)x'$, that is,

$$(21) \qquad\qquad D_u \Phi(u) = f(x(u))x'(u), \quad u \in J.$$

Proof. The proof involves the same principles as that of Theorem I, except that the substitutions are more complicated. The idea is to show that the derivative with respect to x of $\int f(x(u))x'(u)du = \Phi(u(x)) + C$ is equal to $f(x)$, for $x \in I$. To show this we use the chain rule, multiplying $D_u\Phi$ by D_xu, and then substitute $u(x)$ for u, with the aid of (21):

$$(22) \qquad\qquad D_x \Phi(u(x)) = D_u \Phi(u) \cdot D_x u$$
$$= f(x(u))x'(u)u'(x)$$
$$= f(x(u(x)))x'(u(x))u'(x).$$

Since $x(u)$ and $u(x)$ are inverse functions, $x(u(x)) = x$, for $x \in I$, and since $x'(u)$ and $u'(x)$ are nonzero, $x'(u(x))$ and $u'(x)$ are reciprocals (cf. the Theorem, § 618), and their product is identically 1 on I. The last line of (22) therefore simplifies to $f(x) \cdot 1 = f(x)$, and the proof is complete.

In an integration by substitution, with the notation of the preceding discussion, the primary problem is the choice of the expression $u(x)$ to be substituted for u. In the examples given above, we have taken for u either *a quantity raised to a power* (including as a special case *a quantity under a radical sign*) or *a quantity of which a trigonometric function is taken* (as in Example 6). As we shall see in subsequent chapters, these are only two of a great variety of substitutions that are available for integration problems. We give one more illustration of integration by substitution, of a type that is frequently helpful, whereby u is set equal to *the nth root of a linear function.* For this integration we shall use Theorem II.

Example 8.   Evaluate: $\int x\sqrt{3x + 4}\, dx$.

Solution.   If $u \equiv \sqrt{3x + 4}$, then $u^2 = 3x + 4, x = \dfrac{u^2 - 4}{3}, dx = \dfrac{2u}{3}du$, and the given integral can be written

$$\int \frac{u^2 - 4}{3} \cdot u \cdot \frac{2u}{3}\, du = \frac{2}{9} \int (u^4 - 4u^2)du$$

$$= \frac{2}{9}\left(\frac{u^5}{5} - \frac{4u^3}{3}\right) + C = \frac{2}{45}(3x + 4)^{\frac{5}{2}} - \frac{8}{27}(3x + 4)^{\frac{3}{2}} + C.$$

The answer can be verified by differentiation. The result is valid for $x \in I$, where I is any subinterval of $(-\frac{4}{3}, +\infty)$.

1012   DEFINITE INTEGRALS BY SUBSTITUTION

As was illustrated in Examples 4 and 7, § 1011, definite integrals can sometimes be evaluated by the substitution techniques of § 1011. The following theorem shows that in cases where the integration can be performed by substitution, definite integrals can be evaluated without returning to the original variable of integration:

Theorem I.   *If u is a continuously differentiable function of the variable x on an interval I, if the range of u is contained in an interval J of continuity of the function f, if a and b are any two points of I and if c ≡ u(a) and d ≡ u(b), then*

(1)
$$\int_a^b f(u(x))u'(x)dx = \int_a^b f(u(x))du(x) = \int_c^d f(u)du,$$

where the final integral $\int_c^d f(u)du$ is to be interpreted to mean $F(u)\Big|_c^d$, where F is any primitive of f on J.

Proof.   By Theorem I, §1011,

$$\int f(u(x))u'(x)dx = F(u(x)) + C,$$

and therefore

$$\int_a^b f(u(x))u'(x)dx = F(u(x))\Big|_a^b = F(u(b)) - F(u(a))$$

$$= F(d) - F(c) = F(u)\Big|_c^d = \int_c^d f(u)du.$$

Example 1.   Examples 4 and 7, §1011, can be evaluated:

$$\int_0^5 \frac{dx}{\sqrt{3x+1}} = \frac{1}{3}\int_0^5 (3x+1)^{-\frac{1}{2}} d(3x+1) = \frac{1}{3}\int_1^{16} u^{-\frac{1}{2}} du = \frac{1}{3}\cdot\frac{2}{1}u^{\frac{1}{2}}\Big|_1^{16} = \frac{2}{3}(\sqrt{16} - \sqrt{1}) = 2,$$

$$2\pi\int_0^a x\sqrt{a^2 - x^2}\, dx = -\pi\int_0^a (a^2 - x^2)^{\frac{1}{2}} d(a^2 - x^2) = -\pi\int_{a^2}^0 u^{\frac{1}{2}}\, du$$

$$= \pi\int_0^{a^2} u^{\frac{1}{2}}\, du = \frac{2}{3}\pi u^{\frac{3}{2}}\Big|_0^{a^2} = \frac{2}{3}\pi a^3.$$

Theorem I has application to integrals of the form $\int_b^a \phi(x)dx$, where the graph of $y = \phi(x)$ is defined parametrically:

(2) $$x = f(t), \quad y = g(t), \quad \alpha \leq t \leq \beta,$$

where f and g are continuously differentiable functions of t and f is a strictly monotonic function of t, for $\alpha \leq t \leq \beta$, and where $f(\alpha) = a$ and $f(\beta) = b$ (cf. Fig. 1012-1):

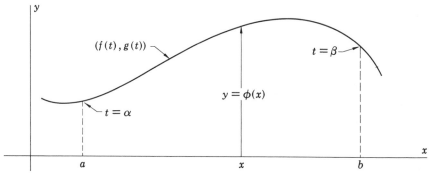

Figure 1012-1

Theorem II. *Under the assumptions of the preceding paragraph,* $y = \phi(x)$ *is a continuous function of x on the interval* $[a, b]$, *and*

(3)
$$\int_a^b y \, dx = \int_a^b \phi(x)dx = \int_\alpha^\beta g(t)f'(t) \, dt.$$

Proof. Since x is a strictly monotonic continuous function of t for $\alpha \leq t \leq \beta$, t must be a strictly monotonic continuous function of x for $a \leq x \leq b$, by §410. Let this inverse function of f be denoted by ψ, so that $t = \psi(x)$. By composition of functions, with $y = g(\psi(x))$, y becomes a continuous function of x by §406, and

(4)
$$\phi(x) = g(\psi(x)), \quad a \leq x \leq b.$$

Since f and ψ are inverse functions, $\psi(f(t)) = t$ for $\alpha \leq t \leq \beta$, and substitution of $x = f(t)$ into (4) gives

(5)
$$\phi(f(t)) = g(t), \quad \alpha \leq t \leq \beta.$$

We now apply Theorem I to the third integral of (3):

$$\int_\alpha^\beta g(t)f'(t)dt = \int_\alpha^\beta \phi(f(t))f'(t)dt = \int_a^b \phi(x)dx,$$

and the proof is complete.

Example 2. Find the area of the set between one arch of the cycloid

(6)
$$x = a\theta - a \sin \theta, \quad y = a - a \cos \theta, a > 0, 0 \leq \theta \leq 2\pi,$$

and the x-axis. (Cf. Example 4, §710.)

Solution. Since $D_\theta x = a(1 - \cos \theta) > 0$ for $0 < \theta < 2\pi$, x is a strictly increasing function of θ on the interval $[0, 2\pi]$, and the conditions of Theorem II, with θ in place of t, are satisfied. Therefore the area requested is

$$\int_0^{2\pi a} y \, dx = \int_0^{2\pi} (a - a \cos \theta)(a - a \cos \theta)d\theta = a^2 \int_0^{2\pi} (1 - 2 \cos \theta + \cos^2 \theta)d\theta.$$

The last integral can be evaluated by means of the half-angle identity $\cos^2 \theta = \frac{1}{2}(1 + \cos 2\theta)$:

$$a^2 \int_0^{2\pi} (1 - 2 \cos \theta + \frac{1}{2} + \frac{1}{2} \cos 2\theta)d\theta$$

$$= \frac{3}{2}a^2 \int_0^{2\pi} d\theta - 2a^2 \int_0^{2\pi} \cos \theta \, d\theta + \frac{1}{4}a^2 \int_0^{2\pi} \cos 2\theta \, d(2\theta)$$

$$= \frac{3}{2} a^2\theta \Big|_0^{2\pi} - 2a^2 \sin \theta \Big|_0^{2\pi} + \frac{1}{4}a^2 \sin 2\theta \Big|_0^{2\pi} = 3\pi a^2.$$

(The use of half-angle formulas in integration is treated in §502, *SCC*.)

1013 EXERCISES

In Exercises 1–20, perform the indicated integration.

1. $\displaystyle\int (4x + 7)^5 \, dx.$

2. $\displaystyle\int \frac{dx}{(4x + 7)^5}.$

3. $\displaystyle\int \frac{du}{\sqrt{6u+1}}.$

4. $\displaystyle\int \sqrt{8v-3}\, dv.$

5. $\displaystyle\int \frac{(6r+5)dr}{(3r^2+5r)^2}.$

6. $\displaystyle\int \frac{(3s^2+1)ds}{\sqrt{s^3+s}}.$

7. $\displaystyle\int w(3w^2+2)^6\, dw.$

8. $\displaystyle\int z\sqrt{2z^2-3}\, dz.$

9. $\displaystyle\int \frac{t\, dt}{\sqrt[3]{4t^2-5}}.$

10. $\displaystyle\int t^2\sqrt[3]{t^3+1}\, dt.$

11. $\displaystyle\int y(y^3+2)^3\, dy.$

12. $\displaystyle\int x^2(x^2-1)^4\, dx.$

13. $\displaystyle\int t\sin t^2\, dt.$

14. $\displaystyle\int \theta\cos(\theta^2+1)d\theta.$

15. $\displaystyle\int \sec 5\alpha\tan 5\alpha\, d\alpha.$

16. $\displaystyle\int \sec^2 2\beta\, d\beta.$

17. $\displaystyle\int x\sqrt{2x+1}\, dx.$

18. $\displaystyle\int r\sqrt[3]{2r+3}\, dr.$

19. $\displaystyle\int \frac{s}{\sqrt{4s-3}}\, ds.$

20. $\displaystyle\int \frac{t}{\sqrt[3]{3t-1}}\, dt.$

In Exercises 21–30, evaluate the definite integral.

21. $\displaystyle\int_1^3 (2x-1)^3\, dx.$

22. $\displaystyle\int_2^4 \frac{dy}{(3y-2)^2}.$

23. $\displaystyle\int_0^2 \frac{dr}{\sqrt{4r+1}}.$

24. $\displaystyle\int_0^3 \sqrt{5s+1}\, ds.$

25. $\displaystyle\int_1^2 t\sqrt{t^2+5}\, dt.$

26. $\displaystyle\int_0^4 \frac{w\, dw}{\sqrt{w^2+9}}.$

27. $\displaystyle\int_0^{\frac{\pi}{6}} \sin 2\theta\, d\theta.$

28. $\displaystyle\int_{\frac{\pi}{12}}^{\frac{\pi}{6}} \cos 3\phi\, d\phi.$

29. $\displaystyle\int_0^1 \frac{u\, du}{\sqrt{5u+4}}.$

30. $\displaystyle\int_1^2 v\sqrt{7v+2}\, dv.$

In Exercises 31–34, find the area of the ordinate set of the given function for the specified interval. Draw a figure.

31. $\dfrac{1}{(2x-1)^2}, 1 \leq x \leq 3.$

32. $\dfrac{1}{\sqrt{3x+1}}, 5 \leq x \leq 8.$

33. $x\sqrt{2x^2+1}, 0 \leq x \leq 2.$

34. $\dfrac{x}{\sqrt{x+4}}, 0 \leq x \leq 5.$

In Exercises 35 and 36, find the area of the bounded region enclosed by the two curves Draw a figure.

35. $y = x+3,\ y = \sqrt{3x+9}.$

36. $y = 9-8x,\ y = \dfrac{9}{(2x+1)^2}.$

In Exercises 37 and 38, find the volume obtained by revolving about the x-axis the ordinate set of the given function for the specified interval. Draw a figure.

37. $y = \dfrac{1}{2x - 1}, 1 \leq x \leq 4.$ **38.** $y = \sqrt[3]{7x + 1}, 0 \leq x \leq 1.$

In Exercises 39 and 40, find the volume obtained by revolving about the y-axis the ordinate set of the given function for the specified interval. Draw a figure.

39. $y = \sqrt{x^2 + 1}, 0 \leq x \leq 3.$ **40.** $y = \sqrt{x + 1}, 0 \leq x \leq 3.$

In Exercises 41–44, find the area of the ordinate set of y as a function of x by evaluating a definite integral with the parameter t as the variable of integration, for the specified interval. Draw a figure.

41. $x = t^3, y = t^2, 0 \leq t \leq 1.$ **42.** $x = t^2, y = t^3, 0 \leq t \leq 1$

43. $x = t^2, y = (t - 1)^2, 0 \leq t \leq 1.$ (Cf. Example 1, §710.)

44. $x = 4 - t^2, y = 4t - t^3, 0 \leq t \leq 2.$ (Cf. Example 3, §710.)

1014   WORK

The concept of *work* was introduced in §211, where it was shown that if F is a nonnegative force that is an integrable function of distance x, where $a \leq x \leq b$, then the work W done by the force F over the interval $[a, b]$ is:

$$(1) \qquad\qquad W = \int_a^b F(x)dx.$$

We are now in a position to solve work problems that were not amenable to solution when we first were studying them. One reason is that techniques of integration given in this chapter permit the handling of more complex functional relations than before. An even more impelling reason is that we now have at our disposal Bliss's theorem of §515, which states that if f and g are integrable on $[a, b]$, then

$$(2) \qquad\qquad \lim_{|\mathfrak{N}| \to 0} \sum_{i=1}^{n} f(x_i)g(x_i')\Delta x_i = \int_a^b fg = \int_a^b f(x)g(x)dx.$$

The problem we shall concentrate on in this section relates to liquids in containers. This problem is of two types, one that of determining the work done in pumping the contents to a certain height above the rim of the container (where this height may be zero), and the other that of determining the work done by the liquid in flowing out of the container. Since the principles are the same we shall limit ourselves in the general formulation to the former type involving pumping.

Assume, then, that a container C has a liquid of constant density (weight per unit volume) ρ and occupies a bounded region R in space.* Assume furthermore that every horizontal plane section S of R, as a function of vertical distance, is either increasing or decreasing, in the sense defined in §209, and that for every S the area of S exists and is a continuous function of vertical distance. Let the x-axis be chosen to be vertical, directed either upward or downward, and let $S(x)$ be the horizontal plane section of R at abscissa x, with area $\alpha(x) = A(S(x))$. If the region R corresponds to

---

*A set in Euclidean space E_3 is **bounded** if and only if it is contained in a sphere. In the present context the word *region* may be considered to be synonymous with the word *set*. (Cf. §201, *SCC*.)

the vertical interval $[a, b]$, and if c is any abscissa corresponding to a point at least as high as the highest point of R (cf. Fig. 1014-1) we have the theorem:

Theorem. *The work done in raising the liquid occupying the region R described above is*

(3) $$\rho \int_a^b \alpha(x)(c - x)dx \text{ if the x-axis is directed upward,}$$

(4) $$\rho \int_a^b \alpha(x)(x - c)dx \text{ if the x-axis is directed downward.}$$

Proof. We give the details for (3) and Figure 1014-1*a*, and leave those for (4) and Figure 1014-1*b* to the reader. Let $\mathfrak{N} = \{a_0, a_1, \cdots, a_n\}$ be any net on $[a, b]$

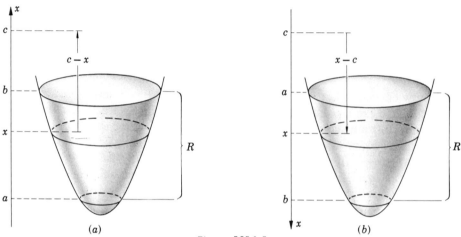

Figure 1014-1

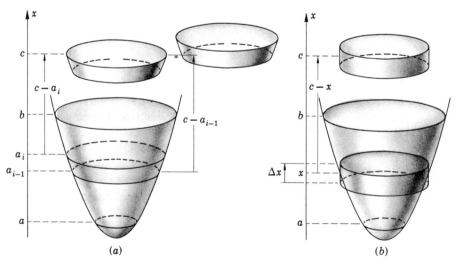

Figure 1014-2

and consider the liquid corresponding to $a_{i-1} \leqq x \leqq a_i$. By the Theorem, §209, the volume ΔV_i of this portion of the liquid is $\int_{a_{i-1}}^{a_i} \alpha(x)dx$, and by the mean value theorem for integrals (§1002), there is a number x_i between a_{i-1} and a_i, such that $\Delta V_i = \alpha(x_i)(a_i - a_{i-1}) = \alpha(x_i)\Delta x_i$. Consequently, the *weight* ΔF_i of this portion of the liquid (that is, the gravitational *force* on it) is got by multiplying the volume by the density:

(5) $$\Delta F_i = \rho\alpha(x_i)\Delta x_i.$$

We now consider the work ΔW_i done in raising the liquid corresponding to the interval $[a_{i-1}, a_i]$ to a point corresponding to c. In the first place, if this liquid were raised uniformly a distance $c - a_i$, the result would be that the newly located liquid would lie *at or below* $x = c$ (cf. Fig. 1014-2a) and as a consequence the work done, which is $\Delta F_i \cdot (c - a_i)$, would be less than or equal to ΔW_i: $\Delta F_i \cdot (c - a_i) \leqq \Delta W_i$. On the other hand, if the liquid for $[a_{i-1}, a_i]$ were raised uniformly a distance $c - a_{i-1}$, the resulting liquid would lie *at or above* $x = c$ (cf. Fig. 1014-2a) and hence $\Delta W_i \leqq \Delta F_i \cdot (c - a_{i-1})$. From the combined inequalities

(6) $$\Delta F_i \cdot (c - a_i) \leqq \Delta W_i \leqq \Delta F_i \cdot (c - a_{i-1}),$$

we infer the existence of a number $x_i' \in [a_{i-1}, a_i]$ such that

(7) $$\Delta W_i = \Delta F_i \cdot (c - x_i').$$

(The number $x_i' \equiv c - (\Delta W_i/\Delta F_i)$ satisfies both the equation (7) and the inequalities $a_{i-1} \leqq x_i' \leqq a_i$.) Substituting from (5), we have

(8) $$\Delta W_i = \rho\alpha(x_i)(c - x_i')\Delta x_i,$$

and consequently the *total* work done is

(9) $$W = \sum_{i=1}^n \Delta W_i = \sum_{i=1}^n \rho\alpha(x_i)(c - x_i')\Delta x_i.$$

Our final problem is to show that the two constants given by (9) and (3) are equal. This is the place where we make use of Bliss's theorem (2), with

(10) $$f(x) \equiv \rho\alpha(x), \quad g(x) \equiv c - x.$$

If ϵ is an arbitrary number there exists a positive number δ such that the inequality $|\mathfrak{N}| < \delta$ implies

(11) $$\left| \sum_{i=1}^n f(x_i)g(x_i')\Delta x_i - \int_a^b fg \right| < \epsilon.$$

Let $\mathfrak{N}$ be *any particular* net on $[a, b]$ of norm less than δ, and let x_i and x_i' be determined as above. Then for the *particular* sum on the right of (9), we have (11), or

(12) $$\left| \sum_{i=1}^n \rho\alpha(x_i)(c - x_i')\Delta x_i - \int_a^b \rho\alpha(x)(c - x)dx \right| < \epsilon,$$

or by (9),

(13) $$\left| W - \rho\int_a^b \alpha(x)(c - x)dx \right| < \epsilon.$$

But the left-hand member of (13) is a nonnegative *constant*, and since ϵ is an arbitrary positive number, this constant must be zero, and the proof is complete.

NOTE. In practice, problems of the type described in the Theorem just proved can be solved by means of a kind of "streamlined" method, as indicated in Figure 1014-2*b*:

(*i*)   Set up a coordinate system, and determine *a*, *b*, and *c*.

(*ii*)   Find the cross section area $\alpha(x)$ for $x \in [a, b]$.

(*iii*)   Find the volume of a "small layer" for x and Δx: $\Delta V = \alpha(x)\Delta x$.

(*iv*)   Find the weight of this "small layer" by multiplying by the density: $\Delta F = \rho\alpha(x)\Delta x$.

(*v*)   Find the distance this "small layer" is raised: $c - x$.

(*vi*)   Find the work done in raising the "small layer" by multiplying (*iv*) and (*v*): $\Delta W = \rho\alpha(x)(c - x)\Delta x$.

(*vii*)   Add the ΔW's and pass to a limit, replacing the summation by an integral and Δx by dx: $W = \rho \int_a^b \alpha(x)(c - x)dx$, where the constant ρ is factored to the front of the integral sign.

In all problems in this book we shall take the density of water to be 62.4 pounds per cubic foot.

Example 1.   A tank has the shape of a right circular cone with vertical axis, vertex at the bottom, altitude 6 feet, and base radius 2 feet. If the tank contains water to a depth of 5 feet, find the work done in pumping water to a height of 4 feet above the top of the tank until the depth is reduced to 2 feet. Also find the work done in pumping to the same height the entire contents of the tank if it is filled to the brim at the start.

Solution.   We draw a sketch in Figure 1014-3*a*, and choose the variable y to measure distances vertically upward from the vertex of the cone. We follow the outline of the preceding Note:

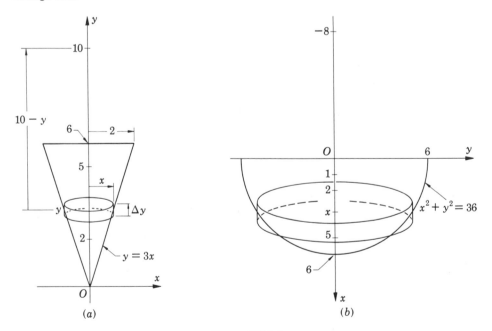

Figure 1014-3

(i) The numbers a, b, and c are $a = 2$, $b = 5$, and $c = 10$.

(ii) The cross section area at distance y is $\pi x^2 = \frac{1}{9}\pi y^2$.

(iii) The volume of a small layer at y of width Δy is $\frac{1}{9}\pi y^2 \Delta y$.

(iv) The weight of this layer is $\frac{1}{9}\pi \rho y^2 \Delta y$.

(v) The distance this layer is raised is $10 - y$.

(vi) The work done in raising the layer is $\frac{1}{9}\pi \rho(10 - y)y^2 \Delta y$.

(vii) The total work done is equal to the integral

$$W = \tfrac{1}{9}\pi\rho \int_2^5 (10 - y)y^2 dy = \tfrac{1}{9}\pi\rho \int_2^5 (10y^2 - y^3)dy = \tfrac{1}{9}\pi\rho[\tfrac{10}{3}y^3 - \tfrac{1}{4}y^4]_2^5$$
$$= \tfrac{1}{9}\pi\rho(\tfrac{3125}{12} - \tfrac{272}{12}) = \tfrac{317}{12}\pi\rho = 5180 \text{ foot-pounds (approximately).}$$

The integral for the work done in emptying the full tank is the same as that just evaluated except for the limits of integration:

$$\tfrac{1}{9}\pi\rho \int_0^6 (10y^2 - y^3)dy = \tfrac{1}{9}\pi\rho[\tfrac{10}{3}y^3 - \tfrac{1}{4}y^4]_0^6 = 44\pi\rho = 8630 \text{ foot-pounds (approximately).}$$

Example 2. A hemispherical tank has a vertical axis of symmetry and radius 6 feet. Water is in the tank to a depth of 4 feet. Find the work done in pumping water from the tank to a height of 8 feet above the top of the tank, until the depth reaches 1 foot.

Solution. As shown in Figure 1014-3b, we shall take a coordinate system with origin at the center of the sphere that includes the hemisphere, for simplicity in relating the variables, with the x-axis directed positively downward and the y-axis directed positively to the right. Then

(i) Depths of 4 feet and 1 foot correspond to $x = 2$ and $x = 5$, respectively, and a height of 8 feet above the tank is given by $x = -8$. Therefore, in Figure 1014-1b, $a = 2$, $b = 5$, and $c = -8$.

(ii) The cross section area at distance x is $\pi y^2 = \pi(36 - x^2)$.

(iii) The volume of a small layer at x of width Δx is $\pi(36 - x^2)\Delta x$.

(iv) The weight of this layer is $\pi\rho(36 - x^2)\Delta x$.

(v) The distance this layer is raised is $x + 8$.

(vi) The work done in raising the layer is $\pi\rho(x + 8)(36 - x^2)\Delta x$.

(vii) The total work done is the integral

$$W = \pi\rho \int_2^5 (x + 8)(36 - x^2)dx = \pi\rho \int_2^5 (288 + 36x - 8x^2 - x^3)dx$$
$$= \pi\rho[288x + 18x^2 - \tfrac{8}{3}x^3 - \tfrac{1}{4}x^4]_2^5 = \pi\rho(288 \cdot 3 + 18 \cdot 21 - 8 \cdot 39 - \tfrac{609}{4})$$
$$= \tfrac{3111}{4}\pi\rho = 152{,}000 \text{ foot-pounds (approximately).}$$

1015 HYDROSTATIC FORCE

A problem whose solution is similar to that of §1014 is that of determining the total force exerted by a liquid on a vertical plane surface immersed in that liquid. Examples are forces on dam walls or on end-plates of fluid containers. The fundamental law of physics that we shall assume is that the pressure (force per unit area) of any liquid is the same in all directions and equal to the product of the density of the liquid and the depth from the surface of the point in question (that is, the pressure is equal to the weight of a column of the liquid having unit horizontal section and height equal to the depth of the point).

Assume that a vertical plane plate P is immersed in a liquid of density ρ. Let the x-axis be chosen to be vertical, directed either upward or downward, with P corresponding to the closed interval $a \leq x \leq b$. Assume that the horizontal section of P at abscissa x is a line segment of length $L(x)$, that $L(x)$ is a continuous function of x, and that for $a \leq u < v \leq b$, the area of the portion of P between u and v is given by the integral $\int_u^v L(x)dx$. If c is the abscissa corresponding to the surface of the liquid (cf. Fig. 1015-1), we have the theorem:

Theorem. *The total force on one side of the plate P described above is*

(1) $\qquad\qquad \rho \displaystyle\int_a^b L(x)(c - x)dx$ *if the x-axis is directed upward,*

(2) $\qquad\qquad \rho \displaystyle\int_a^b L(x)(x - c)dx$ *if the x-axis is directed downward.*

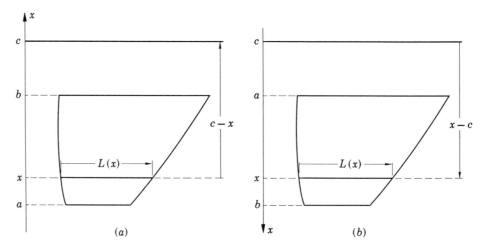

Figure 1015-1

The details of the proof for (1) are very similar to those for (3) of the Theorem, §1014, and are given in §1617, *CWAG* (cf. Fig. 1015-2a). We shall content ourselves here with the analogue of the Note, §1014:

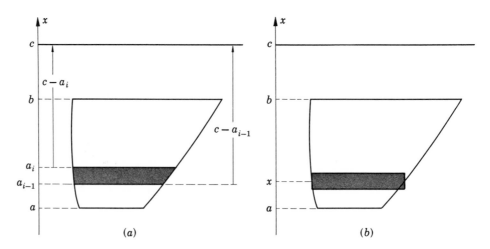

Figure 1015-2

NOTE.   In practice, problems in hydrostatic force of the type just described can be solved by the type of "streamlining" outlined in the Note, §1014, and presented here for case (1) of the preceding Theorem (cf. Fig. 1015-2b):

(*i*)   Set up a coordinate system, and determine a, b, and c.

(*ii*)   Find the cross section length $L(x)$ for $x \in [a, b]$.

(*iii*)   Find the area of a "small strip" for x and Δx: $\Delta A = L(x)\Delta x$.

(*iv*)   Find the depth of this "small strip": $c - x$.

(*v*)   Find the pressure at this "small strip" by multiplying by the density: $\rho \cdot (c - x)$.

(*vi*)   Find the force on the "small strip" by multiplying (*iii*) and (*v*): $\Delta F = \rho L(x)(c - x)\Delta x$.

(*vii*)   Add the ΔF's and pass to a limit, replacing the summation by an integral and Δx by dx: $F = \rho \int_a^b L(x)(c - x)dx$, where the constant ρ is factored to the front of the integral sign.

Example 1.   A vertical plane plate P in the shape of a triangle is immersed in water in such a way that one edge of the plate lies in the surface of the water. Show that the total force on P is equal to the product of its area and the pressure at a point one-third of the distance from the surface of the water to the immersed vertex of P.

Solution.   Choose a coordinate system with origin at the submerged vertex of P, with the x-axis oriented positively upward, let the base of P in the surface of the water have length b, and let the vertical altitude of P be h. (Cf. Fig. 1015-3a.) Since $L(x)$ is a linear function of x, equal to 0 at $x = 0$ and equal to b at $x = h$, $L(x)$ has the form

(3)
$$L(x) = \frac{b}{h}x.$$

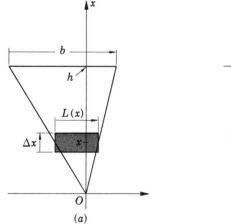

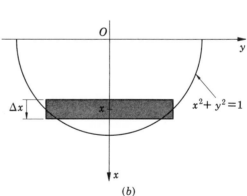

(a)   (b)

Figure 1015-3

We proceed with the seven steps of the preceding Note:

(*i*)   The numbers a, b, and c are $a = 0$, $b = h$, and $c = h$.

(*ii*)   The cross section length at distance x is $L(x) = \dfrac{b}{h}x$.

(*iii*)   The area of a small strip at x of width Δx is $\dfrac{b}{h} x \Delta x$.

(iv)   The depth of this strip is $h - x$.

(v)   The pressure at this strip is $\rho \cdot (h - x)$.

(vi)   The force on this strip is $\rho \dfrac{b}{h} x(h - x)\Delta x$.

(vii)   The total force is equal to the integral

$$F = \rho \frac{b}{h} \int_0^h x(h - x)dx = \frac{\rho b}{h}\left[\tfrac{1}{2}hx^2 - \tfrac{1}{3}x^3\right]_0^h = \tfrac{1}{6}\rho bh^2$$
$$= [\tfrac{1}{2}bh] \cdot [\rho \cdot \tfrac{1}{3}h] = [\text{area of } P] \cdot [\text{pressure at depth } \tfrac{1}{3}h].$$

Example 2. A horizontal trough has a vertical cross section at right angles to its length that is a semicircle of radius 1 foot. (Cf. Fig. 1015-3b.) Find the total force on a vertical end-plate of the trough when it is filled with water.

Solution. As shown in Figure 1015-3b, we choose a coordinate system with origin at the center of the circle containing the semicircle that describes the end-plate, with the x-axis directed positively downward and the y-axis directed positively to the right. Then

(i)   The numbers a, b, and c are $a = 0$, $b = 1$, and $c = 0$.

(ii)   The cross section length at distance x is $2y = 2\sqrt{1 - x^2}$.

(iii)   The area of a small strip at x of width Δx is $2\sqrt{1 - x^2}\,\Delta x$.

(iv)   The depth of this strip is x.

(v)   The pressure at this strip is ρx.

(vi)   The force on this strip is $2\rho x\sqrt{1 - x^2}\,\Delta x$.

(vii)   The total force is equal to the integral

$$F = 2\rho \int_0^1 x\sqrt{1 - x^2}\,dx = -\rho \int_0^1 (1 - x^2)^{\frac{1}{2}}\,d(1 - x^2)$$
$$= -\tfrac{2}{3}\rho(1 - x^2)^{\frac{3}{2}}\,\big|_0^1 = \tfrac{2}{3}\rho = 41.6 \text{ pounds.}$$

1016   EXERCISES

In the following exercises, the density ρ of water should be taken to be 62.4 pounds per cubic foot.

1. A cylindrical tank with vertical axis of symmetry has base radius 3 feet and altitude 7 feet. If the tank is full of water, find the work done in pumping its contents to a point 20 feet above the top of the tank.

2. The tank in Exercise 1 has a tube leading directly to a point 12 feet below the bottom of the tank. Find the work done by the contents in flowing out through the tube.

3. A tank has the shape of a right circular cone with vertical axis, vertex at the bottom, altitude 4 feet, and base radius 3 feet. If the tank is full of water, find the work done in pumping its contents to a point 2 feet above the top of the tank.

4. The tank in Exercise 3 contains water to a depth of 3 feet. Find the work done in pumping this water to the top of the tank.

5. A horizontal trough of length 10 feet has a vertical cross section perpendicular to its length that is a semicircle of radius 2 feet. If the tank is full of water, find the work done in pumping water over the top edge of the trough until the depth reaches 1 foot.

6. In Exercise 5, find the work done in pumping the remaining water, starting at a depth of 1 foot, over the top of the trough.

7. A hemispherical tank has a vertical axis of symmetry and radius 3 feet, and is full of water. Find the work done in lowering the depth by 1 foot if water is pumped to a point 4 feet above the top of the tank.

8. In Exercise 7, find the work done in pumping the remaining water, starting at a depth of 2 feet, to a point 4 feet above the top of the tank.

9. A vertical plane plate P in the shape of a rectangle forms a portion of one face of an aquarium and lies completely below the surface of the water contained in the aquarium. If P has two sides horizontal and two sides vertical, show that the total force on P is equal to the product of the area of P and the pressure at the center of P.

10. If the top edge of P, in Exercise 9, lies in the surface of the water, show that the force on the bottom half of P is 3 times the force on the upper half.

11. The vertical end-plate of a horizontal trough is a trapezoid with vertical axis of symmetry. The two parallel horizontal sides of this trapezoid are of length 1 foot for the lower side and 3 feet for the upper side, and the altitude is 2 feet. Find the total force against this end-plate when the trough is full of water.

12. A horizontal trough has a vertical cross section at right angles to its length that is a semicircle of radius 2 feet, and is filled with water. Find the total force on a vertical end-plate.

11

Logarithmic and Exponential Functions

1101 INTRODUCTION; ALGEBRAIC AND TRANSCENDENTAL FUNCTIONS

The power function* x^b, where b is any rational number, with domain the set $\mathcal{P}$ of all positive numbers, was defined in §411 and its continuity and differentiability properties were discussed in §§411 and 619.   In this chapter we shall present one method of extending the set of values of the exponent b for which the function x^b is defined. This method is to define first the function known as the *natural logarithm function*, denoted ln, and then its inverse, denoted exp. In terms of the latter function we shall define the *general exponential function* a^x and the *general power function* x^b, and establish basic properties for both. Before starting the development of this theory, we should mention that a second method of defining the function x^b for any real b and positive x is by taking limits, or suprema and infima, of values of x^b where b is *rational*. This latter method is used in the author's *The Real Number System*.

As will be seen, the logarithmic and exponential functions defined and treated in this chapter are examples of *transcendental functions*, as opposed to *algebraic functions*, according to the following definition:

Definition. *A function f defined on an interval I is* **algebraic** *there if and only if, for some positive integer n, there exist n + 1 polynomials $A_0(x)$, $A_1(x)$, $\cdots$, $A_n(x)$, where neither $A_0(x)$ nor $A_n(x)$ is the zero polynomial, such that the equation*

$$(1) \qquad A_0(x)f^n(x) + A_1(x)f^{n-1}(x) + \cdots + A_{n-1}(x)f(x) + A_n(x) = 0$$

*In this chapter it will be especially convenient to use elliptic notation, exemplified by letting x^b represent the *function* whose value at x is the *number* x^b.

310

is satisfied identically on I. *(Recall that $f^k(x) \equiv (f(x))^k$.) A function defined on an interval I is* **transcendental** *there if and only if it is not algebraic on I.*

Example 1. The rational function $f(x)/g(x)$, where $f(x)$ and $g(x)$ are polynomials, is algebraic on any interval I where $g(x)$ is nonzero, since if the polynomials $A_0(x)$ and $A_1(x)$ are defined

(2) $$A_0(x) \equiv -g(x), \quad A_1(x) \equiv f(x),$$

then the equation

(3) $$A_0(x)\frac{f(x)}{g(x)} + A_1(x) = 0$$

is satisfied identically on I.

Example 2. The function $\sqrt[n]{x}$ is algebraic on $[0, +\infty)$, since if the polynomials $A_0(x)$, $A_1(x), \cdots, A_n(x)$ are defined

(4) $$A_0(x) \equiv 1, \quad A_1(x) = A_2(x) = \cdots = A_{n-1}(x) \equiv 0, \quad A_n(x) \equiv -x,$$

then the equation

(5) $$A_0(x)(\sqrt[n]{x})^n + A_1(x)(\sqrt[n]{x})^{n-1} + \cdots + A_n(x) = 0$$

is satisfied identically for $x \geq 0$.

Example 3. Show that the function $x/\sqrt{x^2 + 4}$ is algebraic on $(-\infty, +\infty) = \mathcal{R}$.

Solution. Define the polynomials

(6) $$A_0(x) \equiv x^2 + 4, \quad A_1(x) \equiv 0, \quad A_2(x) \equiv -x^2.$$

Then the equation

(7) $$A_0(x)\left(\frac{x}{\sqrt{x^2 + 4}}\right)^2 + A_1(x)\frac{x}{\sqrt{x^2 + 4}} + A_2 = 0$$

is satisfied identically for $x \in \mathcal{R}$.

It can be proved that the set of all functions algebraic on an interval I is an algebra, and therefore closed under linear combinations and products. Furthermore, algebraic functions are closed under composition (an algebraic function of an algebraic function is an algebraic function). Therefore, a function obtained by any finite sequence of sums, products, quotients, formation of nth roots, and multiplication by constants, starting with any rational function, is always an algebraic function. In addition, certain functions satisfying an equation of the form (1), where $n > 4$, are algebraic although they cannot be obtained as the result of a finite sequence of "algebraic operations" of the type described above. (For a discussion of *algebraic numbers*, which form a structure similar to that of algebraic functions, see H. Pollard, *The Theory of Algebraic Numbers* (Carus Mathematical Monograph No. 9, 1950) and I. Niven, *Irrational Numbers* (Carus Mathematical Monograph No. 11, 1956). These monographs are published by The Mathematical Association of America.)

In spite of the apparent generality of the concept of algebraic function, the class of all algebraic functions on an interval I falls far short of exhausting the class of all functions on I, even the restricted class of those that have derivatives of all orders.

The following theorem (a proof of which is given in H§2109, *CWAG*) makes an explicit statement regarding the existence of transcendental functions. (The functions ln and exp of this theorem are defined in §§1102 and 1104 of this chapter.)

Theorem. *The functions* exp, sine, *and* cosine *are transcendental on the interval* $(-\infty, +\infty) = \mathfrak{R}$, *and the function* ln *is transcendental on the interval* $(0, +\infty) = \mathcal{P}$.

1102   THE FUNCTION ln

The **natural logarithm** function ln is the function whose domain is the set $\mathcal{P}$ of positive numbers, and whose value at $x > 0$ is

$$(1) \qquad \ln x \equiv \int_1^x \frac{1}{t}\, dt = \int_1^x \frac{dt}{t}.$$

Since the function $1/t$ is continuous on the interval $(0, +\infty)$, the function ln x exists for every $x > 0$. Evidently, ln $1 = 0$; if $x > 1$, ln x is equal to the area of the ordinate set

$$(2) \qquad \left\{(t, y)\ \Big|\ 1 \leqq t \leqq x, 0 \leqq y \leqq \frac{1}{t}\right\};$$

and if $0 < x < 1$, ln x is the negative of the area of the ordinate set

$$(3) \qquad \left\{(t, y)\ \Big|\ x \leqq t \leqq 1, 0 \leqq y \leqq \frac{1}{t}\right\}.$$

(Cf. Fig. 1102-1.)

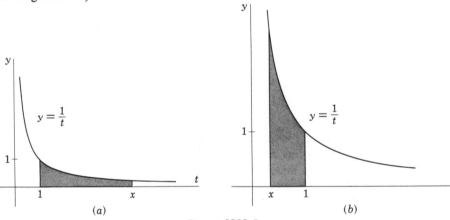

(a)   (b)

Figure 1102-1

If x is any positive number, the *number* ln x is called the **natural logarithm** of x. We shall now describe some of the salient features of the natural logarithm function.

I.   Monotonic behavior. *The function* ln x *is strictly increasing on* $\mathcal{P}$:

$$(4) \qquad 0 < x_1 < x_2 \Rightarrow \ln x_1 < \ln x_2.$$

This fact follows from

$$(5) \qquad \ln x_2 - \ln x_1 = \int_1^{x_2} \frac{dt}{t} - \int_1^{x_1} \frac{dt}{t} = \int_{x_1}^{x_2} \frac{dt}{t},$$

by the Corollary to Theorem I, §1003, and since the function $1/t$ is positive on $[x_1, x_2]$, the last quantity in (5) is *positive* for $x_1 < x_2$ by the Theorem, §1001.

Since $\ln 1 = 0$, it follows that $\ln x > 0$ if $x > 1$ and $\ln x < 0$ if $0 < x < 1$.

II. Continuity and differentiability. Since $\ln x$ is defined as an indefinite integral *it is continuous on* $(0, +\infty)$ by Theorem IV, §1003. Since the integrand $1/t$ in (1) is continuous on $(0, +\infty)$, $\ln x$ *is differentiable on* $(0, +\infty)$ by Theorem I, §1005, *and its derivative is*

$$(6) \qquad\qquad D_x \ln x = \frac{1}{x}, \quad 0 < x < +\infty,$$

or in differential notation,

$$(7) \qquad\qquad d \ln x = \frac{dx}{x}, \quad 0 < x < +\infty.$$

From (6) we see that the derivative of $\ln x$ is everywhere positive, and we have another verification of the fact that $\ln x$ is a strictly increasing function on $(0, +\infty)$.

If u is a positive-valued differentiable function of x, then the chain rule (§ 610) gives a generalization of (6):

$$(8) \qquad\qquad D_x \ln u = \frac{D_x u}{u},$$

or, in terms of differentials,

$$(9) \qquad\qquad d \ln u = \frac{du}{u}.$$

III. Range of ln. *The range of the function* $\ln x$ *is the set* $\Re$ *of all real numbers.* This fact is a consequence of two limit theorems. The first of these is:

$$(10) \qquad\qquad \lim_{x \to +\infty} \ln x = +\infty.$$

Proof. Since $\ln x$ is an increasing function, we have only to prove that $\ln x$ is *unbounded above*. To this end, we consider the particular value of x, $x = 2^n$, where n is a positive integer, and write

$$(11) \qquad \ln 2^n = \int_1^{2^n} \frac{dt}{t} = \int_1^2 \frac{dt}{t} + \int_2^4 \frac{dt}{t} + \int_4^8 \frac{dt}{t} + \cdots + \int_{2^{n-1}}^{2^n} \frac{dt}{t}$$

(cf. Fig. 1102-2). Since for $2^{i-1} \leqq t \leqq 2^i$, $\frac{1}{t} \geqq \frac{1}{2^i}$, for $i = 1, 2, \cdots, n$,

$$(12) \qquad \int_{2^{i-1}}^{2^i} \frac{dt}{t} \geqq \int_{2^{i-1}}^{2^i} \frac{1}{2^i} dt = \frac{1}{2^i}(2^i - 2^{i-1}) = \frac{2^{i-1}}{2^i}(2 - 1) = \frac{1}{2},$$

the right-hand member of (11) is greater than or equal to the sum of n terms each of which is equal to $\frac{1}{2}$, and therefore

$$(13) \qquad\qquad \ln 2^n \geqq \frac{n}{2},$$

and $\ln x$ is unbounded above.

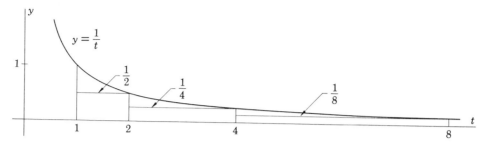

Figure 1102-2

The second limit theorem is:

(14) $$\lim_{x\to 0+} \ln x = -\infty.$$

Proof. Since $\ln x$ is an increasing function, we have only to prove that $\ln x$ is *unbounded below*. To this end, we consider the particular value of x, $x = 2^{-n}$, where n is a positive integer, and write

(15) $$\ln 2^{-n} = \int_1^{2^{-n}} \frac{1}{t}\, dt,$$

and evaluate the integral on the right of (15) by means of the substitution $u = 1/t$, or $t = 1/u$ (cf. Theorem II, § 1011):

(16) $$\int_1^{2^{-n}} \frac{1}{t}\, dt = \int_1^{2^n} u\left(-\frac{1}{u^2}\, du\right) = -\int_1^{2^n} \frac{1}{u}\, du = -\ln 2^n.$$

Since $\ln 2^n$ is unbounded above, by (13), $\ln 2^{-n}$ is unbounded below.

IV. The graph of $\ln x$. The properties of $\ln x$ obtained in I–III, above, enable us to draw its graph. As shown in Figure 1102-3, $\ln x$ crosses the x-axis with slope 1, and although $\ln x$ is an increasing function its rate of increase decreases as $x \to +\infty$. The fact that $\ln x \to -\infty$ as $x \to 0+$ is expressed by the asymptotic nature of the y-axis. Values of $\ln x$ are tabulated in Table III, page 370.

V. Concavity. Since the second derivative of $\ln x$ is everywhere negative:

(17) $$D_x^2 \ln x = D_x(1/x) = -1/x^2 < 0,$$

the graph of $y = \ln x$ is everywhere concave down.

Example 1. Find the equation of the tangent line to the graph of $y = \ln x$ at the point $(x_0, \ln x_0)$.

Solution. Since the slope of the tangent line at $(x, \ln x)$ is $D_x \ln x = 1/x$, the slope at $(x_0, \ln x_0)$ is $1/x_0$, and the equation of the tangent line is

$$y - \ln x_0 = \frac{1}{x_0}(x - x_0).$$

Example 2. Establish the inequality

(18) $$\ln x < x - 1, \quad x \in \mathcal{P}\setminus\{1\}.$$

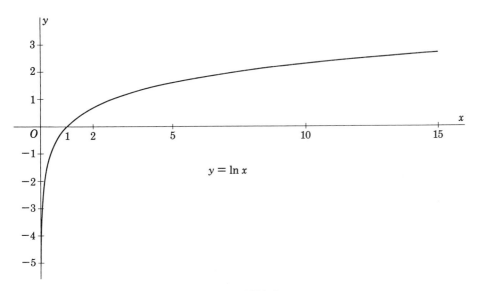

Figure 1102-3

Solution. By Theorem III, § 806, since the second derivative of ln x is everywhere negative, for $x > 0$, the graph of $y = \ln x$ lies below every tangent line, except at the point of tangency. In particular, since the equation of the line tangent to $y = \ln x$ at the point $(1, 0)$ is $y = x - 1$ (cf. Example 1), the preceding statement takes the form of (18).

1103   LAWS OF ln

We shall now establish the following laws of the natural logarithm function:

I. $\ln (xy) = \ln x + \ln y$, x and $y \in \mathcal{P}$.

II. $\ln \left(\dfrac{x}{y} \right) = \ln x - \ln y$, x and $y \in \mathcal{P}$.

IIIa. $\ln (x^n) = n \ln x$, $x \in \mathcal{P}, n \in \mathcal{I}$.

IIIb. $\ln \sqrt[n]{x} = \dfrac{\ln x}{n}$, $x \in \mathcal{P}, n \in \mathcal{R}$.

III. $\ln (x^r) = r \ln x$, $x \in \mathcal{P}, r \in \mathcal{Q}$.

Proof of I.   We start by writing

(1) $\ln (xy) = \displaystyle\int_1^{xy} \frac{dt}{t} = \int_1^x \frac{dt}{t} + \int_x^{xy} \frac{dt}{t} = \ln x + \int_x^{xy} \frac{dt}{t}.$

Since $\ln y = \displaystyle\int_1^y \frac{dt}{t}$, we wish to prove that

(2) $\displaystyle\int_x^{xy} \frac{dt}{t} = \int_1^y \frac{dt}{t}.$

This is done by means of the substitution of $u = t/x$ in the first integral of (2), with $t = xu$ and $dt = x\,du$ since x is constant:

$$(3) \qquad \int_x^{xy} \frac{dt}{t} = \int_1^y \frac{x\,du}{xu} = \int_1^y \frac{du}{u} = \int_1^y \frac{dt}{t}.$$

Proof of II.   By I,

$$(4) \qquad \ln y = \ln\left[x\left(\frac{y}{x}\right)\right] = \ln x + \ln\left(\frac{y}{x}\right),$$

and II follows by subtraction of $\ln x$.

Proof of IIIa.   If n is a *positive* integer, then by the extension of I to n factors,

$$(5) \qquad \ln x^n = \ln(x \cdot x \cdot \, \cdots \, \cdot x) = \ln x + \ln x + \cdots + \ln x = n \ln x.$$

If n is a *negative* integer and $n = -m$ where m is a *positive* integer, then by II and (5),

$$(6) \qquad \ln x^n = \ln x^{-m} = \ln(1/x^m) = \ln 1 - \ln x^m = 0 - m \ln x = n \ln x.$$

Finally, if $n = 0$, IIIa reduces to $\ln 1 = 0$.

Proof of IIIb.   By IIIa,

$$(7) \qquad \ln x = \ln\left(\left(\sqrt[n]{x}\right)^n\right) = n \ln \sqrt[n]{x},$$

and IIIb follows by division by n.

Proof of III.   Let $r = p/q$, where p is an integer and q is a positive integer.   Then by IIIa and IIIb,

$$(8) \qquad \ln x^r = \ln\left(\left(\sqrt[q]{x}\right)^p\right) = p \ln \sqrt[q]{x} = p\left(\frac{1}{q} \ln x\right) = r \ln x.$$

Example.   Prove that for any positive number x,

$$(9) \qquad \ln \frac{1}{x} = -\ln x.$$

First solution.   If $1/x$ is substituted for y in I, we have

$$\ln x + \ln(1/x) = \ln(x/x) = \ln 1 = 0, \text{ whence } \ln(1/x) = -\ln x.$$

Second solution.   Replace x by 1 and y by x in II.

Third solution.   Let $r = -1$ in III.

1104   THE FUNCTION exp

The function ln has an inverse with domain $\mathcal{R}$ and range $\mathcal{P}$, by Theorem I, §410, and properties I, II, and III, §1102.   This inverse is denoted exp, and is thus defined:

$$(1) \qquad y = \exp x = \exp(x) \iff x = \ln y, \quad x \in \mathcal{R}, y \in \mathcal{P}.$$

The graph of $y = \exp x$ is obtained from that of $y = \ln x$ by reflection with respect to the first-quadrant bisector $y = x$ (Fig. 1104-1).

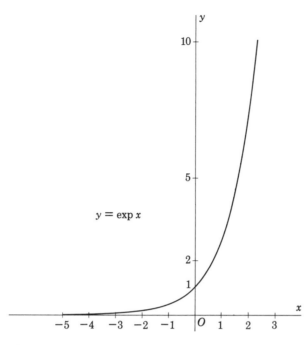

$y = \exp x$

Figure 1104-1

Since ln and exp are inverse functions, we have (cf. (7) and (8), §502, *PCLA*):

(2) $\ln (\exp x) = x$ for $x \in \Re$,

(3) $\exp (\ln x) = x$ for $x \in \wp$.

1105 GENERAL CHARACTERISTICS

I. Monotonic behavior. Since the function $\ln x$ is strictly increasing on $(0, +\infty)$ with range $(-\infty, +\infty)$, *the function* $\exp x$ *is strictly increasing on* $(-\infty, +\infty)$ *with range* $(0, +\infty)$. Since $\ln 1 = 0$, $\exp 0 = 1$, so that $\exp x > 1$ if $x > 0$ and $0 < \exp x < 1$ if $x < 0$.

II. Continuity and differentiability. Since $\ln x$ is continuous and differentiable on $(0, +\infty)$, with a nonzero derivative there, $\exp x$ *is continuous and differentiable on* $(-\infty, +\infty)$ (cf. the Theorem, §618). Furthermore, the derivative $D_x y$ of $y = \exp x$ is the reciprocal of the derivative $D_y x$ of $x = \ln y$, and therefore, from (3), §1102, $D_x y = 1/(1/y) = y = \exp x$, and *the derivative of* $\exp x$ *is* $\exp x$ *itself:*

(1) $D_x \exp x = \exp x$,

or in differential notation,

(2) $d \exp x = (\exp x)dx$.

Since $\exp x$ is everywhere positive, so is its derivative, and we see once more that $\exp x$ is a strictly increasing function.

If u is any differentiable function, then by the chain rule (§ 610), we have from (1):

(3) $$D_x \exp u = (\exp u)D_x u,$$

or in differential notation,

(4) $$d \exp u = (\exp u)du.$$

III. Limits at infinity. The two limit theorems (7) and (11), §1102, for the function ln x take the following forms for the function exp x (cf. Fig. 1104-1):

(5) $$\lim_{x \to +\infty} \exp x = +\infty,$$

(6) $$\lim_{x \to -\infty} \exp x = 0.$$

The x-axis is an asymptote for the graph of $y = \exp x$.

IV. Concavity. Since the second derivative of exp x is everywhere positive:

(7) $$D_x{}^2 \exp x = D_x \exp x = \exp x > 0,$$

the graph of $y = \exp x$ is everywhere concave up.

Example. Find the first and second derivatives of the function exp $(-x^2)$, and sketch its graph, indicating all local extrema, points of inflection, asymptotes, and symmetry.

Solution. If $y = f(x) \equiv \exp(-x^2)$, then, by (4),

(8) $$\frac{dy}{dx} = f'(x) = \exp(-x^2)\frac{d}{dx}(-x^2) = -2x \exp(-x^2),$$

(9) $$\frac{d^2y}{dx^2} = f''(x) = -2 \exp(-x^2) + 4x^2 \exp(-x^2) = 2(2x^2 - 1) \exp(-x^2).$$

Since $f'(x) > 0$ for $x < 0$, and $f'(x) < 0$ for $x > 0$, f is increasing on $(-\infty, 0]$ and decreasing on $[0, +\infty)$, and has a global maximum value of exp $0 = 1$ at $x = 0$. By (9) the graph is concave down on $(-\frac{1}{2}\sqrt{2}, \frac{1}{2}\sqrt{2})$, and is concave up on $(-\infty, -\frac{1}{2}\sqrt{2}) \cup (\frac{1}{2}\sqrt{2}, +\infty)$. Therefore $(-\frac{1}{2}\sqrt{2}, \exp(-\frac{1}{2}))$ and $(\frac{1}{2}\sqrt{2}, \exp(-\frac{1}{2}))$ are points of inflection. The graph, shown in

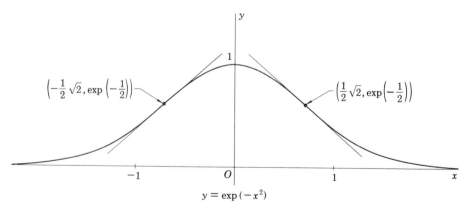

$$y = \exp(-x^2)$$

Figure 1105-1

Figure 1105-1, can be plotted with the aid of values of exp x tabulated in Table V, page 373. It is symmetric with respect to the y-axis and has the x-axis as horizontal asymptote.

The curve in Figure 1105-1 is closely related to the graph of the "density function of a normal distribution," important in probability and statistics.

1106   LAWS OF exp

Corresponding to the laws of ln, §1103, are the following laws of exp:

   I.   exp x exp y = exp$(x + y)$, x and $y \in \mathcal{R}$.
   II.   exp x/exp y = exp$(x - y)$, x and $y \in \mathcal{R}$.
  III.   (exp $x)^y$ = exp(rx), $x \in \mathcal{R}, r \in \mathcal{Q}$.

Proof of I.   Let $u \equiv$ exp x, $v \equiv$ exp y, $w \equiv$ exp$(x + y)$. Then $x = \ln u, y = \ln v$, and $x + y = \ln w$. Since $\ln w = \ln u + \ln v = \ln (uv)$, by I, §1103, it follows that $w = uv$, since ln is a one-to-one mapping, and I is true.

Proof of II.   By I, exp x = exp$((x - y) + y)$ = exp$(x - y)$ exp y, and II follows by division by exp y.

Proof of III.   Let $u \equiv$ exp x and $v \equiv$ exp(rx). Then $x = \ln u$ and $rx = \ln v$. Since $\ln v = r(\ln u) = \ln u^r$, by III, §1103, $v = u^r$ and III is true.

Example.   Prove that for every real number x,

(1)
$$\exp(-x) = \frac{1}{\exp x}.$$

First solution.   If $-x$ is substituted for y in I, we have exp x exp $(-x)$ = exp $(x - x)$ = exp 0 = 1, by I, §1105, whence exp $(-x) = 1/\text{exp } x$.

Second solution.   Replace x by 0 and y by x in II.

Third solution.   Let $r = -1$ in III.

1107   THE NUMBER e

The number e is defined:

(1)
$$e \equiv \exp 1.$$

That is, the number e is the (positive) number whose natural logarithm is equal to 1: $\ln e = 1$, or in other words the number greater than 1 such that the ordinate set

(2)
$$\left\{(x, y) \,\middle|\, 1 \leq x \leq e, \; 0 \leq y \leq \frac{1}{x}\right\}$$

has area 1 (cf. Fig. 1107-1). In §1114, *SCC*, we shall develop methods of computing e to any desired degree of accuracy. A crude approximation can be obtained by use of Figure 1107-1 (cf. Ex. 49, §1108). To five decimal places (cf. Example 1, §1114, *SCC*),

(3)
$$e = 2.71828.$$

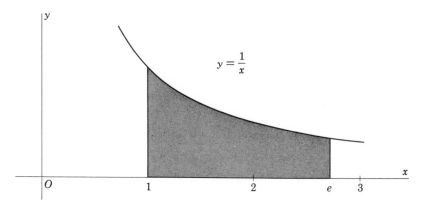

Figure 1107-1

1108 EXERCISES

In Exercises 1–4, show that the given function is algebraic on $\mathfrak{R}$.

1. $\sqrt{x^2 + 5}$.   **2.** $|x|$.   **3.** $x + \sqrt{x^2 + 5}$.   **4.** $|x| + 1$.

In Exercises 5–12, find the indicated derivative or differential, assuming a domain for which the composite function is defined.

5. $D_x \ln(x^2 + 1)$.   **6.** $D_t \ln(3t^4 + t^2)$.   **7.** $D_r (r \ln r)$.   **8.** $D_s \dfrac{\ln s^2}{s}$.

9. $d \ln(u^2 + 2)$.   **10.** $d \ln(v^3 + v)$.   **11.** $d \ln \cos w^2$.   **12.** $d \ln \sin^2 y$.

In Exercises 13–22, estimate to 5 decimal places the value of the given quantity without the use of tables, by means of the following data, given to 5 decimal places:

$$\ln 2 = 0.69315, \quad \ln 3 = 1.09861, \quad \ln 5 = 1.60944.$$

(The digit in the fifth place to the right of the decimal point in the answer may be incorrect because of accumulated round-off error.)

13. $\ln 4$.   **14.** $\ln 6$.   **15.** $\ln 8$.   **16.** $\ln 9$.   **17.** $\ln 10$.

18. $\ln 0.4$.   **19.** $\ln 1.5$.   **20.** $\ln 2.25$.   **21.** $\ln \sqrt{5}$.   **22.** $\ln \sqrt[3]{2}$.

In Exercises 23–30, find the indicated derivative or differential.

23. $D_x \exp x^2$.   **24.** $D_y \exp(y^2 + 3)$.   **25.** $D_u(u \exp u)$.   **26.** $D_v \dfrac{\exp v}{v}$.

27. $d \exp r^3$.   **28.** $d \exp(1 - s^2)$.   **29.** $d \exp \cos w^2$.   **30.** $d \exp \sin^2 z$.

In Exercises 31–34, estimate the value of the given quantity without the use of tables, by means of the following data (cf. Exs. 13–22):

$$\exp 0.69315 = 2, \quad \exp 1.09861 = 3, \quad \exp 1.60944 = 5.$$

Suggestion: Consider sums and differences of the given values of the independent variable.

31. $\exp 2.70805$.   **32.** $\exp 3.21888$.   **33.** $\exp(-0.40546)$.   **34.** $\exp 0.51083$.

35. Show that the equation of the line tangent to the graph of $y = \exp x$ at $(x_0, \exp x_0)$ is

$$y - \exp x_0 = (\exp x_0)(x - x_0).$$

36. Establish the inequality

(1) $$\exp x > 1 + x, \quad x \neq 0.$$

In Exercises 37–44, simplify the given expression.

37. $\ln(\exp(x^2))$.   **38.** $\ln((\exp x)^2)$.   **39.** $\ln((\exp x)^3)$.   **40.** $\ln(\exp(x^3))$.

41. $\exp(\ln(x^2))$.   **42.** $\exp(2 \ln x)$.   **43.** $\exp(3 \ln x)$.   **44.** $\exp(\ln(x^3))$.

In Exercises 45–47, sketch the graph of the given function, and show that there is no point of inflection. (Cf. Tables III and V, pages 370 and 373.)

45. $\ln|x|, \ x \in \mathcal{R} \backslash \{0\}$.   **46.** $\ln x^2, \ x \in \mathcal{R} \backslash \{0\}$.   **47.** $\exp(-x), \ x \in \mathcal{R}$.

48. Sketch the graph of the function $\ln(x^2 + 1)$, and show that the points $(\pm 1, \ln 2)$ are points of inflection and that the origin is an absolute minimum point. (Cf. Table III, p. 370.)

49. Let g be the linear function whose graph is the secant line through the points $(1, 1)$ and $(12/5, 5/12)$ of the curve $y = 1/x$, and let ϕ and ψ be the linear functions whose graphs are the tangent lines to the curve $y = 1/x$ at the points $(3/2, 2/3)$ and $(5/2, 2/5)$, respectively. Establish the inequalities

$$\int_1^{2.4} \frac{dx}{x} < \int_1^{2.4} g = \frac{119}{120} < 1,$$

$$\int_1^3 \frac{dx}{x} > \int_1^2 \phi + \int_2^3 \psi = \frac{2}{3} + \frac{2}{5} = \frac{16}{15} > 1,$$

and thereby conclude that $2.4 < e < 3$.

50. Prove that

(2) $$\lim_{h \to 0} (1 + h)^{1/h} = \lim_{n \to +\infty} \left(1 + \frac{1}{n}\right)^n = e.$$

Suggestions: Since the derivative of $\ln x$ at $x = 1$ is 1, $\lim_{h \to 0} \dfrac{1}{h}[\ln (1 + h) - \ln 1] =$

$\lim_{h \to 0} \ln (1 + h)^{1/h} = 1$. Conclude by using the continuity of exp at 0. (Cf. the Theorem, §506.)

1109   THE GENERAL EXPONENTIAL FUNCTION a^x

If a is any positive number and x any real number, the number a^x is *defined:*

(1) $$a^x \equiv \exp(x \ln a), \quad x \in \mathcal{R}, \quad a \in \mathcal{P}.$$

The number a^x is called a **power** of a, with **base** a and **exponent** x. From the form of (1) we see that a^x is *always a positive number*, and that when $x = 0$ the right-hand member of (1) reduces to $\exp 0 = 1$ (by I, §1105), or:

(2) $$a^0 = 1.$$

If $a = 1$, the right-hand member of (1) again reduces to $\exp 0 = 1$, so that

(3) $$1^x = 1 \text{ for } x \in \mathcal{R}.$$

Furthermore, if x is any rational number, $x = r$, then the right-hand member of (1) is equal to exp (ln a^r), by III, §1103, and by (3), §1104, this in turn reduces to a^r. In other words, the definition (1) is an *extension* of the definition of a^r if r is rational, or, to put it in other terms, if a is a positive constant, the function a^r with domain Q, as defined in §411, is a *restriction* of the function a^x with domain $\Re$, as defined by (1). To put it still differently, the notation a^x is *consistent* with the notation a^r previously used in case x is equal to a rational number r. (For example, $a^1 = a$, and $a^2 = a \cdot a$.)

In case a is the positive number e defined in §1107, the right-hand member of (1) becomes exp $(x \ln e) = \exp (x \cdot 1) = \exp x$. In other words, as functions of x, the two functions exp x and e^x are *identical*:

(4) $\exp x = e^x, \quad x \in \Re.$

In the future we shall use these two notations interchangeably.

Since, for any fixed positive number a, the function a^x is defined as the *composite* of the two functions exp u and $u = (\ln a) \cdot x$ each of which is everywhere continuous and everywhere differentiable, the function a^x is everywhere continuous and everywhere differentiable. Furthermore, by the chain rule (§ 610),

$$D_x(a^x) = D_u(\exp u) \cdot D_x u = \exp u \cdot D_x((\ln a)x) = (a^x)(\ln a),$$

and we have the differentiation formula:

(5) $D_x(a^x) = (\ln a)a^x,$

or in differential notation,

(6) $d(a^x) = (\ln a)a^x \, dx.$

If u is *any* differentiable function (this u is not to be confused with the u of the preceding paragraph), then by the chain rule we have from (5)

(7) $D_x(a^u) = (\ln a)a^u \, D_x u,$

or in differential notation,

(8) $d(a^u) = (\ln a)a^u \, du.$

The monotonic behavior of the function a^x, if $a > 0$ and $a \neq 1$, can be seen from (5): If $a > 1$, then $\ln a > 0$ and hence $D_x(a^x) > 0$, and a^x is strictly increasing; if $0 < a < 1$, then $\ln a < 0$ and hence $D_x(a^x) < 0$, and a^x is strictly decreasing. Furthermore, since for $a > 0$ and $a \neq 1$ the function $(\ln a) \cdot x$ with domain $\Re$ has range $\Re$, we can conclude from the form of (1) and the fact that the range of exp is $\mathcal{P}$ (cf. Fig. 1109-1) the following two statements:

(9)   If $a > 1$, a^x is strictly increasing on $\Re$, with range $\mathcal{P}$, and

$$\lim_{x \to +\infty} a^x = +\infty, \quad \lim_{x \to -\infty} a^x = 0.$$

(10)   If $0 < a < 1$, a^x is strictly decreasing on $\Re$, with range $\mathcal{P}$, and

$$\lim_{x \to +\infty} a^x = 0, \quad \lim_{x \to -\infty} a^x = +\infty.$$

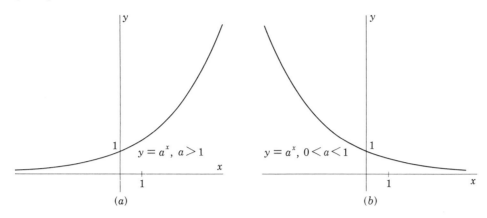

Figure 1109-1

Since the second derivative of a^x is $D_x^2(a^x) = D_x[(\ln a)a^x] = (\ln a)^2\, a^x > 0$, the graph of $y = a^x$ is always concave up for $a > 0$ and $a \neq 1$.

Finally, let us note that (1) is equivalent, by (1), §1104, to

$$(11) \qquad\qquad \ln(a^x) = x \ln a, \quad x \in \mathcal{R}, \quad a \in \mathcal{P}.$$

In other words, law III, §1103, is now extended to arbitrary real exponents r.

Example 1. If $a > 0$, show that a^3, as defined by (1), is equal to $a \cdot a \cdot a$.

Solution. We substitute $x = 3$ in (1), and obtain

$$a^3 = \exp(3 \ln a) = \exp(\ln a + \ln a + \ln a)$$
$$= \exp(\ln(a \cdot a \cdot a)) = a \cdot a \cdot a.$$

NOTE. Multiple-story exponentials are defined "from the top down" thus:

$$(12) \qquad\qquad a^{b^c} \equiv a^{(b^c)}, \; a^{b^{c^d}} \equiv a^{\left(b^{c^d}\right)} = a^{\left(b^{(c^d)}\right)}, \cdots.$$

Example 2. $2^{2^3} = 2^8 = 256, \quad (2^2)^3 = 4^3 = 64, \quad 2^{3^2} = 2^9 = 512, \quad (2^3)^2 = 8^2 = 64,$
$2^{3^3} = 2^{27} = 134{,}217{,}728, \quad (2^3)^3 = 8^3 = 512, \quad 2^{2^{2^2}} = 2^{2^4} = 2^{16} = 65{,}536.$

1110 LAWS OF EXPONENTS

The following laws of exponents follow from the definition (1), §1109, of a^x:

  I. $a^x a^y = a^{x+y}, \quad x$ and $y \in \mathcal{R}, \quad a \in \mathcal{P}.$
  II. $a^x / a^y = a^{x-y}, \quad x$ and $y \in \mathcal{R}, \quad a \in \mathcal{P}.$
  III. $(a^x)^y = a^{xy}, \quad x$ and $y \in \mathcal{R}, \quad a \in \mathcal{P}.$
  IV. $(ab)^x = a^x b^x, \quad x \in \mathcal{R}, \quad a$ and $b \in \mathcal{P}.$
  V. $(a/b)^x = a^x / b^x, \quad x \in \mathcal{R}, \quad a$ and $b \in \mathcal{P}.$

Proof of I. By I, §1106, $a^x a^y = e^{x \ln a}\, e^{y \ln a} = e^{(x \ln a + y \ln a)} = e^{(x+y)\ln a} = a^{x+y}.$

Proof of II. By II, §1106, $a^x / a^y = e^{x \ln a} / e^{y \ln a} = e^{(x \ln a - y \ln a)} = e^{(x-y)\ln a} = a^{x-y}.$

Proof of III. By (11), §1109, $(a^x)^y = e^{y \ln (a^x)} = e^{y(x \ln a)} = e^{xy \ln a} = a^{xy}$.

Proof of IV. By I, §1103, and I, §1106, $(ab)^x = e^{x \ln (ab)} = e^{x (\ln a + \ln x)} = e^{x \ln a + x \ln b} = e^{x \ln a}e^{x \ln b} = a^x b^x$.

Proof of V. By II, §1103, and II, §1106, $(a/b)^x = e^{x \ln(a/b)} = e^{x(\ln a - \ln b)} = e^{x \ln a - x \ln b} = e^{x \ln a}/e^{x \ln b} = a^x/b^x$.

NOTE. With $x = 0$, formula II gives

(1) $$\frac{1}{a^y} = a^{-y}, \quad y \in \mathfrak{R}, \quad a \in \mathcal{P}.$$

Example. Differentiate $\dfrac{\sin x}{e^x}$.

First solution. $D_x \dfrac{\sin x}{e^x} = \dfrac{e^x \cos x - (\sin x)e^x}{(e^x)^2} = \dfrac{e^x(\cos x - \sin x)}{e^{2x}} = \dfrac{\cos x - \sin x}{e^x}$.

Second solution. $D_x(e^{-x} \sin x) = e^{-x} \cos x - e^{-x} \sin x = e^{-x}(\cos x - \sin x)$.

1111   THE GENERAL POWER FUNCTION x^b

If b is any real constant, then the power function x^b with domain $\mathcal{P}$ (the set of positive real numbers) is defined as in §1109:

(1) $$x^b \equiv e^{b \ln x}, \quad x \in \mathcal{P}, \quad b \in \mathfrak{R}.$$

The principal properties of the function x^b are listed (proofs are left to the reader):

I. If $b = 0$, then x^b is the *constant function* 1:

(2) $$x^0 = 1.$$

II. If $b > 0$, then x^b is a *strictly increasing* function with range $\mathcal{P}$, and (cf. **Fig. 1111**-1*a*, *b*):

(3) $$\lim_{x \to +\infty} x^b = +\infty, \quad \lim_{x \to 0+} x^b = 0.$$

III. If $b < 0$, then x^b is a *strictly decreasing* function with range $\mathcal{P}$, and (cf. **Fig. 1111**-1*c*):

(4) $$\lim_{x \to +\infty} x^b = 0, \quad \lim_{x \to 0+} x^b = +\infty.$$

IV. If b is any real constant, then the function x^b is continuous and differentiable on $\mathcal{P}$, and

(5) $$D_x(x^b) = bx^{b-1},$$

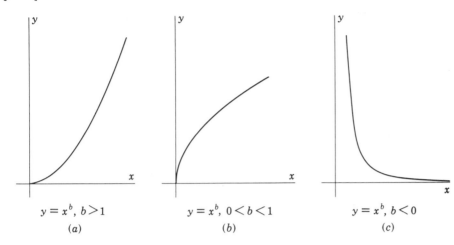

$y = x^b, b > 1$
(a)

$y = x^b, 0 < b < 1$
(b)

$y = x^b, b < 0$
(c)

Figure 1111-1

or in differential notation,

(6) $$d(x^b) = bx^{b-1}\, dx.$$

If u is a positive-valued differentiable function of x, then:

(7) $$D_x(u^b) = bu^{b-1}\, D_x u,$$

or in terms of differentials,

(8) $$d(u^b) = bu^{b-1}\, du.$$

Since $D_x{}^2(x^b) = D_x(bx^{b-1}) = b(b-1)x^{b-2}$, and $x^{b-2} > 0$ for $x > 0$, the second derivative of x^b has the same sign as $b(b-1)$. Consequently: x^b is concave up if $b > 1$ or if $b < 0$, and is concave down if $0 < b < 1$ (cf. Fig. 1111-1).

NOTE. If $b > 0$, 0^b is defined:

(9) $$0^b \equiv 0, \quad b \in \mathcal{P}.$$

From this definition it can be shown that the function x^b, with domain $\mathcal{P} \cup \{0\}$, is continuous at 0 for every positive exponent b, that this function has the right-hand derivative $D_x(x^b) = 0$ at $x = 0$ in case $b > 1$, and that

(10) $$\lim_{h \to 0+} \frac{h^b - 0}{h} = +\infty, \quad \text{if } 0 < b < 1.$$

Example. If $x > \frac{1}{2}$, the derivative of $(2x - 1)^{\sqrt{2}}$ is:

$$D_x(2x - 1)^{\sqrt{2}} = \sqrt{2}(2x - 1)^{\sqrt{2} - 1} \cdot 2 = 2\sqrt{2}(2x - 1)^{\sqrt{2} - 1}.$$

1112 LOGARITHMIC DIFFERENTIATION

A function of the form u^v, where u and v are differentiable functions of x (where *either* u or v may be a constant function), and where u is positive-valued, may be differentiated by the process called **logarithmic differentiation.** This consists of the following steps:

(*i*)   Label the function by a new letter, say $y = u^v$.
(*ii*) Take natural logarithms of both members, and simplify.
(*iii*) Differentiate implicitly with respect to x.
(*iv*) Solve for D_xy, and simplify.

Example 1.   Differentiate x^{2x-1}, where $x > 0$.

Solution.   Write $y = x^{2x-1}$, and take ln of both members: $\ln y = (2x - 1)\ln x$. Differentiate:

$$\frac{y'}{y} = (2x - 1)\frac{1}{x} + 2 \ln x = \frac{2x - 1}{x} + 2 \ln x.$$

Multiplying both members of (1) by y gives:

$$(2)\quad y' = D_xy = y\left[\frac{2x - 1}{x} + 2 \ln x\right] = x^{2x-1}\left[\frac{2x - 1}{x} + 2 \ln x\right]$$

$$= (2x - 1)x^{2x-2} + 2x^{2x-1} \ln x.$$

Example 2.   Obtain a formula for the derivative with respect to x of u^v where u and v are differentiable functions of x and u is positive-valued.

Solution.   With $y = u^v$, $\ln y = v \ln u$ and $\dfrac{y'}{y} = v \cdot \dfrac{u'}{u} + (\ln u)v'$, from which

$$y' = y\left[\frac{v}{u} u' + (\ln u)v'\right] = u^v\left[\frac{v}{u} u' + (\ln u)v'\right],$$

or

$$(3)\qquad\qquad D_xy = vu^{v-1} D_xu + (\ln u)u^v D_xv.$$

We notice that formula (3) is the same as the result that would be obtained by adding the derivatives of (3) obtained in two ways: *first* by differentiating u^v as if v were a constant (u^v being then a *power function*) and *second* by differentiating u^v as if u were a constant (u^v being then an *exponential function*).

Logarithmic differentiation is often helpful in obtaining derivatives of functions expressed as products or quotients involving powers.

Example 3.   Differentiate $x(2x + 1)^5 \sqrt{x^2 + 4}$, $x > 0$.

Solution.   Label the function y and form the natural logarithm:

$$\ln y = \ln x + 5 \ln(2x + 1) + \tfrac{1}{2} \ln(x^2 + 4).$$

Differentiation, followed by multiplication by y, gives

$$\frac{y'}{y} = \frac{1}{x} + \frac{10}{2x + 1} + \frac{x}{x^2 + 4},$$

$$y' = (2x + 1)^5 \sqrt{x^2 + 4} + 10x(2x + 1)^4 \sqrt{x^2 + 4} + \frac{x^2(2x + 1)^5}{\sqrt{x^2 + 4}}$$

$$= \frac{(2x + 1)^4}{\sqrt{x^2 + 4}} [(2x + 1)(x^2 + 4) + 10x(x^2 + 4) + x^2(2x + 1)]$$

$$= \frac{2(2x + 1)^4}{\sqrt{x^2 + 4}} (7x^3 + x^2 + 24x + 2).$$

1113 THE GENERAL LOGARITHMIC FUNCTION

The **general logarithmic function,** with **base** a, where $a > 0$ and $a \neq 1$, is defined as the inverse of the function a^x, and denoted $\log_a x$:

(1) $$y = \log_a x \iff x = a^y, \quad x \in \mathcal{P}, \quad y \in \mathcal{R}.$$

In particular, when $a = e$, since $e^y = \exp y$ and ln and exp are inverse functions,

(2) $$\log_e x = \ln x, \quad x \in \mathcal{P}.$$

From the definition of $\log_a x$ we have immediately (cf. Fig. 1113-1, (9) and (10), §1109):

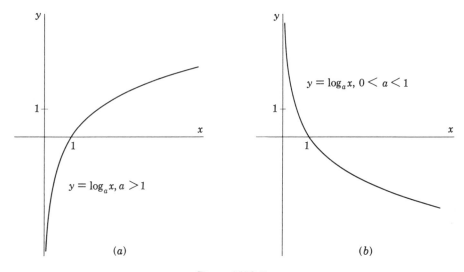

(a)   (b)

Figure 1113-1

(3) If $a > 1$, $\log_a x$ is strictly increasing on $\mathcal{P}$, with range $\mathcal{R}$, and

$$\lim_{x \to +\infty} \log_a x = +\infty, \quad \lim_{x \to 0+} \log_a x = -\infty.$$

(4) If $0 < a < 1$, $\log_a x$ is strictly decreasing on $\mathcal{P}$, with range $\mathcal{R}$, and

$$\lim_{x \to +\infty} \log_a x = -\infty, \quad \lim_{x \to 0+} \log_a x = +\infty.$$

(5) $$\log_a (a^x) = x, \quad x \in \mathcal{R},$$

(6) $$a^{\log_a x} = x, \quad x \in \mathcal{P}.$$

(7) $$\log_a 1 = 0,$$

(8) $$\log_a a = 1.$$

Furthermore, $\log_a x$ is continuous and differentiable on $\mathcal{P}$. Its derivative is most easily obtained from the **change of base formula**:

(9) $$\log_a x = \frac{\ln x}{\ln a}.$$

To prove (9) we write $y = \log_a x$ in the form $x = a^y$, whence $\ln x = \ln(a^y) = y \ln a$, and (5) follows. We have from (9)

(10) $$D_x \log_a x = \frac{1}{\ln a} \cdot \frac{1}{x},$$

or in terms of differentials,

(11) $$d \log_a x = \frac{1}{\ln a} \cdot \frac{dx}{x}.$$

If u is a positive-valued differentiable function of x, from the chain rule:

(12) $$D_x \log_a u = \frac{1}{\ln a} \cdot \frac{1}{u} \cdot D_x u,$$

or, in terms of differentials,

(13) $$d \log_a u = \frac{1}{\ln a} \cdot \frac{du}{u}.$$

Since $D_x^2 \log_a x = \dfrac{1}{\ln a} D_x\left(\dfrac{1}{x}\right) = -\dfrac{1}{\ln a} \cdot \dfrac{1}{x^2}$, the graph of $y = \log_a x$ is concave down if $a > 1$ and concave up if $0 < a < 1$ (cf. Fig. 1113-1).

Formula (9) can be extended to the **general change of base formula**

(14) $$\log_a x = \frac{\log_b x}{\log_b a},$$

where a, b, and x are positive, and $a \neq 1$ and $b \neq 1$. This follows by substitution from (9):

$$\frac{\log_b x}{\log_b a} = \frac{\ln x/\ln b}{\ln a/\ln b} = \frac{\ln x}{\ln a} = \log_a x.$$

(Formula (14) can also be derived directly.) If, in (14), we put x equal to b we conclude that $\log_a b$ and $\log_b a$ are reciprocals:

(15) $$\log_a b = \frac{1}{\log_b a}.$$

The change of base formula (14) can therefore also be written

(16) $$\log_a x = \log_a b \cdot \log_b x.$$

In particular, if $a > 0$ and $a \neq 1$, and if $b = e$, (15) becomes $\log_a e = 1/\ln a$, so that formulas (10) through (13) can be written with the factor $\log_a e$ instead of $1/\ln a$. For example, (10) becomes

(17) $$D_x \log_a x = \frac{\log_a e}{x}.$$

Finally, we state the **general laws of logarithms,** where $a > 0$ and $a \neq 1$ (these follow immediately from laws of ln already established):

   I. $\log_a (xy) = \log_a x + \log_a y$, $\;x$ and $y \in \mathcal{P}$.

   II. $\log_a \left(\dfrac{x}{y}\right) = \log_a x - \log_a y$, $\;x$ and $y \in \mathcal{P}$.

   III. $\log_a (x^b) = b \log_a x$, $\;x \in \mathcal{P}$, $\;b \in \mathcal{R}$.

Example 1. Show how logarithmic differentiation may be used to provide formula (12).

Solution. With $y = \log_a u$, we have $u = a^y$, $\ln u = y \ln a$, and hence $\dfrac{1}{u} D_x u = (\ln a)D_x y$,

so that $D_x y = \left(\dfrac{1}{u} D_x u\right) \Big/ \ln a$.

NOTE. This example illustrates how it is possible to avoid memorization of the formula for differentiation of logarithmic functions where the base is different from e. There are two basic ideas: (*i*) Write the relationship in exponential form. (*ii*) Use logarithmic differentiation.

Example 2. Differentiate $\log_2 x$.

Solution. Label the function y and write the equation $y = \log_2 x$ in the exponential form $x = 2^y$. Taking ln of each side gives $\ln x = \ln(2^y)$, or $\ln x = y \ln 2$, and hence

$$\frac{1}{x} = (D_x y)\ln 2, \quad D_x y = \frac{1}{x \ln 2}.$$

1114   EXERCISES

In Exercises 1–6, find the value of the given logarithm.

  1. $\log_2 \frac{1}{8}$.   **2.** $\log_8 2$.   **3.** $\log_3 \frac{1}{2}$.

  4. $\log_{\frac{1}{2}} 8$.   **5.** $\log_4 8$.   **6.** $\log_8 4$.

In Exercises 7–46, differentiate the given function, assuming a domain for which the function is defined. When it is appropriate, simplify the given function by laws of logarithms or exponents before differentiation.

  7. $\ln \sin \frac{1}{2}x$.   **8.** $\ln(2x^2 - 5)$.   **9.** $\ln \ln x$.   **10.** $x^2 \ln x$.

  11. $(\ln \sin x)(\ln \cos x)$. **12.** $\dfrac{\ln x}{x}$.   **13.** $\dfrac{\ln x^2}{\ln x}$.   **14.** $\dfrac{\ln \sin x}{\cos x}$.

  15. $\log_{10} \sin x$.   **16.** $\log_a x^5$.   **17.** $(\log_{10} x)(\ln x)$.   **18.** $\ln \sqrt{\sin 2x}$.

  19. $\ln \sqrt{x^4 + 3}$.   **20.** $\ln \dfrac{\sqrt{x^2 + 5}}{x}$.   **21.** $\ln \sqrt{\dfrac{1 - \cos x}{1 + \cos x}}$.   **22.** $\ln[x(\sin 2x^4)\ln x]$.

  23. $\sqrt{\ln x}$.   **24.** $\dfrac{1}{(\ln 5x)^2}$.   **25.** $(\ln x^3)^2$.   **26.** e^{2x}.

27. e^{x^2}. **28.** $e^{2x} e^{x^2}$. **29.** $e^{\sqrt{x}}$. **30.** $e^{\sin 2x}$.

31. $e^{3 \ln x}$. **32.** $x^2 e^{-x}$. **33.** $x e^{-x^2}$. **34.** $x^2 e^{2x}$.

35. $\dfrac{x^2}{e^{2x}}$. **36.** $\dfrac{\ln x}{e^x}$. **37.** $\dfrac{e^x - e^{-x}}{e^x + e^{-x}}$. **38.** $\sin e^{2x}$.

39. $\sqrt{e^x}$. **40.** e^{e^x}. **41.** x^e. **42.** π^x.

43. $\ln(xe^x)$. **44.** $\ln a^x$. **45.** $10^{\sin x}$. **46.** $2^{\ln x}$.

In Exercises 47–56, find the derivative by logarithmic differentiation. Assume a domain for which each quantity whose logarithm is formed is positive.

47. $x\sqrt{x^2 + a^2}$. **48.** $\dfrac{x}{\sqrt{x^2 + a^2}}$. **49.** $\dfrac{(2x + 1)^6}{(3x - 1)^5}$. **50.** $\sqrt{\dfrac{4x^2 + 1}{6x^2 + 5}}$.

51. $(3x + 5)^4(x^2 + 3)^5 \sqrt[3]{6x + 1}$. **52.** $(2x - 7)^3(x^3 + 4)^6\sqrt{4x + 3}$.

53. x^x. **54.** $x^{\sin x}$. **55.** x^{x^2}. **56.** $(\ln x)^x$.

In Exercises 57–59, find dy/dx by implicit differentiation. Assume all values of x and y to be positive.

57. $xe^y + ye^x = 4$. **58.** $10x \ln y = ye^x$. **59.** $xe^{-y} = \ln x + \sin y$.

In Exercises 60 and 61, find dy/dx in terms of the parameter t.

60. $x = \sin t, y = e^t$. **61.** $x = \ln t, y = \tan t$.

In Exercises 62–65, sketch the graph of the given function.

62. $2^x, x \in \mathcal{R}$. **63.** $10^x, x \in \mathcal{R}$. **64.** $\log_2 x, x \in \mathcal{P}$. **65.** $\log_{10} x, x \in \mathcal{P}$.

In Exercises 66–69, find the equation of the tangent line to the graph of the given equation at the specified point.

66. $y = xe^x, (1, e)$. **67.** $y = x \ln x, (e, e)$.

68. $\ln xy = 2x + 3y - 5, (1, 1)$. **69.** $xe^y + y = e^2 + \ln x, (e, 1)$.

In Exercises 70–72, obtain an approximation to the given number by means of differentials, using the given "nearness" statement.

70. $\ln 1.02$; 1.02 near 1. **71.** $\ln 0.97$; 0.97 near 1.

72. $e^{-0.02}$; -0.02 near 0.

In Exercises 73 and 74, use differentials to obtain the given linear expression as a linear approximation to the given function of h, for small values of $|h|$. (Cf. §704.)

73. $\ln(1 + h) : h$. **74.** $e^h : 1 + h$.

In Exercises 75 and 76, use the law of the mean (§613) to establish the given inequality for the specified values of the variable and exponent. (Cf. Example 4, §622.)

75. $\dfrac{x}{1 + x} < \ln(1 + x) < x; x \in (-1, 0) \cup (0, +\infty)$.

76. $1 + x < e^x < 1 + xe^x; \ x \in (-\infty, 0) \cup (0, +\infty)$.

In Exercises 77–84, estimate to 3 decimal places the value of the given logarithm without the use of tables, by means of the following data, given to 4 decimal places:

$$\log_{10} 2 = 0.3010, \ \log_{10} 3 = 0.4771, \ \log_{10} 7 = 0.8451, \ \ln 10 = 2.3026.$$

77. ln 2. **78.** ln 3. **79.** ln 4. **80.** ln 5.

81. ln 6. **82.** ln 7. **83.** ln 8. **84.** ln 9.

85. If $x \in \mathcal{P}\backslash\{1\}$, prove that $x^{1/\ln x} = e$.

1115 INTEGRATION FORMULAS

Each of the differentiation formulas of this chapter corresponds to an integration formula. We list these formulas below in terms of the independent variable x, but owing to the role of the differential notation in the process of integration by substitution, each of these formulas has a counterpart where the variable x is replaced by a dependent variable u considered as a function of x. Only formula I requires proof (this is given below), and the integration formula corresponding to (10), §1113, is omitted since it reduces to I. The base a is assumed to be positive and different from 1, and the exponent b is any real number different from -1.

I. $\displaystyle\int \frac{dx}{x} = \ln |x| + C, \quad x > 0 \text{ or } x < 0$.

II. $\displaystyle\int e^x \, dx = e^x + C, \quad x \in \mathcal{R}$.

III. $\displaystyle\int a^x \, dx = \frac{a^x}{\ln a} + C = (\log_a e)a^x, \quad x \in \mathcal{R}, \ a > 0, \ a \neq 1$.

IV. $\displaystyle\int x^b \, dx = \frac{x^{b+1}}{b+1} + C, \quad x > 0, \ b \neq -1$.

Proof of I. The problem is to show that for the interval $(0, +\infty)$, $\ln x$ is a primitive of $1/x$, and that for the interval $(-\infty, 0)$, $\ln(-x)$ is a primitive of $1/x$. For the interval $(0, +\infty)$ the formula $D_x \ln x = 1/x$ is given by (6), §1102. For the interval $(-\infty, 0)$, we have from (8), §1102, with $u = -x$;

$$D_x \ln(-x) = \frac{-1}{-x} = \frac{1}{x}.$$

Example 1. Use laws of logarithms to derive formula III.

Solution. Write $y = a^x$, and take ln of each side: $\ln y = x \ln a$, or $y = e^{x \ln a}$. (Alternatively, we may use III, §1113, to write $a^x = e^{\ln a^x} = e^{x \ln a}$.) Hence

$$\int a^x \, dx = \int e^{(\ln a)x} \, dx,$$

and we integrate by substitution of $u = (\ln a)x$, with $du = (\ln a)dx$:

$$\int a^x \, dx = \int e^u \frac{du}{\ln a} = \frac{1}{\ln a} \int e^u \, du = \frac{e^u}{\ln a} + C = \frac{a^x}{\ln a} + C.$$

(The "point" of this example is that if the laws of logarithms are known, formula III need not be memorized.)

Example 2. Evaluate $\int_{-13}^{-5} \dfrac{dx}{2x + 1}$.

Solution. By I, $\int_{-13}^{-5} \dfrac{dx}{2x + 1} = \dfrac{1}{2} \int_{-13}^{-5} \dfrac{d(2x + 1)}{2x + 1} = \dfrac{1}{2} \ln|2x + 1| \Big|_{-13}^{-5} = \dfrac{1}{2} \ln 9 - \dfrac{1}{2} \ln 25 =$
$\ln 3 - \ln 5 = \ln \frac{3}{5}$.

Example 3. Integrate: $\int x \, e^{-5x^2} \, dx$.

Solution. We let u be substituted for the quantity in the exponent:

$$u = -5x^2, \quad du = -10x \, dx,$$

and multiply and divide by -10:

$$\int x \, e^{-5x^2} \, dx = -\frac{1}{10} \int e^{-5x^2} (-10x) dx = -\frac{1}{10} \int e^{-5x^2} \, d(-5x^2) = -\frac{1}{10} e^{-5x^2} + C.$$

Example 4. Evaluate $\int_0^1 \dfrac{dx}{e^x}$.

Solution. Using the Note, §1110, we write the integral in the form $\int_0^1 e^{-x} \, dx$, whence

$$\int_0^1 e^{-x} \, dx = -\int_0^1 e^{-x} \, d(-x) = -e^{-x} \Big|_0^1 = 1 - e^{-1} = 1 - \frac{1}{e}.$$

Example 5. Evaluate $\lim\limits_{n \to +\infty} \left(\dfrac{1}{n+1} + \dfrac{1}{n+2} + \cdots + \dfrac{1}{2n} \right)$.

Solution. The sum, when rewritten

$$(1) \qquad \left[\frac{1}{1 + \dfrac{1}{n}} + \frac{1}{1 + \dfrac{2}{n}} + \cdots + \frac{1}{1 + \dfrac{n}{n}} \right] \cdot \frac{1}{n},$$

can be interpreted as an approximating sum for the integral $\int_0^1 \dfrac{dx}{1 + x}$, according to the net $\mathfrak{N} = \left\{ 0, \dfrac{1}{n}, \dfrac{2}{n}, \cdots, \dfrac{n}{n} \right\}$ and the points $x_1 = \dfrac{i}{n}$, $i = 1, 2, \cdots, n$. As in the second solution of the Example, §514, the limit of (1) as $|\mathfrak{N}| \to 0$, or equivalently as $n \to +\infty$, is equal to the integral

$$\int_0^1 \frac{dx}{1 + x} = \int_0^1 \frac{d(1 + x)}{1 + x} = \ln(1 + x) \Big|_0^1 = \ln 2.$$

1116 EXERCISES

In Exercises 1–32, perform the indicated integration.

1. $\displaystyle\int \frac{dx}{5x+3}.$ **2.** $\displaystyle\int \frac{du}{5-3u}.$ **3.** $\displaystyle\int \frac{dv}{1-4v}.$ **4.** $\displaystyle\int \frac{dw}{4w-3}.$

5. $\displaystyle\int \frac{z\,dz}{z^2+5}.$ **6.** $\displaystyle\int \frac{x\,dx}{4-x^2}.$ **7.** $\displaystyle\int \frac{t\,dt}{8-5t^2}.$ **8.** $\displaystyle\int \frac{s\,ds}{3s^2+4}.$

9. $\displaystyle\int \frac{\sin x\,dx}{1+\cos x}.$ **10.** $\displaystyle\int \frac{\sec y \tan y\,dy}{3\sec y-2}.$ **11.** $\displaystyle\int \frac{\sec^2 2\theta\,d\theta}{5-6\tan 2\theta}.$ **12.** $\displaystyle\int \frac{\sin 2u\,du}{2+\sin^2 u}.$

13. $\displaystyle\int \frac{e^t-e^{-t}}{e^t+e^{-t}}\,dt.$ **14.** $\displaystyle\int \frac{e^v\,dv}{3+4e^v}.$ **15.** $\displaystyle\int \frac{dx}{x\ln x}.$ **16.** $\displaystyle\int \frac{dr}{\sqrt{r}(\sqrt{r}+1)}.$

17. $\displaystyle\int e^{2-3x}\,dx.$ **18.** $\displaystyle\int e^{5t}\,dt.$ **19.** $\displaystyle\int e^{-2u}\,du.$ **20.** $\displaystyle\int e^{-w}\,dw.$

21. $\displaystyle\int \sqrt{e^s}\,ds.$ **22.** $\displaystyle\int (e^{3y})^4\,dy.$ **23.** $\displaystyle\int \frac{dx}{e^{6x}}.$ **24.** $\displaystyle\int \frac{dz}{e^{3-4z}}.$

25. $\displaystyle\int 10^v\,dv.$ **26.** $\displaystyle\int 2^x\,dx.$ **27.** $\displaystyle\int te^{-t^2}\,dt.$ **28.** $\displaystyle\int \frac{w^3}{e^{w^4}}\,dw.$

29. $\displaystyle\int e^{\cos 3t}\sin 3t\,dt.$ **30.** $\displaystyle\int (e^x-e^{-x})^2\,dx.$ **31.** $\displaystyle\int e^s\sqrt{e^s+1}\,ds.$ **32.** $\displaystyle\int \frac{\sin(\ln x)}{x}\,dx.$

In Exercises 33–48, evaluate the definite integral.

33. $\displaystyle\int_1^2 \frac{dx}{3x+2}.$ **34.** $\displaystyle\int_2^3 \frac{ds}{1-4s}.$ **35.** $\displaystyle\int_2^4 \frac{r\,dr}{1-r^2}.$ **36.** $\displaystyle\int_0^2 \frac{t\,dt}{3t^2+5}.$

37. $\displaystyle\int_{\frac{\pi}{3}}^{\frac{\pi}{2}} \frac{\sin\theta\,d\theta}{1-\cos\theta}.$ **38.** $\displaystyle\int_0^{\frac{\pi}{4}} \frac{\sec^2\phi\,d\phi}{1+\tan\phi}.$ **39.** $\displaystyle\int_e^{e^2} \frac{du}{u\ln u}.$ **40.** $\displaystyle\int_0^1 \frac{e^v\,dv}{e^v+2}.$

41. $\displaystyle\int_0^1 e^{2x}\,dx.$ **42.** $\displaystyle\int_0^{\frac{1}{3}} e^{-3y}\,dy.$ **43.** $\displaystyle\int_0^1 \frac{dw}{e^{1-w}}.$ **44.** $\displaystyle\int_2^4 \sqrt{e^z}\,dz.$

45. $\displaystyle\int_{-1}^0 3^x\,dx.$ **46.** $\displaystyle\int_0^2 \frac{v\,dv}{e^{v^2}}.$ **47.** $\displaystyle\int_{\ln 2}^{\ln 3} \frac{e^s\,ds}{e^s-1}.$ **48.** $\displaystyle\int_1^e \frac{\ln t\,dt}{t}.$

In Exercises 49–51, find the area of the ordinate set of the given function for the specified interval. Use Tables III and V, pages 370 and 373, if necessary, to compute the answer to 3 decimal places. Draw a figure.

49. $\dfrac{1}{x}$, $[2, 6]$. **50.** $\dfrac{x}{x^2+1}$, $[0, \sqrt{3}]$. **51.** xe^{-x^2}, $[0, \sqrt{\ln 10}]$.

In Exercises 52 and 53, find the area of the bounded region determined by the given curves. Use Tables III and V, pages 370 and 373, if necessary, to compute the answer to 2 decimal places. Draw a graph.

52. $xy = e$, $y = e^x$, $x = 2$. *Suggestion:* Substitute $x = 1$.

53. $y = \dfrac{10x}{x^2 + 1}$, $y = \dfrac{x^2 + 4}{x}$. *Suggestion:* Substitute $x = 1$ and $x = 2$.

In Exercises 54 and 55, find the mean value of the given function on the specified interval. Use Tables III and V, pages 370 and 373, if necessary, to compute the answer to 2 decimal places.

54. $\dfrac{1}{x}$, $[1, 3]$.

55. e^x, $[-1, 2]$.

In Exercises 56 and 57, find the volume of revolution obtained by revolving about the indicated coordinate axis the ordinate set of the given function on the specified interval. Use Tables III and V, pages 370 and 373, if necessary, to compute the answer to 2 decimal places. Draw a graph.

56. e^x; $[-1, 1]$; x-axis.

57. e^{-x^2}; $[0, \sqrt{\ln 2}]$; y-axis.

58. Evaluate the limit

$$\lim_{x \to +\infty} \frac{1}{n}\left[\sqrt[n]{2} + \sqrt[n]{2^2} + \sqrt[n]{2^3} + \cdots + \sqrt[n]{2^n} \right].$$

(Cf. the Example, §514, Exs. 1–4, §516, and Exs. 21–23, §1008.)

1117   FUNCTIONAL DEFINITIONS OF SINE AND COSINE

The properties of the sine and cosine functions (and therefore of all the trigonometric functions) can be derived from the following two:

(1) $D_x \sin x = \cos x, \quad D_x \cos x = -\sin x, \, x \in \mathfrak{R},$

(2) $\sin 0 = 0, \quad \cos 0 = 1.$

Properties (1) form a pair of "differential equations" and properties (2) form a pair of "initial conditions" (cf. Chapter 12). A full description of the derivation of the standard properties of the sine and cosine functions, on the basis of (1) and (2) as *assumed properties*, is given in Chapter 19, *CWAG*. (For the *existence* of two functions having properties (1) and (2), see §1108, *SCC*.) In this book we shall limit ourselves to an outline only of the development given in detail in Chapter 19, *CWAG*.

I. Uniqueness.   If f and g are real-valued differentiable functions on $\mathfrak{R}$ such that

(3) $f'(x) = g(x), \quad g'(x) = -f(x), \, x \in \mathfrak{R},$

(4) $f(0) = 0, \quad g(0) = 1,$

then $f(x) = \sin x$ and $g(x) = \cos x.$

II. Identities.   The following identities hold for all real x, a, and b:

(5) $\sin^2 x + \cos^2 x = 1,$

(6) $\sin (a + b) = \sin a \cos b + \cos a \sin b,$

(7) $$\cos (a + b) = \cos a \cos b - \sin a \sin b,$$

(8) $$\sin (-x) = -\sin x, \cos (-x) = \cos x.$$

III. π.   There is a least positive number c such that $\cos c = 0$. The number π is defined to be $2c$. Also, $c = \frac{1}{2}\pi$ is the least positive number whose sine is 1. Furthermore, π is the least positive number whose sine is 0, and 2π is the least positive number whose cosine is 1.

IV. Periodicity.   The functions $\sin x$ and $\cos x$ are periodic with least positive period 2π. That is, the following identities hold for all real x:

(9) $$\sin (x + 2\pi) = \sin x, \quad \cos (x + 2\pi) = \cos x,$$

and whenever either of the following holds identically for $x \in \mathcal{R}$:

(10) $$\sin (x + p) = \sin x, \quad \cos (x + p) = \cos x,$$

then $p = 2\pi n$ for some integer n.

V. The unit circle.   The equations

(11) $$x = \cos t, \quad y = \sin t, 0 \leqq t < 2\pi$$

define a continuous one-to-one mapping (or parametrization) of the interval $[0, 2\pi)$ onto the unit circle $x^2 + y^2 = 1$.

12

Elementary
Differential Equations

1201 THE DIFFERENTIAL EQUATION $dy/dx = f(x)$

An equation involving one or more dependent variables considered as unknown functions of one or more independent variables, together with derivatives of these functions, is called a **differential equation.** An equation involving any number of functions of a single variable, and their derivatives, is called an *ordinary* differential equation, and an equation involving functions of several independent variables, and their derivatives (cf. §§301–303, *SCC*), is called a *partial* differential equation. The **order** of a differential equation is the highest order of a derivative occurring. A particular function is said to **satisfy** or be a **solution** of a differential equation involving a single dependent variable if and only if the equation resulting from the substitution of this function for the dependent variable is an identity in the independent variables. To **solve** a differential equation is to find all of its solutions.

In this chapter we shall limit our considerations to differential equations of only the most elementary nature. The simplest of these is the first order equation

$$(1) \qquad \frac{dy}{dx} = f(x),$$

where $f(x)$ is a given continuous function whose domain is an interval I, and y is to be determined as a function of x. This equation was solved in Chapter 10. In the first place, equation (1) has at least *one* solution, given by any indefinite integral of $f(x)$ on I of the form

$$(2) \qquad \Phi(x) = \int_a^x f(t)dt,$$

336

where a is any point of I. On the other hand, *every* solution $F(x)$ of (1) is a primitive of $f(x)$ and therefore has the form

(3) $F(x) = \Phi(x) + C,$

where C is an arbitrary constant. In other words, the family of solutions of (1) is the family $\{\int_a^x f(t)dt + C\}$, where a is a *fixed* point of I and $C \in \Re$ (cf. Fig. 1201-1).

Another expression for the set of solutions of (1) is given by the family $\{F(x)\}$ such that

(4) $F(x) = G(x) + C,$

where $G(x)$ is an arbitrary primitive of $f(x)$ on I.

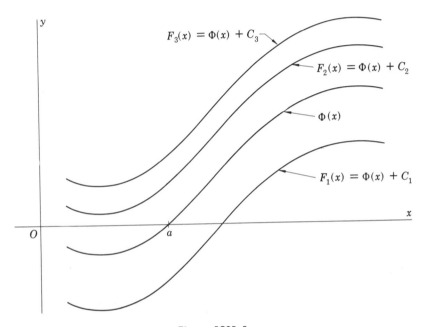

Figure 1201-1

NOTE 1. It will be increasingly convenient in this and the succeeding volume, *SCC*, to use the elliptic notation $f(x)$ as a condensed form for the longer expression "the function f whose value corresponding to the number x is $f(x)$." This is particularly true for such explicit functions as e^{x^2} and $\sin 5t$, where the alternative is to introduce letters to represent the functions, or to appeal to such terminology as "the function given by e^{x^2}" or such notation as $t \rightarrow \sin 5t$. We shall feel free to use elliptic notation henceforth without further comment.

Example 1. Solve the differential equation

(5) $\dfrac{dy}{dx} = \dfrac{1}{x},$ where $x < 0.$

Solution. By the integration formula I, §1115, $\displaystyle\int \dfrac{dx}{x} = \ln|x| + C$ for $x \neq 0$; and therefore a primitive of $1/x$ on the interval $(-\infty, 0)$ is $\ln(-x)$. The solution of (5) is therefore the set of all functions of the form

$$y = \ln(-x) + C.$$

If a *particular* solution of the differential equation (1) is to be determined, some condition on the variables other than the equation itself must be provided. This condition usually takes the form of specifying the value of y corresponding to a particular value of x:

$$(6) \qquad\qquad y(a) = b,$$

where $a \in I$. Such a condition as (6) is called a **boundary condition,** or, if the independent variable represents time, an **initial condition.** The effect of adding the boundary condition (6) is to permit the determination of the constant of integration C in (3) and (4). In (3), to be specific, if we substitute $x = a$ we obtain $F(a) = 0 + C$, or $C = b$, while in (4) we obtain $F(a) = G(a) + C$, or $C = b - G(a)$. The solution of equation (1) with the boundary condition (6) can therefore be written:

$$(7) \qquad\qquad y = \int_a^x f(t)dt + b,$$

or

$$(8) \qquad\qquad y = G(x) - G(a) + b,$$

where $G(x)$ is an arbitrary primitive of $f(x)$ on I.

NOTE 2.   The preceding paragraph exhibits a convenient form of symbolic economy commonly used in connection with boundary conditions of differential equations. In the spirit of the footnote near the beginning of §602, we often allow a *single* letter — in this case y — to represent both the dependent variable and the function that defines this variable in terms of the independent variable. The statement that y is equal to b when the independent variable is equal to a thus reduces to the simple equation $y(a) = b$.

Example 2.   Find the function $f(x)$ on $\Re$ whose derivative is $f'(x) = x$ and whose graph passes through the point (4, 3).

Solution.   One primitive of the function x is $\int_0^x t\, dt = \frac{1}{2}x^2$.   Therefore the solution desired must have the form $f(x) = \frac{1}{2}x^2 + C$ for an appropriate value of C.   Substitution gives

$$3 = f(4) = \frac{1}{2}\cdot 16 + C = 8 + C, \quad C = -5,$$

and the answer is therefore $f(x) = \frac{1}{2}x^2 - 5$.   Equation (7) becomes $y = \int_4^x t\, dt + 3 = \frac{1}{2}x^2 - 5$ and equation (8), with $G(x) \equiv \frac{1}{2}x^2$, reduces to $y = \frac{1}{2}x^2 - \frac{1}{2}\cdot 16 + 3 = \frac{1}{2}x^2 - 5$.

Example 3.   A particle is moving along a straight line with velocity given:

$$(9) \qquad\qquad v(t) = \begin{cases} 6t, 0 \leq t \leq 3, \\ 18, 3 \leq t \leq 5, \end{cases}$$

where time units are seconds and velocity units are feet per second. How far does the particle travel in the time interval $[0, t]$, where $0 \leq t \leq 5$?

Solution.   If distance is denoted $s = s(t)$, with units in feet, then $s'(t) = v(t)$, and hence $s(t)$ must have the form $s(t) = \int_0^t v(x)dx + C$.   Since $s(0) = 0$, the constant C must equal 0, and we have

$$(10) \qquad s(t) = \int_0^t v(x)dx = \begin{cases} \int_0^t 6x\, dx = 3t^2, \ 0 \leq t \leq 3, \\ 27 + \int_3^t 18\, dx = 18t - 27, \ 3 \leq t \leq 5. \end{cases}$$

(Cf. Fig. 1201-2.)

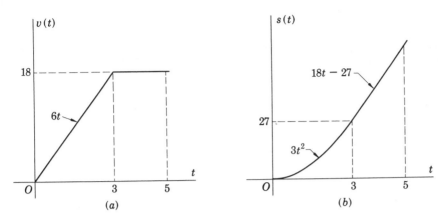

Figure 1201-2

1202 THE DIFFERENTIAL EQUATION $d^2y/dx^2 = f(x)$

The second order differential equation

$$\frac{d^2y}{dx^2} = f(x), \tag{1}$$

where $f(x)$ is continuous on an interval I, can be solved by the methods discussed in §1201. Since the second derivative of y is the first derivative of dy/dx,

$$\frac{dy}{dx} = \int f(x)\, dx = G(x) + C_1, \tag{2}$$

where $G(x)$ is any primitive of $f(x)$ on I, and C_1 is a constant of integration. From (2) we have:

$$y = \int (G(x) + C_1)\, dx = H(x) + C_1 x + C_2, \tag{3}$$

where $H(x)$ is any primitive of $G(x)$.

A boundary condition giving the value of dy/dx for a particular value of x permits the determination of the constant C_1 in (2), and a *second* boundary condition giving the value of y corresponding to a particular value of x permits the determination of the constant C_2 in (3). For a *second* order equation, then, unique solutions are provided by *two* boundary conditions. These two boundary conditions may vary considerably in nature, and need not involve the first derivative explicitly (cf. Example 2).

Example 1. Find the curve $y = f(x)$ passing through the point $(1, 3)$ with slope 7, if $d^2y/dx^2 = 4x + 3$, $x \in \mathfrak{R}$.

Solution. Integration gives $dy/dx = 2x^2 + 3x + C_1$, and substitution gives $7 = 2 + 3 + C_1$, or $C_1 = 2$. From the resulting equation, $dy/dx = 2x^2 + 3x + 2$, we have $y = \frac{2}{3}x^3 + \frac{3}{2}x^2 + 2x + C_2$, and substitution gives $3 = \frac{2}{3} + \frac{3}{2} + 2 + C_2$, or $C_2 = -\frac{7}{6}$. Therefore the curve is the graph of $y = \frac{2}{3}x^3 + \frac{3}{2}x^2 + 2x - \frac{7}{6}$.

Example 2.   Find the curve $y = f(x)$ passing through the two points $(1, 3)$ and $(2, 5)$ if $d^2y/dx^2 = 4x + 3$, $x \in \Re$.

Solution.   We proceed as in the solution of Example 1, except that the second integration must be performed before the constant C_1 is evaluated. We obtain

(4) $y = \frac{2}{3} x^3 + \frac{3}{2} x^2 + C_1 x + C_2.$

Substitution into (4) of both pairs of coordinates gives the two equations $3 = \frac{2}{3} + \frac{3}{2} + C_1 + C_2$ and $5 = \frac{16}{3} + 6 + 2C_1 + C_2$, or

(5) $\begin{cases} C_1 + C_2 = \frac{5}{6}, \\ 2C_1 + C_2 = -\frac{19}{3}. \end{cases}$

Solving the simultaneous system (5) for C_1 and C_2 gives $C_1 = -\frac{43}{6}$ and $C_2 = 8$. Therefore the curve sought is the graph of $y = \frac{2}{3} x^3 + \frac{3}{2} x^2 - \frac{43}{6} x + 8$.

1203   RECTILINEAR MOTION; THE FALLING BODY

Consider a particle p moving along a straight line, let time be represented by the independent variable t, and let distance, velocity, and acceleration be denoted (cf. §§ 602, 603, and 605):

(1)   distance $= s = s(t)$,

(2)   velocity $= v = v(t) = s'(t)$,

(3)   acceleration $= a = a(t) = v'(t) = s''(t)$.

In many physical motion problems the acceleration is specified as a function of t, together with two initial conditions involving distance or velocity. One of the simplest problems of this type is the **falling body problem.** For this problem we assume that an object is in vertical motion near the earth's surface, and neglect the effect of air resistance. In other words, we assume that the object under consideration is being acted upon by a single downward force only, that of the earth's gravity. The effect of this assumption is that if distance $s(t)$ is measured positively upward, then the acceleration $a(t)$ is a negative constant, usually denoted $-g$. In the problems of this section we shall assume that the distance unit is one foot and that the time unit is one second. In these units velocity is measured in feet per second and acceleration is measured in feet per second per second, or feet per second squared, abbreviated respectively

(4)   *velocity:* ft/sec,   *acceleration:* ft/sec/sec or ft/sec^2,

and the constant g is approximately equal to 32. (For convenience we shall assume $g = 32$, although the value of g varies somewhat with altitude and from place to place on the earth's surface; the value 32.2 is often used.) We start, then, with the equation

(5) $a(t) = v'(t) = s''(t) = -g.$

Integration of (5) (with respect to the variable t) gives

(6) $v(t) = s'(t) = -gt + C_1,$

where C_1 is a constant to be determined. If time t is measured from a certain moment considered to be the initial time $t = 0$, and if the velocity at time $t = 0$, called the **initial velocity,** is known, and denoted by

(7) $$v_0 \equiv v(0),$$

then substitution of $t = 0$ in (6) gives $v_0 = 0 + C_1$, whence

(8) $$v(t) = s'(t) = -gt + v_0.$$

Integration of (8) gives

(9) $$s(t) = -\tfrac{1}{2}gt^2 + v_0 t + C_2,$$

where C_2 is a constant to be determined. If the value of $s(t)$ at time $t = 0$, called the **initial distance** or **initial height,** is known, and denoted by

(10) $$s_0 \equiv s(0),$$

then substitution of $t = 0$ in (9) gives $s_0 = 0 + C_2$, and hence

(11) $$s(t) = -\tfrac{1}{2}gt^2 + v_0 t + s_0.$$

In some problems it is convenient to orient the s-axis positively *downward,* in which case the acceleration is a *positive* constant, and equation (11) is replaced by

(12) $$s(t) = \tfrac{1}{2}gt^2 + v_0 t + s_0.$$

In certain situations other than the falling body problem just described, an object may be moving subject to constant acceleration. The result is the same as (11) or (12) except that g is replaced by a different constant, positive or negative depending on orientation. Examples are (*i*) motion on a smooth inclined plane (cf. Example 3), (*ii*) motion near the surface of the moon or another planet, and (*iii*) motion over a short distance approximately two thousand miles (say) above the surface of the earth.

Example 1. An object shot directly upward from a balloon that is located 1000 feet above the surface of the earth reaches a maximum height of 4600 feet. What is the initial velocity of the projectile? How long after firing does the object hit the surface of the earth?

Solution. Letting s represent height above the surface of the earth, measured positively upward, we start from $s''(t) = -32$, and have $v(t) = -32t + v_0$ and $s(t) = -16t^2 + v_0 t + s_0$ $= -16t^2 + v_0 t + 1000$. The maximum value of the quadratic function $-16t^2 + v_0 t + 1000$ (since its second derivative is a negative constant) is given by equating to zero its first derivative:

(13) $$-32t + v_0 = 0, \quad t = v_0/32.$$

Substituting $t = v_0/32$ into $s(t)$ gives

(14) $$s\!\left(\frac{v_0}{32}\right) = 4600 = -\frac{v_0^2}{64} + \frac{v_0^2}{32} + 1000,$$

whence $v_0^2 = 64 \cdot 3600$, and $v_0 = 8 \cdot 60 = 480$ ft/sec. The time t when the projectile hits the earth's surface is found by equating $s(t)$ to 0:

(15) $$-16t^2 + 480t + 1000 = 0, \text{ or } 2t^2 - 60t - 125 = 0,$$

whence

(16)
$$t = \frac{30 \pm \sqrt{1150}}{2} = \frac{30 \pm 33.91}{2}.$$

The negative sign in (16) is without physical significance. Therefore $t = 32$ seconds (to the nearest tenth of a second).

Example 2. A stone is dropped down a vertical mine shaft and hits the bottom in 10 seconds. How deep is the shaft?

Solution. We measure distance positively downward from the opening of the shaft, and with the initial velocity and initial height both equal to 0, we have, from $s''(t) = 32$:

(17)
$$v(t) = 32t + v_0 = 32t, \quad s(t) = 16t^2 + s_0 = 16t^2.$$

Therefore, with $t = 10$, $s = 1600$ feet.

Example 3. A model train car is sent up an inclined plane with an initial velocity of 10 feet per second, and is acted upon by a gravitation force in such a way that its acceleration is constant. In 2 seconds the car has gone 16 feet. How far does it go in the next 2 seconds?

Solution. With distance s measured positively upward along the inclined plane, and with the initial distance taken to be 0, we have

(18)
$$s''(t) = -k, \quad v(t) = -kt + 10, \quad s(t) = -\tfrac{1}{2}kt^2 + 10t.$$

Substitution of $t = 2$ and $s(2) = 16$ gives $16 = -2k + 20$, and $k = 2$. Since $s(t) = -t^2 + 10t$, $s(4) = 24$, and from time $t = 2$ to time $t = 4$ the car goes a distance equal to $s(4) - s(2) = 24 - 16 = 8$ feet.

1204   SEPARABLE EQUATIONS; ORTHOGONAL TRAJECTORIES

If a differential equation is of the form (or is equivalent to one of the form)

(1)
$$g(y) \frac{dy}{dx} = f(x),$$

or in terms of differentials,

(2)
$$g(y)dy = f(x)dx,$$

then the equation is said to be **separable.** The following theorem states the remarkable fact that the solutions of (1) or (2) are given by inserting integral signs in (2) and integrating both resulting members as though the two variables x and y were *both* independent:

(3)
$$\int g(y)dy = \int f(x)dx,$$

where an arbitrary constant of integration is implicity assumed.

Theorem. *Assume that $f(x)$ and $g(y)$ are continuous functions on the intervals I and J, respectively, and let $F(x)$ and $G(y)$ be primitives of $f(x)$ on I and of $g(y)$ on J, respectively. Let $y = \phi(x)$ be a differentiable function whose domain is an interval* *contained in I and whose range is contained in J. Then* $y = \phi(x)$ *is a solution of the differential equation* (1) *or* (2), *if and only if* $y = \phi(x)$ *satisfies the equation*

$$(4) \qquad\qquad G(y) = F(x) + C$$

identically on the domain of $\phi(x)$ *for some constant C.*

Proof. Assume first that $y = \phi(x)$ satisfies (4) identically for some constant C:

$$(5) \qquad\qquad G(\phi(x)) = F(x) + C.$$

Then, since both members of (5) are the same differentiable function of x, and both G and ϕ are differentiable functions, we can apply the chain rule to get $G'(\phi(x)) \phi'(x) = F'(x)$, or

$$(6) \qquad\qquad g(\phi(x))\phi'(x) = f(x),$$

which states that $y = \phi(x)$ is a solution of (1). Now assume that $y = \phi(x)$ is a solution of (1), or in other words that (6) is true for all x in the domain of ϕ. Then the two functions $G(\phi(x))$ and $F(x)$ have the same derivative with respect to x on the domain of ϕ, and since the domain of ϕ is an interval, these two functions must differ by a constant there, and (5) results. This is the meaning of the statement that $y = \phi(x)$ satisfies the equation (4) for some constant C.

Example 1. Find all solutions of the differential equation

$$(7) \qquad\qquad x\,dx + y\,dy = 0.$$

Solution. Any solution $y = \phi(x)$ must satisfy the differential equation

$$(8) \qquad\qquad 2y\,dy = -2x\,dx,$$

and hence the equation

$$(9) \qquad\qquad y^2 = -x^2 + C$$

for some C. Conversely, any solution $y = \phi(x)$ of (9) must satisfy the differential equation (7). Therefore the solutions of (7) are those functions whose graphs are portions of semicircles, given by formulas of the type:

$$(10) \qquad\qquad y = \sqrt{r^2 - x^2}, \quad -r < x < r,$$

and

$$(11) \qquad\qquad y = -\sqrt{r^2 - x^2}, \quad -r < x < r,$$

where r is an arbitrary positive number.

A curve Γ is said to be an **orthogonal trajectory** of a family $\mathfrak{F}$ of curves if and only if (*i*) Γ crosses every curve of $\mathfrak{F}$ and (*ii*) at every point where Γ crosses a curve of the family $\mathfrak{F}$ it crosses that curve orthogonally. If $\mathfrak{F}$ is a given family of curves it is sometimes possible to obtain the family $\mathfrak{G}$ of all orthogonal trajectories of $\mathfrak{F}$. The general method is (*i*) to write the equations of the curves of the family $\mathfrak{F}$ by the use of a general parameter, each value of the parameter corresponding to a curve of the family, (*ii*) to eliminate this parameter by differentiation, thus obtaining a differential equation; (*iii*) to obtain a *new* differential equation from this one by replacing the derivative dy/dx by its *negative reciprocal;* (*iv*) to solve this new differential equation; and (*v*) to interpret these solutions in terms of a family of orthogonal trajectories, taking into account all exceptional cases including vertical tangents.

Example 2.   Find the orthogonal trajectories of the family of curves

(12) $$y = \frac{k}{x^2}, \quad k \text{ and } x \in \mathcal{R} \setminus \{0\},$$

where k is a parameter (cf. Fig. 1204-1).

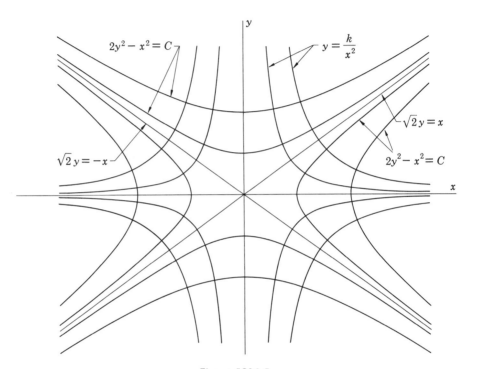

Figure 1204-1

Solution.   The differential equation of the family (12) is obtained by differentiation and then substitution of $k = x^2 y$ to eliminate the parameter k:

(13) $$\frac{dy}{dx} = -\frac{2k}{x^3} = -\frac{2}{x^3} \cdot x^2 y = -\frac{2y}{x}.$$

For all points where $y \neq 0$ (from (12) the equation $y = 0$ is possible only for the curve given by $k = 0$), the differential equation of the orthogonal trajectories is obtained from (13) by replacing $-2y/x$ by its negative reciprocal:

(14) $$\frac{dy}{dx} = \frac{x}{2y}, \quad \text{or} \quad 2y \, dy = x \, dx.$$

Integration of (14) gives

(15) $$2y^2 - x^2 = C,$$

where C is an arbitrary constant of integration. The orthogonal trajectories of (12) are therefore hyperbolas having asymptotes $2y^2 = x^2$, together with the asymptotes.

Example 3. Find the orthogonal trajectories of the family of half-parabolas

$$(16) \qquad\qquad 2x = y^2 + k, \quad y > 0,$$

where k is a parameter.

Solution. Differentiation of (16) gives the differential equation of the family

$$(17) \qquad\qquad \frac{dy}{dx} = \frac{1}{y}, \quad y > 0.$$

The differential equation of the orthogonal trajectories is therefore $dy/dx = -y$, or equivalently,

$$(18) \qquad\qquad dx + \frac{dy}{y} = 0, \quad y > 0,$$

Integration of (18) gives

$$(19) \qquad\qquad x + \ln y = C,$$

where C is an arbitrary constant. This equation can be expressed equivalently as in $y = C - x$, or, by means of exponentials, $e^{\ln y} = e^{C-x} = e^C e^{-x}$, or finally, with $c \equiv e^C$:

$$(20) \qquad\qquad y = ce^{-x}, \quad c > 0.$$

The student should sketch a few of the curves of the families (16) and (19), and display their mutual orthogonality. He should observe that each of these families can be generated by moving any one of its members horizontally.

1205 EXERCISES

In Exercises 1–8, solve the differential equation for the specified interval, subject to the given boundary conditions.

1. $\dfrac{dy}{dx} = \sin x$; $(-\infty, +\infty)$; $y = 2$ when $x = 0$.

2. $\dfrac{dy}{dx} = \sqrt{x}$; $(0, +\infty)$; $y = -3$ when $x = 1$.

3. $\dfrac{dy}{dx} = |x|$; $(-\infty, +\infty)$; $y = 4$ when $x = -2$.

4. $\dfrac{dy}{dx} = \dfrac{1}{|x| + 1}$; $(-\infty, +\infty)$; $y = \ln 4$ when $x = -1$.

5. $\dfrac{d^2y}{dx^2} = \dfrac{1}{x^2}$; $(0, +\infty)$; $\dfrac{dy}{dx} = 1$ and $y = 1$ when $x = 1$.

6. $\dfrac{d^2y}{dx^2} = e^{-2x}$; $(-\infty, +\infty)$; $\dfrac{dy}{dx} = 2$ and $y = 3$ when $x = 0$.

7. $\dfrac{d^2y}{dx^2} = 6x$; $(-\infty, +\infty)$; $y = 3$ when $x = 1$, $y = 13$ when $x = 2$.

8. $\dfrac{d^2y}{dx^2} = \sin \pi x$; $(-\infty, +\infty)$; $y = 3$ when $x = 1$, $y = 1$ when $x = 2$.

In Exercises 9 and 10, find a curve $y = f(x)$ satisfying the given conditions. Draw a graph.

9. Passes through (1, 2) with slope 0; $\dfrac{d^2y}{dx^2} = \dfrac{2}{x^3}$, $x > 0$.

10. Passes through (1, 2) with slope -2; $\dfrac{d^2y}{dx^2} = \dfrac{2}{x^3}$, $x > 0$.

11. A stone is thrown upward from a platform 224 feet above the ground with an initial velocity of 80 feet per second. When does it hit the ground?

12. A stone is thrown downward from the top of a 192-foot smokestack with an initial speed of 64 feet per second. With what speed does the stone hit the ground?

13. A stone is thrown down an abandoned well with an initial speed of 20 feet per second, and hits the bottom with a speed of 100 feet per second. How deep is the well?

14. An object shot directly upward from a balloon 8000 feet high hit the surface of the earth 50 seconds later. How high did it go?

15. Because of brake failure a car parked on the top level of a parking ramp rolled through a defective area in the parapet and fell to the pavement below. If the car struck the pavement at a speed of 56 feet per second (approximately 38 miles per hour), from what height did it fall?

16. A car rolling down a long straight hill was observed to travel a distance of 8 feet during a certain one-second time interval, and a distance of 14 feet during the one-second interval immediately following, How far did it travel during the third one-second interval immediately following this two-second period?

17. A toy cart shot up an inclined plane reaches a maximum height of 20 feet above the point of firing. Three seconds after firing, the cart is moving downward with a speed of 10 feet per second. What was the initial velocity?

18. A stone thrown upward from a window in a building rises to a maximum height from the ground of 64 feet and hits the sidewalk 3 seconds after being thrown. How high is the window?

19. A cannon ball is fired vertically from the surface of a planet, where the constant g of (5), §1803, is replaced by a new gravitational constant γ. Prove that for a given initial velocity v_0, the maximum height reached by the cannon ball varies inversely as γ. How does the total time elapsed between the time of firing and the time the cannon ball strikes the surface of the planet vary?

20. The force of gravitation on any object on the surface of the moon is approximately one-sixth of what it is for the same object on the surface of the earth. Two identical projectiles are fired upward from the surfaces of the moon and the earth, the initial velocity for the projectile on the earth being 6 times that of the projectile on the moon. Compare the two flights as to (*a*) height as a function of elapsed time; (*b*) velocity as a function of elapsed time; (*c*) total time of flight; and (*d*) maximum heights attained. How do the initial velocities compare if the maximum heights are the same?

In Exercises 21–24, solve the differential equation, assuming for simplicity that both x and y are positive. Draw a graph showing the family of curves obtained.

21. $2xy\, dx + (x^2 + 1)dy = 0.$

22. $2y\, dx = x\, dy.$

23. $\dfrac{dy}{dx} = \dfrac{y}{x}.$

24. $\dfrac{dy}{dx} = 2xy.$

In Exercises 25–28, obtain orthogonal trajectories of the given family of curves, where both x and y are assumed to be positive. Draw graphs that show both families. The letter k represents an arbitrary parameter.

25. $y^2 - x^2 = k.$ **26.** $2x + y^2 = k.$

27. $y = kx^2.$ **28.** $y = ke^{-x^2}.$

29. Derive equations (1) of Exercise 38, §713, assuming the following two differential equations and sets of initial conditions:

$$\frac{d^2x}{dt^2} = 0; \quad \frac{dx}{dt} = v_0 \cos \alpha \text{ and } x = 0 \text{ when } t = 0;$$

$$\frac{d^2y}{dt^2} = -32; \quad \frac{dy}{dt} = v_0 \sin \alpha \text{ and } y = 0 \text{ when } t = 0.$$

1206   THE DIFFERENTIAL EQUATION $dy/dt = ky$

As we shall see in the following section, many applied problems of physics and biology are related to the differential equation

(1) $$\frac{dy}{dt} = ky,$$

where k is a nonzero constant (either positive or negative), and the independent variable is denoted by t instead of x since in most applied problems the relevant rates of change are *time* rates of change. Equation (1) states that the rate of change of a certain quantity is proportional to the quantity itself.

It is easy to see that $y = e^{kt}$ is a solution of (1) and, indeed, that $y = ce^{kt}$ is a solution for every constant c. To see that these are the *only* solutions of (1), we assume that $y = \phi(t)$ is a solution for t on some interval I, and form the *quotient* of $\phi(t)$ and e^{kt} (which is possible since e^{kt} is never equal to 0):

(2) $$z = \phi(t)/e^{kt} = \phi(t)e^{-kt}.$$

Our objective is to show that z is a constant. We do this by showing that z (which is a differentiable function of t) has a derivative that is identically zero:

(3) $$\frac{dz}{dt} = \phi(t)[-ke^{-kt}] + \phi'(t)e^{-kt} = [\phi'(t) - k\phi(t)]e^{-kt},$$

and this is equal to zero since the quantity in brackets is identically zero (ϕ being a solution of (1)). Finally, since $dz/dt = 0$, identically in t, on the interval I, z must be equal to a constant c there (Theorem II, §614):

(4) $$\phi(t)/e^{kt} = c, \quad \phi(t) = ce^{kt},$$

and we have the conclusion:

Theorem. *If $y = \phi(t)$ is differentiable on an interval I, then y is a solution of (1) if and only if there exists a constant c such that*

(5) $$y = \phi(t) = ce^{kt}.$$

Example 1. Solve the differential equation $dy/dt = 3y$.

Solution. By the preceding theorem, the general solution is $y = ce^{3t}$, where c is an arbitrary constant.

Example 2. Solve the differential equation $dy/dt = -5y$, subject to the initial condition $y(0) = 200$ (that is, $y = 200$ when $t = 0$).

Solution. From (5), with $k = -5$, we have $y = ce^{-5t}$. Substituting $y = 200$ and $t = 0$, we determine c: $200 = ce^0 = c$. Therefore the solution satisfying the given initial condition is $y = 200e^{-5t}$.

1207 APPLICATIONS TO RADIOACTIVE DECAY AND BACTERIAL GROWTH

In a problem of **radioactive decay,** it is assumed that if y is the amount of a radioactive material present at time t, then the rate of change of y with respect to t is proportional to the amount y. Since the quantity is *decreasing*, the rate of change is *negative*, and the relationship between dy/dt and y is most conveniently expressed by an equation of the form

$$(1) \qquad \frac{dy}{dt} = -ky,$$

where k is a *positive* constant: $k > 0$. By §1206 (with k replaced by $-k$) we have

$$(2) \qquad y = ce^{-kt}.$$

If we denote by y_0 the value $y(0)$ of y at time $t = 0$, we have from (2), $y_0 = ce^0 = c$, and therefore the solution to (1) can be written

$$(3) \qquad y = y_0 e^{-kt}.$$

For a problem in **bacterial growth** it is assumed that if y is the size of a bacterial population, then y can be treated as if it were continuously varying with a rate of change proportional to y itself:

$$(4) \qquad \frac{dy}{dt} = ky,$$

where k is a *positive* constant. As above, the solution of (4) is

$$(5) \qquad y = ce^{kt} = y_0 e^{kt},$$

where $y_0 = y(0)$ is the value of y at time $t = 0$.

As we shall see in the following problems, it is sometimes convenient to use logarithms with a base other than e (for example, base 10 for computations) or powers with a base other than e. The two most useful facts for this purpose are:

I. The quotient of any two logarithms to the same base is independent of that base:

$$(6) \qquad \frac{\log_a x}{\log_a y} = \frac{\log_b x}{\log_b y},$$

where x, y, a, and b are positive, and a and b are different from 1. A particular case of (6) that will be used frequently is given by $a = e$ and $b = 10$:

$$(7) \qquad \frac{\ln x}{\ln y} = \frac{\log x}{\log y},$$

where the notation $\log x$ indicates $\log_{10} x$.

II. If a is any positive number different from 1, the solutions (3) and (5) can be written, respectively,

$$(8) \qquad y = y_0\, a^{-\lambda t},$$

$$(9) \qquad y = y_0\, a^{\lambda t},$$

where k and λ are related by the equations $k = \lambda \ln a$ and $\lambda = k \log_a e$.

Proof of I. From the change of base formula (9), §1113:

$$\frac{\log_a x}{\log_a y} = \frac{\ln x/\ln a}{\ln y/\ln a} = \frac{\ln x/\ln b}{\ln y/\ln b} = \frac{\log_b x}{\log_b y}.$$

Proof of II. For any constant k, $e^{-kt} = a^{\log_a(e^{-kt})} = a^{-kt(\log_a e)} = a^{-(k\log_a e)t} = a^{-\lambda t}$, where $\lambda = k \log_a e = k/\ln a$. This gives (8), and a change in sign gives (9).

NOTE 1.   A concept frequently encountered in connection with radioactive decay is that of *half life*. The **half life** of a radioactive element is the time it takes for any given quantity of the element to be reduced to one half of its original amount. Thus, the half life of the element, obeying the law (1), is the value of t satisfying, from (3),

$$(10) \qquad \tfrac{1}{2}y_0 = y_0\, e^{-kt}, \text{ or } e^{-kt} = \tfrac{1}{2}, \text{ or } e^{kt} = 2,$$

and therefore $kt = \ln 2$, or $t = (\ln 2)/k$. In problems involving half life it is sometimes convenient to use base 2 and formula (8) with $a = 2$. In this case, if t is the half life of the element under consideration, (8) in the form $y = y_0\, 2^{-\lambda t}$ gives $\tfrac{1}{2}y_0 = y_0 2^{-\lambda t}, 2^{\lambda t} = 2$, and therefore $\lambda t = 1$. It follows, then, that the coefficient λ in (8), if $a = 2$, is the reciprocal of the half life.

Example 1.   A radioactive element decomposes at such a rate that out of 1,000,000 atoms at the beginning of a year, only 5,000 remain at the end of the year. What is the half life?

First solution.   Letting y be the number of atoms at time t in years, we have the law $dy/dt = -ky$ for some positive constant k, and therefore, from (3),

$$(11) \qquad y = 1{,}000{,}000e^{-kt}.$$

Substituting $y = 5000$ and $t = 1$ we have $5000 = 1{,}000{,}000e^{-k}$, and hence $e^k = 200$, and $k = \ln 200$. From (10) we have the half life equal to

$$(12) \qquad t = \frac{\ln 2}{k} = \frac{\ln 2}{\ln 200} = \frac{\log 2}{\log 200} = \frac{0.301}{2.301} = 0.131$$

(approximately), where in the middle of (12) we use (7) to make the computation easier. The half life in days is $(0.131)(365) = 48$ days (approximately).

Second solution.   With base 2, (8) becomes

$$(13) \qquad y = 1{,}000{,}000\ 2^{-\lambda t},$$

and substitution of $y = 5000$ and $t = 1$ gives $2^{\lambda} = 200$. The constant λ is computed by means of logarithms to the base 10: $\lambda \log 2 = \log 200$, so that the half life, by Note 1, is

(14)
$$\frac{1}{\lambda} = \frac{\log 2}{\log 200} = \frac{0.301}{2.301} = 0.131,$$

as before.

Example 2. A certain bacterial population increases under a given set of conditions by one percent every 10 days. To what size does a population of 1,000,000 grow in one year?

Solution. If y is the size of the bacterial population and t is time in days from the beginning of the year, then

(15)
$$y = 1,000,000 \, e^{kt}.$$

Substitution of $y = 1,010,000$ and $t = 10$ gives $10k = \ln 1.01$, or $k = \frac{1}{10} \ln 1.01$. Therefore the bacterial population at time $t = 365$ is

(16)
$$1,000,000 \, e^{36.5 \ln 1.01} = 1,000,000 \exp (\ln(1.01^{36.5}))$$
$$= 1,000,000(1.01^{36.5}),$$

and we are led to the evaluation of

(17)
$$x \equiv 1.01^{36.5}.$$

This is most easily done by logarithms to the base 10: $\log x = 36.5 \log 1.01 = 36.5 \cdot 0.0043214 = 0.15773$, and $x = 1.4379$. Therefore the population at the end of 365 days is approximately 1,438,000. This problem can be thought of as being equivalent to computing the result of compound interest of 1 percent on a principal of 1,000,000 with 36.5 periods of compounding.

NOTE 2. The principles in operation with radioactive decay and bacterial growth also apply to certain problems in cooling. A law of physics states that if y denotes the difference between the temperature of an object and the temperature of the surrounding medium, where the surrounding medium remains at constant temperature, then the time rate of change of y is proportional to y, and therefore equation (1) and its solution (3) are appropriate.

Example 3. A cup of coffee at temperature 200° F. is in a room at temperature 70°F. In one minute the temperature of the coffee has fallen to 170° F. Mrs. Jones, who is waiting to drink the coffee, can drink liquids at 130° F. How much longer must she wait?

Solution. If y represents the temperature in degrees Fahrenheit above 70° F., and if t is time in minutes measured from the moment that the coffee has temperature 200°F., then, since the initial value of y is $200 - 70 = 130$,

(18)
$$y = 130 \, e^{-kt}.$$

Substitution of $y = 170 - 70 = 100$ and $t = 1$ gives $100 = 130 \, e^{-k}$, or $e^k = 130/100 = 1.3$, and therefore

(19)
$$k = \ln 1.3.$$

We wish to determine t when $y = 130 - 70 = 60$:

(20)
$$60 = 130 \, e^{-kt} = 130 \, e^{-\ln 1.3)t}.$$

From (20) we have $e^{\ln 1.3)t} = 130/60 = 13/6$, from which $(\ln 1.3)t = \ln(13/6)$, and hence, by (7),

(21)
$$t = \frac{\ln(13/6)}{\ln 1.3} = \frac{\log 2.1667}{\log 1.3} = \frac{0.33579}{0.11394} = 2.947.$$

To the nearest second this is 2 minutes and 57 seconds. Therefore Mrs. Jones must wait an additional minute and 57 seconds beyond the time that the temperature reaches 170° F.

NOTE 3. Certain simple mixing problems involve the same law as that represented by (1) for radioactive decay. Specifically, if a container holding a fixed number of grams of saline solution (salt and water) has a steady flow of fresh water into the tank and a steady overflow at the same rate, with constant mixing, and if y represents the number of grams of salt in the brine at time t, then

$$(22) \qquad \frac{dy}{dt} = -ky,$$

where k is a positive constant equal to the ratio of the amount of fresh water entering the tank in one unit of time divided by the total quantity of liquid in the tank.

Example 4. A tank holds 8000 grams of 20 percent salt brine. Fresh water is flowing in at a rate of 100 grams per minute, with constant mixing and overflow at the same rate. How long will it be before the mixture is 10 percent salt? What percentage of salt is present after 6 hours?

Solution. If y is the number of grams of salt present at time t in minutes, then (22) holds with $k = 100/8000 = 1/80$. Since the amount of salt present initially is 20 percent of 8000, or 1600 grams, y satisfies the equation

$$(23) \qquad y = 1600\, e^{-t/80}.$$

When the mixture is 10 percent salt, $y = 800$ and therefore, from (23), $e^{t/80} = 2$, and $t = 80 \ln 2$. The value of $\ln 2$ is given in Table III, page 370, or it can be computed by means of logarithms to the base 10. In either case, $\ln 2 = 0.69315$, and the value of t corresponding to a 10 percent solution is

$$(24) \qquad \begin{aligned} t &= 80\cdot 0.69315 = 55.452 \text{ minutes} \\ &= 55 \text{ minutes and } 27 \text{ seconds (approximately).} \end{aligned}$$

After 6 hours, or $t = 360$ minutes, the amount of salt present is

$$(25) \qquad y = 1600\, e^{-360/80} = 1600\, e^{-4.5}.$$

In terms of percent this is $100 \cdot \frac{1600}{8000} \cdot e^{-4.5} = 20\, e^{-4.5}$. From Table V, page 373, we evaluate this final quantity:

$$(26) \qquad 20 \cdot 0.011109 = \tfrac{2}{9} \text{ of 1 percent (approximately).}$$

1208   EXERCISES

In Exercises 1 and 2, solve the differential equation.

1. $\dfrac{dy}{dx} + 8y = 0.$

2. $\dfrac{dy}{dt} - \dfrac{y}{3} = 0.$

In Exercises 3 and 4, solve the differential equation, subject to the given initial condition.

3. $\dfrac{dy}{dt} = 5y,\ y_0 = 80$ when $t = 0.$

4. $\dfrac{dy}{dx} = -\dfrac{y}{2},\ y_0 = 100$ when $x = 0.$

5. A certain radioactive isotope decomposes at such a rate that there is a 30 percent loss in 2 years. How much remains at the end of 5 years?

6. How long does it take for the element in Exercise 5 to be reduced to 30 percent of its original amount?

7. A radioactive element decomposes at such a rate that out of 1,000,000 atoms at the beginning of a year, only 5000 remain at the end of the year. What is the half life of this element?

8. For the element in Exercise 7, when will exactly one atom remain? (Explain in what sense this question has any meaning.)

9. How long does it take the bacterial population of Example 2, §1207, to double?

10. The population of the world was approximately 2.49×10^9 in 1950 and approximately 2.98×10^9 in 1960. Assuming that the rate of growth of this population is proportional to its magnitude, estimate when it should be expected to reach approximately 5×10^9.

11. A grocer receives a packaged product with 0.02 percent bacterial contamination which grows at a rate proportional to the amount of contamination. Mr. Robinson purchases a package of this product after it has sat on the grocer's shelf for two months, at which time the contamination has increased to 0.03 percent. Health authorities have determined that the substance is safe provided the contamination does not exceed 0.07 percent. What should Mr. Robinson be advised to do?

12. Suppose the rate of bacterial growth in the product of Exercise 11 is cut in half under refrigeration. Can Mr. Robinson safely keep the package twice as long in his refrigerator as he can on his pantry shelf? Give reasons for your statement.

13. A tank holds 500 cubic centimeters of 20 percent salt brine. Fresh water is flowing in at a rate of 10 cubic centimeters per minute, with constant mixing and overflow at the same rate. How long will it be before the mixture is 2 percent salt?

14. In Exercise 13, what percentage salt is present after one day (24 hours)?

15. On a winter day Mrs. Smith sets outdoors a dish of lemon pie filling to cool. If the temperature outdoors is 20° F. and if it takes 5 minutes for the dish to cool from a temperature of 200° F. to 150° F., how much longer will be needed to cool it to 120° F.?

16. In Exercise 15, what is the temperature of the pie filling if Mrs. Smith forgets it for a total of a half-hour?

17. On a day in early spring Mrs. Smith sets a bowl of gelatine outdoors to cool. If the temperature of the gelatine drops from 200° F. to 150° F. in 5 minutes and from 150° F. to 116° F. in the next 5 minutes, what is the outdoor temperature?

18. On another spring day, when the outdoor temperature is 50° F., Mrs. Smith sets out a kettle of Vichyssoise soup to cool. If the initial temperature of the soup is 200° F., and if the temperature drop during the first 5 minutes is twice what it is during the second 5 minutes, what is the final temperature of the soup after 10 minutes?

19. An electrical current flowing in a circuit is generated by a battery which is suddenly cut off. From the moment when the battery is removed from the circuit, the current i obeys a law of the form $L \, di/dt + Ri = 0$, where L and R are positive constants. If the current drops to half strength in one tenth of a second, how long will it take for the current to be reduced to one percent of its original strength?

20. The intensity I of a light ray passing through a homogeneous medium is reduced in such a way that the rate of change of I with respect to the distance x of the medium through which the light has passed is proportional to the intensity I itself. If the light intensity of a beam passing through a certain portion of the Pacific Ocean is reduced by one percent for each 9-inch distance through which the light has passed, find the percentage of light intensity remaining at a depth of 100 feet.

13

Indeterminate Forms

1301 THE INDETERMINATE FORM 0/0

The derivative of the function x^2 is defined as the limit

$$\lim_{h \to 0} \frac{(x+h)^2 - x^2}{h} = \lim_{h \to 0} \frac{2xh + h^2}{h} = \lim_{h \to 0} \frac{2x + h}{1} = 2x.$$

In this example the evaluation is simplified by the cancellation of a common factor h from numerator and denominator of a fraction.

For the derivative of the function $\ln x$ the evaluation is achieved by other means (cf. §1102), with the following result:

$$\lim_{h \to 0} \frac{\ln (x+h) - \ln x}{h} = \frac{1}{x}.$$

In this second example it is not possible to cancel a common factor h from numerator and denominator.

The two preceding examples have the following feature in common. Each leads to the evaluation of the limit of a quotient of two functions (of the variable h), where the numerator and denominator separately tend toward 0. (In fact, the definition of the derivative of any differentiable function involves the limit of the quotient of two functions each of which has 0 as a limit.) Furthermore, it should be noted that the final results, $2x$ and $1/x$, are distinct.

A limit problem is said to be of the **indeterminate form** 0/0 if and only if the problem is that of determining the limit of a quotient of two functions each of which approaches zero. The word *indeterminate* means that different problems of this same form may lead to different results.

353

In many cases a problem of the indeterminate form $0/0$ can be resolved by simply replacing each of the functions involved by its derivative. This method, known as *l'Hospital's rule* after the French mathematician G. F. A. de l'Hospital (1661–1704), is made specific in the following theorem, whose proof is given in §1302. For the sake of being specific, we have framed the first part of this theorem in terms of right-hand limits, and have then indicated the far greater degree of generality that is available.

Theorem. L'Hospital's Rule. *If f and g are differentiable functions in a deleted right half-neighborhood D_{a+} of the point a, if $g'(x) \neq 0$ for $x \in D_{a+}$, if $\lim_{x \to a+} f(x) = \lim_{x \to a+} g(x) = 0$, and if*

$$(1) \qquad \lim_{x \to a+} \frac{f'(x)}{g'(x)} = L \ (finite, \ +\infty, \ -\infty, \ or \ \infty),$$

then

$$(2) \qquad \lim_{x \to a+} \frac{f(x)}{g(x)} = L.$$

A similar result holds if the deleted right half-neighborhood D_{a+} of a and $x \to a+$ are replaced by any of the following: (i) a deleted left half-neighborhood D_{a-} of a and $x \to a-$, (ii) a deleted neighborhood D_a of a and $x \to a$, (iii) a deleted neighborhood $D_{+\infty}$ of $+\infty$ and $x \to +\infty$, (iv) a deleted neighborhood $D_{-\infty}$ of $-\infty$ and $x \to -\infty$, and (v) a deleted neighborhood D_∞ of ∞ and $x \to \infty$.

Example 1.
$$\lim_{x \to 3} \frac{x^2 - x - 6}{x^2 - 9} = \lim_{x \to 3} \frac{2x - 1}{2x} = \frac{5}{6},$$

$$\lim_{x \to 1} \frac{\ln x}{x - 1} = \lim_{x \to 1} \frac{1/x}{1} = 1,$$

$$\lim_{x \to 0} \frac{\sin x}{x} = \lim_{x \to 0} \frac{\cos x}{1} = 1,$$

$$\lim_{x \to 0} \frac{\sin 2x}{3x} = \lim_{x \to 0} \frac{2 \cos 2x}{3} = \frac{2}{3}.$$

In each case the final equality is true by the continuity of a function whose limit is being evaluated.

Example 2. Evaluate the limit $\lim_{x \to 0} \frac{\sin x - x}{x^3}$.

Solution. In this case l'Hospital's rule must be applied repeatedly before a determinate result is obtained. In the following sequence the existence of each limit implies that of the preceding limit and their equality:

$$\lim_{x \to 0} \frac{\sin x - x}{x^3} = \lim_{x \to 0} \frac{\cos x - 1}{3x^2} = \lim_{x \to 0} \frac{-\sin x}{6x} = \lim_{x \to 0} \frac{-\cos x}{6} = -\frac{1}{6}.$$

The final equality is true by the continuity of $\cos x$ at $x = 0$.

It is important before applying l'Hospital's rule to check on the indeterminacy of the expression being treated. The following example illustrates this:

Example 3. A routine and thoughtless attempt to apply l'Hospital's rule may yield an incorrect result as follows:

$$\lim_{x \to 1} \frac{2x^2 - x - 1}{x^2 - x} = \lim_{x \to 1} \frac{4x - 1}{2x - 1} = \lim_{x \to 1} \frac{4}{2} = 2.$$

The error lies in the fact that the fraction $(4x - 1)/(2x - 1)$ is not a quotient of functions tending toward 0 as $x \to 1$. On the contrary, this function is continuous at $x = 1$, and a correct evaluation is

$$\lim_{x \to 1} \frac{2x^2 - x - 1}{x^2 - x} = \lim_{x \to 1} \frac{4x - 1}{2x - 1} = \frac{4 - 1}{2 - 1} = 3.$$

1302 PROOF OF L'HOSPITAL'S RULE

In this section we give a proof of the Theorem, §1301. We start with the form as originally stated:

Proof for $x \to a+$. Let $f(a)$ and $g(a)$ be defined, or redefined if necessary, to be zero: $f(a) \equiv 0$, $g(a) \equiv 0$. Then f and g are continuous on some closed interval of the form $[a, b]$ in the interior of which f and g are differentiable and $g'(x)$ never vanishes. On any interval $[a, x]$, where $a < x \leq b$, the conditions of the generalized law of the mean (§712) are satisfied, and there exists a number ξ between a and x such that

(1) $$\frac{f'(\xi)}{g'(\xi)} = \frac{f(x) - f(a)}{g(x) - g(a)} = \frac{f(x)}{g(x)}.$$

By hypothesis (1), §1301, if N is any neighborhood of L (where L is either finite or infinite), there exists a positive number δ such that

(2) $$a < x < a + \delta \implies \frac{f'(x)}{g'(x)} \in N.$$

Consequently,

(3) $$a < x < a + \delta \implies a < \xi < a + \delta \implies \frac{f'(\xi)}{f'(\xi)} \in N,$$

and by (1),

(4) $$a < x < a + \delta \implies \frac{f(x)}{g(x)} \in N.$$

Proof for $x \to a-$. This is the same as above except that $[a, b]$ is replaced by $[b, a]$, and such inequalities as $a < \xi < x \leq b$ are replaced by $b \leq x < \xi < a$ and the like.

Proof for $x \to a$. This combines the two preceding results, since the assumption $\lim_{x \to a} f'(x)/g'(x) = L$ implies both $\lim_{x \to a+} f'(x)/g'(x) = L$ and $\lim_{x \to a-} f'(x)/g'(x) = L$.

Proof for $x \to +\infty$. This follows from the case $x \to a+$ with $a = 0$, with the aid of reciprocals. By assumption:

$$(5) \qquad L = \lim_{x \to +\infty} \frac{f'(x)}{g'(x)} = \lim_{t \to 0+} \frac{f'(1/t)}{g'(1/t)}.$$

We now multiply numerator and denominator by $-1/t^2$ and write

$$(6) \qquad L = \lim_{t \to 0+} \frac{f'(1/t)(-1/t^2)}{g'(1/t)(-1/t^2)}.$$

Since $f'\left(\frac{1}{t}\right)\left(-\frac{1}{t^2}\right) = \frac{d}{dt} f\left(\frac{1}{t}\right)$ and $g'\left(\frac{1}{t}\right)\left(-\frac{1}{t^2}\right) = \frac{d}{dt} g\left(\frac{1}{t}\right)$,

we know that

$$(7) \qquad \lim_{t \to 0+} \frac{\dfrac{d}{dt} f\left(\dfrac{1}{t}\right)}{\dfrac{d}{dt} g\left(\dfrac{1}{t}\right)} = L,$$

and hence from the case $x \to a+$,

$$(8) \qquad \lim_{x \to +\infty} \frac{f(x)}{g(x)} = \lim_{t \to 0+} \frac{f(1/t)}{g(1/t)} = L.$$

Proof for $x \to -\infty$. This is the same as the proof for $x \to +\infty$, except that the case $x \to 0-$, instead of the case $x \to 0+$, is used.

Proof for $x \to \infty$. This is the same as the proof for $x \to +\infty$, except that the case $x \to 0$, instead of the case $x \to 0+$, is used.

1303   THE INDETERMINATE FORM ∞/∞

A problem of determining the limit of the quotient of two functions each of which has an infinite limit is said to be of the **indeterminate form** ∞/∞. The technique of using a quotient of derivatives is again appropriate, and the statement is almost identical with that of the Theorem, §1301. The proof, however, is much more difficult and will not be attempted in this book. (For a proof, cf. H§2109, *CWAG*.)

Theorem. L'Hospital's Rule. *If f and g are differentiable functions in a deleted right half-neighborhood D_{a+} of the point a, if $g'(x) \neq 0$ for $x \in D_{a+}$, if $\lim_{x \to a+} f(x) = \infty$ and $\lim_{x \to a+} g(x) = \infty$, and if*

$$(1) \qquad \lim_{x \to a+} \frac{f'(x)}{g'(x)} = L \text{ (finite, } +\infty, -\infty, \text{ or } \infty),$$

then

$$(2) \qquad \lim_{x \to a+} \frac{f(x)}{g(x)} = L.$$

A similar result holds if the deleted right half-neighborhood D_{a+} of a and $x \to a+$ are replaced by any of the following: (i) a deleted left half-neighborhood D_{a-} of a and $x \to a-$, (ii) a deleted neighborhood D_a of a and $x \to a$, (iii) a deleted neighborhood $D_{+\infty}$ of $+\infty$ and $x \to +\infty$, (iv) a deleted neighborhood $D_{-\infty}$ of $-\infty$ and $x \to -\infty$, and (v) a deleted neighborhood D_∞ of ∞ and $x \to \infty$.

Example 1. Show that $\lim\limits_{x \to +\infty} \dfrac{x^a}{e^x} = 0, a \in \Re$.

Solution. If $a \le 0$ the expression is not indeterminate: for $x > 0$, $0 < x^a/e^x \le 1/e^x$, and since by (5), §1105, $\lim_{x \to +\infty} 1/e^x = 0$, $\lim_{x \to +\infty} x^a/e^x = 0$ (cf. Theorem IV, §507). Now assume $a > 0$. Then by (3), §1111, $\lim_{x \to +\infty} x^a = +\infty$, and l'Hospital's rule is applicable:

$$\lim_{x \to +\infty} \frac{x^a}{e^x} = \lim_{x \to +\infty} \frac{ax^{a-1}}{e^x} = \cdots.$$

If this process is continued, an exponent for x in the numerator is ultimately found that is zero or negative. This example shows that the function e^x increases, as $x \to +\infty$, faster than any power of x, and therefore faster than any polynomial. In other words, the result is the same as it would be if the numerator x^a were replaced by the numerator 1.

Example 2. Show that $\lim\limits_{x \to +\infty} \dfrac{\ln x}{x^a} = 0, a \in \mathcal{P}$.

Solution. By (10), §1102, and (3), §1111, $\lim_{x \to +\infty} \ln x = \lim_{x \to +\infty} x^a = +\infty$, and l'Hospital's rule is applicable:

$$\lim_{x \to +\infty} \frac{\ln x}{x^a} = \lim_{x \to +\infty} \frac{1/x}{ax^{a-1}} = \lim_{x \to +\infty} \frac{1}{ax^a} = 0.$$

In other words, the function $\ln x$ increases, as $x \to +\infty$, more slowly than any power of x with positive exponent. The result is the same as it would be if the numerator $\ln x$ were replaced by the numerator 1.

Example 3. Show that $\lim\limits_{x \to +\infty} \dfrac{(\ln x)^b}{x^a} = 0, a$ and $b \in \mathcal{P}$.

Solution. By continuity of the function u^b at $u = 0$ (the limit of the bth power is the bth power of the limit — cf. §506),

$$\lim_{x \to +\infty} \frac{(\ln x)^b}{x^a} = \lim_{x \to +\infty} \left(\frac{\ln x}{x^{a/b}}\right)^b = 0^b = 0,$$

by Example 2.

Example 4. Show that $\lim\limits_{n \to +\infty} \dfrac{e^n}{n!} = 0$.

Solution. This is an indeterminate expression to which l'Hospital's rule does not apply, since the factorial function $n!$ has been defined only for nonnegative integers and hence can not be differentiated. We can establish the limit as follows: Let n be greater than 2. Then

$$\frac{e^n}{n!} = \left(\frac{e}{1} \cdot \frac{e}{2}\right)\left(\frac{e}{3} \cdots \frac{e}{n}\right) \le \frac{e^2}{2}\left(\frac{e}{3}\right)^{n-2}.$$

As $n \to +\infty$, the last factor approaches 0 by (10), §1109, since $0 < e/3 < 1$. (Cf. Ex. 49, §1108.)

Example 5. Criticize the following statement:

$$\lim_{x \to +\infty} \frac{x + \sin x}{x} = \lim_{x \to +\infty} \frac{1 + \cos x}{1},$$

and therefore $\lim_{x \to +\infty} (x + \sin x)/x$ does not exist.

Solution. Although $(x + \sin x)/x$ is an indeterminate expression of the form ∞ / ∞, the hypotheses of l'Hospital's rule are not satisfied, since the function $1 + \cos x$ has no limit, finite or infinite, as $x \to +\infty$. However, the function $(x + \sin x)/x$ does have a limit, as $x \to +\infty$, as we shall now demonstrate. In the first place, by Theorem IV, §507, since

$$0 \leq \left| \frac{\sin x}{x} \right| \leq \frac{1}{x} \to 0,$$

as $x \to +\infty$, $\lim_{x \to +\infty} (\sin x)/x = 0$, and therefore

$$\lim_{x \to +\infty} \frac{x + \sin x}{x} = \lim_{x \to +\infty} 1 + \lim_{x \to +\infty} \frac{\sin x}{x} = 1.$$

This example shows that in the presence of the other hypotheses of l'Hospital's rule, the *nonexistence* of the limit (1) does not imply the *nonexistence* of the limit (2).

1304 EXERCISES

In Exercises 1–25, evaluate the limit, using l'Hospital's rule whenever it is appropriate.

1. $\lim_{x \to 1} \dfrac{2x^2 + x - 3}{4x^2 - 5x + 1}$.

2. $\lim_{x \to 2} \dfrac{x^2 + 3x - 10}{3x^2 - 5x - 2}$.

3. $\lim_{x \to 1} \dfrac{x^3 - x^2 - x + 1}{x^3 - 3x + 2}$.

4. $\lim_{x \to -1} \dfrac{2x^3 + x^2 - 4x - 3}{3x^3 + 8x^2 + 7x + 2}$.

5. $\lim_{x \to \infty} \dfrac{5x^2 - x - 8}{4x^2 + x + 3}$.

6. $\lim_{\theta \to 0} \dfrac{2\theta + \sin \theta}{\tan 4\theta}$.

7. $\lim_{\alpha \to \pi/2} \dfrac{\sin 2\alpha}{\cos 3\alpha}$.

8. $\lim_{t \to 1} \dfrac{\ln t}{\sin \pi t}$.

9. $\lim_{y \to 0} \dfrac{e^{2y} - 1}{\sin 3y}$.

10. $\lim_{x \to 1} \dfrac{e^x - e}{x^3 - 1}$.

11. $\lim_{x \to 1} \dfrac{\sqrt[3]{x} - \sqrt[5]{x}}{\sqrt[4]{x} - \sqrt[6]{x}}$.

12. $\lim_{\beta \to 0} \dfrac{1 - \cos^2 \beta}{\sin^2 3\beta}$.

13. $\lim_{x \to 0} \dfrac{1 - e^{-x^2}}{e^x + e^{-x} - 2}$.

14. $\lim_{x \to 0} \dfrac{\ln(1 + 2x^2)}{x \ln(1 + 3x)}$.

15. $\lim_{x \to 0} \dfrac{\sqrt{1 + x^2} - 1}{x \sin x}$.

16. $\lim_{x \to 0} \dfrac{e^x - e^{-x} - 2x}{x^3}$.

17. $\lim_{x \to 0} \dfrac{\tan x - x}{x^3}$.

18. $\lim_{t \to +\infty} \dfrac{\sqrt{t}}{\ln t}$.

19. $\lim_{u \to +\infty} \dfrac{u^{10} + 5u^2 + 8}{e^{u/2}}$.

20. $\lim_{\theta \to 0} \dfrac{\ln \sin 2\theta}{\ln \tan \theta}$.

21. $\lim_{s \to +\infty} \dfrac{3e^s + 5s}{2e^s + 7s}$.

22. $\lim_{x \to +\infty} \dfrac{\ln(\ln x)}{\ln(x + 1)}$.

23. $\lim_{x \to +\infty} \dfrac{\ln x + \sin x^2}{\ln x}$.

24. $\lim_{n \to +\infty} \dfrac{n!}{n^n}$.

25. $\lim_{n \to +\infty} \dfrac{10^n}{n!}$.

In Exercises 26–29, prove that if a is an arbitrary positive number there exists a positive number N such that the inequality $x > N$ or $n > N$ implies the given inequality.

26. $x^a < e^x$.   **27.** $\ln x < x^a$.

28. $e^n < n!$ **29.** $n! < n^n$.

30. The normal to the curve $y = \ln x$ at the point (a, b) meets the x-axis at the point $(c, 0)$. Prove that $\lim_{a \to +\infty} (c - a) = 0$.

1305 OTHER INDETERMINATE FORMS

In the sense discussed in §1301, each of the following five symbols represents an indeterminate form:

$$(1) \qquad\qquad 0 \cdot \infty, \qquad \infty - \infty, \qquad 0^0, \qquad \infty^0, \qquad 1^\infty.$$

The first of these symbols, for example, represents the case of the product of two functions of which one has the limit 0 and the other has an infinite limit (∞, $+\infty$, or $-\infty$). The following examples and the exercises of §1306 show that the resultant limits in all cases (1) depend on the particular examples concerned.

An expression of the indeterminate form $0 \cdot \infty$ can often be evaluated by writing the product $f(x) \cdot g(x)$ as a quotient and then using l'Hospital's rule (cf. Example 1). An expression of the indeterminate form $\infty - \infty$ sometimes lends itself to rearrangement, use of identities, or judicious multiplication by unity (cf. Examples 2–3). Expressions of indeterminacy of type 0^0, ∞^0, or 1^∞ are usually handled by first taking the natural logarithm: if $y = f(x)^{g(x)}$, then $\ln y = g(x)\ln(f(x))$, and an indeterminacy of the type $0 \cdot \infty$ results. Then, by continuity of the exponential function, $\lim y = \lim \exp(\ln y) = \exp(\lim \ln y)$ (cf. Examples 4–6). Finally, other devices, including substitutions for radicals or reciprocals, and separation of expressions with known limits from indeterminate expressions, are possible (cf. Examples 7–8).

Example 1. Find $\lim\limits_{x \to 0+} x^a \ln x$.

Solution. If $a \leq 0$, the expression is not indeterminate, and the limit is $-\infty$ (cf. (4), §1111, and VI, §1307). If $a > 0$, the limit can be evaluated by l'Hospital's rule, thus (cf. (3) and (4), §1111):

$$\lim_{x \to 0+} \frac{\ln x}{x^{-a}} = \lim_{x \to 0+} \frac{1/x}{-ax^{-a-1}} = \lim_{x \to 0+} \frac{x^a}{-a} = 0.$$

The intuitive idea of this result is that whenever the function $x^a \ln x$ is indeterminate and of the form $0 \cdot \infty$, as $x \to 0+$, the power function x^a is "dominant," and the result is the same as it would be if the logarithmic factor were not present. (Cf. Example 2, §1303.)

Example 2. $\lim\limits_{x \to \pi/2} (\sec x - \tan x) = \lim\limits_{x \to \pi/2} \dfrac{1 - \sin x}{\cos x} = \lim\limits_{x \to \pi/2} \dfrac{-\cos x}{-\sin x} = 0.$

Alternatively, without the use of l'Hospital's rule,

$$\lim_{x \to \pi/2} (\sec x - \tan x) = \lim_{x \to \pi/2} \frac{\sec^2 x - \tan^2 x}{\sec x + \tan x} = \lim_{x \to \pi/2} \frac{\cos x}{1 + \sin x} = 0.$$

Example 3. $\lim_{x \to \infty} (\sqrt{x^2 - a^2} - |x|) = \lim_{x \to \infty} \dfrac{\sqrt{x^2 - a^2} - |x|}{1} \cdot \dfrac{\sqrt{x^2 + a^2} + |x|}{\sqrt{x^2 + a^2} + |x|}$

$$= \lim_{x \to \infty} \frac{-a^2}{\sqrt{x^2 + a^2} + |x|} = 0.$$

Example 4. Find $\lim_{x \to 0+} x^x$.

Solution. If $y = x^x$, then $\ln y = x \ln x$, and, by Example 1, $\lim_{x \to 0+} \ln y = \lim_{x \to 0+} \ln x = 0$. Therefore, by continuity of the function e^x (cf. § 506),

$$\lim_{x \to 0+} y = \lim_{x \to 0+} \exp(\ln y) = \exp(\lim_{x \to 0+} \ln y) = \exp 0 = 1.$$

Example 5. Find $\lim_{x \to +\infty} (1 + ax)^{1/x}, a > 0$.

Solution. If $y = (1 + ax)^{1/x}$, $\ln y = (\ln(1 + ax))/x$, and

$$\lim_{x \to +\infty} \ln y = \lim_{x \to +\infty} \frac{\ln(1 + ax)}{x} = \lim_{x \to +\infty} \frac{a}{1 + ax} = 0.$$

Therefore,

$$\lim_{x \to +\infty} y = \exp \lim_{x \to +\infty} \frac{\ln(1 + ax)}{x} = \exp 0 = 1.$$

Example 6. Show that $\lim_{x \to 0} (1 + ax)^{1/x} = e^a, a \in \mathfrak{R}$.

Solution. If $y = (1 + ax)^{1/x}$, $\ln y = (\ln(1 + ax))/x$, and

$$\lim_{x \to 0} \ln y = \lim_{x \to 0} \frac{\ln(1 + ax)}{x} = \lim_{x \to 0} \frac{a}{1 + ax} = a.$$

Therefore,

$$\lim_{x \to 0} y = \exp \lim_{x \to 0} \frac{\ln(1 + ax)}{x} = \exp a = e^a.$$

Example 7. Find $\lim_{x \to 0+} xe^{1/x}$.

Solution. If this is written $\lim_{x \to 0+} \dfrac{e^{1/x}}{1/x}$, differentiation leads to the answer. However, a simpler evaluation is provided by writing

$$\lim_{t \to +\infty} \frac{e^t}{t} = \lim_{t \to +\infty} \frac{e^t}{1} = +\infty.$$

Example 8. Find $\lim_{x \to 1} \dfrac{12 \sin (\pi/2x) \ln x}{(x^3 + 5)(x - 1)}$.

We separate the factors that tend toward zero:

$$\lim_{x \to 1} \frac{12 \sin (\pi/2x)}{x^3 + 5} \cdot \lim_{x \to 1} \frac{\ln x}{x - 1} = \frac{12 \sin (\pi/2)}{6} \cdot \lim_{x \to 1} \frac{1/x}{1} = 2.$$

1306 EXERCISES

In Exercises 1–27, evaluate the limit, using l'Hospital's rule whenever it is appropriate.

1. $\lim\limits_{x \to +\infty} x e^{-x}$.

2. $\lim\limits_{x \to 0+} \sqrt{x}\, \ln x$.

3. $\lim\limits_{x \to 0+} (\sin x)\ln x$.

4. $\lim\limits_{x \to \frac{1}{2}\pi} (x - \tfrac{1}{2}\pi)\tan x$.

5. $\lim\limits_{x \to 0} (\cot x)\ln(1 + x)$.

6. $\lim\limits_{x \to 0} \left(\dfrac{1}{1 - e^{-x}} - \dfrac{1}{x} \right)$

7. $\lim\limits_{x \to 0} \left(\dfrac{1}{\ln(1 + x)} - \dfrac{1}{x} \right)$.

8. $\lim\limits_{x \to 0} \left(\dfrac{1}{x \sin x} - \dfrac{1}{x^2} \right)$.

9. $\lim\limits_{x \to 0} \left(\dfrac{1}{1 - \cos x} - \dfrac{2}{x^2} \right)$.

10. $\lim\limits_{x \to 0+} x^{\sin x}$.

11. $\lim\limits_{x \to \frac{1}{2}\pi-} (\cos x)^{\cos x}$.

12. $\lim\limits_{x \to 0+} x^{1/\ln x}$.

13. $\lim\limits_{x \to \frac{1}{2}\pi-} (\tan x)^{\cos x}$.

14. $\lim\limits_{x \to +\infty} (1 + x^5)^{2/x}$.

15. $\lim\limits_{x \to +\infty} (1 + 2x e^x)^{1/x}$.

16. $\lim\limits_{x \to 0+} (e^{2/x} - 3)^x$.

17. $\lim\limits_{x \to 0} (1 + x^2)^{1/x}$.

18. $\lim\limits_{x \to 0} (e^{3x} + 2x)^{1/x}$.

19. $\lim\limits_{x \to 0} (\sec x + \tan x)^{\csc x}$.

20. $\lim\limits_{x \to 0} (\cos 4x)^{1/x^2}$.

21. $\lim\limits_{x \to 0} (\sec x)^{1/x^2}$.

22. $\lim\limits_{x \to 0+} \dfrac{1}{x} e^{-1/x}$.

23. $\lim\limits_{x \to +\infty} x \sin \dfrac{1}{x}$

24. $\lim\limits_{x \to 0+} \left(\dfrac{1 + x^5}{x^5} \right)^{2x}$.

25. $\lim\limits_{x \to 0} \dfrac{3 e^{x^2} \sin x \cos \pi x}{5x(2 + 3x^2)}$.

26. $\lim\limits_{x \to 1} \dfrac{5x^2 (2 + \cos \pi x)\ln x}{(x^2 - 1)\tan \frac{1}{3}\pi x}$.

27. $\lim\limits_{x \to +\infty} \dfrac{1}{x^{10}} \displaystyle\int_0^x e^{u^2}\, du$.

1307 DETERMINATE EXPRESSIONS; CURVE SKETCHING

Certain combinations of zero and infinite limits may have a superficial appearance of indeterminacy, and yet have specific determinations. For example, the limit statements of Theorem I, §510, can be expressed as follows:

I. $\dfrac{1}{\infty} = 0$.

II. $\dfrac{1}{0} = \infty$.

III. $\dfrac{m}{0} = \infty$, where $m \neq 0$.

Other determinate expressions are listed below with their determinations, where the behavior of the independent variable is unspecified. Although these limit statements are all plausible intuitively, their proofs are not elementary. For proofs, see H §2109 and H §2110, *CWAG*. The list is not intended to be exhaustive.

IV. $p \cdot (+\infty) = +\infty, p > 0$.

V. $c + \infty = \infty, c \in \Re$.

VI. $\infty \cdot \infty = \infty$.

VII. $(+\infty) + (+\infty) = +\infty$.

VIII. $(0+)^{+\infty} = 0.$

IX. $(+\infty)^{+\infty} = +\infty.$

X. $(+\infty)^{-\infty} = 0.$

XI. $c^{+\infty} = 0, 0 < c < 1.$

XII. $c^{+\infty} = +\infty, c > 1.$

The evaluations of indeterminate expressions by the techniques discussed in the earlier sections of this chapter, together with evaluations of determinate expressions like those listed above, permit curve sketching of functions not previously amenable to analysis.

Example 1.   Discuss the graph of the function $xe^{-x}, x \in \mathfrak{R}.$

Solution.   For use presently we find the first and second derivatives of $y = xe^{-x}$:

(1) $$y' = e^{-x}(1 - x), y'' = e^{-x}(x - 2).$$

From (1) we see that the function xe^{-x} is strictly increasing on the interval $(-\infty, 1]$ and strictly decreasing on the interval $[1, +\infty)$, and that its graph is concave down for $x < 2$ and concave up for $x > 2$. Furthermore, xe^{-x} has a strict global maximum value of $e^{-1} = 1/e$ at $x = 1$, and its graph has a point of inflection at $(2, 2e^{-2}) = (2, 2/e^2)$. By Example 1, §1303, $\lim_{x \to +\infty} xe^{-x} = \lim_{x \to +\infty} x/e^x = 0$, and the x-axis is a horizontal asymptote for the graph. Furthermore, $\lim_{x \to -\infty} xe^{-x} = -\infty$, by VI together with accounting for signs, and there is no vertical asymptote. The graph is shown in Figure 1307-1.

Example 2.   Discuss the graph of the function
$$f(x) \equiv \begin{cases} x \ln x, x > 0, \\ 0, \quad x = 0. \end{cases}$$

Solution.   For use presently we find the first and second derivatives of $y = x \ln x, x > 0$:

(2) $$y' = \ln x + 1, \quad y'' = \frac{1}{x}.$$

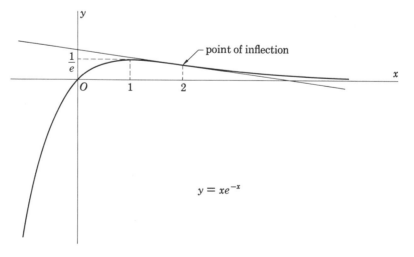

$$y = xe^{-x}$$

Figure 1307-1

By Example 1, §1305, $\lim_{x\to 0+} x \ln x = 0$, and therefore $f(x)$ is continuous on $[0, +\infty)$. By (2), since $y' < 0$ whenever $\ln x < -1$, or equivalently, when $x < e^{-1} = 1/e$, the function $f(x)$ is strictly decreasing on $[0, 1/e]$. Similarly, $f(x)$ is strictly increasing on $[1/e, +\infty)$, and therefore $f(x)$ has a strict global minimum value of $(1/e)(-1) = -1/e$ at $x = 1/e$. Since $y'' > 0$ for $x > 0$, the graph is everywhere concave up, and there are no points of inflection. By VI, together with accounting for signs, $\lim_{x\to +\infty} x \ln x = +\infty$. There is no horizontal asymptote nor vertical asymptote. Since

$$\lim_{h\to 0+} \frac{f(0+h) - f(0)}{h} = \lim_{h\to 0+} \frac{h \ln h}{h} = -\infty,$$

there is a vertical tangent at $(0, 0)$. The graph is shown in Figure 1307-2.

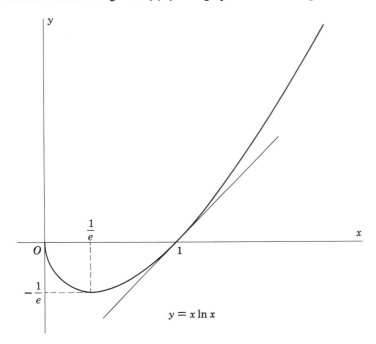

$$y = x \ln x$$

Figure 1307-2

1308   EXERCISES

In Exercises 1–18, use I-XII, §1307, to evaluate the limit.

1. $\lim\limits_{x\to 0} \dfrac{\cos x}{\ln x}$.

2. $\lim\limits_{x\to \pi/2} \dfrac{1+\cos x}{\tan x}$.

3. $\lim\limits_{x\to 1} \dfrac{x^2}{\cos \frac{1}{2}\pi x}$.

4. $\lim\limits_{x\to 0} \dfrac{e^{x^2}}{\sin x}$.

5. $\lim\limits_{x\to 1} \dfrac{e^x}{\ln x}$.

6. $\lim\limits_{x\to 0} \dfrac{\ln(2+x^2)}{\tan x}$.

7. $\lim\limits_{x\to +\infty} \dfrac{x+1}{x} e^x$.

8. $\lim\limits_{x\to +\infty} \dfrac{3x^2}{2x^2+1} \ln x$.

9. $\lim\limits_{x\to \pi/2} (e^x + \tan x)$.

10. $\lim\limits_{x\to +\infty} e^x \ln x$.

11. $\lim\limits_{x\to +\infty} (3^x + \log_{10} x)$.

12. $\lim\limits_{x\to 0+} x^{1/x}$.

13. $\lim\limits_{x\to +\infty} (\ln x)^x$.

14. $\lim\limits_{x\to 0+} |\ln x|^{1/x}$.

15. $\lim\limits_{x\to 0+} |\ln x|^{\ln x}$.

16. $\lim\limits_{x\to+\infty} \left(\dfrac{x}{2x+1}\right)^x.$ **17.** $\lim\limits_{x\to0+} \left(\dfrac{x+1}{x+2}\right)^{1/x}.$ **18.** $\lim\limits_{x\to0+} (1+\cos x)^{\csc x}.$

In Exercises 19–22, discuss and draw the graph of the given function $f(x)$. Give particular attention to asymptotes, extrema, concavity, points of inflection, and limits at infinity.

19. $f(x) \equiv xe^x.$ **20.** $f(x) \equiv x^2e^{-x}.$

21. $f(x) \equiv xe^{-x^2/2}.$ **22.** $f(x) \equiv \begin{cases} x^2 \ln x, & x > 0, \\ 0, & x = 0. \end{cases}$

In Exercise 22 show that the graph has a horizontal tangent line at $(0, 0)$.

In Exercises 23 and 24, show that the given line is an asymptote for the graph of the given function. (Cf. Figures 407-5 and 624-1.)

23. $y = 0, f(x) \equiv \begin{cases} \sin \dfrac{1}{x}, & x \neq 0, \\ 0, & x = 0. \end{cases}$ **24.** $y = 1, f(x) \equiv \begin{cases} x \sin \dfrac{1}{x}, & x \neq 0, \\ 0, & x = 0. \end{cases}$

APPENDIX

Table I.	Squares, cubes, roots, reciprocals	366
Table II.	Four-place common logarithms	368
Table III.	Natural logarithms	370
Table IV.	Numerical constants	372
Table V.	Exponential function	373
Table VI.	Natural trigonometric functions, degree measure	377
Table VII.	Natural trigonometric functions, radian measure	378
Table VIII.	Degrees, minutes, and seconds to radians	379
Table IX.	Radians to degrees, minutes, and seconds	379
Table X.	Formulas from geometry	380
Table XI.	Greek alphabet	380

Table I. Squares, cubes, roots, reciprocals, 1 - 50

n	n^2	n^3	$\sqrt{n}$	$\sqrt{10n}$	$\sqrt[3]{n}$	$\sqrt[3]{10n}$	$\sqrt[3]{100n}$	$10/n$
1	1	1	1.00 000	3.16 228	1.00 000	2.15 443	4.64 159	10.00 00
2	4	8	1.41 421	4.47 214	1.25 992	2.71 442	5.84 804	5.00 00 0
3	9	27	1.73 205	5.47 723	1.44 225	3.10 723	6.69 433	3.33 33 3
4	16	64	2.00 000	6.32 456	1.58 740	3.41 995	7.36 806	2.50 00 0
5	25	125	2.23 607	7.07 107	1.70 998	3.68 403	7.93 701	2.00 00 0
6	36	216	2.44 949	7.74 597	1.81 712	3.91 487	8.43 433	1.66 66 7
7	49	343	2.64 575	8.36 660	1.91 293	4.12 129	8.87 904	1.42 85 7
8	64	512	2.82 843	8.94 427	2.00 000	4.30 887	9.28 318	1.25 00 0
9	81	729	3.00 000	9.48 683	2.08 008	4.48 140	9.65 489	1.11 11 1
10	100	1 000	3.16 228	10.00 00	2.15 443	4.64 159	10.00 00	1.00 00 0
11	121	1 331	3.31 662	10.48 81	2.22 398	4.79 142	10.32 28	.90 90 91
12	144	1 728	3.46 410	10.95 45	2.28 943	4.93 242	10.62 66	.83 33 33
13	169	2 197	3.60 555	11.40 18	2.35 133	5.06 580	10.91 39	.76 92 31
14	196	2 744	3.74 166	11.83 22	2.41 014	5.19 249	11.18 69	.71 42 86
15	225	3 375	3.87 298	12.24 74	2.46 621	5.31 329	11.44 71	.66 66 67
16	256	4 096	4.00 000	12.64 91	2.51 984	5.42 884	11.69 61	.62 50 00
17	289	4 913	4.12 311	13.03 84	2.57 128	5.53 966	11.93 48	.58 82 35
18	324	5 832	4.24 264	13.41 64	2.62 074	5.64 622	12.16 44	.55 55 56
19	361	6 859	4.35 890	13.78 40	2.66 840	5.74 890	12.38 56	.52 63 16
20	400	8 000	4.47 214	14.14 21	2.71 442	5.84 804	12.59 92	.50 00 00
21	441	9 261	4.58 258	14.49 14	2.75 892	5.94 392	12.80 58	.47 61 90
22	484	10 648	4.69 042	14.83 24	2.80 204	6.03 681	13.00 59	.45 45 45
23	529	12 167	4.79 583	15.16 58	2.84 387	6.12 693	13.20 01	.43 47 83
24	576	13 824	4.89 898	15.49 19	2.88 450	6.21 446	13.38 87	.41 66 67
25	625	15 625	5.00 000	15.81 14	2.92 402	6.29 961	13.57 21	.40 00 00
26	676	17 576	5.09 902	16.12 45	2.96 250	6.38 250	13.75 07	.38 46 15
27	729	19 683	5.19 615	16.43 17	3.00 000	6.46 330	13.92 48	.37 03 70
28	784	21 952	5.29 150	16.73 32	3.03 659	6.54 213	14.09 46	.35 71 43
29	841	24 389	5.38 516	17.02 94	3.07 232	6.61 911	14.26 04	.34 48 28
30	900	27 000	5.47 723	17.32 05	3.10 723	6.69 433	14.42 25	.33 33 33
31	961	29 791	5.56 766	17.60 68	3.14 138	6.76 790	14.58 10	.32 25 81
32	1 024	32 768	5.65 685	17.88 85	3.17 480	6.83 990	14.73 61	.31 25 00
33	1 089	35 937	5.74 456	18.16 59	3.20 753	6.91 042	14.88 81	.30 30 30
34	1 156	39 304	5.83 095	18.43 91	3.23 961	6.97 953	15.03 69	.29 41 18
35	1 225	42 875	5.91 608	18.70 83	3.27 107	7.04 730	15.18 29	.28 57 14
36	1 296	46 656	6.00 000	18.97 37	3.30 193	7.11 379	15.32 62	.27 77 78
37	1 369	50 653	6.08 276	19.23 54	3.33 222	7.17 905	15.46 68	.27 02 70
38	1 444	54 872	6.16 441	19.49 36	3.36 198	7.24 316	15.60 49	.26 31 58
39	1 521	59 319	6.24 500	19.74 84	3.39 121	7.30 614	15.74 06	.25 64 10
40	1 600	64 000	6.32 456	20.00 00	3.41 995	7.36 806	15.87 40	.25 00 00
41	1 681	68 921	6.40 312	20.24 85	3.44 822	7.42 896	16.00 52	.24 39 02
42	1 764	74 088	6.48 074	20.49 39	3.47 603	7.48 887	16.13 43	.23 80 95
43	1 849	79 507	6.55 744	20.73 64	3.50 340	7.54 784	16.26 13	.23 25 58
44	1 936	85 184	6.63 325	20.97 62	3.53 035	7.60 590	16.38 64	.22 72 73
45	2 025	91 125	6.70 820	21.21 32	3.55 689	7.66 309	16.50 96	.22 22 22
46	2 116	97 336	6.78 233	21.44 76	3.58 305	7.71 944	16.63 10	.21 73 91
47	2 209	103 823	6.85 565	21.67 95	3.60 883	7.77 498	16.75 07	.21 27 66
48	2 304	110 592	6.92 820	21.90 89	3.63 424	7.82 974	16.86 87	.20 83 33
49	2 401	117 649	7.00 000	22.13 59	3.65 931	7.88 374	16.98 50	.20 40 82
50	2 500	125 000	7.07 107	22.36 07	3.68 403	7.93 701	17.09 98	.20 00 00

Table I (continued). Squares, cubes, roots, reciprocals, 51 - 100

n	n^2	n^3	$\sqrt{n}$	$\sqrt{10n}$	$\sqrt[3]{n}$	$\sqrt[3]{10n}$	$\sqrt[3]{100n}$	$10/n$
51	2 601	132 651	7.14 143	22.58 32	3.70 843	7.98 957	17.21 30	.19 60 78
52	2 704	140 608	7.21 110	22.80 35	3.73 251	8.04 145	17.32 48	.19 23 08
53	2 809	148 877	7.28 011	23.02 17	3.75 629	8.09 267	17.43 51	.18 86 79
54	2 916	157 464	7.34 847	23.23 79	3.77 976	8.14 325	17.54 41	.18 51 85
55	3 025	166 375	7.41 620	23.45 21	3.80 295	8.19 321	17.65 17	.18 18 18
56	3 136	175 616	7.48 331	23.66 43	3.82 586	8.24 257	17.75 81	.17 85 71
57	3 249	185 193	7.54 983	23.87 47	3.84 850	8.29 134	17.86 32	.17 54 39
58	3 364	195 112	7.61 577	24.08 32	3.87 088	8.33 955	17.96 70	.17 24 14
59	3 481	205 379	7.68 115	24.28 99	3.89 300	8.38 721	18.06 97	.16 94 92
60	3 600	216 000	7.74 597	24.49 49	3.91 487	8.43 433	18.17 12	.16 66 67
61	3 721	226 981	7.81 025	24.69 82	3.93 650	8.48 093	18.27 16	.16 39 34
62	3 844	238 328	7.87 401	24.89 98	3.95 789	8.52 702	18.37 09	.16 12 90
63	3 969	250 047	7.93 725	25.09 98	3.97 906	8.57 262	18.46 91	.15 87 30
64	4 096	262 144	8.00 000	25.29 82	4.00 000	8.61 774	18.56 64	.15 62 50
65	4 225	274 625	8 06 226	25.49 51	4.02 073	8.66 239	18.66 26	.15 38 46
66	4 356	287 496	8.12 404	25.69 05	4.04 124	8.70 659	18.75 78	.15 15 15
67	4 489	300 763	8.18 535	25.88 44	4.06 155	8.75 034	18.85 20	.14 92 54
68	4 624	314 432	8.24 621	26.07 68	4.08 166	8.79 366	18.94 54	.14 70 59
69	4 761	328 509	8.30 662	26.26 79	4.10 157	8.83 656	19.03 78	.14 49 28
70	4 900	343 000	8.36 660	26.45 75	4.12 129	8.87 904	19.12 93	.14 28 57
71	5 041	357 911	8.42 615	26.64 58	4.14 082	8.92 112	19.22 00	.14 08 45
72	5 184	373 248	8.48 528	26.83 28	4.16 017	8.96 281	19.30 98	.13 88 89
73	5 329	389 017	8.54 400	27.01 85	4.17 934	9.00 411	19.39 88	.13 69 86
74	5 476	405 224	8.60 233	27.20 29	4.19 834	9.04 504	19.48 70	.13 51 35
75	5 625	421 875	8.66 025	27.38 61	4.21 716	9.08 560	19.57 43	.13 33 33
76	5 776	438 976	8.71 780	27.56 81	4.23 582	9.12 581	19.66 10	.13 15 79
77	5 929	456 533	8.77 496	27.74 89	4.25 432	9.16 566	19.74 68	.12 98 70
78	6 084	474 552	8.83 176	27.92 85	4.27 266	9.20 516	19.83 19	.12 82 05
79	6 241	493 039	8.88 819	28.10 69	4.29 084	9.24 434	19.91 63	.12 65 82
80	6 400	512 000	8.94 427	28.28 43	4.30 887	9.28 318	20.00 00	.12 50 00
81	6 561	531 441	9.00 000	28.46 05	4.32 675	9.32 170	20.08 30	.12 34 57
82	6 724	551 368	9.05 539	28.63 56	4.34 448	9.35 990	20.16 53	.12 19 51
83	6 889	571 787	9.11 043	28.80 97	4.36 207	9.39 780	20.24 69	.12 04 82
84	7 056	592 704	9.16 515	28.98 28	4.37 952	9.43 539	20.32 79	.11 90 48
85	7 225	614 125	9.21 954	29.15 48	4.39 683	9.47 268	20.40 83	.11 76 47
86	7 396	636 056	9.27 362	29.32 58	4.41 400	9.50 969	20.48 80	.11 62 79
87	7 569	658 503	9.32 738	29.49 58	4.43 105	9.54 640	20.56 71	.11 49 43
88	7 744	681 472	9.38 083	29.66 48	4.44 796	9.58 284	20.64 56	.11 36 36
89	7 921	704 969	9.43 398	29.83 29	4.46 475	9.61 900	20.72 35	.11 23 60
90	8 100	729 000	9.48 683	30.00 00	4.48 140	9.65 489	20.80 08	.11 11 11
91	8 281	753 571	9.53 939	30.16 62	4.49 794	9.69 052	20.87 76	.10 98 90
92	8 464	778 688	9.59 166	30.33 15	4.51 436	9.72 589	20.95 38	.10 86 96
93	8 649	804 357	9.64 365	30.49 59	4.53 065	9.76 100	21.02 94	.10 75 27
94	8 836	830 584	9.69 536	30.65 94	4.54 684	9.79 586	21.10 45	.10 63 83
95	9 025	857 375	9.74 679	30.82 21	4.56 290	9.83 048	21.17 91	.10 52 63
96	9 216	884 736	9.79 796	30.98 39	4.57 886	9.86 485	21.25 32	.10 41 67
97	9 409	912 673	9.84 886	31.14 48	4.59 470	9.89 898	21.32 67	.10 30 93
98	9 604	941 192	9.89 949	31.30 50	4.61 044	9.93 288	21.39 97	.10 20 41
99	9 801	970 299	9.94 987	31.46 43	4.62 607	9.96 655	21.47 23	.10 10 10
100	10 000	1 000 000	10.00 000	31.62 28	4.64 159	10.00 000	21.54 43	.10 00 00

Table II. Four-place common logarithms, 10.0 - 54.9

n	0	1	2	3	4	5	6	7	8	9
10	0000	0043	0086	0128	0170	0212	0253	0294	0334	0374
11	0414	0453	0492	0531	0569	0607	0645	0682	0719	0755
12	0792	0828	0864	0899	0934	0969	1004	1038	1072	1106
13	1139	1173	1206	1239	1271	1303	1335	1367	1399	1430
14	1461	1492	1523	1553	1584	1614	1644	1673	1703	1732
15	1761	1790	1818	1847	1875	1903	1931	1959	1987	2014
16	2041	2068	2095	2122	2148	2175	2201	2227	2253	2279
17	2304	2330	2355	2380	2405	2430	2455	2480	2504	2529
18	2553	2577	2601	2625	2648	2672	2695	2718	2742	2765
19	2788	2810	2833	2856	2878	2900	2923	2945	2967	2989
20	3010	3032	3054	3075	3096	3118	3139	3160	3183	3201
21	3222	3243	3263	3284	3304	3324	3345	3365	3385	3404
22	3424	3444	3464	3483	3502	3522	3541	3560	3579	3598
23	3617	3636	3655	3674	3692	3711	3729	3747	3766	3784
24	3802	3820	3838	3856	3874	3892	3909	3927	3945	3962
25	3979	3997	4014	4031	4048	4065	4082	4099	4116	4133
26	4150	4166	4183	4200	4216	4232	4249	4265	4281	4298
27	4314	4330	4346	4362	4378	4393	4409	4425	4440	4456
28	4472	4487	4502	4518	4533	4548	4564	4579	4594	4609
29	4624	4639	4654	4669	4683	4698	4713	4728	4742	4757
30	4771	4786	4800	4814	4829	4843	4857	4871	4886	4900
31	4914	4928	4942	4955	4969	4983	4997	5011	5024	5038
32	5051	5065	5079	5092	5105	5119	5132	5145	5159	5172
33	5185	5198	5211	5224	5237	5250	5263	5276	5289	5302
34	5315	5328	5340	5353	5366	5378	5391	5403	5416	5428
35	5441	5453	5465	5478	5490	5502	5514	5527	5539	5551
36	5563	5575	5587	5599	5611	5623	5635	5647	5658	5670
37	5682	5694	5705	5717	5729	5740	5752	5763	5775	5786
38	5798	5809	5821	5832	5843	5855	5866	5877	5888	5899
39	5911	5922	5933	5944	5955	5966	5977	5988	5999	6010
40	6021	6031	6042	6053	6064	6075	6085	6096	6107	6117
41	6128	6138	6149	6160	6170	6180	6191	6201	6212	6222
42	6232	6243	6253	6263	6274	6284	6294	6304	6314	6325
43	6335	6345	6355	6365	6375	6385	6395	6405	6415	6425
44	6435	6444	6454	6464	6474	6484	6493	6503	6513	6522
45	6532	6542	6551	6561	6571	6580	6590	6599	6609	6618
46	6628	6637	6646	6656	6665	6675	6684	6693	6702	6712
47	6721	6730	6739	6749	6758	6767	6776	6785	6794	6803
48	6812	6821	6830	6839	6848	6857	6866	6875	6884	6893
49	6902	6911	6920	6928	6937	6946	6955	6964	6972	6981
50	6990	6998	7007	7016	7024	7033	7042	7050	7059	7067
51	7076	7084	7093	7101	7110	7118	7126	7135	7143	7152
52	7160	7168	7177	7185	7193	7202	7210	7218	7226	7235
53	7243	7251	7259	7267	7275	7284	7292	7300	7308	7316
54	7324	7332	7340	7348	7356	7364	7372	7380	7388	7396

Table II (continued).   Four-place common logarithms, 55.0 - 99.9

n	0	1	2	3	4	5	6	7	8	9
55	7404	7412	7419	7427	7435	7443	7451	7459	7466	7474
56	7482	7490	7497	7505	7513	7520	7528	7536	7543	7551
57	7559	7566	7574	7582	7589	7597	7604	7612	7619	7627
58	7634	7642	7649	7657	7664	7672	7679	7686	7694	7701
59	7709	7716	7723	7731	7738	7745	7752	7760	7767	7774
60	7782	7789	7796	7803	7810	7818	7825	7832	7839	7846
61	7853	7860	7868	7875	7882	7889	7896	7903	7910	7917
62	7924	7931	7938	7945	7952	7959	7966	7973	7980	7987
63	7993	8000	8007	8014	8021	8028	8035	8041	8048	8055
64	8062	8069	8075	8082	8089	8096	8102	8109	8116	8122
65	8129	8136	8142	8149	8156	8162	8169	8176	8182	8189
66	8195	8202	8209	8215	8222	8228	8235	8241	8248	8254
67	8261	8267	8274	8280	8287	8293	8299	8306	8312	8319
68	8325	8331	8338	8344	8351	8357	8363	8370	8376	8382
69	8388	8395	8401	8407	8414	8420	8426	8432	8439	8445
70	8451	8457	8463	8470	8476	8482	8488	8494	8500	8506
71	8513	8519	8525	8531	8537	8543	8549	8555	8561	8567
72	8573	8579	8585	8591	8597	8603	8609	8615	8621	8627
73	8633	8639	8645	8651	8657	8663	8669	8675	8681	8686
74	8692	8698	8704	8710	8716	8722	8727	8733	8739	8745
75	8751	8756	8762	8768	8774	8779	8785	8791	8797	8802
76	8808	8814	8820	8825	8831	8837	8842	8848	8854	8859
77	8865	8871	8876	8882	8887	8893	8899	8904	8910	8915
78	8921	8927	8932	8938	8943	8949	8954	8960	8965	8971
79	8976	8982	8987	8993	8998	9004	9009	9015	9020	9025
80	9031	9036	9042	9047	9053	9058	9063	9069	9074	9079
81	9085	9090	9096	9101	9106	9112	9117	9122	9128	9133
82	9138	9143	9149	9154	9159	9165	9170	9175	9180	9186
83	9191	9196	9201	9206	9212	9217	9222	9227	9232	9238
84	9243	9248	9253	9258	9263	9269	9274	9279	9284	9289
85	9294	9299	9304	9309	9315	9320	9325	9330	9335	9340
86	9345	9350	9355	9360	9365	9370	9375	9380	9385	9390
87	9395	9400	9405	9410	9415	9420	9425	9430	9435	9440
88	9445	9450	9455	9460	9465	9469	9474	9479	9484	9489
89	9494	9499	9504	9509	9513	9518	9523	9528	9533	9538
90	9542	9547	9552	9557	9562	9566	9571	9576	9581	9586
91	9590	9595	9600	9605	9609	9614	9619	9624	9628	9633
92	9638	9643	9647	9652	9657	9661	9666	9671	9675	9680
93	9685	9689	9694	9699	9703	9708	9713	9717	9722	9727
94	9731	9736	9741	9745	9750	9754	9759	9763	9768	9773
95	9777	9782	9786	9791	9795	9800	9805	9809	9814	9818
96	9823	9827	9832	9836	9841	9845	9850	9854	9859	9863
97	9868	9872	9877	9881	9886	9890	9894	9899	9903	9908
98	9912	9917	9921	9926	9930	9934	9939	9943	9948	9952
99	9956	9961	9965	9969	9974	9978	9983	9987	9991	9996

Table III. Natural logarithms, 0.01 - 5.99

n	0	1	2	3	4	5	6	7	8	9
0.0	S	5.395	6.088	6.493	6.781	7.004	7.187	7.341	7.474	7.592
0.1	u 7.697	7.793	7.880	7.960	8.034	8.103	8.167	8.228	8.285	8.339
0.2	b 8.391	8.439	8.486	8.530	8.573	8.614	8.653	8.691	8.727	8.762
0.3	t 8.796	8.829	8.861	8.891	8.921	8.950	8.978	9.006	9.032	9.058
0.4	r 9.084	9.108	9.132	9.156	9.179	9.201	9.223	9.245	9.266	9.287
	a									
0.5	c 9.307	9.327	9.346	9.365	9.384	9.402	9.420	9.438	9.455	9.472
0.6	t 9.489	9.506	9.522	9.538	9.554	9.569	9.584	9.600	9.614	9.629
0.7	9.643	9.658	9.671	9.685	9.699	9.712	9.726	9.739	9.752	9.764
0.8	10 9.777	9.789	9.802	9.814	9.826	9.837	9.849	9.861	9.872	9.883
0.9	9.895	9.906	9.917	9.927	9.938	9.949	9.959	9.970	9.980	9.990
1.0	0.0 0000	0995	1980	2956	3922	4879	5827	6766	7696	8618
1.1	9531	*0436	*1333	*2222	*3103	*3976	*4842	*5700	*6551	*7395
1.2	0.1 8232	9062	9885	*0701	*1511	*2314	*3111	*3902	*4686	*5464
1.3	0.2 6236	7003	7763	8518	9267	*0010	*0748	*1481	*2208	*2930
1.4	0.3 3647	4359	5066	5767	6464	7156	7844	8526	9204	9878
1.5	0.4 0547	1211	1871	2527	3178	3825	4469	5108	5742	6373
1.6	7000	7623	8243	8858	9470	*0078	*0682	*1282	*1879	*2473
1.7	0.5 3063	3649	4232	4812	5389	5962	6531	7098	7661	8222
1.8	8779	9333	9884	*0432	*0977	*1519	*2058	*2594	*3127	*3658
1.9	0.6 4185	4710	5233	5752	6269	6783	7294	7803	8310	8813
2.0	9315	9813	*0310	*0804	*1295	*1784	*2271	*2755	*3237	*3716
2.1	0.7 4194	4669	5142	5612	6081	6547	7011	7473	7932	8390
2.2	8846	9299	9751	*0200	*0648	*1093	*1536	*1978	*2418	*2855
2.3	0.8 3291	3725	4157	4587	5015	5442	5866	6289	6710	7129
2.4	7547	7963	8377	8789	9200	9609	*0016	*0422	*0826	*1228
2.5	0.9 1629	2028	2426	2822	3216	3609	4001	4391	4779	5166
2.6	5551	5935	6317	6698	7078	7456	7833	8208	8582	8954
2.7	9325	9695	*0063	*0430	*0796	*1160	*1523	*1885	*2245	*2604
2.8	1.0 2962	3318	3674	4028	4380	4732	5082	5431	5779	6126
2.9	6471	6815	7158	7500	7841	8181	8519	8856	9192	9527
3.0	9861	*0194	*0526	*0856	*1186	*1514	*1841	*2168	*2493	*2817
3.1	1.1 3140	3462	3783	4103	4422	4740	5057	5373	5688	6002
3.2	6315	6627	6938	7248	7557	7865	8173	8479	8784	9089
3.3	9392	9695	9996	*0297	*0597	*0896	*1194	*1491	*1788	*2083
3.4	1.2 2378	2671	2964	3256	3547	3837	4127	4415	4703	4990
3.5	5276	5562	5846	6130	6413	6695	6976	7257	7536	7815
3.6	8093	8371	8647	8923	9198	9473	9746	*0019	*0291	*0563
3.7	1.3 0833	1103	1372	1641	1909	2176	2442	2708	2972	3237
3.8	3500	3763	4025	4286	4547	4807	5067	5325	5584	5841
3.9	6098	6354	6609	6864	7118	7372	7624	7877	8128	8379
4.0	8629	8879	9128	9377	9624	9872	*0118	*0364	*0610	*0854
4.1	1.4 1099	1342	1585	1828	2070	2311	2552	2792	3031	3270
4.2	3508	3746	3984	4220	4456	4692	4927	5161	5395	5629
4.3	5862	6094	6326	6557	6787	7018	7247	7476	7705	7933
4.4	8160	8387	8614	8840	9065	9290	9515	9739	9962	*0185
4.5	1.5 0408	0630	0851	1072	1293	1513	1732	1951	2170	2388
4.6	2606	2823	3039	3256	3471	3687	3902	4116	4330	4543
4.7	4756	4969	5181	5393	5604	5814	6025	6235	6444	6653
4.8	6862	7070	7277	7485	7691	7898	8104	8309	8515	8719
4.9	8924	9127	9331	9534	9737	9939	*0141	*0342	*0543	*0744
5.0	1.6 0944	1144	1343	1542	1741	1939	2137	2334	2531	2728
5.1	2924	3120	3315	3511	3705	3900	4094	4287	4481	4673
5.2	4866	5058	5250	5441	5632	5823	6013	6203	6393	6582
5.3	6771	6959	7147	7335	7523	7710	7896	8083	8269	8455
5.4	8640	8825	9010	9194	9378	9562	9745	9928	*0111	*0293
5.5	1.7 0475	0656	0838	1019	1199	1380	1560	1740	1919	2098
5.6	2277	2455	2633	2811	2988	3166	3342	3519	3695	3871
5.7	4047	4222	4397	4572	4746	4920	5094	5267	5440	5613
5.8	5786	5958	6130	6302	6473	6644	6815	6985	7156	7326
5.9	7495	7665	7834	8002	8171	8339	8507	8675	8842	9009

Table III (continued). Natural logarithms, 6.00 - 10.09

n	0	1	2	3	4	5	6	7	8	9
6.0	1.7 9176	9342	9509	9675	9840	*0006	*0171	*0336	*0500	*0665
6.1	1.8 0829	0993	1156	1319	1482	1645	1808	1970	2132	2294
6.2	2455	2616	2777	2938	3098	3258	3418	3578	3737	3896
6.3	4055	4214	4372	4530	4688	4845	5003	5160	5317	5473
6.4	5630	5786	5942	6097	6253	6408	6563	6718	6872	7026
6.5	7180	7334	7487	7641	7794	7947	8099	8251	8403	8555
6.6	8707	8858	9010	9160	9311	9462	9612	9762	9912	*0061
6.7	1.9 0211	0360	0509	0658	0806	0954	1102	1250	1398	1545
6.8	1692	1839	1986	2132	2279	2425	2571	2716	2862	3007
6.9	3152	3297	3442	3586	3730	3874	4018	4162	4305	4448
7.0	4591	4734	4876	5019	5161	5303	5445	5586	5727	5869
7.1	6009	6150	6291	6431	6571	6711	6851	6991	7130	7269
7.2	7408	7547	7685	7824	7962	8100	8238	8376	8513	8650
7.3	8787	8924	9061	9198	9334	9470	9606	9742	9877	*0013
7.4	2.0 0148	0283	0418	0553	0687	0821	0956	1089	1223	1357
7.5	1490	1624	1757	1890	2022	2155	2287	2419	2551	2683
7.6	2815	2946	3078	3209	3340	3471	3601	3732	3862	3992
7.7	4122	4252	4381	4511	4640	4769	4898	5027	5156	5284
7.8	5412	5540	5668	5796	5924	6051	6179	6306	6433	6560
7.9	6686	6813	6939	7065	7191	7317	7443	7568	7694	7819
8.0	7944	8069	8194	8318	8443	8567	8691	8815	8939	9063
8.1	9186	9310	9433	9556	9679	9802	9924	*0047	*0169	*0291
8.2	2.1 0413	0535	0657	0779	0900	1021	1142	1263	1384	1505
8.3	1626	1746	1866	1986	2106	2226	2346	2465	2585	2704
8.4	2823	2942	3061	3180	3298	3417	3535	3653	3771	3889
8.5	4007	4124	4242	4359	4476	4593	4710	4827	4943	5060
8.6	5176	5292	5409	5524	5640	5756	5871	5987	6102	6217
8.7	6332	6447	6562	6677	6791	6905	7020	7134	7248	7361
8.8	7475	7589	7702	7816	7929	8042	8155	8267	8380	8493
8.9	8605	8717	8830	8942	9054	9165	9277	9389	9500	9611
9.0	9722	9834	9944	*0055	*0166	*0276	*0387	*0497	*0607	*0717
9.1	2.2 0827	0937	1047	1157	1266	1375	1485	1594	1703	1812
9.2	1920	2029	2138	2246	2354	2462	2570	2678	2786	2894
9.3	3001	3109	3216	3324	3431	3538	3645	3751	3858	3965
9.4	4071	4177	4284	4390	4496	4601	4707	4813	4918	5024
9.5	5129	5234	5339	5444	5549	5654	5759	5863	5968	6072
9.6	6176	6280	6384	6488	6592	6696	6799	6903	7006	7109
9.7	7213	7316	7419	7521	7624	7727	7829	7932	8034	8136
9.8	8238	8340	8442	8544	8646	8747	8849	8950	9051	9152
9.9	9253	9354	9455	9556	9657	9757	9858	9958	*0058	*0158
10.0	2.3 0259	0358	0458	0558	0658	0757	0857	0956	1055	1154

Table III (continued). Natural logarithms, 10 - 99

n	0	1	2	3	4	5	6	7	8	9
1	2.30259	39790	48491	56495	63906	70805	77259	83321	89037	94444
2	99573	*04452	*09104	*13549	*17805	*21888	*25810	*29584	*33220	*36730
3	3.40120	43399	46574	49651	52636	55535	58352	61092	63759	66356
4	68888	71357	73767	76120	78419	80666	82864	85015	87120	89182
5	91202	93183	95124	97029	98898	*00733	*02535	*04305	*06044	*07754
6	4.09434	11087	12713	14313	15888	17439	18965	20469	21951	23411
7	24850	26268	27667	29046	30407	31749	33073	34381	35671	36945
8	38203	39445	40672	41884	43082	44265	45435	46591	47734	48864
9	49981	51086	52179	53260	54329	55388	56435	57471	58497	59512

Table III (continued).   Natural logarithms, 100 - 509

n	0	1	2	3	4	5	6	7	8	9
10	4.6 0517	1512	2497	3473	4439	5396	6344	7283	8213	9135
11	4.7 0048	0953	1850	2739	3620	4493	5359	6217	7068	7912
12	8749	9579	*0402	*1218	*2028	*2831	*3628	*4419	*5203	*5981
13	4.8 6753	7520	8280	9035	9784	*0527	*1265	*1998	*2725	*3447
14	4.9 4164	4876	5583	6284	6981	7673	8361	9043	9721	*0395
15	5.0 1064	1728	2388	3044	3695	4343	4986	5625	6260	6890
16	7517	8140	8760	9375	9987	*0595	*1199	*1799	*2396	*2990
17	5.1 3580	4166	4749	5329	5906	6479	7048	7615	8178	8739
18	9296	9850	*0401	*0949	*1494	*2036	*2575	*3111	*3644	*4175
19	5.2 4702	5227	5750	6269	6786	7300	7811	8320	8827	9330
20	9832	*0330	*0827	*1321	*1812	*2301	*2788	*3272	*3754	*4233
21	5.3 4711	5186	5659	6129	6598	7064	7528	7990	8450	8907
22	9363	9816	*0268	*0717	*1165	*1610	*2053	*2495	*2935	*3372
23	5.4 3808	4242	4674	5104	5532	5959	6383	6806	7227	7646
24	8064	8480	8894	9306	9717	*0126	*0533	*0939	*1343	*1745
25	5.5 2146	2545	2943	3339	3733	4126	4518	4908	5296	5683
26	6068	6452	6834	7215	7595	7973	8350	8725	9099	9471
27	9842	*0212	*0580	*0947	*1313	*1677	*2040	*2402	*2762	*3121
28	5.6 3479	3835	4191	4545	4897	5249	5599	5948	6296	6643
29	6988	7332	7675	8017	8358	8698	9036	9373	9709	*0044
30	5.7 0378	0711	1043	1373	1703	2031	2359	2685	3010	3334
31	3657	3979	4300	4620	4939	5257	5574	5890	6205	6519
32	6832	7144	7455	7765	8074	8383	8690	8996	9301	9606
33	9909	*0212	*0513	*0814	*1114	*1413	*1711	*2008	*2305	*2600
34	5.8 2895	3188	3481	3773	4064	4354	4644	4932	5220	5507
35	5793	6079	6363	6647	6930	7212	7493	7774	8053	8332
36	8610	8888	9164	9440	9715	9990	*0263	*0536	*0808	*1080
37	5.9 1350	1620	1889	2158	2426	2693	2959	3225	3489	3754
38	4017	4280	4542	4803	5064	5324	5584	5842	6101	6358
39	6615	6871	7126	7381	7635	7889	8141	8394	8645	8896
40	9146	9396	9645	9894	*0141	*0389	*0635	*0881	*1127	*1372
41	6.0 1616	1859	2102	2345	2587	2828	3069	3309	3548	3787
42	4025	4263	4501	4737	4973	5209	5444	5678	5912	6146
43	6379	6511	6843	7074	7304	7535	7764	7993	8222	8450
44	8677	8904	9131	9357	9582	9807	*0032	*0256	*0479	*0702
45	6.1 0925	1147	1368	1589	1810	2030	2249	2468	2687	2905
46	3123	3340	3556	3773	3988	4204	4419	4633	4847	5060
47	5273	5486	5698	5910	6121	6331	6542	6752	6961	7170
48	7379	7587	7794	8002	8208	8415	8621	8826	9032	9236
49	9441	9644	9848	*0051	*0254	*0456	*0658	*0859	*1060	*1261
50	6.2 1461	1661	1860	2059	2258	2456	2654	2851	3048	3245

Table IV.   Numerical constants

$$\pi = 3.14159\ 26536 \qquad 1/\pi = 0.318\ 3099$$
$$e = 2.71828\ 18285 \qquad \sqrt{\pi} = 1.772\ 4539$$
$$1/e = 0.36787\ 94412 \qquad 1/\sqrt{\pi} = 0.564\ 1896$$
$$\ln 10 = 2.30258\ 50930 \qquad \pi^2 = 9.869\ 6044$$
$$\log_{10} e = 0.43429\ 44819 \qquad 1/\pi^2 = 0.101\ 3212$$
$$\log_{10} \log_{10} e = 9.63778\ 43113 \qquad \pi^3 = 31.006\ 2767$$
$$-10 \qquad 1/\pi^3 = 0.032\ 2515$$
$$\ln 2 = 0.69314\ 71806 \qquad \sqrt{2\pi} = 2.506\ 6283$$
$$\log_{10} 2 = 0.30102\ 99957 \qquad \sqrt[3]{\pi} = 1.464\ 5919$$
$$\ln \pi = 1.14472\ 98858 \qquad \pi/180 = 0.017\ 4533$$
$$\log_{10}\pi = 0.49714\ 98727 \qquad 180/\pi = 57.295\ 7795$$

Table V. Exponential function, 0.00 - 1.00

x	e^x	$\log_{10} e^x$	e^{-x}	x	e^x	$\log_{10} e^x$	e^{-x}
0.00	1.0000	.00 000	1.00 000	**0.50**	1.6487	.21 715	.60 653
0.01	1.0101	.00 434	0.99 005	0.51	1.6653	.22 149	.60 050
0.02	1.0202	.00 869	.98 020	0.52	1.6820	.22 583	.59 452
0.03	1.0305	.01 303	.97 045	0.53	1.6989	.23 018	.58 860
0.04	1.0408	.01 737	.96 079	0.54	1.7160	.23 452	.58 275
0.05	1.0513	.02 171	.95 123	**0.55**	1.7333	.23 886	.57 695
0.06	1.0618	.02 606	.94 176	0.56	1.7507	.24 320	.57 121
0.07	1.0725	.03 040	.93 239	0.57	1.7683	.24 755	.56 553
0.08	1.0833	.03 474	.92 312	0.58	1.7860	.25 189	.55 990
0.09	1.0942	.03 909	.91 395	0.59	1.8040	.25 623	.55 433
0.10	1.1052	.04 343	.90 484	**0.60**	1.8221	.26 058	.54 881
0.11	1.1163	.04 777	.89 583	0.61	1.8404	.26 492	.54 335
0.12	1.1275	.05 212	.88 692	0.62	1.8589	.26 926	.53 794
0.13	1.1388	.05 646	.87 810	0.63	1.8776	.27 361	.53 259
0.14	1.1503	.06 080	.86 936	0.64	1.8965	.27 795	.52 729
0.15	1.1618	.06 514	.86 071	**0.65**	1.9155	.28 229	.52 205
0.16	1.1735	.06 949	.85 214	0.66	1.9348	.28 663	.51.685
0.17	1.1853	.07 383	.84 366	0.67	1.9542	.29 098	.51 171
0.18	1.1972	.07 817	.83 527	0.68	1.9739	.29 532	.50 662
0.19	1.2092	.08 252	.82 696	0.69	1.9937	.29 966	.50 158
0.20	1.2214	.08 686	.81 873	**0.70**	2.0138	.30 401	.49 659
0.21	1.2337	.09 120	.81 058	0.71	2.0340	.30 835	.49 164
0.22	1.2461	.09 554	.80 252	0.72	2.0544	.31 269	.48 675
0.23	1.2586	.09 989	.79 453	0.73	2.0751	.31 703	.48 191
0.24	1.2712	.10 423	.78 663	0.74	2.0959	.32 138	.47 711
0.25	1.2840	.10 857	.77 880	**0.75**	2.1170	.32 572	.47 237
0.26	1.2969	.11 292	.77 105	0.76	2.1383	.33 006	.46 767
0.27	1.3100	.11 726	.76 338	0.77	2.1598	.33 441	.46 301
0.28	1.3231	.12 160	.75 578	0.78	2.1815	.33 875	.45 841
0.29	1.3364	.12 595	.74 826	0.79	2.2034	.34 309	.45 384
0.30	1.3499	.13 029	.74 082	**0.80**	2.2255	.34 744	.44 933
0.31	1.3634	.13 463	.73 345	0.81	2.2479	.35 178	.44 486
0.32	1.3771	.13 897	.72 615	0.82	2.2705	.35 612	.44 043
0.33	1.3910	.14 332	.71 892	0.83	2.2933	.36 046	.43 605
0.34	1.4049	.14 766	.71 177	0.84	2.3164	.36 481	.43 171
0.35	1.4191	.15 200	.70 469	**0.85**	2.3396	.36 915	.42 741
0.36	1.4333	.15 635	.69 768	0.86	2.3632	.37 349	.42 316
0.37	1.4477	.16 069	.69 073	0.87	3.3869	.37 784	.41 895
0.38	1.4623	.16 503	.68 386	0.88	2.4109	.38 218	.41 478
0.39	1.4770	.16 937	.67 706	0.89	2.4351	.38 652	.41 066
0.40	1.4918	.17 372	.67 032	**0.90**	2.4596	.39 087	.40 657
0.41	1.5068	.17 806	.66 365	0.91	2.4843	.39 521	.40 252
0.42	1.5220	.18 240	.65 705	0.92	2.5093	.39 955	.39 852
0.43	1.5373	.18 675	.65 051	0.93	2.5345	.40 389	.39 455
0.44	1.5527	.19 109	.64 404	0.94	2.5600	.40 824	.39 063
0.45	1.5683	.19 543	.63 763	**0.95**	2.5857	.41 258	.38 674
0.46	1.5841	.19 978	.63 128	0.96	2.6117	.41 692	.38 289
0.47	1.6000	.20 412	.62 500	0.97	2.6379	.42 127	.37 908
0.48	1.6161	.20 846	.61 878	0.98	2.6645	.42 561	.37 531
0.49	1.6323	.21 280	.61 263	0.99	2.6912	.42 995	.37 158
0.50	1.6487	.21 715	.60 653	**1.00**	2.7183	.43 429	.36 788

Table V (continued). Exponential function, 1.00 - 2.00

x	e^x	$\log_{10} e^x$	e^{-x}	x	e^x	$\log_{10} e^x$	e^{-x}
1.00	2.7183	.43 429	.36 788	**1.50**	4.4817	.65 144	.22 313
1.01	2.7456	.43 864	.36 422	1.51	4.5267	.65 578	.22 091
1.02	2.7732	.44 298	.36 059	1.52	4.5722	.66 013	.21 871
1.03	2.8011	.44 732	.35 701	1.53	4.6182	.66 447	.21 654
1.04	2.8292	.45 167	.35 345	1.54	4.6646	.66 881	.21 438
1.05	2.8577	.45 601	.34 994	**1.55**	4.7115	.67 316	.21 225
1.06	2.8864	.46 035	.34 646	1.56	4.7588	.67 750	.21 014
1.07	2.9154	.46 470	.34 301	1.57	4.8066	.68 184	.20 805
1.08	2.9447	.46 904	.33 960	1.58	4.8550	.68 619	.20 598
1.09	2.9743	.47 338	.33 622	1.59	4.9037	.69 053	.20 393
1.10	3.0042	.47 772	.33 287	**1.60**	4.9530	.69 487	.20 190
1.11	3.0344	.48 207	.32 956	1.61	5.0028	.69 921	.19 989
1.12	3.0649	.48 641	.32 628	1.62	5.0531	.70 356	.19 790
1.13	3.0957	.49 075	.32 303	1.63	5.1039	.70 790	.19 593
1.14	3.1268	.49 510	.31 982	1.64	5.1552	.71 224	.19 398
1.15	3.1582	.49 944	.31 664	**1.65**	5.2070	.71 659	.19 205
1.16	3.1899	.50 378	.31 349	1.66	5.2593	.72 093	.19 014
1.17	3.2220	.50 812	.31 037	1.67	5.3122	.72 527	.18 825
1.18	3.2544	.51 247	.30 728	1.68	5.3656	.72 961	.18 637
1.19	3.2871	.51 681	.30 422	1.69	5.4195	.73 396	.18 452
1.20	3.3201	.52 115	.30 119	**1.70**	5.4739	.73 830	.18 268
1.21	3.3535	.52 550	.29 820	1.71	5.5290	.74 264	.18 087
1.22	3.3872	.52 984	.29 523	1.72	5.5845	.74 699	.17 907
1.23	3.4212	.53 418	.29 229	1.73	5.6407	.75 133	.17 728
1.24	3.4556	.53 853	.28 938	1.74	5.6973	.75 567	.17 552
1.25	3.4903	.54 287	.28 650	**1.75**	5.7546	.76 002	.17 377
1.26	3.5254	.54 721	.28 365	1.76	5.8124	.76 436	.17 204
1.27	3.5609	.55 155	.28 083	1.77	5.8709	.76 870	.17 033
1.28	3.5966	.55 590	.27 804	1.78	5.9299	.77 304	.16 864
1.29	3.6328	.56 024	.27 527	1.79	5.9895	.77 739	.16 696
1.30	3.6693	.56 458	.27 253	**1.80**	6.0496	.78 173	.16 530
1.31	3.7062	.56 893	.26 982	1.81	6.1104	.78 607	.16 365
1.32	3.7434	.57 327	.26 714	1.82	6.1719	.79 042	.16 203
1.33	3.7810	.57 761	.26 448	1.83	6.2339	.79 476	.16 041
1.34	3.8190	.58 195	.26 185	1.84	6.2965	.79 910	.15 882
1.35	3.8574	.58 630	.25 924	**1.85**	6.3598	.80 344	.15 724
1.36	3.8962	.59 064	.25 666	1.86	6.4237	.80 779	.15 567
1.37	3.9354	.59 498	.25 411	1.87	6.4883	.81 213	.15 412
1.38	3.9749	.59 933	.25 158	1.88	6.5535	.81 647	.15 259
1.39	4.0149	.60 367	.24 908	1.89	6.6194	.82 082	.15 107
1.40	4.0552	.60 801	.24 660	**1.90**	6.6859	.82 516	.14 957
1.41	4.0960	.61 236	.24 414	1.91	6.7531	.82 950	.14 808
1.42	4.1371	.61 670	.24 171	1.92	6.8210	.83 385	.14 661
1.43	4.1787	.62 104	.23 931	1.93	6.8895	.83 819	.14 515
1.44	4.2207	.62 538	.23 693	1.94	6.9588	.84 253	.14 370
1.45	4.2631	.62 973	.23 457	**1.95**	7.0287	.84 687	.14 227
1.46	4.3060	.63 407	.23 224	1.96	7.0993	.85 122	.14 086
1.47	4.3492	.63 841	.22 993	1.97	7.1707	.85 556	.13 946
1.48	4.3929	.64 276	.22 764	1.98	7.2427	.85 990	.13 807
1.49	4.4371	.64 710	.22 537	1.99	7.3155	.86 425	.13 670
1.50	4.4817	.65 144	.22 313	**2.00**	7.3891	.86 859	.13 534

Table V. (continued). Exponential function, 2.00 - 3.00

x	e^x	$\log_{10} e^x$	e^{-x}	x	e^x	$\log_{10} e^x$	e^{-x}
2.00	7.3891	.86 859	.13 534	**2.50**	12.182	1.08 574	.082 085
2.01	7.4633	.87 293	.13 399	2.51	12.305	1.09 008	.081 268
2.02	7.5383	.87 727	.13 266	2.52	12.429	1.09 442	.080 460
2.03	7.6141	.88 162	.13 134	2.53	12.554	1.09 877	.079 659
2.04	7.6906	.88 596	.13 003	2.54	12.680	1.10 311	.078 866
2.05	7.7679	.89 030	.12 873	**2.55**	12.807	1.10 745	.078 082
2.06	7.8460	.89 465	.12 745	2.56	12.936	1.11 179	.077 305
2.07	7.9248	.89 899	.12 619	2.57	13.066	1.11 614	.076 536
2.08	8.0045	.90 333	.12 493	2.58	13.197	1.12 048	.075 774
2.09	8.0849	.90 768	.12 369	2.59	13.330	1.12 482	.075 020
2.10	8.1662	.91 202	.12 246	**2.60**	13.464	1.12 917	.074 274
2.11	8.2482	.91 636	.12 124	2.61	13.599	1.13 351	.073 535
2.12	8.3311	.92 070	.12 003	2.62	13.736	1.13 785	.072 803
2.13	8.4149	.92 505	.11 884	2.63	13.874	1.14 219	.072 078
2.14	8.4994	.92 939	.11 765	2.64	14.013	1.14 654	.071 361
2.15	8.5849	.93 373	.11 648	**2.65**	14.154	1.15 088	.070 651
2.16	8.6711	.93 808	.11 533	2.66	14.296	1.15 522	.069 948
2.17	8.7583	.94 242	.11 418	2.67	14.440	1.15 957	.069 252
2.18	8.8463	.94 676	.11 304	2.68	14.585	1.16 391	.068 563
2.19	8.9352	.95 110	.11 192	2.69	14.732	1.16 825	.067 881
2.20	9.0250	.95 545	.11 080	**2.70**	14.880	1.17 260	.067 206
2.21	9.1157	.95 979	.10 970	2.71	15.029	1.17 694	.066 537
2.22	9.2073	.96 413	.10 861	2.72	15.180	1.18 128	.065 875
2.23	9.2999	.96 848	.10 753	2.73	15.333	1.18 562	.065 219
2.24	9.3933	.97 282	.10 646	2.74	15.487	1.18 997	.064 570
2.25	9.4877	.97 716	.10 540	**2.75**	15.643	1.19 431	.063 928
2.26	9.5831	.98 151	.10 435	2.76	15.800	1.19 865	.063 292
2.27	9.6794	.98 585	.10 331	2.77	15.959	1.20 300	.062 662
2.28	9.7767	.99 019	.10 228	2.78	16.119	1.20 734	.062 039
2.29	9.8749	.99 453	.10 127	2.79	16.281	1.21 168	.061 421
2.30	9.9742	.99 888	.10 026	**2.80**	16.445	1.21 602	.060 810
2.31	10.074	1.00 322	.09 9261	2.81	16.610	1.22 037	.060 205
2.32	10.176	1.00 756	.09 8274	2.82	16.777	1.22 471	.059 606
2.33	10.278	1.01 191	.09 7296	2.83	16.945	1.22 905	.059 013
2.34	10.381	1.01 625	.09 6328	2.84	17.116	1.23 340	.058 426
2.35	10.486	1.02 059	.09 5369	**2.85**	17.288	1.23 774	.057 844
2.36	10.591	1.02 493	.09 4420	2.86	17.462	1.24 208	.057 269
2.37	10.697	1.02 928	.09 3481	2.87	17.637	1.24 643	.056 699
2.38	10.805	1.03 362	.09 2551	2.88	17.814	1.25 077	.056 135
2.39	10.913	1.03 796	.09 1630	2.89	17.993	1.25 511	.055 576
2.40	11.023	1.04 231	.09 0718	**2.90**	18.174	1.25 945	.055 023
2.41	11.134	1.04 665	.08 9815	2.91	18.357	1.26 380	.054 476
2.42	11.246	1.05 099	.08 8922	2.92	18.541	1.26 814	.053 934
2.43	11.359	1.05 534	.08 8037	2.93	18.728	1.27 248	.053 397
2.44	11.473	1.05 968	.08 7161	2.94	18.916	1.27 683	.052 866
2.45	11.588	1.06 402	.08 6294	**2.95**	19.106	1.28 117	.052 340
2.46	11.705	1.06 836	.08 5435	2.96	19.298	1.28 551	.051 819
2.47	11.822	1.07 271	.08 4585	2.97	19.492	1.28 985	.051 303
2.48	11.941	1.07 705	.08 3743	2.98	19.688	1.29 420	.050 793
2.49	12.061	1.08 139	.08 2910	2.99	19.886	1.29 854	.050 287
2.50	12.182	1.08 574	.08 2085	**3.00**	20.086	1.30 288	.049 787

Table V (continued). Exponential function, 3.00 - 10.00

x	e^x	$\log_{10} e^x$	e^{-x}	x	e^x	$\log_{10} e^x$	e^{-x}
3.00	20.086	1.30 288	.049 787	**5.50**	244.69	2.38 862	.004 0868
3.05	21.115	1.32 460	.047 359	5.55	257.24	2.41 033	.003 8875
3.10	22.198	1.34 631	.045 049	5.60	270.43	2.43 205	.003 6979
3.15	23.336	1.36 803	.042 852	5.65	284.29	2.45 376	.003 5175
3.20	24.533	1.38 974	.040 762	5.70	298.87	2.47 548	.003 3460
3.25	25.790	1.41 146	.038 774	**5.75**	314.19	2.49 719	.003 1828
3.30	27.113	1.43 317	.036 883	5.80	330.30	2.51 891	.003 0276
3.35	28.503	1.45 489	.035 084	5.85	347.23	2.54 062	.002 8799
3.40	29.964	1.47 660	.033 373	5.90	365.04	2.56 234	.002 7394
3.45	31.500	1.49 832	.031 746	5.95	383.75	2.58 405	.002 6058
3.50	33.115	1.52 003	.030 197	**6.00**	403.43	2.60 577	.002 4788
3.55	34.813	1.54 175	.028 725	6.10	445.86	2.64 920	.002 2429
3.60	36.598	1.56 346	.027 324	6.20	492.75	2.69 263	.002 0294
3.65	38.475	1.58 517	.025 991	6.30	544.57	2.73 606	.001 8363
3.70	40.447	1.60 689	.024 724	6.40	601.85	2.77 948	.001 6616
3.75	42.521	1.62 860	.023 518	**6.50**	665.14	2.82 291	.001 5034
3.80	44.701	1.65 032	.022 371	6.60	735.10	2.86 634	.001 3604
3.85	46.993	1.67 203	.021 280	6.70	812.41	2.90 977	.001 2309
3.90	49.402	1.69 375	.020 242	6.80	897.98	2.95 320	.001 1138
3.95	51.935	1.71 546	.019 255	6.90	992.27	2.99 663	.001 0078
4.00	54.598	1.73 718	.018 316	**7.00**	1 096.6	3.04 006	.000 9119
4.05	57.397	1.75 889	.017 422	7.10	1 212.0	3.08 349	.000 8251
4.10	60.340	1.78 061	.016 573	7.20	1 339.4	3.12 692	.000 7466
4.15	63.434	1.80 232	.015 764	7.30	1 480.3	3.17 035	.000 6755
4.20	66.686	1.82 404	.014 996	7.40	1 636.0	3.21 378	.000 6113
4.25	70.105	1.84 575	.014 264	**7.50**	1 808.0	3.25 721	.000 5531
4.30	73.700	1.86 747	.013 569	7.60	1 998.2	3.30 064	.000 5005
4.35	77.478	1.88 918	.012 907	7.70	2 208.3	3.34 407	.000 4528
4.40	81.451	1.91 090	.012 277	7.80	2 440.6	3.38 750	.000 4097
4.45	85.627	1.93 261	.011 679	7.90	2 697.3	3.43 093	.000 3707
4.50	90.017	1.95 433	.011 109	**8.00**	2 981.0	3.47 436	.000 3355
4.55	94.632	1.97 604	.010 567	8.10	3 294.5	3.51 779	.000 3035
4.60	99.484	1.99 775	.010 052	8.20	3 641.0	3.56 121	.000 2747
4.65	104.58	2.01 947	.009 5616	8.30	4 023.9	3.60 464	.000 2485
4.70	109.95	2.04 118	.009 0953	8.40	4 447.1	3.64 807	.000 2249
4.75	115.58	2.06 290	.008 6517	**8.50**	4 914.8	3.69 150	.000 2035
4.80	121.51	2.08 461	.008 2297	8.60	5 431.7	3.73 493	.000 1841
4.85	127.74	2.10 633	.007 8284	8.70	6 002.9	3.77 836	.000 1666
4.90	134.29	2.12 804	.007 4466	8.80	6 634.2	3.82 179	.000 1507
4.95	141.17	2.14 976	.007 0834	8.90	7 332.0	3.86 522	.000 1364
5.00	148.41	2.17 147	.006 7379	**9.00**	8 103.1	3.90 865	.000 1234
5.05	156.02	2.19 319	.006 4093	9.10	8 955.3	3.95 208	.000 1117
5.10	164.02	2.21 490	.006 0967	9.20	9 897.1	3.99 551	.000 1010
5.15	172.43	2.23 662	.005 7994	9.30	10 938	4.03 894	.000 0914
5.20	181.27	2.25 833	.005 5166	9.40	12 088	4.08 237	.000 0827
5.25	190.57	2.28 005	.005 2475	**9.50**	13 360	4.12 580	.000 0749
5.30	200.34	2.30 176	.004 9916	9.60	14 765	4.16 923	.000 0677
5.35	210.61	2.32 348	.004 7482	9.70	16 318	4.21 266	.000 0613
5.40	221.41	2.34 519	.004 5166	9.80	18 034	4.25 609	.000 0555
5.45	232.76	2.36 690	.004 2963	9.90	19 930	4.29 952	.000 0502
5.50	244.69	2.38 862	.004 0868	**10.00**	22 026	4.34 294	.000 0454

Table VI. Natural trigonometric functions, degree measure

radians	degrees	sin	cos	tan	cot	sec	csc		
0.0000	0	0.0000	1.0000	0.0000		1.0000		90	1.5708
0.0175	1	0.0175	0.9998	0.0175	57.290	1.0002	57.299	89	1.5533
0.0349	2	0.0349	0.9994	0.0349	28.636	1.0006	28.654	88	1.5359
0.0524	3	0.0523	0.9986	0.0524	19.081	1.0014	19.107	87	1.5184
0.0698	4	0.0698	0.9976	0.0699	14.301	1.0024	14.336	86	1.5010
0.0873	5	0.0872	0.9962	0.0875	11.430	1.0038	11.474	85	1.4835
0.1047	6	0.1045	0.9945	0.1051	9.5144	1.0055	9.5668	84	1.4661
0.1222	7	0.1219	0.9925	0.1228	8.1443	1.0075	8.2055	83	1.4486
0.1396	8	0.1392	0.9903	0.1405	7.1154	1.0098	7.1853	82	1.4312
0.1571	9	0.1564	0.9877	0.1584	6.3138	1.0125	6.3925	81	1.4137
0.1745	10	0.1736	0.9848	0.1763	5.6713	1.0154	5.7588	80	1.3963
0.1920	11	0.1908	0.9816	0.1944	5.1446	1.0187	5.2408	79	1.3788
0.2094	12	0.2079	0.9781	0.2126	4.7046	1.0223	4.8097	78	1.3614
0.2269	13	0.2250	0.9744	0.2309	4.3315	1.0263	4.4454	77	1.3439
0.2443	14	0.2419	0.9703	0.2493	4.0108	1.0306	4.1336	76	1.3265
0.2618	15	0.2588	0.9659	0.2679	3.7321	1.0353	3.8637	75	1.3090
0.2793	16	0.2756	0.9613	0.2867	3.4874	1.0403	3.6280	74	1.2915
0.2967	17	0.2924	0.9563	0.3057	3.2709	1.0457	3.4203	73	1.2741
0.3142	18	0.3090	0.9511	0.3249	3.0777	1.0515	3.2361	72	1.2566
0.3316	19	0.3256	0.9455	0.3443	2.9042	1.0576	3.0716	71	1.2392
0.3491	20	0.3420	0.9397	0.3640	2.7475	1.0642	2.9238	70	1.2217
0.3665	21	0.3584	0.9336	0.3839	2.6051	1.0711	2.7904	69	1.2043
0.3840	22	0.3746	0.9272	0.4040	2.4751	1.0785	2.6695	68	1.1868
0.4014	23	0.3907	0.9205	0.4245	2.3559	1.0864	2.5593	67	1.1694
0.4189	24	0.4067	0.9135	0.4452	2.2460	1.0946	2.4586	66	1.1519
0.4363	25	0.4226	0.9063	0.4663	2.1445	1.1034	2.3662	65	1.1345
0.4538	26	0.4384	0.8988	0.4877	2.0503	1.1126	2.2812	64	1.1170
0.4712	27	0.4540	0.8910	0.5095	1.9626	1.1223	2.2027	63	1.0996
0.4887	28	0.4695	0.8829	0.5317	1.8807	1.1326	2.1301	62	1.0821
0.5061	29	0.4848	0.8746	0.5543	1.8040	1.1434	2.0627	61	1.0647
0.5236	30	0.5000	0.8660	0.5774	1.7321	1.1547	2.0000	60	1.0472
0.5411	31	0.5150	0.8572	0.6009	1.6643	1.1666	1.9416	59	1.0297
0.5585	32	0.5299	0.8480	0.6249	1.6003	1.1792	1.8871	58	1.0123
0.5760	33	0.5446	0.8387	0.6494	1.5399	1.1924	1.8361	57	0.9948
0.5934	34	0.5592	0.8290	0.6745	1.4826	1.2062	1.7883	56	0.9774
0.6109	35	0.5736	0.8192	0.7002	1.4281	1.2208	1.7434	55	0.9599
0.6283	36	0.5878	0.8090	0.7265	1.3764	1.2361	1.7013	54	0.9425
0.6458	37	0.6018	0.7986	0.7536	1.3270	1.2521	1.6616	53	0.9250
0.6632	38	0.6157	0.7880	0.7813	1.2799	1.2690	1.6243	52	0.9076
0.6807	39	0.6293	0.7771	0.8098	1.2349	1.2868	1.5890	51	0.8901
0.6981	40	0.6428	0.7660	0.8391	1.1918	1.3054	1.5557	50	0.8727
0.7156	41	0.6561	0.7547	0.8693	1.1504	1.3250	1.5243	49	0.8552
0.7330	42	0.6691	0.7431	0.9004	1.1106	1.3456	1.4945	48	0.8378
0.7505	43	0.6820	0.7314	0.9325	1.0724	1.3673	1.4663	47	0.8203
0.7679	44	0.6947	0.7193	0.9657	1.0355	1.3902	1.4396	46	0.8029
0.7854	45	0.7071	0.7071	1.0000	1.0000	1.4142	1.4142	45	0.7854
		cos	sin	cot	tan	csc	sec	degrees	radians

Table VII. Natural trigonometric functions, radian measure
0.00 - 1.19

radians	sin	cos	tan	cot	radians	sin	cos	tan	cot
.00	.0000	1.0000	.0000		.60	.5646	.8253	.6841	1.462
.01	.0100	1.0000	.0100	99.997	.61	.5729	.8196	.6989	1.431
.02	.0200	.9998	.0200	49.993	.62	.5810	.8139	.7139	1.401
.03	.0300	.9996	.0300	33.323	.63	.5891	.8080	.7291	1.372
.04	.0400	.9992	.0400	24.987	.64	.5972	.8021	.7445	1.343
.05	.0500	.9988	.0500	19.983	.65	.6052	.7961	.7602	1.315
.06	.0600	.9982	.0601	16.647	.66	.6131	.7900	.7761	1.288
.07	.0699	.9976	.0701	14.262	.67	.6210	.7838	.7923	1.262
.08	.0799	.9968	.0802	12.473	.68	.6288	.7776	.8087	1.237
.09	.0899	.9960	.0902	11.081	.69	.6365	.7712	.8253	1.212
.10	.0998	.9950	.1003	9.967	.70	.6442	.7648	.8423	1.187
.11	.1098	.9940	.1104	9.054	.71	.6518	.7584	.8595	1.163
.12	.1197	.9928	.1206	8.293	.72	.6594	.7518	.8771	1.140
.13	.1296	.9916	.1307	7.649	.73	.6669	.7452	.8949	1.117
.14	.1395	.9902	.1409	7.096	.74	.6743	.7385	.9131	1.095
.15	.1494	.9888	.1511	6.617	.75	.6816	.7317	.9316	1.073
.16	.1593	.9872	.1614	6.197	.76	.6889	.7248	.9505	1.052
.17	.1692	.9856	.1717	5.826	.77	.6961	.7179	.9697	1.031
.18	.1790	.9838	.1820	5.495	.78	.7033	.7109	.9893	1.011
.19	.1889	.9820	.1923	5.200	.79	.7104	.7038	1.009	.9908
.20	.1987	.9801	.2027	4.933	.80	.7174	.6967	1.030	.9712
.21	.2085	.9780	.2131	4.692	.81	.7243	.6895	1.050	.9520
.22	.2182	.9759	.2236	4.472	.82	.7311	.6822	1.072	.9331
.23	.2280	.9737	.2341	4.271	.83	.7379	.6749	1.093	.9146
.24	.2377	.9713	.2447	4.086	.84	.7446	.6675	1.116	.8964
.25	.2474	.9689	.2553	3.916	.85	.7513	.6600	1.138	.8785
.26	.2571	.9664	.2660	3.759	.86	.7578	.6524	1.162	.8609
.27	.2667	.9638	.2768	3.613	.87	.7643	.6448	1.185	.8437
.28	.2764	.9611	.2876	3.478	.88	.7707	.6372	1.210	.8267
.29	.2860	.9582	.2984	3.351	.89	.7771	.6294	1.235	.8100
.30	.2955	.9553	.3093	3.233	.90	.7833	.6216	1.260	.7936
.31	.3051	.9523	.3203	3.122	.91	.7895	.6137	1.286	.7774
.32	.3146	.9492	.3314	3.018	.92	.7956	.6058	1.313	.7615
.33	.3240	.9460	.3425	2.920	.93	.8016	.5978	1.341	.7458
.34	.3335	.9428	.3537	2.827	.94	.8076	.5898	1.369	.7303
.35	.3429	.9394	.3650	2.740	.95	.8134	.5817	1.398	.7151
.36	.3523	.9359	.3764	2.657	.96	.8192	.5735	1.428	.7001
.37	.3616	.9323	.3879	2.578	.97	.8249	.5653	1.459	.6853
.38	.3709	.9287	.3994	2.504	.98	.8305	.5570	1.491	.6707
.39	.3802	.9249	.4111	2.433	.99	.8360	.5487	1.524	.6563
.40	.3894	.9211	.4228	2.365	1.00	.8415	.5403	1.557	.6421
.41	.3986	.9171	.4346	2.301	1.01	.8468	.5319	1.592	.6281
.42	.4078	.9131	.4466	2.239	1.02	.8521	.5234	1.628	.6142
.43	.4169	.9090	.4586	2.180	1.03	.8573	.5148	1.665	.6005
.44	.4259	.9048	.4708	2.124	1.04	.8624	.5062	1.704	.5870
.45	.4350	.9004	.4831	2.070	1.05	.8674	.4976	1.743	.5736
.46	.4439	.8961	.4954	2.018	1.06	.8724	.4889	1.784	.5604
.47	.4529	.8916	.5080	1.969	1.07	.8772	.4801	1.827	.5473
.48	.4618	.8870	.5206	1.921	1.08	.8820	.4713	1.871	.5344
.49	.4706	.8823	.5334	1.875	1.09	.8866	.4625	1.917	.5216
.50	.4794	.8776	.5463	1.830	1.10	.8912	.4536	1.965	.5090
.51	.4882	.8727	.5594	1.788	1.11	.8957	.4447	2.014	.4964
.52	.4969	.8678	.5726	1.747	1.12	.9001	.4357	2.066	.4840
.53	.5055	.8628	.5859	1.707	1.13	.9044	.4267	2.120	.4718
.54	.5141	.8577	.5994	1.668	1.14	.9086	.4176	2.176	.4596
.55	.5227	.8525	.6131	1.631	1.15	.9128	.4085	2.234	.4475
.56	.5312	.8473	.6269	1.595	1.16	.9168	.3993	2.296	.4356
.57	.5396	.8419	.6410	1.560	1.17	.9208	.3902	2.360	.4237
.58	.5480	.8365	.6552	1.526	1.18	.9246	.3809	2.427	.4120
.59	.5564	.8309	.6696	1.494	1.19	.9284	.3717	2.498	.4003

Table VII (continued). Natural trigonometric functions, radian measure, 1.20 - 1.60

radians	sin	cos	tan	cot	radians	sin	cos	tan	cot
1.20	.9320	.3624	2.572	.3888	1.40	.9854	.1700	5.798	.1725
1.21	.9356	.3530	2.650	.3773	1.41	.9871	.1601	6.165	.1622
1.22	.9391	.3436	2.733	.3659	1.42	.9887	.1502	6.581	.1519
1.23	.9425	.3342	2.820	.3546	1.43	.9901	.1403	7.055	.1417
1.24	.9458	.3248	2.912	.3434	1.44	.9915	.1304	7.602	.1315
1.25	.9490	.3153	3.010	.3323	1.45	.9927	.1205	8.238	.1214
1.26	.9521	.3058	3,113	.3212	1.46	.9939	.1106	8.989	.1113
1.27	.9551	.2963	3.224	.3102	1.47	.9949	.1006	9.887	.1011
1.28	.9580	.2867	3.341	.2993	1.48	.9959	.0907	10.983	.0910
1.29	.9608	.2771	3.467	.2884	1.49	.9967	.0807	12.350	.0810
1.30	.9636	.2675	3.602	.2776	1.50	.9975	.0707	14.101	.0709
1.31	.9662	.2579	3.747	.2669	1.51	.9982	.0608	16.428	.0609
1.32	.9687	.2482	3.903	.2562	1.52	.9987	.0508	19.670	.0508
1.33	.9711	.2385	4.072	.2456	1.53	.9992	.0408	24.498	.0408
1.34	.9735	.2288	4.256	.2350	1.54	.9995	.0308	32.461	.0308
1.35	.9757	.2190	4.455	.2245	1.55	.9998	.0208	48.078	.0208
1.36	.9779	.2092	4.673	.2140	1.56	.9999	.0108	92.620	.0108
1.37	.9799	.1994	4.913	.2035	1.57	1.0000	.0008	1255.8	.0008
1.38	.9819	.1896	5.177	.1931	1.58	1.0000	−.0092	−108.65	−.0092
1.39	.9837	.1798	5.471	.1828	1.59	.9998	−.0192	−52.067	−.0192
					1.60	.9996	−.0292	−34.233	−.0292

Table VIII. Degrees, minutes, and seconds to radians

degrees	radians	minutes	radians	seconds	radians
1	0.01745 33	1	0.00029 09	1	0.00000 48
2	0.03490 66	2	0.00058 18	2	0.00000 97
3	0.05235 99	3	0.00087 27	3	0.00001 45
4	0.06981 32	4	0.00116 36	4	0.00001 94
5	0.08726 65	5	0.00145 44	5	0.00002 42
6	0.10471 98	6	0.00174 53	6	0.00002 91
7	0.12217 30	7	0.00203 62	7	0.00003 39
8	0.13962 63	8	0.00232 71	8	0.00003 88
9	0.15707 96	9	0.00261 80	9	0.00004 36
10	0.17453 29	10	0.00290 89	10	0.00004 85
20	0.34906 59	20	0.00581 78	20	0.00009 70
30	0.52359 88	30	0.00872 66	30	0.00014 54
40	0.69813 17	40	0.01163 55	40	0.00019 39
50	0.87266 46	50	0.01454 44	50	0.00024 24
60	1.04719 76	60	0.01745 33	60	0.00029 09
70	1.22173 05				
80	1.39626 34				
90	1.57079 63				

Table IX. Radians to degrees, minutes, and seconds

radians		radians		radians		radians		radians	
1	57°17′44″.8	.1	5°43′46″.5	.01	0°34′22″.6	.001	0° 3′26″.3	.0001	0°0′20″.6
2	114°35′29″.6	.2	11°27′33″.0	.02	1° 8′45″.3	.002	0° 6′52″.5	.0002	0°0′41″.3
3	171°53′14″.4	.3	17°11′19″.4	.03	1°43′07″.9	.003	0°10′18″.8	.0003	0°1′01″.9
4	229°10′59″.2	.4	22°55′05″.9	.04	2°17′30″.6	.004	0°13′45″.1	.0004	0°1′22″.5
5	286°28′44″.0	.5	28°38′52″.4	.05	2°51′53″.2	.005	0°17′11″.3	.0005	0°1′43″.1
6	343°46′28″.8	.6	34°22′38″.9	.06	3°26′15″.9	.006	0°20′37″.6	.0006	0°2′03″.8
7	401° 4′13″.6	.7	40° 6′25″.4	.07	4° 0′38″.5	.007	0°24′03″.9	.0007	0°2′24″.4
8	458°21′58″.4	.8	45°50′11″.8	.08	4°35′01″.2	.008	0°27′30″.1	.0008	0°2′45″.0
9	515°39′43″.3	.9	51°33′58″.3	.09	5° 9′23″.8	.009	0°30′56″.4	.0009	0°3′05″.6

Table X. Formulas from geometry

In these formulas the following notation is used: A = area, V = volume, b = base, h = altitude, r = radius (including base radius), C = circumference, B = base area.

1. *Triangle:* $A = \frac{1}{2}bh$.
2. *Parallelogram:* $A = bh$.
3. *Trapezoid:* $A = \frac{1}{2}(a + b)h$ (*a* and *b* lengths of parallel sides).
4. *Circle:* $C = 2\pi r$, $A = \pi r^2$.
5. *Ellipse:* $A = \pi ab$ (*a* and *b* semiaxes).
6. *Parallelepiped:* $V = Bh$.
7. *Tetrahedron:* $V = \frac{1}{3}Bh$.
8. *Right circular cylinder:* Curved surface $A = 2\pi rh$, $V = \pi r^2h$.
9. *Right circular cone:* Curved surface $A = \pi r\sqrt{r^2 + h^2}$, $V = \frac{1}{3}\pi r^2h$.
10. *General cone or pyramid:* $V = \frac{1}{3}Bh$.
11. *Sphere:* $A = 4\pi r^2$, $V = \frac{4}{3}\pi r^3$.
12. *Ellipsoid:* $V = \frac{4}{3}\pi abc$ (*a*, *b*, and *c* semiaxes).

Table XI. Greek alphabet

Name	Letter		Name	Letter	
Alpha	α	A	Nu	ν	N
Beta	β	B	Xi	ξ	Ξ
Gamma	γ	Γ	Omicron	o	O
Delta	δ	Δ	Pi	π	Π
Epsilon	$\epsilon\ \varepsilon$	E	Rho	ρ	P
Zeta	ζ	Z	Sigma	$\sigma\ s$	Σ
Eta	η	H	Tau	τ	T
Theta	$\theta\ \vartheta$	Θ	Upsilon	υ	Υ
Iota	ι	I	Phi	$\phi\ \varphi$	Φ
Kappa	κ	K	Chi	χ	X
Lambda	λ	Λ	Psi	ψ	Ψ
Mu	μ	M	Omega	ω	Ω

Answers and Hints

5. 5, 8, 13.   **6.** 2, -16, -14.   **7.** 5, 8, -1.   **8.** 2, -16, 38.

1. 21.   **2.** 32.   **3.** 110.   **4.** 624.   **5.** -32.   **6.** $\frac{163}{3}$.
7. $\frac{39}{4}$.   **8.** 174.   **9.** 1.   **10.** 0.   **11.** $\frac{3}{2}$.   **12.** 1.
13. 30.   **14.** 0.   **15.** 138.   **16.** 29.

1. 36.   **2.** 12.   **3.** $\frac{88}{3}$.   **4.** 78.   **5.** 12   **6.** 8.
7. $\frac{4}{3}$.   **8.** $\frac{32}{3}$.   **9.** 36.   **10.** $\frac{1}{6}$.   **11.** $\frac{4}{3}$.   **12.** $\frac{500}{3}$.
13. $\frac{32}{3}$.   **14.** $\frac{57}{2}$.   **15.** 54.   **16.** $\frac{9}{2}$.   **17.** 36.   **18.** 36.
19. $\frac{9}{2}$.   **20.** $\frac{37}{12}$.   **21.** $\frac{71}{6}$.   **22.** $\frac{23}{4}$.   **23.** $\frac{35}{3}$.   **24.** 13.
25. $\frac{53}{2}$.   **26.** 5.   **27.** 11.   **28.** 27.   **29.** 13.   **30.** 32.

1. $\frac{243}{5}\pi$.   **2.** 3π.   **3.** 55π.   **4.** 2π.   **5.** $\frac{16}{3}\pi$.   **6.** 64π.
7. $\frac{1}{5}\pi$.   **8.** $\frac{1}{2}\pi$.   **9.** $\frac{2}{35}\pi$.   **10.** $\frac{1}{6}\pi$.   **11.** $\frac{459}{10}\pi$.   **12.** $\frac{243}{5}\pi$.
13. $\frac{4}{45}\pi$.   **14.** $\frac{2}{15}\pi$.   **15.** $\frac{128}{3}\pi$.   **16.** $\frac{27}{2}\pi$.
17. $\frac{23}{210}\pi$.   **18.** $\frac{1024}{5}\pi$.   **19.** $\frac{8}{45}\pi$.   **20.** $\frac{8}{15}\pi$.

1. $\frac{81}{2}\pi$.   **2.** $\frac{44}{3}\pi$.   **3.** 34π.   **4.** $\frac{26}{3}\pi$.   **5.** $\frac{32}{3}\pi$.
6. 384π.   **7.** $\frac{1}{2}\pi$.   **8.** $\frac{1}{6}\pi$.   **9.** $\frac{1}{10}\pi$.   **10.** $\frac{27}{2}\pi$.
11. $\frac{1}{6}\pi$.   **12.** $\frac{27}{2}\pi$.   **13.** $\frac{1}{6}\pi$.   **14.** $\frac{1}{6}\pi$.   **15.** $\frac{1}{12}\pi$.
16. $\frac{625}{6}\pi$.   **17.** $\frac{1}{15}\pi$.   **18.** $\frac{64}{3}\pi$.   **19.** $\frac{1}{10}\pi$.   **20.** π.
21. $\frac{16}{3}a^3$.   **22.** $\frac{4}{3}\sqrt{3}a^3$.   **23.** 228.   **24.** $\frac{56}{3}$.
25. 8.   **26.** $\frac{203}{15}$.   **27.** $\frac{16}{3}$ cubic feet.

§ 213   Page 63

1. 1700 foot-pounds.   **2.** 446 foot-pounds.   **3.** 1650 foot-pounds.

4. 118,560 foot-pounds.   **5.** $53\frac{1}{3}$ inch-pounds.

6. Total length $= 7 + 6\sqrt{2}$ inches.   **7.** 24 inch-pounds.

8. $12\frac{1}{2}$ inches.   **9.** $937\frac{1}{2}$ foot-pounds.

10. $25(2 - \sqrt{2}) = 14.65$ feet (approximately).

11. 45,000 foot-pounds.   **12.** 6,250 foot-pounds.

13. 350 feet.   **14.** 180 feet.   **15.** 96 feet.   **16.** 238 inches.

§ 305   Page 78

1. $\delta = \frac{1}{5}\epsilon$.   **2.** $\delta = \frac{1}{7}\epsilon$.   **3.** $\delta = \frac{1}{12}\epsilon$.   **4.** $\delta = 9\epsilon$.

5. $\delta = 25\epsilon$.   **6.** $\delta = \frac{16}{3}\epsilon$.   **7.** $\delta = \sqrt{3}\epsilon$.   **8.** $\delta = \frac{2}{3}\sqrt{5}\epsilon$.

9. $x_2 = \min(\sqrt{3}, \delta)$, $x_1 = \frac{1}{2}x_2$.   **10.** $x_2 = \min(1, \delta)$, $x_1 = \frac{1}{4}x_2$.

11. $x_1 = \dfrac{4}{3\delta^2}$, $x_2 = \dfrac{4}{3\delta^2} + \dfrac{\delta}{2}$.

§ 402   Page 90

1. $\delta = \frac{1}{3}\epsilon$.   **2.** $\delta = \frac{1}{2}\epsilon$.   **3.** $\delta = \min(1, \frac{1}{11}\epsilon)$.

4. $\delta = \min(1, \frac{1}{14}\epsilon)$.   **5.** $\delta = \min(1, \frac{1}{6}\epsilon)$.   **6.** $\delta = \min(1, \frac{1}{3}\epsilon)$.

7. $\delta = \min(1, \frac{1}{13}\epsilon)$.   **8.** $\delta = \min(1, 24\epsilon)$.   **9.** $\delta = \min(1, 20\epsilon)$.

10. $\delta = \min(\frac{1}{10}, \frac{1}{10}\epsilon) = \frac{1}{10}\min(1, \epsilon)$.   **11.** $\delta = \min(\frac{1}{12}, \frac{1}{12}\epsilon) = \frac{1}{12}\min(1, \epsilon)$.

12. $\delta = \min(1, \frac{20}{21}\epsilon)$.

§ 405   Page 93

1. $x = \frac{1}{2}\delta$.   **2.** $x = 2 - \frac{1}{2}\delta$.   **3.** $x = 1 - \frac{1}{2}\delta$.   **4.** $x = \min(1, \frac{1}{2}\delta)$.

5. $x = \min(1, \frac{1}{2}\delta)$.

§ 408   Page 101

20. Infinite discontinuity at $x = 2$.   **21.** Infinite discontinuity at $x = \pm 2$.

22. Jump discontinuity at $x = 1$. Left-hand continuity at $x = 1$.

23. Removable discontinuity at $x = 1$.   **24.** Everywhere continuous.

25. Jump discontinuity at $x = 1$.

26. Oscillatory discontinuity at $x = 0$. Left-hand continuity at $x = 0$.

27. Dense discontinuities everywhere.

§ 412   Page 109

7. $[-1, 2]$.   **8.** $(1, 2)$.   **9.** $(4, +\infty)$.   **10.** $[-3, +\infty)$.

Hint for 11 and 12: Complete a square.

11. $(-16, 0]$.   **12.** $(-9, 0]$.   **13.** $x = y^3$, $[-1, 2]$.

14. $x = \sqrt{y^3}$, $(1, 2)$.   **15.** $x = \sqrt[3]{y - 4}$, $(4, +\infty)$.   **16.** $x = \sqrt[4]{y + 3}$, $[-3, +\infty)$.

17. $x = 4 + \sqrt{y + 16}$, $(-16, 0]$.   **18.** $x = 3 - \sqrt{y + 9}$, $(-9, 0]$.

§ 505   Page 121

1. No.   **2.** Yes.   **3.** Yes.   **4.** No.   **5.** Yes.   **6.** No.

7. Yes.   **8.** Yes.   **9.** $\delta = \min(4, 2\epsilon)$.   **10.** $\delta = \min(2, \sqrt{2}\epsilon)$.

11. $\delta = \min(1, \frac{1}{4}\epsilon)$.   **12.** $\delta = \min(1, \frac{1}{3}\epsilon)$.   **13.** $\delta = \min(\frac{1}{3}, \frac{2}{3}\epsilon)$.   **14.** $\delta = \min(\frac{1}{2}, \frac{3}{4}\epsilon)$.

15. 0.   **16.** $3b^3$.   **17.** $\frac{1}{2}$.   **18.** $\frac{1}{3}$.   **19.** $\sqrt[3]{3}$.

20. 1.   **21.** -13.   **22.** 21.   **23.** 81.

§ 508   Page 129

1. 10.   **2.** 12.   **3.** $\frac{1}{6}$.   **4.** $\frac{1}{10}$.   **5.** $-\dfrac{1}{a^2}$.   **6.** $-\frac{5}{9}$.

7. $\frac{5}{4}$.   **8.** $-\frac{3}{4}$.

§ 511   Page 139

1. $p(\epsilon) = 1/\epsilon^2$.   **2.** $p(\epsilon) = 1/\sqrt{\epsilon}$.   **3.** $p(\epsilon) = 7/8\epsilon$ or $1/\epsilon$.

7. $\frac{5}{7}$.   **8.** $\frac{11}{5}$.   **9.** $\frac{3}{8}$.   **10.** $\frac{6}{5}$.

11. 0.   **12.** 0.   **19.** $\delta = 1/\sqrt{p}$.   **20.** $\delta = 1/p^2$.

21. $\delta = \min(1, 1/p)$.   **22.** $\delta = 1/\sqrt[3]{p}$.   **23.** $\delta = 1/p$.   **24.** $\delta = \min(1, 1/5p)$.

25. $y = \frac{3}{4}, x = -\frac{3}{2}$.   **26.** $y = \frac{5}{3}, x = \frac{1}{3}$.   **27.** $y = 0, x = \pm 2$.   **28.** $y = 0, x = -3, 1$.

29. $y = \frac{3}{4}$.   **30.** $y = \frac{5}{3}$.   **31.** $x = 2$.   **32.** $x = 1$.   **33.** ∞.

34. $\frac{1}{2}$.   **35.** 0.   **36.** ∞.   **37.** 4.   **38.** 0.

§ 516   Page 145

1. $\frac{1}{2}$.   **2.** $\frac{1}{4}$.   **3.** $\frac{1}{5}$.   **4.** $\frac{1}{6}$.   **5.** $\frac{1}{3}$.

6. $\frac{1}{4}$.   **7.** $\frac{1}{5}$.   **8.** 1.   **9.** $\frac{4}{3}$.   **10.** 2.

§ 604   Page 157

1. $10a + 3, y + 5a^2 - 7 = (10a + 3)x, x - a + (10a + 3)(y - 5a^2 - 3a - 7) = 0$.

2. $12a - 4, y + 6a^2 + 9 = (12a - 4)x, x - a + (12a - 4)(y - 6a^2 + 4a + 9) = 0$.

3. $-\dfrac{1}{(a + 5)^2}, x + (a + 5)^2 y = 2a + 5, (a + 5)^3(x - a) - (a + 5)y + 1 = 0$.

4. $-\dfrac{2}{(a + 3)^2}, 2x + (a + 3)^2 y = 4a + 6, (a + 3)^3(x - a) - 2(a + 3)y + 4 = 0$.

5. $v = -4, \sigma = 4$.   **6.** $v = 6, \sigma = 6$.

7. $v = -4t + 8, \sigma = 4|t - 2|$.   **8.** $v = -8t + 7, \sigma = 8|t - \frac{7}{8}|$.

17. $4x + 9$.   **18.** $6x - 8$.   **19.** $-16t - 5$.

20. $-\dfrac{6}{(2x + 7)^2}$.   **21.** $-\dfrac{6}{(3x + 1)^2}$.   **22.** $-\dfrac{17}{(3x - 1)^2}$.

23. $\dfrac{1}{2\sqrt{x + 2}}$.   **24.** $\dfrac{1}{2\sqrt{x + 5}}$.   **25.** $\dfrac{1}{\sqrt{2x + 3}}$.

§ 606   **Page 161**

1. $f'(x) = 24x^5 - 21x^2, f''(x) = 120x^4 - 42x.$

2. $f'(x) = 15x^2 + 18, f''(x) = 30x.$ **3.** $f'(s) = 50s^4 - 32s, f''(s) = 200s^3 - 32.$

4. $f'(t) = 24t^2 - 24t - 24, f''(t) = 48t - 24.$

5. $f'(u) = 10u^9 + 6u^5 + 2u, f''(u) = 90u^8 + 30u^4 + 2.$

6. $f'(v) = 12v^{11} - 8v^7 - 1, f''(v) = 132v^{10} - 56v^6.$

7. $f'(y) = 32y^{15} - 32y^7 - 32y^3, f''(y) = 480y^{14} - 224y^6 - 96y^2.$

8. $f'(z) = 77z^6 + 20z^3 - 6, f''(z) = 462z^5 + 60z^2.$

9. $f'(x) = 4x^3 + 12x - 5, \ f''(x) = 12x^2 + 12, \ f'''(x) = 24x, \ f''''(x) = 24, \ f^{(n)}(x) = 0$ for $n \geqq 5.$

10. $f'(x) = 5x^4 - 6x^2, f''(x) = 20x^3 - 12x, f'''(x) = 60x^2 - 12, f''''(x) = 120x, f^{(5)}(x) = 120, f^{(n)}(x) = 0$ for $n \geqq 6.$

16. $2|x|.$ **17.** $3x|x|.$

§ 608   **Page 164**

1. $12x + 7.$ **2.** $60x - 23.$ **3.** $5x^4 + 12x^2 + 2x.$

4. $5x^4 - 20x^3 + 3x^2.$ **5.** $12x^3 + 20x.$ **6.** $80x^3 + 34x.$

7. $\dfrac{13}{(2x + 5)^2}.$ **8.** $-\dfrac{13}{(5x - 3)^2}.$ **9.** $\dfrac{-x^4 + 4x^2 + 2x}{(x^3 + 4x + 1)^2}.$

10. $\dfrac{x^4 - 10x^3 + 3x^2}{(x^2 - 5x + 1)^2}.$ **11.** $-\dfrac{28x}{(3x^2 - 2)^3}.$ **12.** $\dfrac{14x}{(5x^2 + 3)^2}.$

13. $\dfrac{5x^2 + 12x - 7}{2\sqrt{x}}.$ **14.** $\dfrac{5x^2 - 9x + 9}{2\sqrt{x}}.$ **15.** $\dfrac{-x - 3}{2\sqrt{x}(x - 3)^2}.$

16. $\dfrac{-x + 2}{2\sqrt{x}(x + 2)^2}.$ **17.** $\tfrac{3}{2}\sqrt{x}.$ **18.** $\tfrac{5}{2}x\sqrt{x}.$

§ 611   **Page 169**

1. $60(6x + 5)^9.$ **2.** $80(10x - 3)^7.$

3. $60(x + 1)(5x^2 + 10x + 3)^5.$ **4.** $28(3x + 1)(6x^2 + 4x - 5)^6.$

5. $72u(4u^2 + 5)^8.$ **6.** $50v(5v^2 + 8)^4.$ **7.** $-70\dfrac{(3x + 4)^4}{(5x + 2)^6}.$

8. $12\dfrac{(4x + 5)^5}{(2x + 3)^7}.$ **9.** $16x\dfrac{(x^2 + 2)^3}{(x^2 + 4)^5}.$ **10.** $-12x\dfrac{(3x^2 + 1)^2}{(5x^2 + 1)^4}.$

13. $\dfrac{3x}{\sqrt{3x^2 + 4}}.$ **14.** $\dfrac{5x}{\sqrt{5x^2 - 2}}.$ **15.** $\dfrac{x + 5}{\sqrt{x^2 + 10x + 30}}.$

16. $\dfrac{4x - 10}{\sqrt{4x^2 - 20x + 5}}.$ **17.** $-\dfrac{6x}{(3x^2 + 4)^2}.$ **18.** $-\dfrac{10x}{(5x^2 - 2)^2}.$

19. $-\dfrac{2x + 10}{(x^2 + 10x + 30)^2}.$ **20.** $\dfrac{-8x + 20}{(4x^2 - 20x + 5)^2}.$

21. $(130x + 153)(2x + 3)^5(5x + 4)^6.$ **22.** $(189y + 2)(3y - 1)^4(7y + 2)^3.$

23. $4s(5s^2 + 19)(s^2 + 3)^3(s^2 + 5)^5.$ **24.** $6t(32t^2 + 13)(3t^2 + 2)^4(4t^2 + 1)^2.$

25. $-\dfrac{(10u + 57)(2u + 3)^5}{(5u + 4)^8}.$ **26.** $\dfrac{(21v + 58)(3v - 1)^4}{(7v + 2)^5}.$

27. $\dfrac{4r(-r^2 + 1)(r^2 + 3)^3}{(r^2 + 5)^7}.$

28. $\dfrac{6z(8z^2 - 3)(3z^2 + 2)^4}{(4z^2 + 1)^4}.$

29. $32x(8x + 13).$

30. $18(3x + 2)(9x^2 + 12x + 5)^2.$

31. $-50\,\dfrac{4x + 5}{(5x + 6)^3}.$

32. $-10\,\dfrac{x + 4}{(5x^2 + 40x + 86)^2}.$

§ 616   Page 180

1. 1 and 3.   **2.** -1 and 3.   **3.** 2 and 3.   **4.** 4 and -1.

5. $c = 2, \theta = \frac{1}{2}.$ **6.** $c = \frac{3}{2}, \theta = \frac{1}{2}.$

7. $c = \frac{2}{3}\sqrt{3}, \theta = \frac{1}{3}\sqrt{3}.$ **8.** $c = \sqrt{2}, \theta = \sqrt{2} - 1.$

9. Strict increase: $(-\infty, 3]$; strict decrease: $[3, +\infty).$

10. Strict increase: $[\frac{5}{2}, +\infty)$; strict decrease: $(-\infty, \frac{5}{2}].$

11. Strict increase: $(-\infty, -1]$ and $[2, +\infty)$; strict decrease $[-1, 2].$

12. Strict increase: $[0, 6]$; strict decrease: $(-\infty, 0]$ and $[6, +\infty).$

13. Strict increase: $[-3, 3]$; strict decrease: $(-\infty, -3]$ and $[3, +\infty).$

14. Strict increase: $(-\infty, -2]$ and $[2, +\infty)$; strict decrease: $[-2, 0)$ and $(0, 2].$

15. Strict increase: $(-\infty, -2]$ and $[2, +\infty)$; strict decrease: $[-2, 0)$ and $(0, 2].$

16. Strict increase: $(0, 2]$; strict decrease: $(-\infty, 0)$ and $[2, +\infty).$

§ 620   Page 186

1. $x^{\frac{5}{2}} - x^{\frac{3}{2}} + x^{\frac{1}{2}}.$

2. $x^{\frac{4}{3}} + x^{\frac{1}{3}} - x^{-\frac{2}{3}}.$

3. $10r^{\frac{2}{3}} + 10r^{-\frac{9}{4}}.$

4. $4s^{-\frac{3}{5}} + 15s^{-\frac{8}{3}}.$

5. $\frac{1}{2}y^{-\frac{1}{2}} + \frac{1}{4}y^{-\frac{3}{4}} + \frac{1}{6}y^{-\frac{5}{6}}.$

6. $\frac{2}{3}z^{-\frac{1}{3}} + \frac{4}{5}z^{-\frac{1}{5}} + \frac{6}{7}z^{-\frac{1}{7}}.$

7. $\frac{7}{3}u^{-\frac{2}{3}} + \frac{10}{3}u^{-\frac{5}{3}} = \frac{1}{3}u^{-\frac{5}{3}}(7u + 10).$

8. $\frac{6}{5}v^{-\frac{3}{5}} + \frac{6}{5}v^{-\frac{8}{5}} = \frac{6}{5}\sqrt[5]{v^2}(v + 1)/v^2.$

9. $x^3(x^4 + 5)^{-\frac{3}{4}} = x^3/\sqrt[4]{(x^4 + 5)^3}.$

10. $3x/\sqrt{3x^2 + 8}.$

11. $4(\sqrt{t} + 5)^7/\sqrt{t}.$

12. $2(\sqrt[3]{w} - 4)^5/\sqrt[3]{w^2}.$

13. $27r\sqrt{9r^2 + 4}.$

14. $-10s\sqrt{(5 - 2s^2)^3}.$

15. $(9 - 2u^2)/\sqrt{9 - u^2}.$

16. $(2v^2 + 9)/\sqrt{v^2 + 9}.$

17. $\sqrt{3/4x} = \sqrt{3x}/2x.$

18. $\sqrt[3]{2x}/3x.$

19. $\frac{4}{3}\sqrt[3]{4x}.$

20. $\frac{3}{2}\sqrt{5x}.$

21. $6(x - 4)(2x + 5)^2(3x + 1)^{-3}.$

22. $(-20x + 9)(4x + 1)(5x + 3)^{-4}.$

23. $-2x(2x^2 + 3)(x^2 + 9)^{-4}.$

24. $-2x(x^2 + 8)(x^2 + 2)^{-3}.$

25. $-x(x^2 + 4)^{-\frac{3}{2}}.$

26. $x(9 - x^2)^{-\frac{3}{2}}.$

27. $3(2x^2 + 3)^{-\frac{3}{2}}.$

28. $2(3x^2 + 2)^{-\frac{3}{2}}.$

29. $-132(2x + 7)^3(5x + 1)^{-5}.$

30. $57(3x + 2)^2(4x + 9)^{-4}.$

31. $5x(x^2 + 4)^{-\frac{1}{2}}(x^2 + 9)^{-\frac{3}{2}}.$

32. $5x(9 - x^2)^{-\frac{1}{2}}(4 - x^2)^{-\frac{3}{2}}.$

33. $36(2x + 1)(2x + 7)^3(8x + 1)^{-\frac{1}{2}}.$

34. $2(95x + 78)(5x + 3)^5(6x + 5)^{-\frac{2}{3}}.$

35. $(10x + 11)(4x + 3)^{-\frac{1}{2}}(3x + 4)^{-\frac{2}{3}}.$

36. $2x(x^3 + 2x + 4)(x^2 + 4)^{-\frac{1}{2}}(x^3 + 8)^{-\frac{2}{3}}.$

37. $4(14x - 5)(2x + 7)^3(8x + 1)^{-\frac{3}{2}}.$

38. $2(85x + 72)(5x + 3)^5(6x + 5)^{-\frac{4}{3}}.$

39. $(2x + 5)(4x + 3)^{-\frac{1}{2}}(3x + 4)^{-\frac{4}{3}}.$

40. $4x(2 - x)(x^2 + 4)^{-\frac{1}{2}}(x^3 + 8)^{-\frac{4}{3}}.$

41. $3x - y - 8 = 0, x + 3y - 6 = 0.$

42. $x - y + 1 = 0, x + y - 7 = 0.$

43. $4x - 3y + 1 = 0$, $3x + 4y - 18 = 0$.   **44.** $x + 2y - 10 = 0$, $2x - y = 0$.

45. $y = 6 - \frac{3}{2}x$, $D_x y = -\frac{3}{2}$; $x = 4 - \frac{2}{3}y$, $D_y x = -\frac{2}{3}$.

46. $y = \frac{4}{5}x - 4$, $D_x y = \frac{4}{5}$; $x = \frac{5}{4}y + 5$, $D_y x = \frac{5}{4}$.

47. $y = \frac{1}{3}x^2 + \frac{5}{3}$, $D_x y = \frac{2}{3}x$; $x = \pm\sqrt{3y - 5}$, $D_y x = \pm 3/2\sqrt{3y - 5} = 3/2x$.

48. $y = \pm\sqrt{2x - 8}$, $D_x y = \pm 1/\sqrt{2x - 8} = 1/y$; $x = \frac{1}{2}y^2 + 4$, $D_y x = y$.

49. $y = x^{\frac{5}{3}}$, $D_x y = \frac{5}{3}x^{\frac{2}{3}}$; $x = y^{\frac{3}{5}}$, $D_y x = \frac{3}{5}y^{-\frac{2}{5}} = 3/5(x^{\frac{5}{3}})^{\frac{2}{5}} = 3/5x^{\frac{2}{3}}$.

50. $y = x^{\frac{4}{7}}$, $D_x y = \frac{4}{7}x^{-\frac{3}{7}} = 4/7x^{\frac{3}{7}}$; $x = y^{\frac{7}{4}}$, $D_y x = \frac{7}{4}y^{\frac{3}{4}} = \frac{7}{4}(x^{\frac{4}{7}})^{\frac{3}{4}} = \frac{7}{4}x^{\frac{3}{7}}$.

51. $3(26x^2 + 20x + 1)(3x + 1)^4(4x + 3)^{-\frac{1}{2}}$.

52. $(90x^2 + 59x + 5)(2x + 5)^5(6x + 1)^{-\frac{1}{2}}$.

§ 623   Page 190

1. $\pi \cos \pi x$.   **2.** $-3\pi \sin 3\pi t$.   **3.** $2 \sec^2 2s$.   **4.** $-4 \csc^2 4u$.

5. $\frac{1}{2}\pi \sec \frac{1}{2}\pi t \tan \frac{1}{2}\pi t$.   **6.** $-\frac{1}{3}\pi \csc \frac{1}{3}\pi r \cot \frac{1}{3}\pi r$.

7. $\dfrac{\cos \sqrt{x}}{2\sqrt{x}}$.   **8.** $-\dfrac{\sin \sqrt{t + 1}}{2\sqrt{t + 1}}$.   **9.** $\dfrac{1}{(t + 1)^2} \sec \dfrac{t}{t + 1} \tan \dfrac{t}{t + 1}$.

10. $-2y \csc y^2 \cot y^2$.   **11.** $\dfrac{\pi}{u^2} \csc \dfrac{\pi}{u}$.   **12.** $2(r - 1)\sec^2 (r - 1)^2$.

13. $3 \sin^2 x \cos x$.   **14.** $-4 \csc^2 u \cot^3 u$.   **15.** $-\dfrac{\sin t}{2\sqrt{\cos t}}$.

16. $3 \sec^3 s \tan s$.   **17.** $-\frac{1}{2}\sqrt{\csc v} \cot v$.   **18.** $2 \sec^2 w \tan w$.

19. $-6 \sin(3y - 1) \cos (3y - 1)$.   **20.** $-12 \csc^2 4w \cot^2 4w$.

21. $6 \sin^2 2x \cos 2x$.   **22.** $\dfrac{3 \sec^2 6w}{\sqrt{\tan 6w}}$.   **23.** $2\sqrt{\sec 4t} \tan 4t$.

24. $-10 \csc^2 5u \cot 5u$.   **25.** $3x^2 \sin x + x^3 \cos x$.

26. $2x \cos 2x - 2x^2 \sin 2x$.   **27.** $\dfrac{1}{2\sqrt{t}} \tan 4t + 4\sqrt{t} \sec^2 4t$.

28. $\sec u^2 + 2u^2 \sec u^2 \tan u^2$.

29. $3 \cos 3x \cos 2x - 2 \sin 3x \sin 2x$.

30. $2 \sin t \cos t \cos 4t - 4 \sin^2 t \sin 4t$.

31. $2 \cos 2z \cos^2 3z - 6 \sin 2z \sin 3z \cos 3z$.

32. $4 \sin 2y \cos 2y \cos^2 5y - 10 \sin^2 2y \sin 5y \cos 5y$.

33. $\dfrac{2 \sin x}{(1 + \cos x)^2}$.   **34.** $\dfrac{2 \sec^2 x}{(1 - \tan x)^2}$.   **35.** $-\dfrac{2}{(\cos x + \sin x)^2}$.

36. $\dfrac{1}{1 - \sin x}$.   **37.** $y = 2x$.   **38.** $6x - 4\sqrt{3}y = \pi - 2\sqrt{3}$.

39. $2x + 4\sqrt{3}y = \pi + 3\sqrt{3}$.   **40.** $12x - 3y = 4\pi - 3\sqrt{3}$.

41. $12 \sin^2 x \cos^2 x - 4 \sin^4 x$.   **42.** $6 \sin^2 x \cos x - 3 \cos^3 x$.

43. $x^2(12 - x^2)\cos x - 8x^3 \sin x$.   **44.** $4x \cos x + (2 - x^2)\sin x$.

45. *Hint:* Use $\dfrac{\tan x - \tan 0}{x - 0} = \sec^2 c$.

46. *Hint:* Use $\dfrac{\cos x - \cos \frac{1}{2}\pi}{x - \frac{1}{2}\pi} = -\sin c$.

§ 703　　Page 201

1. $dy = 10x\,dx, \dfrac{dy}{dx} = 10x.$

2. $dy = 3t^2\,dt, \dfrac{dy}{dt} = 3t^2.$

3. $du = (2s + 3)ds, \dfrac{du}{ds} = 2s + 3.$

4. $dv = 2(r - r^{-3})dr, \dfrac{dv}{dr} = \dfrac{2(r^4 - 1)}{r^3}.$

5. $dw = \dfrac{dv}{2\sqrt{v}}, \dfrac{dw}{dv} = \dfrac{1}{2\sqrt{v}}.$

6. $dz = \tfrac{7}{3}y^{\frac{4}{3}}\,dy, \dfrac{dz}{dy} = \tfrac{7}{3}y^{\frac{4}{3}}.$

7. $dy = \dfrac{4\,dx}{\sqrt{4x^2 + 9}}, \dfrac{dy}{dx} = \dfrac{4}{\sqrt{4x^2 + 9}}.$

8. $dv = -\dfrac{9u\,du}{\sqrt{4 - 9u^2}}, \dfrac{dv}{du} = -\dfrac{9u}{\sqrt{4 - 9u^2}}.$

9. $dx = 2t \cos t^2\,dt, \dfrac{dx}{dt} = 2t \cos t^2.$

10. $dy = \dfrac{1}{t^2} \sin \dfrac{1}{t}\,dt, \dfrac{dy}{dt} = \dfrac{1}{t^2} \sin \dfrac{1}{t}.$

11. $du = 15 \sin^2 5z \cos 5z\,dz, \dfrac{du}{dz} = 15 \sin^2 5z \cos 5z.$

12. $dv = 6y^2 \sec^2 y^3 \tan y^3\,dy, \dfrac{dv}{dy} = 6y^2 \sec^2 y^3 \tan y^3.$

13. $n(n - 1)x^{n-2}.$

14. $4(\cos 2t - t \sin 2t).$

15. $-12t \sin t^2 - 8t^3 \cos t^2.$

16. $-8 \sin x \cos x.$

17. $\dfrac{(-1)^n\, n!}{x^{n+1}}.$

18. $(-1)^n \dfrac{1 \cdot 3 \cdot 5 \cdots (2n - 1)}{2^n}\, y^{-n-\frac{1}{2}}.$

19. $dy = \tfrac{2}{5}dx.$

20. $dy = \tfrac{3}{4}dx.$

21. $dy = 3y^{\frac{2}{3}}dx = 3x^2\,dx.$

22. $dy = \dfrac{dx}{2y} = \dfrac{dx}{2\sqrt{x}}.$

23. $dy = (3t^4)(2t\,dt).$

24. $dy = (30t + 20)(3dt).$

25. $dy = \left(\dfrac{1}{2\sqrt{t^2 + 4}}\right)(2t\,dt).$

26. $dy = \left(\dfrac{1}{3\sqrt[3]{(t^3 + 1)^2}}\right)(3t^2\,dt).$

27. $-\dfrac{16}{x^2}\left(\dfrac{2}{x} + 1\right)^7.$

28. $-\dfrac{9x}{\sqrt{9x^2 + 4}}.$

29. $6 \sin 3x \cos 3x.$

30. $-6 \sin 2x \cos^2 2x.$

31. $2(42x + 41)(2x + 5)^3(6x - 1)^2\,dx.$

32. $(2u^2 + a^2)(u^2 + a^2)^{-\frac{1}{2}}\,du.$

33. $a^2(v^2 + a^2)^{-\frac{3}{2}}\,dv.$

34. $2(6y - 49)(2y + 5)^3(6y - 1)^{-4}\,dy.$

35. $40t \sin^3 5t^2 \cos 5t^2\,dt.$

36. $8\alpha(\alpha^2 + 1)^3 \cos(\alpha^2 + 1)^4\,d\alpha.$

§ 705　　Page 204

1. $dy = 2, \Delta y = 2.01.$

2. $dy = 2, \Delta y = 1.99.$

3. $dy = -1.2, \Delta y = -1.141.$

4. $dy = 0.03, \Delta y = 0.030301.$

5. $dy = -0.0008, \Delta y = -0.000797$ (approx.).

6. $dy = 0.0004$, $\Delta y = 0.0004016$ (approx.).

7. $dy = -0.0975$, $\Delta y = -0.1$.   **8.** $dy = 0.1005$, $\Delta y = 0.1$.

9. $\lim\limits_{\Delta x \to 0} \dfrac{(2x\Delta x + \Delta x^2) - 2x\Delta x}{\Delta x} = \lim\limits_{\Delta x \to 0} \Delta x = 0$, $\lim\limits_{\Delta x \to 0} \dfrac{2x\Delta x + \Delta x^2}{2x\Delta x} = \lim\limits_{\Delta x \to 0} \dfrac{2x + \Delta x}{2x} = 1$, $\eta(h) = h$.

10. $\lim\limits_{\Delta x \to 0} \dfrac{(3x^2\Delta x + 3x\Delta x^2 + \Delta x^3) - 3x^2\Delta x}{\Delta x} = \lim\limits_{\Delta x \to 0} (3x\Delta x + \Delta x^2) = 0$,

$\lim\limits_{\Delta x \to 0} \dfrac{3x^2\Delta x + 3x\Delta x^2 + \Delta x^3}{3x^2\Delta x} = \lim\limits_{\Delta x \to 0} \dfrac{3x^2 + 3x\Delta x + \Delta x^2}{3x^2} = 1$, $\eta(h) = 3xh + h^2$.

11. $\lim\limits_{\Delta x \to 0} \dfrac{1}{\Delta x}\left[-\dfrac{\Delta x}{x(x + \Delta x)} + \dfrac{\Delta x}{x^2} \right] = \lim\limits_{\Delta x \to 0} \dfrac{\Delta x}{x^2(x + \Delta x)} = 0$,

$\lim\limits_{\Delta x \to 0} \dfrac{-\Delta x/x(x + \Delta x)}{-\Delta x/x^2} = \lim\limits_{\Delta x \to 0} \dfrac{x}{x + \Delta x} = 1$, $\eta(h) = \dfrac{h}{x^2(x + h)}$.

12. $\lim\limits_{\Delta x \to 0} \dfrac{1}{\Delta x}\left[\sqrt{x + \Delta x} - \sqrt{x} - \dfrac{\Delta x}{2\sqrt{x}} \right] = \lim\limits_{\Delta x \to 0} \left[\dfrac{1}{\sqrt{x + \Delta x} + \sqrt{x}} - \dfrac{1}{2\sqrt{x}} \right] = 0$,

$\lim\limits_{\Delta x \to 0} \dfrac{\sqrt{x + \Delta x} - \sqrt{x}}{\Delta x/2\sqrt{x}} = \lim\limits_{\Delta x \to 0} \dfrac{2\sqrt{x}}{\sqrt{x + \Delta x} + \sqrt{x}} = 1$,

$\eta(h) = \dfrac{1}{\sqrt{x + h} + \sqrt{x}} - \dfrac{1}{2\sqrt{x}} = -\dfrac{h}{2\sqrt{x}(\sqrt{x + h} + \sqrt{x})^2}$.

17. 9.1111.   **18.** 3.9375.   **19.** 1.261.   **20.** 1.73205.

21. 0.003936.   **22.** 0.083912.

23. 7040 square yards; true area $= 7044$ square yards.

24. 0.4π square inches; true area $= 0.4016\pi$ square inches.

25. 0.27π cubic inches.   **26.** 0.384 cubic inches.

27. $\frac{100}{3}\pi = 105$ (approx.) cubic feet.

§ 709   Page 209

1. $2xy^3 + 3x^2y^2y'$.   **2.** $(2xy - 3x^2y')y^{-4}$.

3. $(1 + yy')(2x + y^2)^{-\frac{1}{2}}$.

4. $2(x + yy')\cos(x^2 + y^2)$.   **5.** $-\dfrac{y + xy'}{2\sqrt{xy}} \sin\sqrt{xy}$.

6. $2(2 + 3y')\sec^2(2x + 3y)\tan(2x + 3y)$.

7. $-\dfrac{y}{x + 2y}$.   **8.** $-\dfrac{6xy + y^2 - 1}{3x^2 + 2xy - 1}$.   **9.** $\dfrac{3x^2 - y}{x - 3y^2}$.

10. $-\dfrac{4x^{\frac{3}{2}}y^{\frac{5}{2}} - y^{\frac{1}{2}}}{4x^{\frac{5}{2}}y^{\frac{3}{2}} - x^{\frac{1}{2}}}$.   **11.** $-\dfrac{3x + 4y}{4x - y}$.   **12.** $\dfrac{5x - y}{x - 7y}$.

13. $\dfrac{3x^2 - 4y^2}{8xy + 6y^2 + 5}$.   **14.** $-2\dfrac{x^2 + xy + 1}{x^2 - y^2}$.

15. $-\dfrac{2\sqrt{x^2y + xy^2} + y\sqrt{x + y} + \sqrt{xy}}{x\sqrt{x + y} + \sqrt{xy}}$.   **16.** $-\dfrac{\sqrt[3]{y^2}(\sqrt[3]{x^2} + \sqrt[3]{(x + y)^2})}{\sqrt[3]{x^2}(\sqrt[3]{y^2} + \sqrt[3]{(x + y)^2})}$.

17. $\dfrac{y\cos xy - 1}{1 - x\cos xy}$.   **18.** $\dfrac{x\sec^2(x^2 + y^2) - y}{x - y\sec^2(x^2 + y^2)}$.

19. $x + 7y = 7$.   **20.** $5x + 7y = 1$.   **21.** $4x - 5y + 6 = 0$.

22. $5x + 8y = 18.$

23. $\sqrt{3}\pi x + (\sqrt{3}\pi - 9)y = 3\sqrt{3}\pi - 18.$

24. $\pi x + (2\pi - 4)y = 4\pi - 4.$

25. $\dfrac{30}{(x - 2y)^3}.$

26. $\dfrac{50}{(x - 2y)^3}.$

27. $\dfrac{36}{(x - 5y)^3}.$

28. $\dfrac{24}{(x - 5y)^3}.$

29. $-\dfrac{8x}{25y^5}.$

30. $\dfrac{24(x^2 - 9xy - 3y^2)}{(x^2 + 3y^2)^3}.$

§713   Page 218

1. $dx/dt = 3,\ dy/dt = -2,\ dy/dx = -\frac{2}{3}.$ Everywhere regular. No horizontal or vertical tangents, general tangent: $y + 2t - 4 = -\frac{2}{3}(x - 3t + 3),$ or $y - 4 = -\frac{2}{3}(x + 3).$ $2x + 3y = 6.$

2. $dx/dt = 6t,\ dy/dt = -4t,\ dy/dx = -\frac{2}{3},\ t \neq 0.$ Regular where $t \neq 0.$ No horizontal or vertical tangents, general tangent: $y + 2t^2 - 6 = -\frac{2}{3}(x - 3t^2 + 6),$ or $y - 6 = -\frac{2}{3}(x + 6).$ $2x + 3y = 6.$

3. $dx/dt = 2,\ dy/dt = 2t,\ dy/dx = t.$ Everywhere regular. Horizontal tangent where $t = 0,$ general tangent: $y - t^2 = t(x - 2t).$ Symmetric with respect to the y-axis. $4y = x^2.$

4. $dx/dt = -2t,\ dy/dt = 3,\ dy/dx = -3/2t,\ t \neq 0.$ Everywhere regular. Vertical tangent where $t = 0,$ general tangent: $3(x - 1 + t^2) + 2t(y - 3t) = 0.$ Symmetric with respect to the x-axis. $9x + y^2 = 9.$

5. $\dfrac{dx}{dt} = 2t,\ \dfrac{dy}{dt} = -\dfrac{2t}{(t^2 + 1)^2},\ \dfrac{dy}{dx} = -\dfrac{1}{(t^2 + 1)^2},\ t \neq 0.$ Regular where $t \neq 0.$ No horizontal or vertical tangents, general tangent: $x + (t^2 + 1)^2 y = 2t^2 + 2.$ $xy = 1,\ x \geq 1,$ $0 < y \leq 1.$

6. $\dfrac{dx}{dt} = 1 + \dfrac{1}{t^2},\ \dfrac{dy}{dt} = -\dfrac{t^2 + 1}{(t^2 - 1)^2},\ \dfrac{dy}{dx} = -\dfrac{t^2}{(t^2 - 1)^2}.$ Everywhere regular ($t^2 \neq 0, 1$). No horizontal or vertical tangents, general tangent: $t^2 x + (t^2 - 1)y = 2t^3 - 2t.$ Symmetric with respect to the line $y = x.$ $xy = 1.$

7. $\dfrac{dx}{dt} = 6t^5,\ \dfrac{dy}{dt} = 4t^3,\ \dfrac{dy}{dx} = \dfrac{2}{3t^2},\ t \neq 0.$ Regular where $t \neq 0.$ Vertical tangent where $t = 0,$ general tangent: $2x - 3t^2 y + t^6 = 0.$ $x^2 = y^3$ or $y = x^{\frac{2}{3}},\ x \geq 0.$

8. $\dfrac{dx}{dt} = 3t^2,\ \dfrac{dy}{dt} = 2t,\ \dfrac{dy}{dx} = \dfrac{2}{3t},\ t \neq 0.$ Regular where $t \neq 0.$ Cusp where $t = 0,$ general tangent: $2x - 3ty + t^3 - 2 = 0.$ Symmetric with respect to the line $x = 1.$ $(x - 1)^2 = y^3$ or $y = (x - 1)^{\frac{2}{3}}.$

9. $\dfrac{dx}{dt} = 2t + 1,\ \dfrac{dy}{dt} = 2t - 1,\ \dfrac{dy}{dx} = \dfrac{2t - 1}{2t + 1},\ t \neq -\frac{1}{2}.$ Everywhere regular. Horizontal tangent where $t = \frac{1}{2},$ vertical tangent where $t = -\frac{1}{2},$ general tangent: $(2t - 1)x - (2t + 1)y = 2t^2.$ Symmetric with respect to the line $y = x,\ x^2 - 2xy + y^2 - 2x - 2y = 0.$

10. $\dfrac{dx}{dt} = 2t,\ \dfrac{dy}{dt} = 1 - 2t,\ \dfrac{dy}{dx} = \dfrac{1 - 2t}{2t},\ t \neq 0.$ Everywhere regular. Horizontal tangent where $t = \frac{1}{2},$ vertical tangent where $t = 0,$ general tangent: $2tx + (2t - 1)y = t + 3t^2.$ $x^2 + 2xy + y^2 - 3x - 2y + 2 = 0.$

11. $\dfrac{dx}{dt} = 2t,\ \dfrac{dy}{dt} = 3t^2 - 1,\ \dfrac{dy}{dx} = \dfrac{3t^2 - 1}{2t},\ t \neq 0.$ Everywhere regular. Horizontal tangents where $t = \pm\frac{1}{3}\sqrt{3},$ vertical tangent where $t = 0,$ general tangent: $(3t^2 - 1)x - 2ty = (t^2 - 1)^2.$ Symmetric with respect to the x-axis. $y^2 = x^2(x + 1).$

12. $\dfrac{dx}{dt} = 3 - 3t^2, \dfrac{dy}{dt} = -2t, \dfrac{dy}{dx} = \dfrac{2t}{3t^2 - 3}, \ t^2 \neq 1$. Everywhere regular. Horizontal tangent where $t = 0$, vertical tangents where $t = \pm 1$, general tangent: $2tx + 3(1 - t^2)y = (3 - t^2)^2$. Symmetric with respect to the y-axis. $x^2 = y^2(3 - y)$.

13. $\dfrac{dx}{dt} = -\sin t, \dfrac{dy}{dt} = \cos t, \dfrac{dy}{dx} = -\cot t, t \neq n\pi, n \in \mathcal{G}$. Everywhere regular. Horizontal tangent where $t = (n + \tfrac{1}{2})\pi, n \in \mathcal{G}$, vertical tangent where $t = n\pi, n \in \mathcal{G}$, general tangent: $x \cos t + y \sin t = 1$. Symmetric with respect to each coordinate axis and the origin. $x^2 + y^2 = 1$.

14. $\dfrac{dx}{dt} = -\sin t, \dfrac{dy}{dt} = 2 \sin t \cos t, \dfrac{dy}{dx} = -2 \cos t, t \neq n\pi, n \in \mathcal{G}$. Regular where $t \neq n\pi$, $n \in \mathcal{G}$. Horizontal tangent where $t = (n + \tfrac{1}{2})\pi, n \in \mathcal{G}$, general tangent: $2x \cos t + y = 1 + \cos^2 t$. Symmetric with respect to the y-axis. $y = 1 - x^2$.

15. $\dfrac{dx}{dt} = -\dfrac{4t}{(1 + t^2)^2}, \dfrac{dy}{dt} = \dfrac{2 - 2t^2}{(1 + t^2)^2}, \dfrac{dy}{dx} = \dfrac{t^2 - 1}{2t}, t \neq 0$. Everywhere regular. Horizontal tangents where $t = \pm 1$, vertical tangent where $t = 0$, general tangent: $(1 - t^2)x + 2ty = 2$. Symmetric with respect to the x-axis. $x^2 + y^2 = 2x, x \neq 0$.

16. $\dfrac{dx}{dt} = \dfrac{2 - 2t^2}{(1 + t^2)^2}, \dfrac{dy}{dt} = \dfrac{4t}{(1 + t^2)^2}, \dfrac{dy}{dx} = \dfrac{2t}{1 - t^2}, t^2 \neq 1$. Everywhere regular. Horizontal tangent where $t = 0$, vertical tangents where $t = \pm 1$, general tangent: $2tx + (t^2 - 1)y = 2t^2$. $x^2 + y^2 = 2y, y \neq 2$.

17. 0.   **18.** 0.   **19.** $\tfrac{1}{2}$.   **20.** $-\dfrac{3}{4t^3}$.   **21.** $\dfrac{4t}{(t^2 + 1)^3}$.

22. $\dfrac{2t^3}{(t^2 - 1)^3}$.   **23.** $-\dfrac{2}{9t^8}$.   **24.** $-\dfrac{2}{9t^4}$.   **25.** $\dfrac{4}{(2t + 1)^3}$.

26. $-\dfrac{1}{4t^3}$.   **27.** $\dfrac{3t^2 + 1}{4t^3}$.   **28.** $\dfrac{2(t^2 + 1)}{9(t^2 - 1)^3}$.   **29.** $-\csc^3 t$.

30. -2.   **31.** $-\left(\dfrac{1 + t^2}{2t}\right)^3$.   **32.** $\left(\dfrac{1 + t^2}{1 - t^2}\right)^2$.   **33.** $\xi = 1$.

34. $\xi = \tfrac{14}{9}$.   **35.** $\xi = \tfrac{1}{2}b$.   **36.** $\xi = \sqrt{2} - 1$.

38. $\dfrac{dy}{dx} = -\tan \theta, \dfrac{d^2y}{dx^2} = \dfrac{1}{3a \sin \theta \cos^4 \theta}$.

§ 802   Page 223

1. $\xi = 0, \max = 16, \min = 0$.   **2.** $\xi = 0, \max = 1, \min = -8$.

3. No $\xi, \max = \tfrac{5}{3}, \min = -3$.   **4.** $\xi = 2, \max = 5, \min = 4$.

5. $\xi = 1, \max = 3, \min = -1$.   **6.** $\xi = 2, \max = 4, \min = 0$.

7. $\xi = 2, \max = -9, \min = -16$.   **8.** $\xi = 3, \max = \tfrac{1}{6}, \min = \tfrac{2}{13}$.

9. No $\xi, \max = 1, \min = \tfrac{2}{5}$.   **10.** $\xi \in [-1, 0] \cup [1, 2], \max = 1, \min = -1$.

11. $\xi = 0, 1, \max = 3, \min = -1$.   **12.** $\xi = 0, 1, \max = 1, \min = -3$.

13. $\xi = 0, \max = 1, \min = 0$.   **14.** $\xi = 0, \max = 1, \min = 0$.

§ 805   Page 232

1. Global minimum of -6 at $x = 3$; $x^2 - 6x + 3 \geq -6, (x - 3)^2 \geq 0$.

2. Global maximum of 32 at $x = 5$; $7 + 10x - x^2 \leq 32, (x - 5)^2 \geq 0$.

3. Global minimum of 6 at $x = 3$; $x + \dfrac{9}{x} \geqq 6$, $\dfrac{(x-3)^2}{x} \geqq 0$.

4. Global minimum of 8 at $x = 2$; $x^2 + \dfrac{16}{x^2} \geqq 8$, $\dfrac{(x^2-4)^2}{x^2} \geqq 0$.

5. Global minimum of 0 at $x = 0$; global maximum of $\dfrac{1}{6}$ at $x = 3$; $\dfrac{x}{x^2+9} \leqq \dfrac{1}{6}$, $(x-3)^2 \geqq 0$.

6. Global minimum of 0 at $x = 0$; global maximum of $\dfrac{1}{4}$ at $x = 2$; $\dfrac{x}{x^2+4} \leqq \dfrac{1}{4}$, $(x-2)^2 \geqq 0$.

7. Min of -41 at $x = -6$.   **8.** Max of $\frac{73}{4}$ at $x = -\frac{7}{2}$.

9. Max of 9 at $x = 1$, min of 5 at $x = 3$.

10. Min of -12 at $x = -2$, max of 96 at $x = 4$.

11. No extrema; point of inflection $(1, 4)$.   **12.** No extrema; point of inflection $(-2, 2)$.

13. No extrema; point of inflection $(1, 0)$.   **14.** Min of 0 at $x = -3$.

15. Max of 1 at $x = 0$; min of 0 at $x = \pm 1$.

16. Max of 1 at $x = 1$; point of inflection $(0, 0)$.

17. Max of $\frac{1}{4}$ at $x = 2$.   **18.** Min of $-\frac{1}{4}$ at $x = -1$.

19. Min of 0 at $x = 1$.   **20.** Min of $-\frac{1}{3}$ at $x = 3$.

21. Max of 4 at $x = 2$.   **22.** Max of $\frac{1}{16}\sqrt{2}$ at $x = 2$.

23. Min of 0 at $x = 0$.   **24.** Min of $-\frac{1}{4}$ at $x = \frac{1}{16}$.

25. Min of 0 at $x = 0$.   **26.** Min of 0 at $x = 0$.

27. Max of 1 at $x = 0$.   **28.** No critical points.

29. Min of 0 at $x = 0$.   **30.** No extrema; point of inflection $(0, 0)$.

§ 808   **Page 242**

1. Everywhere concave up.   **2.** Everywhere concave down.

3. Concave up: $x > 0$; concave down: $x < 0$.

4. Concave up: $x < 0$; concave down: $x > 0$.

5. Concave up: $x < 0$, $x > 2$; concave down: $0 < x < 2$.

6. Concave up: $x < 1$, $x > 3$; concave down: $1 < x < 3$.

7. Concave up: $x < -2$, $x > 0$; concave down: $-2 < x < 0$.

8. Everywhere concave up ($x \neq 0$).

9. Concave up: $x > 6$; concave down: $x < 0$, $0 < x < 6$.

10. Min of 5 at $x = 5$.   **11.** Max of 17 at $x = 2$.

12. Min of -10 at $x = 2$, max of -6 at $x = 4$.

13. Max of 2 at $x = 1$, min of 1 at $x = 2$.   **14.** Min of 0 at $x = 0$.

15. Max of 1 at $x = 0$.   **16.** Min of $3\sqrt[3]{9}$ at $x = \sqrt[3]{3}$.

17. Min of $\frac{3}{2}\sqrt[3]{12}$ at $x = \sqrt[3]{12}$.   **18.** Max of $\frac{1}{8}$ at $x = 4$.

28. Max of $\frac{5}{4}$ at $x = \frac{3}{4}$.   **29.** Min of $\frac{5}{4}$ at $x = 4$.

30. Max of $\frac{1}{32}$ at $x = 2$.   **31.** Max of 4 at $x = 2$.

32. Min of 32 at $x = 2$.   **33.** Max of $\frac{3}{8}$ at $x = \frac{1}{4}$.

34. Max of $\frac{2}{9}\sqrt{3}$ at $x = \frac{2}{3}$.   **35.** Max of 1 at $x = 1$.

36. Max of $\frac{1}{2}$ at $x = 1$.   **37.** Min of $\frac{1}{9}$ at $x = 4$.

§ 812   Page 254

1. $7\frac{11}{27}$ cubic feet.   **2.** 18 cubic feet.   **3.** $\frac{1}{4}ab$.

4. *Hint:* If any two sides are unequal, a triangle of greater area can be found with a vertex on the perpendicular bisector of the third side.

5. 24 feet.   **6.** 11 feet by 11 feet.   **7.** 4 feet by 8 feet.

8. He should aim at the point of the shore 3 miles toward his goal from the point of the shore nearest the island.

9. He should row directly toward his goal.   **10.** $\theta = \dfrac{\pi}{6}$.

11. $30\sqrt{3}$ cubic feet.   **13.** 27 feet.

14. 20 miles per hour.   **15.** 41.6 miles per hour.

16. The maximum speed of 60 miles per hour. **17.** $x = 14$.

18. $x = 20$.   **19.** No profit is possible with the new formula.

20. *Hint:* Choose a coordinate system such that the river shore is the x-axis and his house and barn are represented by the points $(0, c)$ and (a, b), where a, b, and c are positive. Consider the shortest route between $(0, c)$ and $(a, -b)$ and reflect. $x = ac/(b + c)$.

21. $(1, 1)$.   **22.** $(1, \frac{1}{2})$.   **23.** $\frac{288}{49}$.   **24.** 10 square feet.   **26.** $\alpha = \frac{1}{4}\pi$.

§ 814   Page 258

4. Area $= 2ab$.   **5.** 40 yards by 80 yards.

6. $20\sqrt{2}$ yards by $80\sqrt{2}$ yards.   **7.** Length $=$ twice width.

8. 4 feet by 4 feet by 2 feet.   **9.** 4 feet by 4 feet by 3 feet.

10. $2x_1y_1$.   **11.** $h^2 = 2r^2$.   **12.** $r = \frac{1}{3}\sqrt{6}a,\ h = \frac{1}{3}\sqrt{3}a$.

13. $x = \sqrt{ab}$.   **14.** $7\frac{1}{2}$ inches by 12 inches.

15. $6\sqrt{3}$ inches by $6\sqrt{6}$ inches (approximately 10.4 in. by 14.7 in.).

16. 9 inches by $9\sqrt{3}$ inches (approximately 9 in. by 15.6 in.).

17. $r = \sqrt{2}a,\ h = 4a$.   **18.** $\frac{9}{4}\pi r^2 h$.

§ 816   Page 262

1. -1.   **2.** -10.

3. $\dfrac{4096}{5\pi}$ (approximately 261) feet per second.

4. $\dfrac{1}{36\pi}$ feet per second $= \dfrac{5}{3\pi}$ feet per minute $= \dfrac{20}{\pi}$ (approximately 6.37) inches per minute.

5. $R = \frac{5}{2}\sqrt{3}$ (approximately 4.33).

6. $-\frac{2}{5}\sqrt{39}$ (approximately -2.50) feet per minute.

7. $b' = -2$ inches per minute.   **8.** 240 miles per hour.

9. -5 miles per hour; approaching; $11\frac{1}{13}$ seconds after noon; 90 miles per hour.

10. 1 foot per second.   **11.** 16 square inches per second.

12. $2/5\pi$ feet per minute; 16 square feet per minute.

14. 7π (approximately 22) feet per minute.

15. -0.12 pounds per square inch per minute.

16. 7 seconds after noon.

17. $-500/\sqrt{41}$ feet per second; $1500/\sqrt{61}$ feet per second.

§ 902   Page 268

1. None.   **2.** None.   **3.** $(0, -4)$.   **4.** $(0, 2)$.

5. $(0, 0)$, $(2, -16)$.   **6.** $(1, 11)$, $(3, 27)$.   **7.** $(-2, 0)$.

8. None.   **9.** $(6, \frac{1}{9})$.

10. $(\pm a/\sqrt{3}, \frac{3}{4})$; axis $x = 0$; asymptote $y = 0$; maximum point $(0, 1)$; points of inflection $(\pm 1, \frac{3}{4})$.

11. $(\pm \sqrt{3}a, \pm \sqrt{3}/4a)$; center $(0, 0)$; asymptote $y = 0$; extreme points $(\pm \frac{1}{3}\sqrt{3}, \pm \frac{1}{2}\sqrt{3})$; points of inflection $(0, 0)$, $(\pm 1, \pm \frac{3}{4})$.

12. Asymptotes $x = 0$ and $y = 0$; maximum point $(1, 1)$; point of inflection $(\frac{3}{2}, \frac{8}{9})$.

13. Asymptote $y = 1$; minimum point $(0, -1)$; points of inflection $(\pm 1, -\frac{1}{2})$.

14. Asymptote $y = 0$; maximum point $(\sqrt[3]{2}, \sqrt[3]{2}) = (1.26, 1.26)$; point of inflection $(2, 1)$.

§ 906   Page 273

17. $(0, 3)$.   **18.** $(-\infty, -1] \cup [2, +\infty)$.   **19.** $(-\infty, -1] \cup \{0\}$.

20. $(-\infty, 0) \cup (0, 1) = (-\infty, 1) \setminus \{0\}$.   **21.** $(-\infty, +\infty) = \mathcal{R}$.

22. $\varnothing$.   **23.** $[-1, 3]$.   **24.** $(-\infty, -6) \cup (-2, +\infty)$.

§ 1004   Page 280

1. $c = 2$.   **2.** $c = \sqrt[3]{39}$. **3.** $\frac{1}{2}$.   **4.** $-\frac{1}{2}$.   **5.** 0.   **6.** -3.

7. -39.   **8.** 246.   **13.** $\frac{1}{4}x^4$.   **14.** $x^3 - 2x^4$.   **15.** $|x|$.

16. $\frac{1}{2}x|x|$.

§ 1008   Page 289

5. $x^4 - x^3$.   **6.** $7x - 5x^2$.   **9.** $\frac{1}{9}x^9 + C$.   **10.** $\frac{1}{11}x^{11} + C$.

11. $\frac{1}{7}x^7 + C$.   **12.** $\frac{1}{12}x^{12} + C$.   **13.** $8^8 - 5^8$.   **14.** $11^7 - 1$.

15. $-\frac{4}{21}$.   **16.** $-\frac{3}{40}$.   **17.** $\sqrt{15} - \sqrt{7}$.   **18.** $\sqrt{30} - 3$.

19. $\frac{7}{8}$.   **20.** 3.   **21.** $\frac{2}{3}$.   **22.** $\frac{1}{2}$.   **23.** $\sqrt{2} - 1$.

§ 1010   Page 292

1. $x + C$.

2. $3x^2 + 8x + C$.

3. $-\frac{1}{2}r^4 + \frac{5}{3}r^3 + C$.

4. $3s^6 - 4s^4 + C$.

5. $-\dfrac{1}{w} + C$.

6. $-\dfrac{3}{z} + \dfrac{5}{2z^2} + C$.

7. $u + \dfrac{1}{u} + C$.

8. $v - \dfrac{2}{v} + \dfrac{3}{2v^2} + C$.

9. $\frac{2}{3}x\sqrt{x} + C$.

10. $\frac{2}{5}x^2\sqrt{x} + C$.

11. $\frac{6}{5}u^{\frac{5}{2}} + \frac{8}{3}u^{\frac{3}{2}} + C$.

12. $2\sqrt{v}(v + 4) + C$.

13. $2w^{\frac{3}{2}} + 3w^{\frac{4}{3}} + C$.

14. $3z^{\frac{5}{3}} - 4z^{\frac{7}{4}} + C$.

15. $-\cos r + C$.

16. $\sin s + C$.

17. $-3 \csc u + C$.

18. $-6 \cot v + C$.

19. $5 \tan w + C$.

20. $2 \sec z + C$.

21. 36.   **22.** 32.   **23.** 14.   **24.** 45.   **25.** $\frac{1}{36}$.   **26.** $\frac{1}{20}$.

27. $\frac{1}{2}$.   **28.** $\frac{1}{2}$.   **29.** $\frac{2}{3}\sqrt{3}$.   **30.** $\sqrt{2} - 1$.

§ 1013   **Page 299**

1. $\frac{1}{24}(4x + 7)^6 + C$.   2. $-\frac{1}{16}(4x + 7)^{-4} + C$.

3. $\frac{1}{3}\sqrt{6u + 1} + C$.   4. $\frac{1}{12}(8v - 3)^{\frac{3}{2}} + C$.

5. $-(3r^2 + 5r)^{-1} + C$.   6. $2\sqrt{s^3 + s} + C$.

7. $\frac{1}{42}(3w^2 + 2)^7 + C$.   8. $\frac{1}{6}(2z^2 - 3)^{\frac{3}{2}} + C$.

9. $\frac{3}{16}(4t^2 - 5)^{\frac{2}{3}} + C$.   10. $\frac{1}{4}(t^3 + 1)^{\frac{4}{3}} + C$.

11. $\frac{1}{11}y^{11} + \frac{3}{4}y^8 + \frac{12}{5}y^5 + 4y^2 + C$.

12. $\frac{1}{11}x^{11} - \frac{4}{9}x^9 + \frac{6}{7}x^7 - \frac{4}{5}x^5 + \frac{1}{3}x^3 + C$.

13. $-\frac{1}{2}\cos t^2 + C$.   14. $\frac{1}{2}\sin(\theta^2 + 1) + C$.

15. $\frac{1}{5}\sec 5\alpha + C$.   16. $\frac{1}{2}\tan 2\beta + C$.

17. $\frac{1}{10}(2x + 1)^{\frac{5}{2}} - \frac{1}{6}(2x + 1)^{\frac{3}{2}} + C$.   18. $\frac{3}{28}(2r + 3)^{\frac{7}{3}} - \frac{9}{16}(2r + 3)^{\frac{4}{3}} + C$.

19. $\frac{1}{24}(4s - 3)^{\frac{3}{2}} + \frac{3}{8}(4s - 3)^{\frac{1}{2}} + C$.   20. $\frac{1}{15}(3t - 1)^{\frac{5}{3}} + \frac{1}{6}(3t - 1)^{\frac{2}{3}} + C$.

21. 78.   22. $\frac{1}{20}$.   23. 1.   24. $\frac{42}{5}$.   25. $9 - 2\sqrt{6}$.

26. 2.   27. $\frac{1}{4}$.   28. $\frac{1}{6}(2 - \sqrt{2})$.   29. $\frac{14}{75}$.   30. $\frac{3946}{735}$.

31. $\frac{2}{5}$.   32. $\frac{2}{3}$.   33. $\frac{13}{3}$.   34. $\frac{14}{3}$.   35. $\frac{3}{2}$.   36. 2.

37. $\frac{3}{7}\pi$.   38. $\frac{93}{35}\pi$.   39. $\frac{2}{3}(10\sqrt{10} - 1)\pi$.   40. $\frac{232}{15}\pi$.

41. $\frac{3}{5}$.   42. $\frac{2}{5}$.   43. $\frac{1}{6}$.   44. $\frac{128}{15}$.

§ 1016   **Page 308**

1. $\frac{2961}{2}\pi\rho$ (= 290,000 approx.) foot-pounds.

2. $\frac{1953}{2}\pi\rho$ (= 191,000 approx.) foot-pounds.

3. $36\pi\rho$ (= 7060 approx.) foot-pounds.

4. $\frac{567}{64}\pi\rho$ (= 1740 approx.) foot-pounds.

5. $20(\frac{8}{3} - \sqrt{3})\rho$ (= 1170 approx.) foot-pounds.

6. $20\sqrt{3}\rho$ (= 2160 approx.) foot-pounds.

7. $\frac{467}{12}\pi\rho$ (= 7630 approx.) foot-pounds.

8. $\frac{160}{3}\pi\rho$ (= 10500 approx.) foot-pounds.

11. $\frac{10}{3}\rho$ (= 208 approx.) foot-pounds.

12. $\frac{16}{3}\rho$ (= 333 approx.) foot-pounds.

§ 1108   **Page 320**

1. Satisfies $y^2 - (x^2 + 5) = 0$.   2. Satisfies $y^2 - x^2 = 0$.

3. Satisfies $y^2 - 2xy - 5 = 0$.   4. Satisfies $y^2 - 2y + (1 - x^2) = 0$.

5. $\dfrac{2x}{x^2 + 1}$.   6. $\dfrac{12t^2 + 2}{3t^3 + t}$ 7. $\ln r + 1$.   8. $\dfrac{2 - \ln s^2}{s^2}$.

11. $\dfrac{2u\, du}{u^2 + 2}$.   12. $\dfrac{3v^2 + 1}{v^3 + v}\, dv$.

11. $-2w \tan w^2\, dw$.   12. $2 \cot y\, dy$.   13. 1.38630 (actually 1.38629).

14. 1.79176.   15. 2.07945 (actually 2.07944). 16. 2.19722.

17. 2.30259.   18. $9.08371 - 10$.   19. 0.40546 (actually 0.40547).

20. 0.81092 (actually 0.81093). 21. 0.80472.   22. 0.23105.

23. $2x \exp x^2$.   24. $2y \exp(y^2 + 3)$.   25. $(u + 1)\exp u$.

26. $\dfrac{v-1}{v^2}\exp v.$ **27.** $3r^2\exp r^3\,dr.$ **28.** $-2s\exp(1-s^2)ds.$

29. $-2w\sin w^2\exp\cos w^2\,dw.$ **30.** $2\sin z\cos\exp\sin^2 z\,dz.$

31. $15.$ **32.** $25.$ **33.** $\frac{2}{3}.$ **34.** $\frac{5}{3}.$ **37.** $x^2.$ **38.** $2x.$

39. $3x.$ **40.** $x^3.$ **41.** $x^2.$ **42.** $x^2.$ **43.** $x^3.$ **44.** $x^3.$

§ 1114   Page 329

1. $-3.$ **2.** $\frac{1}{3}.$ **3.** $-\frac{1}{3}.$ **4.** $-3.$ **5.** $\frac{3}{2}.$ **6.** $\frac{2}{3}.$

7. $\frac{1}{2}\cot\frac{1}{2}x.$ **8.** $\dfrac{4x}{2x^2-5}.$ **9.** $\dfrac{1}{x\ln x}.$ **10.** $x+2x\ln x.$

11. $(\cot x)\ln\cos x-(\tan x)\ln\sin x).$ **12.** $\dfrac{1-\ln x}{x^2}.$

13. $0.$ **14.** $\dfrac{\cos^2 x+\sin^2 x\ln\sin x}{\sin x\cos^2 x}.$

15. $\dfrac{\cot x}{\ln 10}.$ **16.** $\dfrac{5}{x\ln a}.$

17. $\dfrac{\ln x}{x\ln 10}+\dfrac{\log_{10} x}{x}=\dfrac{2\log_{10} x}{x}.$ **18.** $\cot 2x.$

19. $\dfrac{2x^3}{x^4+3}.$ **20.** $\dfrac{x}{x^2+5}-\dfrac{1}{x}=-\dfrac{5}{x(x^2+5)}.$

21. $\csc x.$ **22.** $\dfrac{1}{x}+8x^3\cot 2x^4+\dfrac{1}{x\ln x}.$ **23.** $\dfrac{1}{2x\sqrt{\ln x}}.$

24. $-\dfrac{2}{x(\ln 5x)^3}.$ **25.** $\dfrac{18\ln x}{x}.$ **26.** $2e^{2x}.$

27. $2xe^{x^2}.$ **28.** $2(x+1)e^{x^2+2x}.$ **29.** $e^{\sqrt{x}}/2\sqrt{x}.$ **30.** $2\cos 2x\,e^{\sin 2x}.$

31. $3x^2.$ **32.** $(2x-x^2)e^{-x}.$ **33.** $(1-2x^2)e^{-x^2}.$ **34.** $2(x^2+x)e^{2x}.$

35. $2(x-x^2)e^{-2x}.$ **36.** $e^{-x}\left(\dfrac{1}{x}-\ln x\right).$ **37.** $4(e^x+e^{-x})^{-2}.$ **38.** $2e^{2x}\cos e^{2x}.$

39. $\frac{1}{2}e^{\frac{1}{2}x}.$ **40.** $e^x\,e^{e^x}=e^{x+e^x}.$ **41.** $exe^{-1}.$ **42.** $(\ln\pi)\pi^x.$

43. $\dfrac{x+1}{x}.$ **44.** $\ln a.$ **45.** $(\ln 10)(\cos x)10^{\sin x}.$

46. $\dfrac{\ln 2}{x}2^{\ln x}.$ **47.** $\dfrac{2x^2+a^2}{\sqrt{x^2+a^2}}.$ **48.** $a^2(x^2+a^2)^{-\frac{3}{2}}.$

49. $\dfrac{3(2x-9)(2x+1)^5}{(3x-1)^6}.$ **50.** $14x(4x^2+1)^{-\frac{1}{2}}(6x^2+5)^{-\frac{3}{2}}.$

51. $(3x+5)^4(x^2+3)^5\sqrt[3]{6x+1}\left[\dfrac{12}{3x+5}+\dfrac{10x}{x^2+3}+\dfrac{2}{6x+1}\right].$

52. $(2x-7)^3(x^3+4)^6\sqrt{4x+3}\left[\dfrac{6}{2x-7}+\dfrac{18x^2}{x^3+4}+\dfrac{2}{4x+3}\right].$

53. $(1+\ln x)x^x.$ **54.** $\left(\dfrac{\sin x}{x}+(\cos x)\ln x\right)x^{\sin x}.$

55. $(1+2\ln x)x^{x^2+1}.$ **56.** $\left(\dfrac{1}{\ln x}+\ln\ln x\right)(\ln x)^x.$

57. $-\dfrac{e^y+ye^x}{xe^y+e^x}.$ **58.** $\dfrac{y^2 e^x-10y\ln y}{10x-ye^x}.$ **59.** $\dfrac{xe^{-y}-1}{x^2 e^{-y}+x\cos y}.$

60. $e^t \sec t$.   **61.** $t \sec^2 t$.

66. $2ex - y = e$.   **67.** $2x - y = e$.

68. $x + 2y = 3$.   **69.** $(e^2 - 1)x + e(e^2 + 1)y = 2e^3$.

70. 0.02.   **71.** -0.03.   **72.** 0.98.

75. *Hint:* Use $\dfrac{\ln(1 + x) - \ln(1 + 0)}{(1 + x) - (1 + 0)} = \dfrac{1}{1 + c}$.

76. *Hint:* Use $\dfrac{e^x - e^0}{x - 0} = e^c$.

77. 0.693.   **78.** 1.099.   **79.** 1.386.

80. 1.610 (actually 1.609).   **81.** 1.792.   **82.** 1.946.

83. 2.079.   **84.** 2.197.

§ 1116   Page 333

1. $\frac{1}{5} \ln |5x + 3| + C$.   **2.** $-\frac{1}{3} \ln |5 - 3u| + C$.

3. $-\frac{1}{4} \ln |1 - 4v| + C$.   **4.** $\frac{1}{4} \ln |4w - 3| + C$.

5. $\frac{1}{2} \ln(z^2 + 5) + C$.   **6.** $-\frac{1}{2} \ln |4 - x^2| + C$.

7. $-\frac{1}{10} \ln |8 - 5t^2| + C$.   **8.** $\frac{1}{6} \ln(3s^2 + 4) + C$.

9. $-\ln(1 + \cos x) + C$.   **10.** $\frac{1}{3} \ln |3 \sec y - 2| + C$.

11. $-\frac{1}{12} \ln |5 - 6 \tan 2\theta| + C$.   **12.** $\ln(2 + \sin^2 u) + C$.

13. $\ln(e^t + e^{-t}) + C$.   **14.** $\frac{1}{4} \ln(3 + 4e^v) + C$.

15. $\ln |\ln x| + C$.   **16.** $2 \ln(\sqrt{r} + 1) + C$.   **17.** $-\frac{1}{3} e^{2-3x} + C$.

18. $\frac{1}{5} e^{5t} + C$.   **19.** $-\frac{1}{2} e^{-2u} + C$.   **20.** $-e^{-w} + C$.

21. $2e^{\frac{1}{2}s} + C = 2\sqrt{e^s} + C$.   **22.** $\frac{1}{12} e^{12y} + C$.

23. $-\frac{1}{6} e^{-6x} + C$.   **24.** $\frac{1}{4} e^{4z-3} + C$.   **25.** $\dfrac{10^v}{\ln 10} + C$.

26. $\dfrac{2^x}{\ln 2} + C$.   **27.** $-\frac{1}{2} e^{-t^2} + C$.   **28.** $-\frac{1}{4} e^{-w^4} + C$.

29. $-\frac{1}{3} e^{\cos 3t} + C$.   **30.** $\frac{1}{2}(e^{2x} - e^{-2x}) - 2x + C$.

31. $\frac{2}{3}(e^s + 1)^{\frac{3}{2}} + C$.   **32.** $-\cos(\ln x) + C$.

33. $\frac{1}{3} \ln \frac{8}{5}$.   **34.** $-\frac{1}{4} \ln \frac{11}{7}$.   **35.** $-\frac{1}{2} \ln 5$.   **36.** $\frac{1}{6} \ln \frac{17}{5}$.   **37.** $\ln 2$.

38. $\ln 2$.   **39.** $\ln 2$.   **40.** $\ln \dfrac{e + 2}{3}$.   **41.** $\frac{1}{2}(e^2 - 1)$.   **42.** $\dfrac{e - 1}{3e}$.

43. $\dfrac{e - 1}{e}$.   **44.** $2(e^2 - e)$.   **45.** $\dfrac{2}{3 \ln 3}$.   **46.** $\dfrac{e^4 - 1}{2e^4}$.   **47.** $\ln 2$.

48. $\frac{1}{2}$.   **49.** $\ln 3 = 1.099$.   **50.** $\ln 2 = 0.693$.   **51.** $\frac{9}{20} = 0.450$.

52. $e^2 - e \ln 2 - e = 2.79$.   **53.** $5 \ln 5 - \frac{3}{2} - 9 \ln 2 = 0.31$.

54. $\frac{1}{2} \ln 3 = 0.55$.   **55.** $\frac{1}{3}(e^2 - e^{-1}) = 2.34$.

56. $\frac{1}{2}\pi(e^2 - e^{-2}) = 11.39$ **57.** $\frac{1}{2}\pi = 1.57$.   **58.** $\dfrac{1}{\ln 2}$.

§ 1205   Page 345

1. $y = -\cos x + 3$.   **2.** $y = \frac{1}{3}(2x^{\frac{3}{2}} - 11)$.

3. $y = \frac{1}{2}x|x| + 6$.   **4.** $y = \begin{cases} \ln(1 + x) + \ln 8, & x \geqq 0, \\ -\ln(1 - x) + \ln 8, & x \leqq 0. \end{cases}$

5. $y = -\ln x + 2x - 1$.

6. $y = \frac{1}{4}(e^{-2x} + 10x + 11)$.

7. $y = x^3 + 3x - 1$.

8. $y = -\dfrac{\sin \pi x}{\pi^2} - 2x + 5$.

9. $y = x + \dfrac{1}{x}$.

10. $y = -x + \dfrac{1}{x} + 2$.

11. 7 seconds later.

12. 128 feet per second.

13. 150 feet.

14. 14,400 feet.

15. 49 feet.

16. 20 feet.

17. 20 feet per second.

18. 48 feet.

19. Inversely as γ.

20. (*a*), (*b*) and (*d*): ratio of 6 to 1; (*c*): same. Ratio of $\sqrt{6}$ to 1.

21. $y = \dfrac{c}{x^2 + 1}$, $c > 0$.

22. $y = cx^2$, $c > 0$.

23. $y = cx$, $c > 0$.

24. $y = ce^{x^2}$, $c > 0$.

25. $xy = C$, $C > 0$.

26. $y = ce^x$, $c > 0$.

27. $x^2 + 2y^2 = C$, $C > 0$.

28. $x = ce^{y^2}$, $c > 0$.

§ 1208   Page 351

1. $y = ce^{-8x}$.

2. $y = ce^{\frac{1}{3}t}$.

3. $y = 80e^{5t}$.

4. $y = 100\, e^{-\frac{1}{2}x}$.

5. Approximately 41 percent.

6. Approximately 6 years and 9 months.

7. Approximately 48 days.

8. After approximately 2.6 years. This has meaning only in the crude sense that after $2\frac{1}{2}$ or 3 years one could expect the substance to have disintegrated completely.

9. Between 696 and 697 days.

10. Approximately 1989.

11. He should consume the package within 6.2 months after it was packaged or, for the sake of safety, within 4 months of the time he purchases it from the grocer.

12. Yes. It is the product kt in the formula y_0e^{kt} that must be controlled.

13. Approximately 1 hour, 55 minutes, and 8 seconds.

14. Less than one one hundred billionth of one percent.

15. Approximately 4 minutes and 2 seconds more.

16. Approximately 45.5°F.

17. $43\frac{3}{4}$°F.

18. $87\frac{1}{2}$°F.

19. Approximately $\frac{2}{3}$ of a second.

20. Approximately 26 percent.

§ 1304   Page 358

1. $\frac{5}{3}$.

2. 1.

3. $\frac{2}{3}$.

4. 5.

5. $\frac{5}{4}$.

6. $\frac{3}{4}$.

7. $-\frac{2}{3}$.

8. $-\dfrac{1}{\pi}$.

9. $\frac{2}{3}$.

10. $\dfrac{e}{3}$.

11. $\frac{8}{5}$.

12. $\frac{2}{9}$.

13. 1.

14. $\frac{2}{3}$.

15. $\frac{1}{2}$.

16. $\frac{1}{3}$.

17. $\frac{1}{3}$.

18. $+\infty$.

19. 0.

20. 1.

21. $\frac{3}{2}$.

22. 0.

23. 0.

24. 0.

25. 0.

§ 1306   Page 361

1. 0.

2. 0.

3. 0.

4. -1.

5. 1.

6. $\frac{1}{2}$.

7. $\frac{1}{2}$.

8. $\frac{1}{6}$.

9. $\frac{1}{6}$.

10. 1.

11. 1.

12. e.

13. 1.

14. 1.

15. e.

16. e^2.

17. 1.

18. e^5.

19. *e.*　　　　**20.** e^{-2}.　　　　**21.** $\sqrt{e}$.　　　　**22.** 0.　　　　**23.** 1.　　　　**24.** 1.

25. $\frac{3}{10}$.　　　　　　　　**26.** $\frac{5}{6}\sqrt{3}$.　　　　　　　　　　**27.** $+\infty$.

§ 1308　　　Page 363

1. 0.　　　　**2.** 0.　　　　**3.** ∞.　　　　**4.** ∞.　　　　**5.** ∞.　　　　**6.** ∞.

7. $+\infty$.　　　　**8.** $+\infty$.　　　　**9.** ∞.　　　　**10.** $+\infty$.　　　　**11.** $+\infty$.　　　　**12.** 0.

13. $+\infty$.　　　**14.** $+\infty$.　　　**15.** 0.　　　　**16.** 0.　　　　**17.** 0.　　　　**18.** $+\infty$.

19. Asymptote $y = 0$; global minimum $-e^{-1}$ at $x = -1$; concave down for $x < -2$, concave up for $x > -2$; point of inflection $(-2, -2e^{-2})$; $\lim\limits_{x \to -\infty} f(x) = 0$; $\lim\limits_{x \to +\infty} f(x) = +\infty$.

20. Asymptote $y = 0$; global minimum 0 at $x = 0$, local maximum $4e^{-2}$ at $x = 2$; concave up for $|x - 2| > \sqrt{2}$, concave down for $|x - 2| < \sqrt{2}$; points of inflection $(2 \pm \sqrt{2}, (6 \pm 4\sqrt{2})e^{-2\mp\sqrt{2}})$; $\lim\limits_{x \to -\infty} f(x) = +\infty$, $\lim\limits_{x \to +\infty} f(x) = 0$.

21. Asymptote $y = 0$; global extrema $\pm e^{-\frac{1}{2}}$ at $x = \pm 1$; concave down for $x \in (-\infty, -\sqrt{3}) \cup (0, \sqrt{3})$, concave up for $x \in (-\sqrt{3}, 0) \cup (\sqrt{3}, +\infty)$; points of inflection $(\pm\sqrt{3}, \pm\sqrt{3}e^{-\frac{3}{2}})$; $\lim\limits_{x \to -\infty} f(x) = \lim\limits_{x \to +\infty} f(x) = 0$.

22. Local maximum 0 at $x = 0$, global minimum $-\frac{1}{2}e^{-1}$ at $x = e^{-\frac{1}{2}}$; concave down for $0 < x < e^{-\frac{3}{2}}$, concave up for $x > e^{-\frac{3}{2}}$; point of inflection $(e^{-\frac{3}{2}}, -\frac{3}{2}e^{-3})$; $\lim\limits_{x \to +\infty} f(x) = +\infty$.

SPECIAL SYMBOLS

Symbol	Meaning	Page
A	area function	1
$\cong$	congruence of sets	1
$\int_a^b s = \int_a^b s(x)dx$	Riemann integral of a step-function	4
$\mathcal{L}_f$	lower class for f	9
$\mathcal{U}_f$	upper class for f	9
$\mathcal{D}$	vector space of integrable functions	10
$\int_a^b f = \int_a^b f(x)dx$	Riemann integral in general	16
$\mathcal{E}$	ring of sets	30
$\mathcal{J}, \mathcal{J}_2$	ring of sets having area	31, 42
$\mathcal{J}, \mathcal{J}_3$	ring of sets having volume	42
V	volume function	43
$\mathcal{U}$	vector space of uniformly continuous functions	75
N_{c+}, N_{c-}	one-sided neighborhoods	101
$\sqrt[n]{x}$	nth root of x	106
x^r	rational power of x	107
D_c	deleted neighborhood	114
$\lim_{x \to c} f(x)$	limit of a function	116
$f(x) \to d$ as $x \to c$	limit of a function	116
$\lim_{x \to c+} f(x), \lim_{x \to c-} f(x)$	one-sided limits	117–118
D_{c+}, D_{c-}	deleted one-sided neighborhoods	118
$D_{+\infty}, D_{-\infty}, D_{\infty}$	deleted neighborhoods of infinity	130, 132, 133
$\lim_{x \to +\infty} f(x), \lim_{x \to -\infty} f(x), \lim_{x \to \infty} f(x)$	limits at infinity	130, 133
$N_{+\infty}, N_{-\infty}, N_{\infty}$	neighborhoods of infinity	136
$|\mathfrak{N}|$	norm of a net	142
$\lim_{|\mathfrak{N}| \to 0} \sum_{i=1}^{n} f(x_i)\Delta x_i$	limit of a sum	142
$v(t), \sigma(t)$	velocity, speed	151
$f', Df, f'(x), Df(x)$	derivative of f	154
$y', Dy, D_x y$	derivative of y with respect to x	154

Symbol	Meaning	Page
$\Delta x,\ \Delta y$	increments $h,\ f(x+h)-f(x)$	156
f'', $D^2 f$, $f''(x)$, $D^2 f(x)$, y'', $D^2 y$, $D_x^2 y$	second derivative	160
$f^{(n)}$, $D^n f$, $f^{(n)}(x)$, $D^n f(x)$, $y^{(n)}$, $D^n y$, $D_x^n y$	nth derivative	160
$a(t)$	acceleration	160
$dx,\ dy,\ df,\ df(x)$	differentials	194
AM	arithmetic mean	275
$\displaystyle\int f,\ \int f(x)dx$	indefinite integral of f	284
$\displaystyle F(x)\Big|_a^b,\ \Big[F(x)\Big]_a^b$	$F(b)-F(a)$	288
$\displaystyle F(u)\Big|^{u=\phi(x)},\ \Big[F(u)\Big]^{u=\phi(x)}$	$F(\phi(x))$	295
ln	natural logarithm function	312
exp	exponential function	316
e	natural logarithm base	319
a^x	general exponential function	321
e^x	exponential function	322
x^b	power function	324
$\log_a x$	logarithmic function	327
π	pi	335
$\log x$	$\log_{10} x$	349
$0/0,\ \infty/\infty$	indeterminate forms	353–357
$0\cdot\infty,\ \infty-\infty,\ 0^0,\ \infty^0,\ 1^\infty$	indeterminate forms	359–360

INDEX

(The numbers refer to pages)

Abscissa set, 35
Absolute extremum, 220 (footnote)
Acceleration, 160
Additivity, for area, 2, 31
  for the Riemann integral, 18, 21
  for volume, 43
  for work, 60
Algebra, of functions continuous at a point, 92
  of integrable functions, 15
  of uniformly continuous functions, 77
Algebraic function, 310
Algebraic number, 311
Annulus, circular, 50
Answers and hints, 381
Antiderivative, 282
Applications of the definite integral, 30–64,
    301–309
  to area, 30–41
  to hydrostatic force, 305–309
  to volume, 43–59
  to work, 60–62, 301–305
Applications of differential equations, 336–352
  to bacterial growth, 348–352
  to cooling, 350–352
  to falling bodies, 340–342
  to mixing, 351
  to orthogonal trajectories, 343–347
  to radioactive decay, 348–352
Applications of extrema, 247–259
Approximations, by differentials, 202–205
  linear, 204
Area, 1–3, 30–41
  of a circular disk, 43
Arithmetic mean, 275
Asymptote, horizontal, 133
  vertical, 137
Average, 275
Average rate of change, 155
Average velocity, 150

Bacterial growth, 348–352
Base, 321–328
Bliss, G. A., 144
Bliss's theorem, 144
Boundary condition, 338
Bounded from zero, 96

Bounded function, locally, 92
Bounded set, 1, 301 (footnote)
Boundedness of a continuous function, 111

Chain rule, 166–168
  with differentials, 200
Change of base formula, 328
Circular disk, area of, 43
Circular functions, 334–335
Class, lower, upper, 9
Closed rectangle, 2
Closed triangle, 36
Cluster point, 115, 130, 132, 133
Common logarithms, table of, 368
Completeness, of an area function, 2, 32
  of a volume function, 43
Composite function, derivative of, 166–168
  limit of, 122, 132
Composite of continuous functions, 94
Composite of uniformly continuous functions,
  79
Composition of ordinates, 272
Concavity, 233–239
Cone, volume of, 46
Congruence-invariant, 1, 31, 43
Constant of integration, 285
Constants, table of numerical, 372
Content, Jordan, 31, 33
Continuity, and differentiability, 161
  and uniform continuity, 110
  at a point, 84–113
  for area, 2
  one-sided, 97–100
  uniform, 65–83
Continuous image of an interval, 104, 111
Continuously differentiable, 155
Cooling problems, 350–352
Cosine function, 334–335
  derivative of, 189
Counterexample, 191–193
Critical point of a function, 221
Critical-point test for extrema, 222
Critical value of a variable, 221
Cube roots, table of, 366
Cubes, table of, 366

Curve, defined parametrically, 211–215
    regular, 211
Curve sketching, 140–141, 265–273, 361–364
Cusp, 178
Cycloid, 214
Cylinder, open or closed, 43
Cylinders and washers, 43–48
Cylindrical set, 42
Cylindrical shells, 49–54

Definite integral, 4, 16
    as the limit of a sum, 142
Degrees to radians, table, 379
Deleted half-neighborhood, 118
Deleted neighborhood, 114
    of infinity, 129–130, 132–133
Deleted one-sided neighborhood, 118
Dense set of discontinuities, 101
Derivative, 153–157
    higher order, 160
    of a composite function, 166–169
    of an inverse function, 182
    one-sided, 170
    right-hand (left-hand), 170
Derivatives, laws of, 157–163
Determinate expressions, 361–362
Differentiability, and continuity, 161
    of a composite function, 166–168
    of an inverse function, 182
Differentiable function, 155
    continuously, 155
Differential equation, 336–352
    separable, 342
Differentials, 194–204
    approximations by, 202–205
Differentiation, 155
    implicit, 205–207
    logarithmic, 325–326
    of composite functions, 166–168
    of inverse functions, 182
    of rational powers, 185
Discontinuity, in a dense set, 101
    jump, 99–100
    one-sided, 98
    oscillatory, 100
    removable, 99
    unbounded, 99
Discontinuous function, 91
Disk, area of, 43
Distance and velocity, 62, 149–152
Dominant terms in graphing, 272–273
Dummy variable, 5

e, 319
Equation, differential, 336–352
Exhaustion, method of, 2
Exp, 316–319
Exponent, 107, 321
Exponential function, 316–319, 321–323
    table of, 373

Exponents, laws of, 108, 323
Extended law of the mean, 244–247
Extended mean value theorem, 244–247
Extrema, 220–264
    of a continuous function, 111
Extremum, global, 220
    local, 224

Falling body problem, 340–342
Finite additivity for area, 2, 31
Finite limit, 116, 130
First derivative test, 227
First mean value theorem, 275
Force, and work, 60–62, 301–305
    hydrostatic, 305–309
Forms, indeterminate, 353–365
Formulas, integration, 285, 290–291, 331
Formulas from geometry, table of, 380
Function, algebraic, 310
    area, 1–3, 30–41
    circular, 334–335
    continuous, 84–113
    continuously differentiable, 155
    cosine, 189, 334–335
    differentiable, 155
    discontinuous, 91
    exponential, 316–319, 321–323
    implicit, 205–209
    integrable, 9
    locally bounded, 92
    locally unbounded, 92
    logarithmic, 312–316, 327
    natural logarithm, 312–316
    nth root, 106
    periodic, 335
    power, 107–109, 324
    sectionally linear, 24
    sectionally monotonic, 24
    sine, 188, 334–335
    transcendental, 311
    trigonometric, 334–335
    uniformly continuous, 65
Fundamental theorem of calculus, 286–288

Generalized law of the mean, 216
Generalized mean value theorem, 216
Geometry formulas, table of, 380
Global extremum, 220
Global maximum, 220
Global minimum, 220
Global property, 84
Graphical solution of inequalities, 271
Greek alphabet, 380

Half life, 349
Half-neighborhood, 101
    deleted, 118
Higher order derivatives, 160

Hints and answers, 381
Hooke's law, 61
l'Hospital, G. F. A. de, 354
l'Hospital's rule, 354–356
Hydrostatic force, 305–309
Hypocycloid of four cusps, 219 (Ex. 39)

Image of an interval, continuous, 104, 111
Implicit differentiation, 205–207
Implicit function, 205–209
Implicit functions and extrema, 256–259
In the large, property, 84
In the small, property, 84
Increment, 156
Indefinite integral, 278–279
Indefinite integration, 285
Indeterminate forms, 353–365
Inequalities, graphical solution of, 271
Infinitesimal, 202
Infinity, minus, 132, 135
    plus, 130, 135
    unsigned, 133, 135
Inflection point, 230, 265–268
Initial condition, 338
Initial distance, 341
Initial velocity, 341
Instantaneous rate of change, 155
Instantaneous speed, 151
Instantaneous velocity, 151
Integrability, of a continuous function, 110
    of a monotonic function, 13–15
    of a polynomial, 15
    of a uniformly continuous function, 80
    of $|f|$, 15
    of fg, 15
    sufficient conditions, 13, 15, 80, 110
Integrable function, 9
Integral, as the limit of a sum, 142
    definite, 4, 16
    indefinite, 278–279
    Riemann, 4, 16
Integral sign, 4, 5, 284
Integrand, 4, 16, 285
Integration, 16, 285
    by substitution, 293–299
Integration formulas, 285, 290–291, 331
Intermediate-value property, for continuous
        functions, 103
    for derivatives, 180–182
Inverse of a monotonic function, 104–105
Inverse function, differentiability of, 182
Isolated point, 115

Jordan, C., 31
Jordan content, 31, 33
Jump discontinuity, 99–100

Law of the mean, 171–174
    extended, 244–247

generalized, 216
Laws, of derivatives, 157–163
    of exp, 319
    of exponents, 108, 323
    of ln, 315
    of logarithms, 315, 329
Lebesgue, H., 33
Lebesgue measure, 33
Leibniz, G. W., 5, 84, 195, 294
l'Hospital, G. F. A. de, 354
l'Hospital's rule, 354–356
Limit, finite, 116, 130
    from the right (left), 117–118
    infinite, 135–139
    of integration, 16
    of a sum, 142
    one-sided, 117–118
Limit at infinity, 129–135
Limit point, 115, 130, 132, 133
Limit theorems, 123–128
Line, normal, 148
    tangent, 147
Linear approximation, 204
Linear function, sectionally, 24
Local behavior of curves, 272–273
Local boundedness, 92
Local extremum, 224
Local maximum, 224
Local minimum, 224
Local property, 84
Locally bounded function, 92
Locally unbounded function, 92
Logarithm, general, 327
    natural, 312–316
Logarithmic differentiation, 325–326
Logarithms, table of common, 368
Logarithms, table of natural, 370
Lower class, 9
Lower limit of integration, 16
Lower step-function, 9

Maximal interval of monotonicity, 177
Maximum, global, 220
    local, 224
    of a continuous function, 111
Mean, arithmetic, 275
Mean, law of the, 171–174, 216, 244–247
Mean value, 275
Mean value theorem for derivatives, 171–174
    extended, 244–247
    generalized, 216
Mean value theorem for integrals, 275
Measure, Lebesgue, 33
Minimum, global, 220
    local, 224
    of a continuous function, 111
Minus infinity, 132, 135
Mixing problems, 351
Monotonic function, differentiable, 175–177
    integrability of, 13–15
    inverse of, 104–105

Monotonic function (cont'd)
  limit of, 118, 134, 138–139
  sectionally, 24
Motion, rectilinear, 62, 149, 340–342
Multiple-story exponentials, 323

Natural logarithm function, 312–316
Natural logarithms, table of, 370
Negation, of continuity at a point, 90
  of integrability, 11
  of uniform continuity, 70
Neighborhood, deleted, 114, 129–130, 132–133
  of infinity, 135
  one-sided, 101
Newton, Sir Isaac, 84
Norm of a net, 142
Normal line, 148
Number, algebraic, 311
Numerical constants, table of, 372

One-sided continuity, 97–100
One-sided derivative, 170
One-sided discontinuity, 98
One-sided limit, 117–118
One-sided neighborhood, 101
  deleted, 118
Open-ended intervals and extrema, 239–242
Open rectangle, 2
Open triangle, 36
Order n, derivative of, 160
Order of a differential equation, 336
Ordinate set, 3
  area of, 33
Orthogonal trajectory, 343
Oscillatory discontinuity, 100

Parallelepiped, volume of, 57
Parameter, 211
Parametric curves, 211–215
Period of a function, 335
Periodic function, 335
π, 335
Plus infinity, 130, 135
Point, isolated, 115
  limit, 115, 130, 132, 133
  of inflection, 230, 265–268
Point property, 84
Polynomials in factored form, 269–270
Power, 107, 321, 324
Power function, 107–109, 324
Pressure, hydrostatic, 305–309
Primitive, 282
Pumping problems, 301–305
Pyramid, volume of, 57

Quotient of continuous functions, 95

Radians to degrees, table, 379
Radioactive decay, 348–352
Rate of change, 155
Rates, related, 260–262
Rational power function, 107–109
Rational powers, differentiation of, 185–186
Reciprocals, table of, 366
Rectangle, closed, 2
  open, 2
Rectilinear motion, 62, 149, 340–342
Reflection property, of an ellipse, 210 (Ex. 35)
  of a hyperbola, 210 (Ex. 36)
  of a parabola, 210 (Ex. 34)
Regular curve, 211
Related rates, 260–262
Removable discontinuity, 99
Riemann, G. F. B., 4 (footnote)
Riemann-integrable, 9
Riemann integral, 4, 16
  as the limit of a sum, 142
Right (left) half-neighborhood, 101
Right-hand (left-hand) continuity, 97–100
Right-hand (left-hand) derivative, 170
Right-hand (left-hand) discontinuity, 98
Right-hand (left-hand) limit, 117–118
Ring of sets, 30
Rolle, Michel, 172
Rolle's theorem, 172
Root, nth, 106
  square, 106
Rule, l'Hospital's, 354–356

Second derivative, 160
Second derivative test, 235
Sectionally linear, 24
Sectionally monotonic, 24
Semicubical parabola, 178
Separable differential equation, 342
Sequence, infinite, 132
Set, bounded, 1, 301 (footnote)
  cylindrical, 42
  ordinate, 3
Set between two graphs, 37
Sine function, 334–335
  derivative of, 188
Slope of a curve, 147
Solution of a differential equation, 336
Solving inequalities, 271
Special symbols, list, 399
Speed, 151
Spherical ball, volume of, 45–46
Square root of, 106
Square roots, table of, 366
Squares, table of, 366
Step-function, lower, upper, 9
Strict extremum, 220, 224
Substitution, integration by, 293–299
Symbols, special list of, 399

Tables,
  I.   Squares, cubes, roots, reciprocals, 366
  II. Four-place common logarithms, 368
  III. Natural logarithms, 370
  IV. Numerical constants, 372
  V.   Exponential function, 373
  VI. Natural trigonometric functions, degree measure, 377
  VII. Natural trigonometric functions, radian measure, 378
  VIII. Degrees, minutes, and seconds to radians, 379
  IX. Radians to degrees, minutes, and seconds, 379
  X.   Formulas from geometry, 380
  XI. Greek alphabet, 380
Tangent line, 147
  for an ellipse, 210 (Ex. 32)
  for a hyperbola, 210 (Ex. 33)
  for a parabola, 210 (Ex. 31)
  for a parametric curve, 211-212
  vertical, 177–179
Taylor's formula with a remainder, 245
Trajectory, orthogonal, 343
Transcendental function, 311
Triangle, 36
Triangular set, 36
Trigonometric functions, 334–335
  derivatives of, 188–190
  table for degrees, 377
  table for radians, 378

Unbounded, locally, 92
Unbounded discontinuity, 99
Uniform continuity, 65–83
  negation of, 70
Unit circle, 335
Upper class, 9
Upper limit of integration, 16
Upper step-function, 9

Variable, dummy, 5
  of integration, 5, 16, 285
Vector space, of functions continuous at a point, 92
  of integrable functions, 11
  of uniformly continuous functions, 75
Vector space Venn diagram, 82
Velocity, 62, 149–153
  average, 150
  instantaneous, 151
Venn diagram for vector spaces, 82
Vertical tangent line, 177–179
Volume, 42–59
  of known cross section area, 54–58
  of a parallelepiped, 57
  of a pyramid, 57
  of revolution, 43–54
  of a right circular cone, 46
  of a spherical ball, 45–46

Work, 60–62, 301–305